*Oxidases and*
*Related Redox Systems*

Rodin

# Oxidases and Related Redox Systems

Proceedings of a Symposium Held
in Amherst, Massachusetts, July 15–19, 1964

*Volume One*

*Edited by*

TSOO E. KING

HOWARD S. MASON

MARTIN MORRISON

John Wiley & Sons, Inc.
New York · London · Sydney

# Participants

Helmut Beinert, Institute for Enzyme Research, University of Wisconsin, Madison, Wisconsin

P. D. Boyer, Division of Biochemistry, Department of Chemistry, University of California, Los Angeles, California

R. C. Bray, Chester Beatty Research Institute, Institute of Cancer Research: Royal Cancer Hospital, London, England

Winslow S. Caughey, Department of Physiological Chemistry, The Johns Hopkins University School of Medicine, Baltimore, Maryland

Britton Chance, Johnson Research Foundation, University of Pennsylvania, Philadelphia, Pennsylvania

Freeman W. Cope, Biochemistry Division, Aviation Medical Acceleration Laboratory, U.S. Naval Air Development Center, Johnsville, Pennsylvania

Dana I. Crandall, Department of Biological Chemistry, University of Cincinnati College of Medicine, Cincinnati, Ohio

Charles R. Dawson, Department of Chemistry, Columbia University, New York, New York

Anders Ehrenberg, The Nobel Medical Institute, Department of Biochemistry, Stockholm, Sweden

Lars Ernster, Wenner-Gren Institute, University of Stockholm, Stockholm, Sweden

Ronald W. Estabrook, Johnson Research Foundation, University of Pennsylvania, Philadelphia, Pennsylvania

E. Frieden, Department of Chemistry and the Institute of Molecular Biophysics, Florida State University, Tallahassee, Florida

Philip George, John Harrison Laboratory of Chemistry, University of Pennsylvania, Philadelphia, Pennsylvania

Q. H. Gibson, Johnson Research Foundation, University of Pennsylvania, Philadelphia, Pennsylvania

D. E. Green, Institute for Enzyme Research, University of Wisconsin, Madison, Wisconsin

D. E. Griffiths, Department of Biochemistry, Oxford University, Oxford, England

I. C. Gunsalus, Biochemistry Division, Department of Chemistry and Chemical Engineering, University of Illinois, Urbana, Illinois

Philip Handler, Department of Biochemistry, Duke University, Durham, North Carolina

Osamu Hayaishi, Department of Medical Chemistry, Faculty of Medicine, Kyoto University, Kyoto, Japan

Peter Hemmerich, Institute for Inorganic Chemistry, University of Basel, Basel, Switzerland

Lloyd L. Ingraham, Department of Biochemistry and Biophysics, University of California, Davis, California

Earl E. Jacobs, Biophysics Laboratory, Stanford University, Stanford, California

Martin D. Kamen, Department of Chemistry, University of California at San Diego, La Jolla, California

Tsoo E. King, Laboratory for Respiratory Enzymology, Oregon State University, Corvallis, Oregon

W. Eugene Knox, Department of Biological Chemistry, Harvard Medical School, and Cancer Research Institute, New England Deaconess Hospital, Boston, Massachusetts

Anthony W. Linnane, Department of Biochemistry, Monash University, Clayton, Victoria, Australia

B. G. Malmström, Department of Biochemistry, University of Göteborgs, Göteborg, Sweden

Howard S. Mason, Department of Biochemistry, University of Oregon Medical School, Portland, Oregon

V. Massey, Department of Biological Chemistry, University of Michigan, Ann Arbor, Michigan

Martin Morrison, Department of Biochemistry, City of Hope Medical Center, Duarte, California

Peter Nicholls, Department of Biochemistry, University of Buffalo School of Medicine, Buffalo, New York

R. O. C. Norman, The Dyson Perrins Laboratory, Oxford University, Oxford, England

Yasuyuki Ogura, Department of Biophysics and Biochemistry, Faculty of Science, University of Tokyo, Tokyo, Japan

K. Okunuki, Department of Biology, Faculty of Science, University of Osaka, Osaka, Japan

L. E. Orgel, Salk Institute, San Diego, California

E. Racker, Department of Biochemistry, The Public Health Research Institute of the City of New York, New York, New York

E. R. Redfearn, Department of Biochemistry, University of Leicester, Leicester, England

Barnett Rosenberg, Department of Biophysics, Michigan State University, East Lansing, Michigan

Ryo Sato, Institute for Protein Research, Osaka University, Osaka, Japan

Thomas P. Singer, Enzyme Division, Edsel B. Ford Institute for Medical Research, Henry Ford Hospital, Detroit, Michigan

E. C. Slater, Laboratory of Physiological Chemistry, University of Amsterdam, Amsterdam, The Netherlands

Lucile Smith, Department of Biochemistry, Dartmouth University Medical School, Hanover, New Hampshire

Hj. Staudinger, Physiologisch-chemisches Institut der Justus Liebig-Universitat Giessen, Giessen, Germany

N. Sutin, Department of Chemistry, Brookhaven National Laboratory, Upton, New York, and Isotope Department, Weizmann Institute of Science, Rehovoth, Israel

Shigeki Takemori, Department of Biology, Faculty of Science, University of Osaka, Osaka, Japan

Charles L. Wadkins, Department of Physiological Chemistry, The Johns Hopkins University School of Medicine, Baltimore, Maryland

W. W. Wainio, Department of Physiology and Biochemistry and the Bureau of Biological Research, Rutgers—The State University, New Brunswick, New Jersey

M. E. Winfield, Division of Physical Chemistry, Commonwealth Scientific and Industrial Research Organization, Melbourne, Australia

I. Yamazaki, Biophysics Division, Research Institute of Applied Electricity, Hokkaido University, Sapporo, Japan

T. Yonetani, Johnson Research Foundation, University of Pennsylvania, Philadelphia, Pennsylvania

# *Preface*

These volumes contain the collected papers and discussion given at An International Symposium on Oxidases and Related Oxidation–Reduction Systems, which was held at Amherst College, Amherst, Massachusetts, during July 15–19, 1964.

This Symposium was organized in order to develop an over-all picture of the state of knowledge in the oxidase field, to clarify the nature of the problems still facing it, and by wide-ranging discussion to stimulate a creative exchange of ideas for their solution. With these aims in mind, and with the advice of a committee consisting of Professors B. Chance, P. George, M. Kamen, and E. C. Slater, to whom the organizers are grateful, a group of fifty specialists was convened. In order to give ample time to prepare for discussion, the papers themselves were preprinted and distributed in early June.

The editorial policy adopted was to consider the preprint as an uncorrected proof, and no substantive changes were allowed without due acknowledgement with reasons for the changes set forth in the final publication. With two exceptions all the preprinted material arrived at Duarte, California, by the end of May, 1964. Two papers were not precirculated before the meeting and are so designated in the volume.

The meeting itself was devoted primarily to a discussion of the preprinted manuscripts. The authors were given opportunity to correct, amend, or extend the material in their papers. After these remarks, general discussion took place. The entire proceedings were recorded, and transcripts were presented to participants for correction. The papers are organized in the following manner: (1) fundamental aspects of oxidation-reduction, (2) oxidases, discussed according to the nature of their prosthetic groups, and (3) organized systems for biological oxidation-reduction. The general discussion of cytochromes $a$ and $a_3$ (pp. 539–548) was organized *impromptu* at the meeting.

Amherst College, through the good offices of Dr. George Kidder and the courtesy of President Calvin H. Plimpton, provided the facilities for the meeting and the staffing. Miss Margaret Boyd, Secretary to Dr. Plimpton, acted as Executive with competence and charm. The National Institutes of Health and the Office of Naval Research provided grants which made the Symposium possible. We wish finally to thank Joyce Morrison for indexing, Walter Vanneste for checking transcripts against master tapes, and the staff of our publishers, John Wiley & Sons, particularly Mrs. Ruth Flohn, for efficient professional assistance throughout the preparation of these volumes.

Tsoo E. King
Howard S. Mason
Martin Morrison

July, *1965*

# Contents

## Part III. Iron-Containing Oxidases

## *Part IV. Flavin-Containing Oxidases*

# Part V. Heme-Containing Oxidases, I

## A MECHANISM AND MODEL OF PEROXIDASE–OXIDASE REACTION    *I. Yamazaki, K. Yokota, and R. Nakajima*    485

# List of Symbols and Abbreviations

Standard symbols and abbreviations as outlined by the *Journal of Biological Chemistry* have been employed. Less commonly employed abbreviations are as follows:

| | |
|---|---|
| BV | benzyl viologen |
| CP | ceruloplasmin |
| *p*-CMB | *p*-chloromercuribenzoate |
| *p*-CMS | *p*-chloromercuriphenylsulfonate |
| DEAE | diethylaminoethyl cellulose |
| DHF | dihydroxyfumarate |
| DHOA | dihydroorotic acid |
| DHOD | dihydroorotic acid dehydrogenase |
| EDTA | ethylenediaminetetraacetic acid |
| EPR | electron paramagnetic resonance |
| ESR | electron spin resonance |
| ETP | electron transport particle |
| $ETP_H$ | electron-transport particle with a limited capability for phosphorylation |
| FlH | flavin, quinonoid form |
| $FlH_2$ | flavin, semiquinonoid form |
| $FlH_3$ | flavin, hydroquinonoid form |
| FMN | riboflavin-5′-phosphate |
| *g* | *g* value of an ESR spectrum |
| Hfs | hyperfine structure (in EPR spectroscopy) |
| *p*-HPP | *p*-hydroxyphenylpyruvate oxidase |
| IMS | inner membrane subunit |
| Lf (or LF) | lumiflavin |
| MORD | magnetically induced optical rotatory dispersion |

| | |
|---|---|
| MV | methyl viologen |
| NMR | nuclear magnetic resonance |
| ORD | optical rotatory dispersion |
| PMS | phenazine methosulfate, N-methylphenazinium methyl sulfate |
| Rf (or RF) | riboflavin |
| RHP | *Rhodospirillum* hemoprotein |
| SDH | succinate dehydrogenase |
| STK | succinate thiokinase |
| TCBQ | tetrachlorobenzoquinone |
| TMPD | N, N, N′, N′-tetramethyl-$p$-phenylenediamine |
| TNP- | trinitrophenyl- |
| TTA | thenoyltrifluoroacetone |

# The Fitness of Oxygen

. . . PHILIP GEORGE

## I. 1913–1963: THE FIFTIETH ANNIVERSARY OF "THE FITNESS OF THE ENVIRONMENT"

With this symposium on oxidases following so closely upon the fiftieth anniversary of the publication of Lawrence J. Henderson's remarkable book, *The Fitness of the Environment* (1), it seems very appropriate that in considering some aspects of the fundamental physical chemistry of oxygen we should re-examine its particular fitness as a terminal oxidant in the light of modern knowledge.

One is immediately struck by the enormous advances bearing on the problem of biological fitness that have been made in chemistry and biochemistry since 1913. For thermodynamic data Henderson could turn only to heats of combustion and formation that were available through the pioneering work of Berthelot and Thomsen in thermochemistry toward the end of the nineteenth century. The systematic determination of standard free energies, the more significant quantities, was only just being undertaken, and ten years were to elapse before Lewis and Randall brought together the data then available in their book, *Thermodynamics and the Free Energy of Chemical Substances* (2). Although the study of chemical kinetics also has a history stretching back into the nineteenth century, the extensive investigation of the role of free radicals in gas-phase reactions and the mechanism of organic and inorganic oxidation-reduction processes in aqueous solution was a development of the 1920's and 1930's. The electronic theory of valence, and with it the electronic interpretation of the chemical reactivity of molecules, have been built up in their entirety since 1913. The brilliant experimental studies of metabolism and biosynthesis, including those which established the nature and sequence of the enzymes that transport electrons or reduction equivalents, almost all date from that time too.

3

The range of topics for a present-day inquiry following Henderson's lead is thus enormously greater. Moreover the advances in physical chemistry enable more telling observations to be made. New correlations can be set up, and more penetrating questions can be raised.

In a thorough treatment of the fitness of oxygen, its properties at both the macroscopic and molecular levels would have to be considered; kinetic and thermodynamic aspects of its reactivity would have to be explored in terms of electronic theory. However, the uncertainty which still surrounds the precise nature of the mechanism of its most important biochemical reactions severely limits any discussion of kinetic aspects. This paper, therefore, will be devoted mainly to thermodynamic aspects which are not subject to this limitation. It seems a natural choice in developing Henderson's theme, and a very fitting one, because the role that oxygen is able to play depends ultimately on the favorable free energy change associated with its reduction from the gaseous elemental state to liquid water.

## II. OXYGEN AS THE TERMINAL OXIDANT COMPARED TO OTHER ELEMENTS OF LOW ATOMIC WEIGHT

Given that the favorable free energy of reduction of oxygen to water is of paramount importance biologically, and assuming that only chemical elements need be considered in this role, one is confronted with three questions. First, are any other elements better than oxygen in this respect? Second, could any other element reasonably be expected to replace oxygen? And,

TABLE 1

Standard Entropies and Enthalpies of Atomization for Several Elements of Low Atomic Weight, Together with the Thermochemical Bond Energies for Their Simple Hydrides, All at 25°C

Standard states: fugacities of 1 atm, and the most stable solid states as specified.

| Element | State | $S°$, eu | $\Delta H_a°$, kcal/mole | Hydride | $E_{X-H}$, kcal/mole |
|---------|-------|----------|--------------------------|---------|----------------------|
| $H_2$ | g | 31.211 | 52.09 | ... | ... |
| $F_2$ | g | 48.6 | 18.5 | HF | 135 |
| $O_2$ | g | 49.003 | 59.54 | $H_2O$ | 110.75 |
| $N_2$ | g | 45.767 | 112.9 | $NH_3$ | 93.4 |
| C | Graphite | 1.3609 | 170.9 | $CH_4$ | 99.3 |
| $Cl_2$ | g | 53.286 | 28.94 | HCl | 103.1 |
| S | Rhombic | 7.62 | ~57 | $H_2S$ | 83 |
| P | White | 10.6 | 75.3 | $PH_3$ | 76.8 |
| Si | Cond. | 4.47 | 105 | $SiH_4$ | 76.5 |

third, to what particular properties does oxygen owe the very favorable value for its free energy of reduction?

Qualitatively, the answer to the first question has long been commonplace inorganic chemistry; the elements that are strong oxidizing agents are those of lower atomic weight in Groups VI and VII of the periodic table. So we would expect only $F_2$, $Cl_2$, $Br_2$, and possibly $I_2$ and S to be serious contenders. In the present context, however, a quantitative approach is called for, and a detailed one. It will be necessary to examine critically the individual terms that make up the standard free energy change, and the elements in the first two rows of the periodic table will be considered first to establish some important trends.

## A. Sources of Data*

The thermodynamic data in Tables 1, 2, and 3 have been taken mostly from the *National Bureau of Standards Circular* No. 500 (3) and Latimer's book on oxidation potentials (4). The enthalpies of atomization and thermochemical bond energies are those adopted by Cottrell (5); it should be noted that the value for $\Delta H_a^\circ(O_2)_g$, 59.54 kcal/g atom, is a little greater than that listed in the NBS publication, i.e., 59.16 kcal/g atom. The values of $\Delta F_f^\circ$, $\Delta H_f^\circ$, and $\bar{S}^\circ$ for aqueous HF have been calculated from the corresponding values for aqueous $F^-$ by utilizing the ionization data of Broeue and DeVries (6); the numbers in the NBS tables are identical for $HF_{aq}$ and $F_{aq}^-$, which would be acceptable on the convention that $\Delta F_f^\circ$, $\Delta H_f^\circ$, and $\bar{S}^\circ$ are zero for the hydrogen ion only if HF were a strong acid like HCl, HBr, etc. The data for $PH_3$ and $SiH_4$ incorporate the most recent values for $\Delta H_f^\circ$ from the experimental studies of Gunn and Green (7); the values for aqueous $CH_4$ are based on the measurements of Claussen and Polglase (8).

## B. Thermodynamic Data for the Formation of the Hydrides of Carbon, Nitrogen, Oxygen, Fluorine, Silicon, Phosphorus, Sulfur, and Chlorine

In comparing gas-phase reactions of the same chemical type it is often found that differences in chemical affinity, as expressed by the standard free

---

* *Symbols:* Standard free energies, enthalpies, and entropies of formation of substances from their component elements in their standard states, at 25°C, are denoted by the symbols $\Delta F_f^\circ$, $\Delta H_f^\circ$, and $\Delta S_f^\circ$, respectively.

Standard entropies for gases, liquids, and solids at 25°C are denoted by $S^\circ$, and standard partial molal entropies for 1 molal aqueous solutions by the symbol $\bar{S}^\circ$.

Enthalpies of atomization, often referred to as "heats" of atomization, are denoted by the symbol $\Delta H_a^\circ$.

When the need arises to specify any of these quantities for a particular compound, its formula is added in parentheses after the symbol with a subscript to indicate the physical state; e.g., $\Delta F_f^\circ(H_2O_2)_g$ denotes the standard free energy of formation of gaseous hydrogen peroxide.

Bond dissociation energies and thermochemical bond energies at 25°C are denoted by the symbols $D$ and $E$, respectively, with an appropriate subscript to identify the bond.

energy changes, arise chiefly through differences in the enthalpy changes, the similarity in number and nature of reactants and products leading to entropy changes that are not very different in magnitude.

This is true for the formation of the gaseous hydrides of the lighter elements in Groups IV, V, VI, and VII, as can be seen from the values of $\Delta H_f^\circ$ and $\Delta S_f^\circ$

TABLE 2

Thermodynamic Data for the Hydrides of F, O, N, C, Cl, S, P, and Si at 25°C

Standard states: fugacities of 1 atm, and 1 molal solutions.

| Hydride | State | $\Delta H_f^\circ$, kcal/mole | $\Delta F_f^\circ$, kcal/mole | $\Delta S_f^\circ$, eu | $S^\circ$, eu | $\bar{S}^\circ$, eu |
|---|---|---|---|---|---|---|
| HF | g | −64.2 | −64.7 | +1.56 | 41.47 | ... |
|  | aq | −75.48 | −70.41 | −17.0 | ... | 22.9 |
| F⁻ | aq | −78.66 | −66.08 | −42.2 | ... | −2.3 |
| $H_2O$ | g | −57.80 | −54.64 | −10.60 | 45.11 | ... |
|  | l | −68.32 | −56.69 | −38.99 | ... | 16.72 |
|  | "aq" | −68.32 | −59.11 | −30.9 | ... | 24.8 |
| $NH_3$ | g | −11.04 | −3.98 | −23.69 | 46.01 | ... |
|  | aq | −19.32 | −6.36 | −43.3 | ... | 26.4 |
| $NH_4^+$ | aq | −31.72 | −18.97 | −44.0 | ... | 25.7 |
| $CH_4$ | g | −17.89 | −12.14 | −19.28 | 44.50 | ... |
|  | aq | −20.94 | −8.25 | −42.5 | ... | 21.3 |
| HCl | g | −22.06 | −22.77 | +2.37 | 44.62 | ... |
|  | aq | −40.02 | −31.35 | −29.0 | ... | 13.2 |
| Cl⁻ | aq | −40.02 | −31.35 | −29.0 | ... | 13.2 |
| $H_2S$ | g | −4.82 | −7.89 | +10.32 | 49.15 | ... |
|  | aq | −9.2 | −6.54 | +9.6 | ... | 29.2 |
| HS⁻ | aq | −4.22 | +3.01 | −24.2 | ... | 14.6 |
| $PH_3$ | g | +1.3 | +3.45 | −7.2 | 50.2 | ... |
| $SiH_4$ | g | +7.3 | +12.7 | −18.2 | 48.7 | ... |

in Table 2 and from the plots of $\Delta H_f^\circ$ and $\Delta F_f^\circ$ in Fig. 1, which follow each other quite closely. On closer inspection, however, it appears that the entropy change makes a small but important contribution to $\Delta F_f^\circ$ in an irregular manner. With the first-row elements $\Delta S_f^\circ$ becomes progressively more negative as we go from fluorine to oxygen to nitrogen, but there is a discontinuity between nitrogen and carbon; on the other hand, with the second-row elements there is a discontinuity between chlorine and sulfur, and then the values become progressively more negative as we go from sulfur to phosphorus to silicon. Two effects are superimposed here. The nature of the stoichiometry of the reactions in which the hydrides are formed is such that the entropy change should become progressively more negative as we go from Group VII to Group IV because the consumption of hydrogen increases per mole of hydride, e.g.,

$$\text{Fluorine} + \tfrac{1}{2}H_2 \rightarrow HF \tag{1}$$

$$\text{Oxygen} + H_2 \rightarrow H_2O \tag{2}$$

$$\text{Nitrogen} + \tfrac{3}{2}H_2 \rightarrow NH_3 \tag{3}$$

$$\text{Carbon} + 2H_2 \rightarrow CH_4 \tag{4}$$

But the physical character of the elements in each row is not identical in the standard state at 25°. In the first row, fluorine, oxygen, and nitrogen are

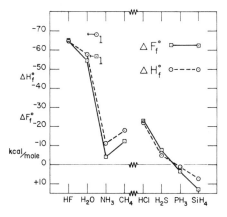

**Fig. 1.** Trends in the values of $\Delta H_f^\circ$ and $\Delta F_f^\circ$ for the gaseous hydrides of the Group IV to Group VII elements in the first and second rows of the periodic table. For $H_2O$ the subsidiary points indicate the values for the formation of water.

diatomic gases, whereas carbon is the solid, graphite; in the second row, chlorine is a diatomic gas, but the remaining elements, sulfur, phosphorus, and silicon, are solid. These differences in the character of the standard state of the element account for the discontinuities in the trend of $\Delta S_f^\circ$ because $S^\circ$ for the diatomic gases ranges from 45 to 53 eu, whereas $S^\circ$ for the solid elements is much smaller, ranging from 1 to 10 eu.

Effects arising from the stoichiometry of the reactions and from the character of the standard states can also be traced in the values of $\Delta H_f^\circ$, although there are no clear-cut discontinuities. The properties which determine the magnitude of $\Delta H_f^\circ$ are the enthalpies of atomization of the element and of hydrogen, and the thermochemical bond energy of the "X-H" bond in the hydride. When HF is taken to illustrate the interplay between these quantities, the Born-Haber cycle

$$
\begin{array}{c}
\text{F} \; + \; \text{H} \quad\underline{\quad E_{\text{F}-\text{H}}\quad} \\
\end{array}
$$

$$\Delta H_a^\circ(\text{F}_2)_\text{g} \qquad \Delta H_a^\circ(\text{H}_2)_\text{g}$$

$$\tfrac{1}{2}\text{F}_2 + \tfrac{1}{2}\text{H}_2 \longrightarrow \text{HF} + \Delta H_f^\circ(\text{HF})_\text{g}$$

shows that

$$\Delta H_f^\circ(\text{HF})_\text{g} = \Delta H_a^\circ(\text{F}_2)_\text{g} + \Delta H_a^\circ(\text{H}_2)_\text{g} - E_{\text{F}-\text{H}} \tag{5}$$

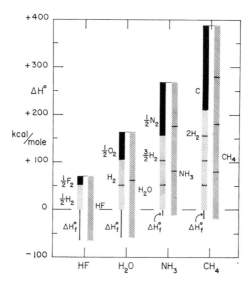

**Fig. 2.** Bar-graph representations of the Born-Haber cycles for the formation of HF, H$_2$O, NH$_3$, and CH$_4$ in the gas phase at 25°C.

For the other elements in the first row the corresponding equations are

$$\Delta H_f^\circ(\text{H}_2\text{O})_\text{g} = \Delta H_a^\circ(\text{O}_2)_\text{g} + 2\Delta H_a^\circ(\text{H}_2)_\text{g} - 2E_{\text{O}-\text{H}} \tag{6}$$

$$\Delta H_f^\circ(\text{NH}_3)_\text{g} = \Delta H_a^\circ(\text{N}_2)_\text{g} + 3\Delta H_a^\circ(\text{H}_2)_\text{g} - 3E_{\text{N}-\text{H}} \tag{7}$$

$$\Delta H_f^\circ(\text{CH}_4)_\text{g} = \Delta H_a^\circ(\text{C})_\text{graph} + 4\Delta H_a^\circ(\text{H}_2)_\text{g} - 4E_{\text{C}-\text{H}} \tag{8}$$

These equations, and those for the second-row elements with the appropriate values for the various quantities, are presented as bar graphs in Figs. 2 and 3, respectively, with the thick vertical line denoting $\Delta H_f^\circ$ in each case.

For given values of $\Delta H_a^\circ$ for the elements and $E_{\text{X}-\text{H}}$ for the hydrides, the effect of the varying stoichiometry is to make $\Delta H_a^\circ$ relatively less important as we go from the elements in Group VII to those in Group IV, because, as can be seen from equations 5–8, while $1 \times \Delta H_a^\circ$ is involved in each case, $E_{\text{X}-\text{H}}$ is involved to the extent of $1\times$, $2\times$, $3\times$, and $4\times$, respectively.

The physical character of the element in its standard state is reflected in the value of $\Delta H_f^\circ$ in that $\Delta H_a^\circ$ for fluorine, oxygen, nitrogen, and chlorine is half the bond dissociation energy for the diatomic gases, whereas for carbon, sulfur, phosphorus, and silicon it refers to the production of atoms from the more (most) stable solid form at 25°C. Although this is an important distinction with respect to $\Delta S_f^\circ$ because of the big difference between the entropies of diatomic gaseous elements and those of solid elements, it is less significant in the case of $\Delta H_f^\circ$ because the values of $\Delta H_a^\circ$ for the solid elements are as

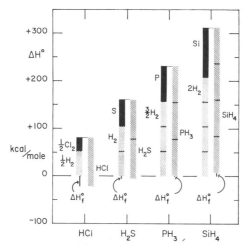

**Fig. 3.** Bar-graph representations of the Born-Haber cycles for the formation of HCl, $H_2S$, $PH_3$, and $SiH_4$ in the gas phase at 25°C.

large as or larger than the bond dissociation energies. This is only to be expected, since covalent bonds are also broken in the atomization of these solid elements, namely, the bonds in the graphite structure of carbon, in the $P_4$ tetrahedral structure of phosphorus, etc. In fact, when the values of $\Delta H_a^\circ$ are plotted, as in Fig. 4, there is a smooth decrease with increasing atomic number which is in keeping with the increase in electronegativity.

This increase in electronegativity is also responsible for the trend in the values of $E_{X-H}$, which increase with atomic number from nitrogen to fluorine and from phosphorus to chlorine. However, unlike the values of $\Delta H_a^\circ$, which decrease progressively for all four elements in each row, $E_{N-H}$ is appreciably less than $E_{C-H}$, and $E_{P-H}$ is almost the same as $E_{Si-H}$.

Reference to equations 5–8 shows that $\Delta H_f^\circ$ makes the more favorable contribution to $\Delta F_f^\circ$ (i.e., is more negative) the lower the value of $\Delta H_a^\circ$ and the higher the value of $E_{X-H}$. Since $E_{X-H}$ increases and $\Delta H_a^\circ$ decreases as we go from the elements of Group IV to those of Group VII (see Fig. 4), the underlying trend is for progressively more favorable values of $\Delta H_f^\circ$ in this order.

But, although $\Delta H_a^\circ$ decreases more rapidly than $E_{X-H}$ increases, the stoichiometry of the reactions calls for different relative contributions from these two terms and from $\Delta H_a^\circ(H_2)_g$ as shown above, and the final outcome is an irregular trend in the values of $\Delta H_f^\circ$ for the first-row elements, namely, HF $-64.2$, H$_2$O $-57.8$, NH$_3$ $-11.0$, and CH$_4$ $-17.9$ kcal/mole, even though a regular trend does appear for the second-row elements, HCl $-22.1$, H$_2$S $-4.8$, PH$_3$ $+1.3$, and SiH$_4$ $+7.3$ kcal/mole.

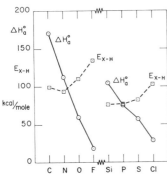

**Fig. 4.** The variation of $\Delta H_a^\circ$ and $E_{X-H}$ with atomic number for the Group IV to Group VII elements in the first and second rows of the periodic table.

The discontinuities we have noted in the values of $\Delta S_f^\circ$, which arise from the different physical characters of the elements in their standard states, are not such as to alter these relationships when the contribution of $T\Delta S_f^\circ$ to $\Delta F_f^\circ$ is taken into account. With the first-row elements the trend is also irregular for the values of $\Delta F_f^\circ$: HF $-64.7$, H$_2$O $-54.6$, NH$_3$ $-4.0$, and CH$_4$ $-12.1$ kcal/mole; and it is regular again for the second-row elements, HCl $-22.8$, H$_2$S $-7.9$, PH$_3$ $+3.5$, and SiH$_4$ $+12.7$ kcal/mole. It is to be noted that, except in the case of fluorine, chlorine, and sulfur, $T\Delta S_f^\circ$ makes an unfavorable contribution to $\Delta F_f^\circ$.

In considering the reactions in which the *aqueous* hydrides are formed, and liquid water in the case of oxygen, the thermodynamic data for the intermolecular solution and condensation process enter as additional terms modifying those for the gas-phase reactions. Data for all except PH$_3$ and SiH$_4$ are available; see Table 2. These terms are not large in comparison to those for the intramolecular bond breaking and making steps in the gas phase, but there are some significant differences. Hydrogen fluoride and NH$_3$ have quite favorable enthalpies of solution, $-11.3$ and $-8.3$ kcal/mole, respectively, which are similar to the enthalpy of condensation of water, $-10.5$ kcal/mole. The entropies of solution and condensation are all unfavorable, but the $T\Delta S^\circ$ terms are smaller in magnitude than the enthalpies, so the resulting free energies of solution and condensation favor the process. This is not the case for CH$_4$; the enthalpy of solution is still favorable but is much smaller, $-3.1$ kcal/mole; so that with an unfavorable entropy of solution, almost the same as that for HF and NH$_3$, the resulting free energy of solution is unfavorable to the extent of $+3.9$ kcal/mole. This difference in behavior is clearly attributable to hydrogen bond formation between HF, NH$_3$, and the water, which cannot occur with CH$_4$.

In the case of the second-row elements, the data for HCl resemble those for HF, although it must be remembered that in a 1 molal solution HCl is completely ionized, whereas HF, with a $pK^\circ$ of 3.17, is not. On the other hand, the data for $H_2S$ are like those for $CH_4$ rather than $H_2O$; a small favorable enthalpy of solution is outweighed by the $T\Delta S^\circ$ term, and the free energy of solution is unfavorable to the extent of $+1.35$ kcal/mole. Weaker hydrogen bonding is presumably responsible.

Hence, in calculating $\Delta H_f^\circ$ and $\Delta F_f^\circ$ for the aqueous hydrides, these data for the solution (condensation) process serve only to change the values for the gaseous hydrides by a few kilocalories per mole, and the general trends in the values remain substantially unaltered. For the aqueous hydrides, $\Delta H_f^\circ$ has the following values: HF $-75.5$, $H_2O_1$ $-68.3$, $NH_3$ $-19.3$, $CH_4$ $-20.9$, HCl $-40.0$, and $H_2S$ $-9.4$ kcal/mole; and $\Delta F_f^\circ$: HF $-70.4$, $H_2O_1$ $-56.7$, $H_2O_{aq}$ $-59.1$, $NH_3$ $-6.4$, $CH_4$ $-8.3$, HCl $-31.4$, and $H_2S$ $-6.5$ kcal/mole. It is to be noted that $T\Delta S_f^\circ$ makes an unfavorable contribution to $\Delta F_f^\circ$ for all the aqueous hydrides except $H_2S$.

Further changes are brought about by the ionization of the weak acids HF and $H_2S$ and by the formation of the $NH_4^+$ ion; see Table 2. But only the latter reaction affects the general trends; the values of both $\Delta H_f^\circ$ and $\Delta F_f^\circ$ for $NH_4^+$ are appreciably more negative than those for $CH_4$, in contrast to the values for $NH_3$, which are slightly more positive.

### C. The Fitness of Oxygen from the Point of View of Its Favorable Free Energy of Reduction to Water

We have now assembled all the data necessary for an evaluation of oxygen compared to the other first- and second-row elements in Groups IV, V, VI, and VII with respect to the over-all reduction processes yielding the aqueous hydrides.

The values of $\Delta F_f^\circ$ for the aqueous hydrides are, of course, per *mole*; and on this basis, with 1 molal $H_2O$ as the standard state for water, oxygen is inferior only to fluorine, by 11.3 kcal/mole. It is superior to chlorine by 27.7 kcal/mole and to nitrogen in its reduction to the ammonium ion by 40.1 kcal/mole, and much superior to carbon and sulfur, by more than 50 kcal/mole. With the exception of sulfur, for which the $T\Delta S_f^\circ$ term is slightly favorable, $\Delta H_f^\circ$ constitutes the sole driving force, more than compensating for substantially unfavorable $T\Delta S_f^\circ$ terms.

However, since the "lowest common factor" in oxidation-reduction reactions is not the *mole* but the *equivalent*, it has been customary to make comparisons of relative oxidizing power on this basis, dividing $\Delta F_f^\circ$ by $nF$, where $n$ is the number of equivalents and $F$ the Faraday, to give the $E^0$ values for the corresponding standard electrode reactions at $[H^+] = 1$ (see Table 3). On this more familiar basis chlorine is a little better oxidizing agent than oxygen, and fluorine is far superior. The values of $\Delta F^\circ$, $\Delta H^\circ$, and $\Delta S^\circ$ per equivalent are given in Table 4. For each element the enthalpy and entropy terms make

### TABLE 3

**Oxidation-Reduction Potentials at 25°C for Element/Hydride Couples in Acidic Solution and at pH 7.0**

Standard states: elements, the physical state at 25°C; hydrides, 1 molal solution of the appropriate species at $[H^+] = 1$, and $10^{-7}$, respectively.

| Acidic Solution, $[H^+] = 1$ | | At pH 7.0 | |
|---|---|---|---|
| Electrode Reaction | $E^0$, volts | Electrode Reaction | $E^{0\prime}$, volts |
| $\frac{1}{2}F_2 + H^+ + e^- \rightleftharpoons HF$ | +3.06 | $\frac{1}{2}F_2 + e^- \rightleftharpoons F^-$ | +2.87 |
| $\frac{1}{4}O_2 + H^+ + e^- \rightleftharpoons \frac{1}{2}H_2O$ | +1.23 | $\frac{1}{4}O_2 + H^+ + e^- \rightleftharpoons \frac{1}{2}H_2O$ | +0.82 |
| $\frac{1}{6}N_2 + \frac{4}{3}H^+ + e^- \rightleftharpoons \frac{1}{3}NH_4^+$ | +0.27 | $\frac{1}{6}N_2 + \frac{4}{3}H^+ + e^- \rightleftharpoons \frac{1}{3}NH_4^+$ | -0.28 |
| $\frac{1}{4}C + H^+ + e^- \rightleftharpoons \frac{1}{4}CH_4$ | +0.09 | $\frac{1}{4}C + H^+ + e^- \rightleftharpoons \frac{1}{4}CH_4$ | -0.32 |
| $\frac{1}{2}Cl_2 + e^- \rightleftharpoons Cl^-$ | +1.36 | $\frac{1}{2}Cl_2 + e^- \rightleftharpoons Cl^-$ | +1.36 |
| $\frac{1}{2}S + H^+ + e^- \rightleftharpoons \frac{1}{2}H_2S$ | +0.14 | $\frac{1}{2}S + 0.74H^+ + e^- \rightleftharpoons$ $0.24H_2S + 0.26HS^-$ | -0.27 |
| $\frac{1}{2}Br_2 + e^- \rightleftharpoons Br^-$ | +1.07 | $\frac{1}{2}Br_2 + e^- \rightleftharpoons Br^-$ | +1.07 |
| $\frac{1}{2}Se + H^+ + e^- \rightleftharpoons \frac{1}{2}H_2Se$ | -0.40 | $\frac{1}{2}Se + \frac{1}{2}H^+ + e^- \rightleftharpoons \frac{1}{2}HSe^-$ | -0.72 |
| $\frac{1}{2}I_2 + e^- \rightleftharpoons I^-$ | +0.54 | $\frac{1}{2}I_2 + e^- \rightleftharpoons I^-$ | +0.54 |
| $\frac{1}{2}Te + H^+ + e^- \rightleftharpoons \frac{1}{2}H_2Te$ | -0.74 | $\frac{1}{2}Te + \frac{1}{2}H^+ + e^- \rightleftharpoons \frac{1}{2}HTe^-$ | -1.02 |

the same relative contributions to the standard free energy change as on the mole basis, but, since the stoichiometry of the reduction reaction differs, the trends in the values for the free energy, enthalpy, and entropy terms are all modified somewhat. As can be seen from Table 4, $\Delta F^\circ$ becomes progressively more favorable in going from carbon to fluorine, as does $\Delta H^\circ$, whereas the values of $\Delta S^\circ$ are no longer so unfavorable for oxygen, nitrogen, and carbon in relation to fluorine.

### TABLE 4

**Thermodynamic Data per Equivalent for the Standard Cell Reactions Involving the Element/Hydride Couples of F, O, N, C, Cl, and S at 25°C**

Standard states: as in Table 3.

| Reaction | $\Delta F^\circ$ | $\Delta H^\circ$ | $\Delta S^\circ$ |
|---|---|---|---|
| $\frac{1}{2}F_2 + \frac{1}{2}H_2 \rightleftharpoons HF$ | -70.41 | -75.48 | -17.0 |
| $\frac{1}{4}O_2 + \frac{1}{2}H_2 \rightleftharpoons \frac{1}{2}H_2O$ | -28.35 | -34.16 | -19.5 |
| $\frac{1}{6}N_2 + \frac{1}{2}H_2 + \frac{1}{3}H^+ \rightleftharpoons \frac{1}{3}NH_4^+$ | -6.32 | -10.57 | -14.7 |
| $\frac{1}{4}C + \frac{1}{2}H_2 \rightleftharpoons \frac{1}{4}CH_4$ | -2.06 | -5.24 | -10.6 |
| $\frac{1}{2}Cl_2 + \frac{1}{2}H_2 \rightleftharpoons Cl^- + H^+$ | -31.35 | -40.02 | -29.0 |
| $\frac{1}{2}S + \frac{1}{2}H_2 \rightleftharpoons \frac{1}{2}H_2S$ | -3.27 | -4.7 | +4.8 |

The $E^{0\prime}$ values at pH 7.0 for the first- and second-row elements in Groups IV–VII are also given in Table 3. Because $H^+$ is involved in a different manner and to a different extent in the various reactions—i.e., HF and $H_2S$ ionize, ammonia is present as the ammonium ion, and HCl is a strong acid so that $H^+$ does not participate at all in the electrode reaction—the relative values of $E^{0\prime}$ are different from those of $E^0$. But these effects are not great enough to change the elements in their order of oxidizing power.

Exactly the same considerations hold for the elements of higher atomic weight. To complete these comparisons, the $E^0$ and $E^{0\prime}$ values for selenium, bromine, tellurium, and iodine are also included in Table 3.

We thus have answers to the first two questions posed at the beginning of section II. No matter whether we compare the free energy data per mole or per equivalent, fluorine is a much better oxidizing agent than oxygen. This more advantageous thermodynamic reactivity, however, is matched by extreme kinetic reactivity, and the very ready attack by fluorine on R-H and other bonds renders it quite unsuitable as the terminal oxidant for biological systems. Moreover, oxygen would be evolved in an aqueous environment by the reaction

$$2F_{2\,g} + 2H_2O_1 \rightarrow O_{2\,g} + 4HF_{aq} \qquad (9)$$

which has the highly favorable standard free energy change of $-168.3$ kcal/mole.

Chlorine and bromine have $E^0$ values very similar to oxygen, but their kinetic reactivity, although less than that of fluorine, again makes them unsuitable as biological oxidizing agents. Furthermore, in aqueous solution the highly reactive hypochlorite and hypobromite ions are formed, e.g.,

$$Cl_2 + H_2O \rightarrow H^+ + Cl^- + HOCl \qquad (10)$$

Iodine is quite a good oxidizing agent but appreciably weaker than oxygen; and, on the basis of the $E^0$ values for nitrogen, carbon, sulfur, selenium, and tellurium, and the $\Delta F_f^\circ$ values for phosphorus and silicon, it is clear that none of these other elements merits consideration in relation to oxygen.

In regard to the third question, namely, to what particular properties does oxygen owe the very favorable value for its free energy of reduction, the various fundamental quantities which determine the standard enthalpy and entropy of formation of water, and hence its free energy of formation, have already been discussed in section IIB. The salient points may be summarized as follows:

1. $\Delta H_f^\circ$ is solely responsible for the favorable $\Delta F_f^\circ$ of gaseous, liquid, and "aqueous" $H_2O$ ("aqueous" referring to the standard state of 1 molal, instead of the pure liquid). In all cases, $T\Delta S_f^\circ$ is unfavorable.

2. $\Delta H_f^\circ$ for gaseous $H_2O$, which contains the intramolecular bond energy terms, makes by far the largest contribution, although the enthalpy change for

the transition from the gaseous to the liquid (solution) phase is by no means insignificant. The hydrogen bonding in liquid water is thus an important factor.

3. From the trend in $\Delta H_f^{\circ}$ values for the gaseous hydrides it is apparent that the especially favorable value for $H_2O$, exceeded only by that for HF, arises from the combination of a "low" enthalpy of atomization with a "high" thermochemical bond energy in the hydride. In other words, although there is a double bond in the oxygen molecule, it is not a particularly strong one, whereas the O-H bond in $H_2O$ is one of the strongest "X-H" bonds. The property underlying this relationship is the increase in electronegativity from the Group IV to the Group VII elements, which is greatest for the elements of lowest atomic weight.

Even though the double bond in the oxygen molecule, with a dissociation energy of 119.08 kcal/mole at 25°C, is not as strong, e.g., as C=C 145.8, C=N 147, and C=O 179 kcal/mole, it is nevertheless much stronger than the single bond in the halogens, $F_2$ 37, $Cl_2$ 57.9, $Br_2$ 53.4, and $I_2$ 51.0 kcal/mole. This is undoubtedly an important factor contributing to the usually more sluggish kinetic reactivity of oxygen as compared to the halogens. Furthermore, the high electronegativity of oxygen in relation to carbon severely limits the type of double bond addition reaction that can occur. Hence, in oxygen we have the element with the most favorable free energy of reduction coupled with a rather sluggish kinetic reactivity, at least in the absence of appropriate catalysts. These criteria make it exceptionally suitable for the role of biological oxidant.

### D. The Fitness of Oxygen from the Point of View of Its Physical State and Solubility

In the foregoing discussion the physical state of the element was passed over, except to note its bearing upon the enthalpy of atomization and its influence on the entropy change for the reduction reaction. The physical state has, however, a more direct and more obvious significance. A solid or liquid substance as oxidant would have to be taken in as food by living organisms and would thus restrict their habitat to regions where it was available. On the other hand a gaseous oxidant, by its very ubiquity in the atmosphere, poses no such limitation. Moreover, since the reductants, i.e., the substrates, are derived almost invariably from solid or liquid foods, the combination of both oxidant and reductant in these physical states would accentuate the limitation even more, and only in the hydrosphere would conditions be reasonably favorable for life, provided of course that the oxidant was fairly soluble.

Among the relevant elements, only fluorine, chlorine, bromine (by virtue of its high vapor pressure), oxygen, and nitrogen are gases, and thus meet the first of these criteria of fitness. With regard to solubility in water, fluorine undergoes rapid chemical reaction; and although chlorine and bromine react more slowly, they are quite soluble, giving saturated solutions of about $9 \times 10^{-2}$ and $2.2 \times 10^{-1}$ $M$, respectively. Nitrogen and oxygen at 1 atm pressure are less soluble, giving about 0.8 and $1.4 \times 10^{-3}$ $M$ solutions at 25°C. In a careful comparative study of the solubility of argon, nitrogen, and oxygen, Klots and Benson (9) have shown unambiguously that a previous notion of a unique water-oxygen complex is untenable. Even so, oxygen has a fair solubility, eminently useful, and far greater than that of the solid elements—carbon, sulfur, phosphorus, etc.

As we have seen, the kinetic reactivity of the halogens makes them unsuitable as biological oxidants, and nitrogen is too poor an oxidizing agent. Oxygen is thus the only element in the most appropriate physical state, with a satisfactory solubility in water, and with the desirable combination of kinetic and thermodynamic properties.

## III. INTERMEDIATES IN THE REDUCTION OF OXYGEN TO WATER

The reduction of the halogens involves the fission of single bonds, and although the gas-phase reaction with hydrogen is extremely complicated for all the halogens except iodine, the intermediates are restricted in chemical type to the halogen atom and excited molecular species because the reduction is necessarily a two-equivalent process.

With oxygen, however, the fission of the double bond is necessarily a four-equivalent process, and as a consequence there is a greater variety of chemical species as possible reaction intermediates. Besides oxygen atoms and excited molecular species, the radicals $HO_2$ and $HO$ need to be considered, and in addition the stable two-equivalent reduction stage—hydrogen peroxide. The reaction with hydrogen in the gas phase is notoriously complicated, and in aqueous solution it has proved no less difficult to establish unequivocally the mechanism of the reduction of oxygen to water. Just as in the gas-phase reaction the mechanism evidently depends upon physical factors which influence the mode of chain initiation and termination and the type of chain carrier, so in solution different mechanisms evidently operate, depending upon experimental conditions and the nature of the reducing agent.

The mechanism by which reduction occurs at the terminus of the cytochrome system is also very obscure. Two points serve to guide us. First, through the reaction pathway provided by cytochrome oxidase, the process responds rapidly and is able to hold the chemical potential of reducing equivalents in the cytochrome system at a low level. Second, the pathway appears to be self-contained, in that there is no evidence for the escape of intermediates and their subsequent reaction with other components of the cytochrome system or cellular constituents in general.

This second point, in relation to enzyme specificity, was appreciated many years ago [see, for example, Oppenheimer and Stern (10)], and it has been used as a telling argument against the participation of free-radical intermediates. The supposition that adsorbed radicals are involved is in itself too facile an explanation, for, were this to be true, the problems would still remain of specifying the nature of the adsorption and accounting for the altered reactivity.

Thermodynamic data for the simple reduction pathways involving the radical intermediates are nevertheless important for two reasons. First, any unfavorable step or steps may be indicative of stages in the reduction process where the participation of the oxidase is essential, not merely to ensure an adequate rate of reaction, but also to establish a new type of pathway with favorable characteristics in order to achieve an adequate rate. Second, by using these data together with those for various hemoprotein couples, estimates can be made for certain steps in some of the reaction mechanisms which have been postulated.

The high reactivity of the radicals $HO_2$ and $HO$ precludes any direct determination of data for the four-step reduction of oxygen to water, and all values must necessarily be calculated from enthalpy and entropy data obtained indirectly in various ways. In the following sections new calculations are presented for the reduction pathway via $H_2O_2$ which are based upon more recent data than those used in a previous discussion of this topic [George and Griffith (11)]. In addition, values have been calculated for the alternative pathway via "$H_2O + O$" as the two-equivalent reduction stage.

## A. Sources of Data

The values for the enthalpies of formation of the various species in the gas phase and the bond dissociation energies listed in Tables 5 and 6 are those given by Gray (12) in his critical review, with but one modification. The value of 59.54 kcal/atom is used for $\Delta H_a^\circ(O_2)_g$, following Cottrell (5), instead of 59.16 kcal/atom (3). As a consequence a corresponding small change is introduced in the value for $\Delta H_f^\circ(HO)_g$ and in several of the bond dissociation energies. Because of their usefulness for certain other purposes the thermochemical bond energies $E_{O-O}$ in $HO_2$ and $H_2O_2$ have been calculated from these data, taking $E_{O-H} = 110.8$ kcal, the value for water. No distinction can be made, of course, between $D$ and $E$ for the diatomic molecules $O_2$ and OH.

The values of $\Delta H_f^\circ$ for the aqueous solution species, calculated from the corresponding gas-phase values and the enthalpies of solution, likewise follow those of Gray. It is to be noted that values have to be assumed for the enthalpies of solution of the highly reactive species O, HO, and $HO_2$. Gray adopted the value of $-2 \pm 1$ kcal/mole for oxygen suggested by Evans, Hush, and Uri (13); but in the case of HO and $HO_2$ he presented several reasons for choosing somewhat lower values than those of these authors, namely, $-7 \pm 2.5$ and $-8 \pm 2.5$ kcal/mole instead of $-10.5$ and $-12.3$ kcal/mole, respectively.

### TABLE 5

**Thermodynamic Data for Calculations Relating to the Reduction of Oxygen to Water at 25°C via the Radicals $HO_2$ and HO, with Hydrogen Peroxide, or Water and an Oxygen Atom, as the Two-Equivalent Intermediate[a,b]**

Standard states: fugacities of 1 atm, and 1 molal solutions.

| Com-pound | State | $\Delta H_f^\circ$, kcal/mole | $\Delta F_f^\circ$, kcal/mole | $\Delta S_f^\circ$, eu | $S^\circ$, eu | $\bar{S}^\circ$, eu |
|---|---|---|---|---|---|---|
| $H_2$ | g | 0 | 0 | 0 | 31.21 | ... |
| $O_2$ | g | 0 | 0 | 0 | 49.00 | ... |
| O | g | 59.54 | 55.37 | 13.97 | 38.47 | ... |
| O | aq | $57.5 \pm 1$ | $60.9 \pm 1$ | $-11.5 \pm 1$ | ... | $13 \pm 1$ |
| HO | g | $9.2 \pm 0.5$ | $8.1 \pm 0.5$ | $+3.8$ | 43.88 | ... |
| HO | aq | $2 \pm 3$ | $6.8 \pm 3$ | $-16.1 \pm 1$ | ... | $24 \pm 1$ |
| $H_2O$ | g | $-57.80$ | $-54.64$ | $-10.60$ | 45.11 | ... |
| $H_2O$ | l | $-68.32$ | $-56.69$ | $-38.99$ | 16.72 | ... |
| $H_2O$ | "aq" | $-68.32$ | $-59.11$ | $-30.9$ | ... | 24.8 |
| $HO_2$ | g | $4.9 \pm 4$ | $9.3 \pm 5$ | $-14.6 \pm 2$ | $50 \pm 2$ | ... |
| $HO_2$ | aq | $-3 \pm 5$ | $7.3 \pm 6$ | $-34.6 \pm 2$ | ... | $30 \pm 2$ |
| $H_2O_2$ | g | $-32.53$ | $-23.5 \pm 1$ | $-30.2 \pm 2$ | $50 \pm 2$ | ... |
| $H_2O_2$ | aq | $-45.88$ | $-31.47$ | $-48.4$ | ... | 31.8 |

[a] The values not in italics are based solely on experimental data; see *NBS Circ.* C500 (3), Cottrell (5) for the revised value of $\Delta H_a^\circ$ for $O_2$, and Gray (11).

[b] The values in italics involve an estimate for one or more of the fundamental quantities, as described in section IIIA.

The standard entropies, $S^\circ$, listed in Table 5, are taken from *NBS Circular* 500 (3) with the exception of those for $HO_2$ and $H_2O_2$, which are the values estimated by Evans, Hush, and Uri (13). The partial molal entropy of $H_2O_2$ aq is found to be 31.8 eu from Gray's value of $\Delta H_f^\circ$ and Lewis and Randall's indirect experimental measurement of $\Delta F^\circ$ (2). Calculation by means of Cobble's (14) empirical equation for partial molal entropies of neutral solutes in aqueous solution gives 33.6 eu, within 1.8 eu of this experimental value.

As with the enthalpies of solution for O, HO, and $HO_2$, values also have to be assumed for their partial molal entropies. Those in Table 5 have been assigned on the basis of the experimental values for molecules of almost the

## TABLE 6

### Bond Dissociation Energies and Thermochemical Bond Energies for Hydrogen-Oxygen and Oxygen-Oxygen Bonds in the Gas Phase at 25°C

Hydrogen-Oxygen Bond Dissociation Energies, kcal/mole

(i)   $H_2O \rightarrow H + HO$ $\qquad\qquad\qquad$ $D_{H—OH} = 119.1 \pm 0.5$
(ii)  $HO \rightarrow H + O$ $\qquad\qquad\qquad\quad$ $D_{H—O} = 102.4 \pm 0.5$
(iii) $H_2O_2 \rightarrow H + HO_2$ $\qquad\qquad\quad$ $D_{H—O_2H} = 89.5 \pm 4$
(iv)  $HO_2 \rightarrow H + O_2$ $\qquad\qquad\qquad$ $D_{H—O_2} = 47.2 \pm 4$

Oxygen-Oxygen Bond Dissociation Energies, kcal/mole

(i)   $O_2 \rightarrow O + O$ $\qquad\qquad\qquad\qquad$ $D_{O—O} = 119.08$
(ii)  $HO_2 \rightarrow HO + O$ $\qquad\qquad\qquad$ $D_{HO—O} = 63.9 \pm 4.5$
(iii) $H_2O_2 \rightarrow HO + OH$ $\qquad\qquad$ $D_{HO—OH} = 51.1 \pm 0.7$

Thermochemical Bond Energies,[a] kcal/mole

$E_{H—O} = 110.8$ $\qquad\qquad\qquad\qquad$ $E_{O=O}$ same as $D_{O=O}$
$E_{H—O'}$ same as $D_{H—O}$ $\qquad\qquad$ $E_{O—O'} = 55.5 \pm 4.5$
$\qquad\qquad\qquad\qquad\qquad\qquad\quad$ $E_{O—O} = 34.3 \pm 0.7$

[a] The subscripts H—O′ and O—O′ denote the bonds in the HO and $HO_2$ radicals, respectively.

same mass and comparable structure in terms of Cobble's equation, namely, the value of 14.2 eu for Ne leads to 13 eu for O, the values of 22.9 eu for HF and 24.8 eu for $H_2O$ lead to 24 eu for HO, and the value of 31.8 eu for $H_2O_2$ leads to 30 eu for $HO_2$. In view of the applicability of Cobble's equation, these values should not be in error by more than $\pm 1$, $\pm 1$, and $\pm 2$ eu, respectively. It may be noted that these values happen to give the same entropy of solution for HO and $HO_2$, namely $-20$ eu, as compared to the

## TABLE 7

### Standard Enthalpies, Entropies, and Free Energies of Solution in Water at 25°C

Standard states: gases, fugacities of 1 atm; solution species, including $H_2O$, 1 molal solutions.

| Species | $\Delta H°$, kcal/mole | $\Delta S°$, eu | $\Delta F°$, kcal/mole |
|---------|------------------------|-----------------|------------------------|
| O       | $-2$                   | $-25$           | $+5.5$                 |
| HO      | $-7.2$                 | $-20$           | $-1.2$                 |
| $H_2O$  | $-10.52$               | $-20.3$         | $-4.47$                |
| $O_2$   | $-2.89$                | $-22.9$         | $+3.95$                |
| $HO_2$  | $-7.9$                 | $-20$           | $-1.9$                 |
| $H_2O_2$| $-13.35$               | $-18.2$         | $-8.0$                 |

value of $-25$ eu for both radicals which Evans, Hush, and Uri (13) assumed for their calculations.

For easy reference these enthalpies and entropies of solution and the corresponding standard free energy changes have been collected in Table 7, together with the experimental values for $H_2O$ and $O_2$ for comparison (the values of $\Delta S^\circ$ and $\Delta F^\circ$ for water refer to the 1 molal standard state, as for the other species).

Except in the case of aqueous $H_2O_2$ (see above), the remaining values of $\Delta F_f^\circ$ in Table 5 have been calculated from the equation $\Delta F_f^\circ = \Delta H_f^\circ - T \Delta S_f^\circ$, the values of $\Delta S_f^\circ$ being obtained from the $S^\circ$ and $\bar{S}^\circ$ data, together with the $S^\circ$ values for the elements given in Table 1.

## B. Reduction via Hydrogen Peroxide

From the values of $\Delta H_f^\circ$, $S^\circ$, $\bar{S}^\circ$, and $\Delta F_f^\circ$ in Table 5, the standard enthalpy, entropy, and free energy changes associated with the four single-equivalent steps,

$$O_2 + \tfrac{1}{2}H_2 \rightarrow HO_2, \qquad \text{step i} \qquad (11)$$

$$HO_2 + \tfrac{1}{2}H_2 \rightarrow H_2O_2, \qquad \text{step ii} \qquad (12)$$

$$H_2O_2 + \tfrac{1}{2}H_2 \rightarrow HO + H_2O, \quad \text{step iii} \qquad (13)$$

$$HO + \tfrac{1}{2}H_2 \rightarrow H_2O, \qquad \text{step iv} \qquad (14)$$

and the two-equivalent steps,

$$O_2 + H_2 \rightarrow H_2O_2 \qquad (15)$$

$$H_2O_2 + H_2 \rightarrow 2H_2O \qquad (16)$$

have been calculated for both the gas-phase and aqueous-solution reactions at $[H^+] = 1$ and are listed in Table 8. $E^0$, and $E^{0\prime}$ at pH 7.0, have been calculated from the free energy values (see Table 9), taking the p$K$ for the $HO_2$ radical to be 2.2 as before (11).

The further refinement of experimental data has led to very little change in $E^0$ (and $E^{0\prime}$) for steps iii and iv involving the HO radical, the previous values for $E^0$ being $+0.78$ and $+2.77$ volts respectively, compared to the present values of $+0.80$ and $+2.74$ volts. But the new data for the $HO_2$ radical, especially its enthalpy of formation, lead to appreciably more positive $E^0$ (and $E^{0\prime}$) values for the first step, and correspondingly lower values for the second step, the present $E^0$ values being $-0.32$ and $+1.68$ volts, respectively, compared to the previous values of $-0.74$ and $+2.11$ volts. Nevertheless the values for the first step are still appreciably *negative*, and it seems unlikely that any new experimental data in the future will alter the conclusion that in this first single-equivalent step oxygen is a remarkably poor oxidizing agent. This conclusion, of course, is very much in keeping with the sluggish kinetic behavior observed in many reactions, and it suggests that with cytochrome

### TABLE 8

Thermodynamic Data for the Four-Step Reduction of Oxygen to Water Via
Hydrogen Peroxide at 25°C

| Reaction | $\Delta H°$, kcal/mole | $\Delta S°$, eu | $T\Delta S°$, kcal/mole | $\Delta F°$, kcal/mole |
|---|---|---|---|---|
| (a) Gas Phase | | | | |
| (i)   $O_2 + \frac{1}{2}H_2 \rightleftharpoons HO_2$ | +4.9 | −14.6 | −4.4 | +9.3 |
| (ii)  $HO_2 + \frac{1}{2}H_2 \rightleftharpoons H_2O_2$ | −37.4 | −15.6 | −4.6 | −32.8 |
| (iii) $H_2O_2 + \frac{1}{2}H_2 \rightleftharpoons HO + H_2O$ | −16.1 | +23.4 | +7.0 | −23.1 |
| (iv)  $HO + \frac{1}{2}H_2 \rightleftharpoons H_2O$ | −67.0 | −14.4 | −4.3 | −62.7 |
| $O_2 + H_2 \rightleftharpoons H_2O_2$ | −32.5 | −30.2 | −9.0 | −23.5 |
| $H_2O_2 + H_2 \rightleftharpoons 2H_2O$ | −83.1 | +9.0 | +2.7 | −85.8 |
| $O_2 + 2H_2 \rightleftharpoons 2H_2O$ | −115.6 | −21.2 | −6.3 | −109.3 |
| (b) Aqueous Solution, $[H^+] = 1$ | | | | |
| (i)   $O_2 + \frac{1}{2}H_2 \rightleftharpoons HO_2$ | −3.0 | −34.6 | −10.3 | +7.3 |
| (ii)  $HO_2 + \frac{1}{2}H_2 \rightleftharpoons H_2O_2$ | −42.9 | −13.8 | −4.1 | −38.8 |
| (iii) $H_2O_2 + \frac{1}{2}H_2 \rightleftharpoons HO + H_2O_l$ | −20.4 | −6.7 | −2.0 | −18.4 |
| (iv)  $HO + \frac{1}{2}H_2 \rightleftharpoons H_2O_l$ | −70.3 | −22.9 | −6.8 | −63.5 |
| $O_2 + H_2 \rightleftharpoons H_2O_2$ | −45.9 | −48.4 | −14.4 | −31.5 |
| $H_2O_2 + H_2 \rightleftharpoons 2H_2O_l$ | −90.7 | −29.6 | −8.8 | −81.9 |
| $O_2 + 2H_2 \rightleftharpoons 2H_2O_l$ | −136.6 | −78.0 | −23.2 | −113.4 |

### TABLE 9

Oxidation-Reduction Potentials for the Reduction of Oxygen to Water via Hydrogen
Peroxide at 25°C, in Acidic Solution and at pH 7.0

Standard states: $O_2$, fugacity of 1 atm; other species, 1 molal solutions, except
water for which the values refer to the liquid state.

| Acidic Solution, $[H^+] = 1$ | | At pH 7.0 | |
|---|---|---|---|
| Electrode Reaction | $E^0$, volts | Electrode Reaction | $E^{0'}$, volts |
| $O_2 + H^+ + e^- \rightleftharpoons HO_2$ | −0.32 | $O_2 + e^- \rightleftharpoons O_2^-$ | −0.45 |
| $HO_2 + H^+ + e^- \rightleftharpoons H_2O_2$ | +1.68 | $O_2^- + 2H^+ + e^- \rightleftharpoons H_2O_2$ | +0.98 |
| $H_2O_2 + H^+ + e^-$ | | $H_2O_2 + H^+ + e^-$ | |
| $\rightleftharpoons HO + H_2O$ | +0.80 | $\rightleftharpoons HO + H_2O$ | +0.38 |
| $HO + H^+ + e^- \rightleftharpoons H_2O$ | +2.74 | $HO + H^+ + e^- \rightleftharpoons H_2O$ | +2.33 |
| $\frac{1}{2}O_2 + H^+ + e^- \rightleftharpoons \frac{1}{2}H_2O_2$ | +0.68 | $\frac{1}{2}O_2 + H^+ + e^- \rightleftharpoons \frac{1}{2}H_2O_2$ | +0.27 |
| $\frac{1}{2}H_2O_2 + H^+ + e^- \rightleftharpoons H_2O$ | +1.77 | $\frac{1}{2}H_2O_2 + H^+ + e^- \rightleftharpoons H_2O$ | +1.35 |
| $\frac{1}{4}O_2 + H^+ + e^- \rightleftharpoons \frac{1}{2}H_2O$ | +1.23 | $\frac{1}{4}O_2 + H^+ + e^- \rightleftharpoons \frac{1}{2}H_2O$ | +0.81 |

oxidase an entirely different pathway may be made available which does not suffer from this thermodynamic handicap.

The driving force in the reduction of $O_2$ to $H_2O_2$ comes with the second single-equivalent step in which the reduction of the $HO_2$ radical occurs; there is a similar relationship between the two steps in the reduction of $H_2O_2$ to water. Although $H_2O_2$ is quite a good oxidizing agent in the third single-equivalent step giving $HO + H_2O$, it is nothing like so powerful as the HO radical in its reduction to water in the fourth step.

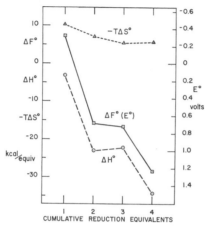

**Fig. 5.** Trends in the values of $\Delta H°$, $-T\Delta S°$, and $\Delta F°$ per cumulative equivalent, and in the corresponding $E°$ values, for the reduction of $O_2$ to $H_2O$ via the radicals $HO_2$ and HO, with $H_2O_2$ as the two-equivalent reduction stage.

If the cumulative values are considered as the reduction proceeds through the several steps, rather than the individual values for each step (i.e., dividing $\Delta F°$ for step i by 1, $\Delta F°$ for steps i and ii by 2, $\Delta F°$ for steps i, ii, and iii by 3, and $\Delta F°$ for steps i, ii, iii, and iv by 4, etc.), the trends in $E^0$ and in the various thermodynamic quantities per cumulative equivalent are as shown in Fig. 5. $\Delta F°$ and $\Delta H°$ per cumulative equivalent follow each other rather closely because $-T\Delta S°$ per cumulative equivalent does not vary very much. The successive $E^0$ values for the one-, two-, three-, and four-equivalent reduction stages are $-0.32$, $+0.68$, $+0.72$, and $+1.23$ volts respectively. Those for the two- and three-equivalent stages are quite similar, but the HO radical is such a powerful oxidizing agent that the inclusion of the data for the fourth step to give the over-all four-equivalent reduction process profoundly affects both $\Delta H°$ and $\Delta F°$, increasing $E^0$ by half a volt.

It is instructive at this point to look back into the enthalpy and entropy data for each individual step to see how the driving force is made up, just as we did in the case of the formation of water in relation to other hydrides in section II. For the gas-phase reactions it can be seen from Table 8a that $\Delta H^\circ$ is again more important than $T\Delta S^\circ$ in determining the sign and magnitude of $\Delta F^\circ$ for all but the first step. Reference to the appropriate Born-Haber cycles shows that these values of $\Delta H^\circ$ are in turn determined by the thermochemical bond energies according to the following equations:

$$\Delta H^\circ \text{ (step i)} = E_{O-O} + \tfrac{1}{2}E_{H-H} - [E_{H-O} + E_{O-O'}] \qquad (17)$$

$$\Delta H^\circ \text{ (step ii)} = [E_{H-O} + E_{O-O'}] + \tfrac{1}{2}E_{H-H} - [2E_{H-O} + E_{O-O}] \qquad (18)$$

$$\Delta H^\circ \text{ (step iii)} = [2E_{H-O} + E_{O-O}] + \tfrac{1}{2}E_{H-H} - E_{H-O'} - 2E_{H-O} \qquad (19)$$

$$\Delta H^\circ \text{ (step iv)} = E_{H-O'} + \tfrac{1}{2}E_{H-H} - 2E_{H-O} \qquad (20)$$

These equations are presented as bar graphs in Fig. 6 with the thick vertical line denoting $\Delta H^\circ$ in each case.

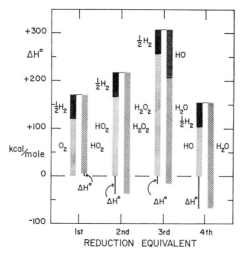

**Fig. 6.** Bar-graph representations of the Born-Haber cycles for the four-step reduction of $O_2$ to $H_2O$ via the radicals $HO_2$ and $HO$, with $H_2O_2$ as the two-equivalent reduction stage.

Although it is not possible to single out any one bond energy as more important than the others in determining $\Delta H^\circ$ for a particular step, the relative values for the various steps, i.e.,

$$\Delta H^\circ \text{ (step iv)} \gg \Delta H^\circ \text{ (step ii)} > \Delta H^\circ \text{ (step iii)} > \Delta H^\circ \text{ (step i)}$$

are primarily governed by the O-O bond energies, as the following argument shows. $\tfrac{1}{2}E_{H-H}$, which of course is the same as $\Delta H_a^\circ(H_2)_g$, is common to all four steps, and to a first approximation we can take $E_{HO} \approx E_{HO'}$ because the difference is only about 8 kcal/mole. Hence, it follows from equations 17–20 that, relative to $\Delta H^\circ$ for step iv, the values for steps ii, iii, and i are less favorable by approximately $(E_{O-O'} - E_{O-O})$, $E_{O-O}$, and $(E_{O=O} - E_{O-O'})$, i.e., 21, 34, and 64 kcal/mole, respectively. A major factor contributing to the unfavorable character of the first step in the reduction of oxygen is thus the very substantial difference between the bond energy in the oxygen molecule and in the $HO_2$ radical.

The $T\Delta S^\circ$ term is almost identical for steps i, ii, and iv because the reactions are of the same type, two simple reactant species giving one simple product species. As a consequence the values are unfavorable, i.e., negative, whereas for step iii, in which two simple product species are formed, the value is less unfavorable and happens to be positive to a small extent. However, the $T\Delta S$ terms for all four reactions are relatively small in magnitude, so the values of $\Delta F^\circ$ follow the same order as those for $\Delta H^\circ$ given above.

Even when the enthalpies and entropies of solution are taken into account to give $\Delta H^\circ$, $T\Delta S^\circ$, and $\Delta F^\circ$ for the aqueous-solution reactions, the differences between the values of $\Delta H^\circ$ for the gas-phase reactions still predominate and the order remains unchanged.

It is interesting to note that, with the present values for $\Delta H_f^\circ(HO_2)_g$ and its enthalpy of solution, $\Delta H^\circ$ for step i in aqueous solution is actually favorable to the extent of $-3$ kcal/mole. Nevertheless, the entropy change is quite negative, i.e., $-34.6$ eu, because two gases are reacting to give one species in solution. As a consequence the resulting standard free energy change is almost as unfavorable as that for the gas-phase reaction: $+7.3$, compared to $+9.3$ kcal/mole.

## C. Reduction via Water and an Oxygen Atom

An alternative pathway to reduction via $H_2O_2$ involves water and an oxygen atom as the two-equivalent reduction stage. The first and fourth steps are necessarily the same, but the second and third steps differ:

$$HO_2 + \tfrac{1}{2}H_2 \rightarrow H_2O + O, \quad \text{step ii}' \tag{21}$$

$$O + \tfrac{1}{2}H_2 \rightarrow HO, \quad \text{step iii}' \tag{22}$$

The two two-equivalent steps are likewise different:

$$O_2 + H_2 \rightarrow H_2O + O \tag{23}$$

$$O + H_2 \rightarrow H_2O \tag{24}$$

The thermodynamic data for these steps, calculated from the fundamental quantities in Table 5, are listed in Table 10 for both the gas-phase and aqueous-solution reactions. $E^0$, and $E^{0'}$ at pH 7.0, derived from the standard free energy changes, are listed in Table 11, and the trends in $E^0$, and in $\Delta F^\circ$, $\Delta H^\circ$, and $-T\Delta S^\circ$ per cumulative equivalent, are shown in Fig. 7.

In view of the magnitude of the over-all standard free energy change,

## TABLE 10

### Thermodynamic Data for the Four-Step Reduction of Oxygen to Water via an Oxygen Atom at 25°C

| Reaction | $\Delta H°$, kcal/mole | $\Delta S°$, eu | $T\Delta S°$, kcal/mole | $\Delta F°$, kcal/mole |
|---|---|---|---|---|
| (a) Gas Phase | | | | |
| (i) $O_2 + \frac{1}{2}H_2 \rightleftharpoons HO_2$ | +4.9 | −14.6 | −4.4 | +9.3 |
| (ii') $HO_2 + \frac{1}{2}H_2 \rightleftharpoons H_2O + O$ | −3.2 | +18.0 | +5.4 | −8.6 |
| (iii') $O + \frac{1}{2}H_2 \rightleftharpoons HO$ | −50.3 | −10.2 | −3.0 | −47.3 |
| (iv) $HO + \frac{1}{2}H_2 \rightleftharpoons H_2O$ | −67.0 | −14.4 | −4.3 | −62.7 |
| $O_2 + H_2 \rightleftharpoons H_2O + O$ | +1.7 | +3.4 | +1.0 | +0.7 |
| $O + H_2 \rightleftharpoons H_2O$ | −117.3 | −24.6 | −7.3 | −110.0 |
| $O_2 + 2H_2 \rightleftharpoons 2H_2O$ | −115.6 | −21.2 | −6.3 | −109.3 |
| (b) Aqueous Solution, $[H^+] = 1$ | | | | |
| (i) $O_2 + \frac{1}{2}H_2 \rightleftharpoons HO_2$ | −3.0 | −34.6 | −10.3 | +7.3 |
| (ii') $HO_2 + \frac{1}{2}H_2 \rightleftharpoons H_2O_1 + O$ | −7.8 | −15.9 | −4.7 | −3.1 |
| (iii') $O + \frac{1}{2}H_2 \rightleftharpoons HO$ | −55.5 | −4.6 | −1.4 | −54.1 |
| (iv) $HO + \frac{1}{2}H_2 \rightleftharpoons H_2O_1$ | −70.3 | −22.9 | −6.8 | −63.5 |
| $O_2 + H_2 \rightleftharpoons H_2O_1 + O$ | −10.8 | −50.5 | −15.0 | +4.2 |
| $O + H_2 \rightleftharpoons H_2O_1$ | −125.8 | −27.5 | −8.2 | −117.6 |
| $O_2 + 2H_2 \rightleftharpoons 2H_2O_1$ | −136.6 | −78.0 | −23.2 | −113.4 |

## TABLE 11

### Oxidation-Reduction Potentials for the Reduction of Oxygen to Water via an Oxygen Atom at 25°C, in Acidic Solution and at pH 7.0

Standard states: $O_2$, fugacity of 1 atm; other species 1 molal solutions, except water for which the values refer to the liquid state.

| Acidic Solution, $[H^+] = 1$ | | At pH 7.0 | |
|---|---|---|---|
| Electrode Reaction | $E^0$, volts | Electrode Reaction | $E^{0'}$, volts |
| $O_2 + H^+ + e^- \rightleftharpoons HO_2$ | −0.32 | $O_2 + e^- \rightleftharpoons O_2^-$ | −0.45 |
| $HO_2 + H^+ + e^- \rightleftharpoons H_2O + O$ | +0.13 | $O_2^- + 2H^+ + e^- \rightleftharpoons H_2O + O$ | −0.57 |
| $O + H^+ + e^- \rightleftharpoons HO$ | +2.34 | $O + H^+ + e^- \rightleftharpoons HO$ | +1.92 |
| $HO + H^+ + e^- \rightleftharpoons H_2O$ | +2.74 | $HO + H^+ + e^- \rightleftharpoons H_2O$ | +2.33 |
| $\frac{1}{2}O_2 + H^+ + e^-$ $\rightleftharpoons \frac{1}{2}H_2O + \frac{1}{2}O$ | −0.09 | $\frac{1}{2}O_2 + H^+ + e^-$ $\rightleftharpoons \frac{1}{2}H_2O + \frac{1}{2}O$ | −0.51 |
| $\frac{1}{2}O + H^+ + e^- \rightleftharpoons \frac{1}{2}H_2O$ | +2.54 | $\frac{1}{2}O + H^+ + e^- \rightleftharpoons \frac{1}{2}H_2O$ | +2.12 |
| $\frac{1}{4}O_2 + H^+ + e^- \rightleftharpoons \frac{1}{2}H_2O$ | +1.23 | $\frac{1}{4}O_2 + H^+ + e^- \rightleftharpoons \frac{1}{2}H_2O$ | +0.81 |

namely, more than $-100$ kcal/mole, the most striking feature of this alternative pathway is the small positive values for the two-equivalent reduction stage giving $H_2O$ and an oxygen atom. According to the present data, the reaction is almost balanced in the gas phase with $\Delta F° = +0.7$ kcal/mole, and even in solution the value is only $+4.2$ kcal/mole. This feature is brought out very clearly in Fig. 7, where the swing to large negative values for $\Delta F°$ (and $E^0$) can be seen to occur with the third and fourth equivalent. Although

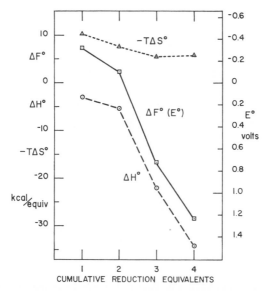

**Fig. 7.** Trends in the values of $\Delta H°$, $-T\Delta S°$, and $\Delta F°$ per cumulative equivalent, and in the corresponding $E°$ values, for the reduction of $O_2$ to $H_2O$ via the radicals $HO_2$ and $HO$, with "$H_2O + O$" as the two-equivalent reduction stage.

the $T\Delta S$ terms are similar in magnitude to those for the other pathway, with the positive value for step ii′ instead of step iii in accord with the number of product species, they are of comparable significance to $\Delta H°$ in determining the sign and magnitude of $\Delta F°$ for the first two steps, and the values of $\Delta H°$ for the gas-phase reactions are the dominant quantities for only the last two steps.

Reference to the appropriate Born-Haber cycles shows that the values of $\Delta H°$ for steps ii′ and iii′ are determined by the thermochemical bond energies:

$$\Delta H° \text{ (step ii′)} = [E_{H-O} + E_{O-O'}] + \tfrac{1}{2}E_{H-H} - 2E_{H-O} \quad (25)$$

$$\Delta H° \text{ (step iii′)} = \tfrac{1}{2}E_{H-H} - E_{H-O'} \quad (26)$$

The bar-graph representation of the cycles for all four steps of this alternative pathway given in Fig. 8 shows very clearly the small values of $\Delta H°$ for the first two steps in comparison to the large favorable values for the last two steps.

The value of $\Delta H°$ for step ii′ is less favorable than that for step ii in the other pathway, as can be seen by comparing equations 18 and 25, because the reaction lacks the additional driving force provided by the formation of the O-O bond in $H_2O_2$. But, as can be seen from equations 19 and 26, the value for step iii′ is more favorable than that for step iii by exactly the same bond energy because the bond is already broken.

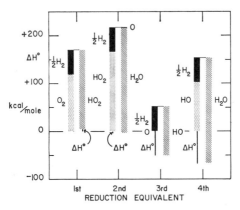

**Fig. 8.** Bar-graph representations of the Born-Haber cycles for the four-step reduction of $O_2$ to $H_2O$ via the radicals $HO_2$ and $HO$, with "$H_2O + O$" as the two-equivalent reduction stage.

The key difference between the two pathways thus lies in the following reaction of $H_2O_2$ itself:

$$H_2O_2 \rightarrow H_2O + O \tag{27}$$

for which the thermodynamic data are listed in Table 12. The $T\Delta S°$ term is appreciably less favorable for the aqueous-solution reaction, largely because the entropy of liquid $H_2O$ is much less than that of the gas. This reaction is of some interest in view of the old controversy as to whether the structure of $H_2O_2$ is

$$HO—OH \qquad or \qquad \begin{matrix} H \\ \diagdown \\ O \rightarrow O \\ \diagup \\ H \end{matrix}$$

Modern methods for determining structure have shown unequivocally that the first structure is the correct one; and for aqueous solutions, the standard free energy change in Table 12 gives a vanishingly small concentration for the oxygen atom at equilibrium, namely, $H_2O_2 : O = 10^{26} : 1$.

## TABLE 12

### Thermodynamic Data at 25°C for the Reaction $H_2O_2 \rightarrow H_2O + O$

Standard states: gases, fugacities of 1 atm; 1 molal solutions of $H_2O_2$ and O, liquid water.

|  | $\Delta H°$, kcal/mole | $\Delta S°$, eu | $T\Delta S°$, kcal/mole | $\Delta F°$, kcal/mole |
|---|---|---|---|---|
| Gas phase: | +34.2 | +33.6 | +10.0 | +24.2 |
| Aqueous solution: | +35.1 | −2.1 | −0.6 | +35.7 |

## IV. CATALYSIS OF THE REDUCTION OF OXYGEN TO WATER BY METAL IONS AND COMPLEXES, ESPECIALLY HEMOPROTEINS

The principle underlying the straightforward catalysis of the reduction of oxygen to water by oxidation-reduction couples of metal ions, etc., is quite simple. The primary reducing agent reacts with the oxidized state of the catalyst, giving the reduced state. The reduced state of the catalyst then reacts with oxygen and such intermediates in the reduction pathway as required, reducing the oxygen to water, and regenerating the oxidized state of the catalyst to react with the primary reducing agent once again. It will be noted that one important consideration has been omitted, namely, reactions between intermediates in the reduction pathway and the primary reducing agent itself. However, since this type of reaction does not appear to occur at the terminus of the cytochrome system, it will not be discussed further, and attention will be directed toward the kind of mechanism by which cytochrome oxidase may catalyse the reduction of oxygen to water with ferrocytochrome $c$ as the primary reducing agent.

With all catalytic mechanisms of this kind there are two interrelated problems:

1. What is the nature of the reduction pathway? Does it involve one-equivalent steps? or two-equivalent steps? or some special co-operative mechanism in which four equivalents are transferred within a reaction "cage"?

2. What is the chemical nature of the oxidation states of the catalyst that participate at each stage of the reduction process if the four equivalents are not transferred to oxygen at once?

If the special structural environment of cytochrome oxidase and cytochrome $c$ within the mitochondrion makes possible a co-operative four-equivalent transfer directly to oxygen, any problems that remain lie beyond the scope of this paper, and only the discussion of the factors which determine the favorable free energy change for the over-all reduction has its place. But, if one- or two-equivalent steps are involved, or some four-equivalent step which takes the reduction of oxygen only part way, then the thermodynamic data for the principal reduction pathways also have their place, and the question of oxidation states immediately becomes important.

Higher oxidation states of iron have long been considered as possible intermediates in the reaction of iron salts with oxygen and $H_2O_2$. In 1929 Hale reviewed much of the previous literature, which goes back at least to 1900 (15). In this earlier period the derivatives were usually formulated as the higher oxides $Fe_2O_4$ and $Fe_2O_5$, although Bray and Gorin in 1932 proposed the ferryl ion, $FeO^{2+}$, analogous to the vanadyl ion, $VO^{2+}$, as the intermediate in "compensating" reactions to account for the catalytic decomposition of $H_2O_2$ (16). With the advent of free-radical mechanisms, reaction mechanisms were advanced in terms of the $HO_2$ and $HO$ radicals, but with only the more familiar ferrous and ferric oxidation states participating. [See, for example, Haber and Weiss (17), Weiss (18), Baxendale, Evans, and Park (19), and Barb, Baxendale, George, and Hargrave (20).] However, Barb *et al.* observed certain kinetic behavior which suggested that the ferryl ion replaced the $HO$ radical at high ferric ion concentrations (21), i.e.,

$$Fe^{3+} + HO \rightleftharpoons FeO^{2+} + H^+ \qquad (28)$$

and subsequently mechanisms have been proposed by Cahill and Taube (22) and Kremer (23) involving both higher oxidation states in the form of species such as Fe(IV) (unspecified), $FeO_2H^{3+}$ [peroxide complex of Fe(IV)], and $FeO^{3+}$ (the perferryl ion). Yet, the nature of the evidence is largely indirect, being based on kinetic measurements and experiments with $^{18}O$ as tracer. Like the free radicals, these higher oxidation states would apparently be highly reactive and have a very transitory existence. The only relatively stable intermediate formed in these systems is the ferric ion complex with the anion of $H_2O_2$, i.e., $FeO_2H^{2+}$ [Evans, George, and Uri (24)], which is not strictly a higher oxidation state.

On the other hand, there is now good evidence for the formation of relatively stable higher oxidation states of the iron protoporphyrin prosthetic group in myoglobin, hemoglobin, peroxidase, and catalase. Spectrophotometric titrations have shown that the compounds originally described as a peroxide complex of ferrimyoglobin and the "second" peroxide complex of ferriperoxidase are one oxidizing equivalent above the ferric state and thus react as Fe(IV) derivatives [George and Irvine (25), George (26)]. The "first" peroxide complex is one equivalent above this state [Chance (27)]; hence in principle it can be either a true peroxide complex or an Fe(V) derivative. The observation that other strong oxidizing agents besides peroxides can give what appear to be identical compounds [George and Irvine (28), George (29)] favors the higher oxidation state formulation, and the close similarity in spectroscopic properties between the compounds of peroxidase and catalase indicates that the catalase compounds are also of this type.

In setting up possible mechanisms for the catalytic reduction of oxygen to water by cytochrome oxidase, and for oxidase action in general in which hemoproteins are involved, all four oxidation states, Fe(II), Fe(III), Fe(IV), and Fe(V), thus need to be considered [George (30)]. To put the discussion on a quantitative basis, values at least for the oxidation-reduction potentials are required. In the case of the Fe(III)/Fe(II) couples, $E^{0'}$ at pH 7 is about +0.1 to +0.2 volt for myoglobin and hemoglobin [Hanania (31); see George (32)] and about −0.25 volt for peroxidase [Harbury (32)]. The $E^{0'}$ values for the Fe(IV)/Fe(III) couples of myoglobin and peroxidase, and for the Fe(V)/Fe(IV) couple of peroxidase, are all approximately 1 volt [George (29, 32)]. The peroxidase values are interpolated from qualitative observations on the position of equilibrium in reactions of ferriperoxidase with strong oxidizing agents, whereas the value of +0.84 volt for myoglobin is based on spectrophotometric measurements of the equilibrium constant for the reaction of ferrimyoglobin with chloriridate [George and Irvine (34)]. The enthalpy change was determined also for both myoglobin couples, so the following survey of various reaction steps has been based on these data because they are the most complete at present, namely,

$$Fe(III) + e^- \rightleftharpoons Fe(II), \quad E^{0'} = +0.12 \text{ volt}, \quad \Delta H^\circ = -14 \text{ kcal/mole} \quad (29)$$

$$Fe(IV) + 2H^+ + e^- \rightleftharpoons Fe(III), \quad E^{0'} = +0.84 \text{ volt}, \quad \Delta H^\circ = -40 \text{ kcal/mole} \quad (30)$$

In Table 13, $A$ and $B$, the direction of the arrows indicates the position of equilibrium in the various steps of both pathways, via $HO_2$ and via "$H_2O + O$," in which Fe(II) and Fe(III), respectively, take the place of hydrogen as the reducing agent. The calculated standard free energy changes are given above the arrows, and the enthalpy changes in parentheses below the arrows.

The value of +13 kcal/mole for step i with Fe(II) as the reducing agent emphasizes the point made earlier about the difficulty in getting the reduction under way; and even with a hemoprotein like ferroperoxidase, $E^{0'} = -0.25$ volt, the value would still be unfavorable to the extent of about +5 kcal/mole. It can be very fairly objected, however, that the free energy changes for the steps generating a radical are misleading because the subsequent more favored step in which the radical reacts can serve to pull the reaction through. Presumably this happens in the case of the reaction of ferrimyoglobin with $H_2O_2$ if it proceeds according to step iii, because the reaction definitely occurs despite an unfavorable free energy change of +12 kcal/mole; but there is a possibility of a different mechanism involving an Fe(V) state [George and Irvine (35)].

Even so the enthalpy changes provide additional crucial information, since, for an endothermic reaction, $\Delta H°$ fixes a minimum value for the activation energy. With the present data, step i with Fe(II) would have an activation energy of at least 11 kcal/mole, an extremely high value should this be the rate-determining step for the over-all reduction of oxygen, which is known to occur very rapidly.

## TABLE 13

**Reactions of Typical Fe(II), Fe(III), and Fe(IV) Oxidation States of Hemoproteins in the Reduction of Oxygen to Water via the Radicals $HO_2$ and HO, and $H_2O_2$ or "$H_2O + O$" as the Two-Equivalent Reduction Stage**

The oxidation-reduction potentials for the Fe(III)/Fe(II) and Fe(IV)/Fe(III) couples have been taken as +0.12 and +0.84 volt, respectively, at pH 7 and 25°, and the corresponding enthalpy changes as −14 and −40 kcal/mole.

The direction of the arrow indicates the position of equilibrium for the various steps, with the values of $\Delta F°$ at pH 7 above the arrow, and those of $\Delta H°$, in parentheses, below the arrow.

| Reducing Couple | Step i | Step ii | Step ii′ | Step iii | Step iii′ | Step iv |
|---|---|---|---|---|---|---|
| A. Fe(II) → Fe(III) | ← +13 (+11) | −20 → (−29) | ← +16 (+6) | −6 → (−6) | −42 → (−42) | −51 → (−56) |
| B. Fe(III) → Fe(IV) | ← +30 (+37) | −3 → (−3) | ← +34 (+32) | +11 → (+20) | −25 → (−16) | −34 → (−30) |

| Reducing Couple | Steps i + ii | Steps iii + iv | Steps i + ii′ | Steps iii′ + iv |
|---|---|---|---|---|
| C. Fe(II) → Fe(IV) | ← +10 (+8) | −40 → (−37) | ← +46 (+43) | −76 → (−72) |

With Fe(III) as the reducing agent instead of Fe(II), the values of both $\Delta F°$ and $\Delta H°$ are much less favorable (see Table 13, B), and, as is evident from the $E^{0'}$ values, the over-all reduction

$$4Fe(III) + O_2 \rightarrow 4Fe(IV) + 4H^+ + 2H_2O \qquad (31)$$

is slightly unfavorable, with $\Delta F° = +3$ kcal/mole. Were these the only reactions in which the Fe(IV)/Fe(III) couple could participate they would clearly be of little significance, but in combination with the Fe(III)/Fe(II) couple the resulting two-equivalent couple, i.e.,

$$Fe(IV) + 2H^+ + 2e^- \rightleftharpoons Fe(II), \quad E^{0'} = +0.48 \text{ volt}, \quad \Delta H° = -54 \text{ kcal/mole} \qquad (32)$$

opens up further possibilities.

As a comparison of the $E^{0'}$ values shows, Fe(II) is capable of reducing $O_2$ to $H_2O$, giving Fe(IV), with $\Delta F° = -30$ kcal/mole. The values of $\Delta F°$ and $\Delta H°$ for the two two-equivalent steps of both reduction pathways are noted in Table 13, C. But even for the more favorable pathway via $H_2O_2$, the value of neither $\Delta F°$ nor $\Delta H°$ is appropriate for reactions that have to play a catalytic role.

There is, however, another possibility. In the "straightforward" catalytic mechanisms discussed above, the alternative pathway via "$H_2O + O$" is much less favored because the free energy release occurs entirely with the third and fourth equivalents; see section IIIC. Yet if the oxygen atom could be trapped as an integral part of the catalytic mechanism a more favorable energy release might ensue.

The ferryl ion structure, which has been shown to account satisfactorily for the reactions of the Fe(IV) state of myoglobin [George and Irvine (34)], provides one way in which this could occur. When the structures are written with ionic charges so that the stoichiometry can be followed more readily, the two steps in terms of electrode reactions are:

$$O_2 + Fe^{2+} + 2H^+ + 2e^- \rightleftharpoons FeO^{2+} + H_2O, \quad E^{0\prime} = +1.14 \text{ volt} \quad (33)$$

$$FeO^{2+} + 2H^+ + 2e^- \rightleftharpoons Fe^{2+} + H_2O, \quad E^{0\prime} = +0.48 \text{ volt} \quad (32')$$

or, for the reduction by hydrogen as the primary reducing agent,

$$O_2 + Fe^{2+} + H_2 \rightleftharpoons FeO^{2+} + H_2O, \quad \Delta F° = -72.0, \quad \Delta H° = -83 \text{ kcal/mole} \quad (34)$$

$$FeO^{2+} + H_2 \rightleftharpoons Fe^{2+} + H_2O, \quad \Delta F° = -41.4, \quad \Delta H° = -54 \text{ kcal/mole} \quad (35)$$

It will be apparent immediately that the first step is actually a four-equivalent reduction and could be considered as being mediated by the formation of an oxygen complex:

$$Fe^{2+} + O_2 \rightleftharpoons Fe^{2+}\!-\!O_2, \quad \Delta F° = -x \text{ kcal/mole} \quad (36)$$

$$Fe^{2+}\!-\!O_2 + H_2 \rightleftharpoons FeO^{2+} + H_2O, \quad \Delta F° = -72 + x \text{ kcal/mole} \quad (37)$$

Such a mechanism illustrates one of probably several ways by which the adverse free energy and enthalpy changes associated with the reduction pathways via the simple inorganic intermediates could be circumvented. Similar mechanisms can be set up bringing in the Fe(V) state, and, in principle, the same kind of mechanism can be formulated with various oxidation states of copper, molybdenum, etc.

# V. CONCLUSIONS

In section IV we lost touch somewhat with our original intention to examine the fitness of oxygen. But in so doing a further consideration has emerged.

Oxygen has physical properties, thermodynamic properties, and kinetic properties which make it admirably suitable as a terminal oxidant, and it is abundantly clear from the earlier discussion that no other element could effectively replace it. Nevertheless in looking over the "electron-transport" chain it is obvious that the trend toward a greater simplicity of reaction type is abruptly broken at the terminus. Two-equivalent organic substrates and coenzymes are followed by the one-equivalent cytochromes, but oxygen apparently is unable to respond equivalent by equivalent. It is almost as if the major part of the chain had evolved for a different terminal oxidant capable of reacting in this simpler fashion, and when oxygen became available, the oxidase evolved as a special but very necessary appendage.

Whether or not biochemical evolution followed this course, the point still remains that the very thermodynamic and kinetic properties which contribute so much to the fitness of oxygen impose limitations of their own kind on the biochemical system. At this chemical level of organization, which underlies the more complex biochemical level with its sequences and cycles of reactions, there is thus an important component of determinism.

## ACKNOWLEDGMENT

This paper is part of a study of hemoprotein structure and specificity and the thermodynamics of biochemical reactions, supported by Research Grants AM-03187 and AM-04764, respectively, from the United States Public Health Service.

## REFERENCES

1. L. J. Henderson, *The Fitness of the Environment*, Macmillan, New York, 1913; Beacon paperback, Boston, 1958.
2. G. N. Lewis and M. Randall, *Thermodynamics and the Free Energy of Chemical Substances*, McGraw-Hill, New York, 1923.
3. F. D. Rossini, D. D. Wagman, W. H. Evans, S. Levine, and I. Jaffe, "Selected Values of Chemical Thermodynamic Properties," *Natl. Bur. Standards Circ.* No. 500, Washington, D.C., 1952.
4. W. M. Latimer, *The Oxidation States of the Elements and Their Potentials in Aqueous Solution*, Prentice-Hall, Englewood Cliffs, N.J., 1952.
5. T. L. Cottrell, *The Strengths of Chemical Bonds*, Butterworths, London, 1958.
6. H. H. Broeue and T. DeVries, *J. Am. Chem. Soc.*, **69**, 1644 (1947).
7. S. R. Gunn and LeRoy G. Green, *J. Phys. Chem.*, **65**, 779 (1961).
8. W. F. Claussen and M. F. Polglase, *J. Am. Chem. Soc.*, **74**, 4817 (1952).
9. C. E. Klots and B. B. Benson, *J. Phys. Chem.*, **67**, 933 (1933).
10. C. Oppenheimer and K. G. Stern, *Biological Oxidation*, W. Junk, The Hague, 1939, pp. 44–49.
11. P. George and J. S. Griffith, "Electron Transfer and Enzyme Catalysis," in P. D. Boyer, H. Lardy, and K. Myrbäck, Ed., *The Enzymes*, Vol. 1. Academic Press, New York, 1959, p. 347.
12. P. Gray, *Trans. Faraday Soc.*, **55**, 408 (1959).

13. M. G. Evans, N. S. Hush, and N. Uri, *Quart. Rev. Chem. Soc. (London)*, **6**, 186 (1952).
14. J. W. Cobble. *J. Chem. Phys.*, **21**, 1451 (1953).
15. D. R. Hale, *J. Phys. Chem.*, **2**, 1633 (1929).
16. W. C. Bray and M. H. Gorin, *J. Am. Chem. Soc.*, **54**, 2124 (1932).
17. F. Haber and J. Weiss, *Proc. Roy. Soc. (London)*, **A147**, 332 (1934).
18. J. Weiss, *Naturwiss.*, **23**, 64 (1935).
19. J. H. Baxendale, M. G. Evans, and G. S. Park, *Trans. Faraday Soc.*, **42**, 155 (1946).
20. W. G. Barb, J. H. Baxendale, P. George, and K. H. Hargrave, *Trans. Faraday Soc.*, **47**, 462 (1951).
21. W. G. Barb, J. H. Baxendale, P. George, and K. H. Hargrave, *Trans. Faraday Soc.*, **47**, 591 (1951).
22. A. E. Cahill and H. Taube, *J. Am. Chem. Soc.*, **74**, 2312 (1952).
23. M. L. Kremer, *Trans. Faraday Soc.*, **58**, 702 (1962), and **59**, 2537 (1963).
24. M. G. Evans, P. George, and N. Uri, *Trans. Faraday Soc.*, **45**, 230 (1949).
25. P. George and D. H. Irvine, *Biochem. J.*, **52**, 511 (1952), and *J. Chem. Soc.*, 3142 (1954).
26. P. George, *Biochem. J.*, **54**, 267 (1953).
27. B. Chance, *Arch. Biochem.*, **37**, 235 (1952).
28. P. George and D. H. Irvine, *Biochem. J.*, **58**, 188 (1954).
29. P. George, *J. Biol. Chem.*, **201**, 413 (1953), and *Science*, **117**, 220 (1953).
30. P. George, *Discussions Faraday Soc.*, **20**, 297 (1955).
31. G. I. H. Hanania, Ph.D. thesis, Cambridge University, 1953; see ref. 32 below.
32. P. George, "On the Nature of Hemoprotein Reactions," in D. E. Green, Ed., *Currents in Biochemical Research*, Interscience, New York, 1956.
33. H. A. Harbury, *J. Biol. Chem.*, **225**, 1009 (1957).
34. P. George and D. H. Irvine, *Biochem. J.*, **60**, 596 (1955).
35. P. George and D. H. Irvine, *J. Colloid Sci.*, **11**, 327 (1956).

*Discussion*

INGRAHAM: You state that adsorbed free radicals are too facile an explanation; then the problem really would still require an explanation of the altered reactivity of an adsorbed free radical. I just want to point out that this alteration clearly occurs in many organic reactions. For example, in the chlorination reactions, atomic chlorine has an entirely different reactivity in benzene from what it has in *n*-hexane, and I think that this is probably an example of an adsorbed free radical altering reactivity. It's also clear that many transition metals will change the product in certain free-radical reactions, and I think the explanation here again can be that the free radical is stabilized to altered reactivity by the transition metal. Moreover, it's clear that, for example, the equilibrium constant of flavins is different when they are attached to proteins from where they are in free solution. This may be another example of altered reactivity by adsorption of a free radical. In fact, I think that $FeO^{2+}$ could be thought of as a free radical, $HO\cdot$, in another viewpoint as stabilized by ferric iron.

GEORGE: I'm sorry that I gave a misleading impression. I didn't mean to imply that the adsorption of a radical could not alter the reactivity, but rather to say that the burden of explanation was merely shifted, and that the theoreticians would then be faced with accounting for the altered reactivity.

SUTIN: I would like to make two brief comments on Dr. George's paper. The first is concerned with the $E^{\circ\prime}$ values given in Tables 9 and 11. These $E^{\circ\prime}$ values are based on a p$K$ of 2.2 for the perhydroxyl radical. Recent studies [G. Czapski and L. M. Dorfman, *J. Phys. Chem.*, **68**, 1169 (1964)] have provided good evidence that this p$K$ is in fact 4.5 $\pm$ 0.2 at 25°C. This new p$K$ changes the $E^{\circ\prime}$ values for the first two steps in the reduction of oxygen to water by 0.14 volt. Consequently the $E^{\circ\prime}$ values presented for the first and second steps in Tables 9 and 11 become $-0.59$ and $+1.12$, and $-0.59$ and $-0.43$ volts, respectively. The $E^{\circ\prime}$ is thus more negative for the first step in the reduction of oxygen than for the remaining steps in both mechanisms.

I would also like to comment on formal potentials and standard free energy changes and their application to reaction rates. Free energies calculated from formal potentials, $\Delta G^{\circ\prime}$, are related to the "driving force" of an over-all reaction. They do not necessarily refer to a particular oxidation-reduction step or to a sequence of steps which are of a rate-determining nature. It is the latter free energy changes which are important in a discussion of reaction rates.

Consider, for example, two of the possible mechanisms for the reaction of $Fe^{2+}$ ions and OH radicals at pH = 7. For convenience we will neglect the hydrolysis of $Fe^{2+}$ at this pH.

(*a*) The oxidation-reduction reaction proceeds via an electron-transfer mechanism

$$Fe^{2+} + OH \rightarrow Fe^{3+} + OH^- \qquad \Delta G_1^{\circ}$$

$$Fe^{3+} + OH^- \rightarrow FeOH^{2+} \qquad \Delta G_2^{\circ}$$

$$FeOH^{2+} + OH^- \rightarrow \text{Further hydrolysis} \quad \Delta G_3^{\circ}$$

In this case $\Delta G_E^{\circ}$, the standard free energy change for the oxidation-reduction step, is equal to $\Delta G_1^{\circ}$. It does not include the free energy change for the subsequent hydrolysis reactions.

(*b*) The oxidation-reduction reaction proceeds via a hydrogen atom transfer mechanism:

$$Fe^{2+} + OH \rightarrow FeOH^{2+} + H_2O \qquad (\Delta G_1^{\circ} + \Delta G_2^{\circ})$$

$$FeOH^{2+} + OH^- \rightarrow \text{Further hydrolysis} \quad \Delta G_3^{\circ}$$

In this case $\Delta G_H^{\circ}$, the standard free energy change for the oxidation-reduction step, is equal to $(\Delta G_1^{\circ} + \Delta G_2^{\circ})$, i.e., it includes the free energy change for the first hydrolysis reaction. It is perhaps worth emphasizing that, if the mechanism corresponds to (*a*), then the contribution from the hydrolysis is irrelevant to the "driving force" for the oxidation-reduction reaction. However, if $\Delta G_1^{\circ}$ were very small, so that appreciable back-reaction occurred in this step, then the over-all rate of the reaction would be influenced by the free energy of hydrolysis, but not otherwise.

Finally, the value of $\Delta G^{\circ\prime}$ calculated from the formal potential of the Fe(II)/Fe(III) couple is related to $(\Delta G_1^{\circ} + \Delta G_2^{\circ} + \Delta G_3^{\circ})$, the free energy change for the over-all reaction. It is not equal to the standard free energy change for any of the rate-determining steps.

KING: I would like to ask whether the following over-all reaction 1 is feasible? This, $[FeO^{2+}]$, is the familiar ferryl compound.

$$FeO^{2+} + H^+ + Fe^{2+} \rightarrow 2Fe^{3+} + OH^- \qquad (1)$$

GEORGE: Are we referring here to iron in a hemoprotein or ionic iron? In both cases reaction 1 would be favorable, I think.

KING: Very good. Then would you comment on reaction 2?

$$FeOOH^{2+} + Fe^{2+} \rightarrow FeO^{2+} + Fe^{3+} \tag{2}$$

The compound $FeOOH^{2+}$, which you studied some time ago in considerable detail, is actually not a high-valenced iron. It is really a ferric ion complex with an anion of hydrogen peroxide.

GEORGE: I should like to have five minutes with a pencil to work this one out. It is not really too dissimilar from leaving the ferric iron out and just writing $H_2O_2 + Fe^{2+} \rightarrow FeO^{2+}$; here we would be dealing with the two-equivalent reduction stage of the peroxide. My suspicion is that this again would be a favorable reaction in the case of hemoproteins.

KING: Very good if this is favorable. Now I wonder what you think about reaction 3?

$$Fe^{2+} + HO_2^{\cdot} \rightarrow Fe^{3+} + HO_2^{-} \tag{3}$$

GEORGE: This again is a favorable reaction, I think; so where do we go from here?

KING: Would you care to comment on reaction 4?

$$FeO_2^{2+} + H^+ \rightarrow Fe^{3+} + HO_2^{\cdot} \tag{4}$$

GEORGE: This is in a sense electron transfer inside the ferrous oxygen complex to give, transitorally, $Fe^{3+}$ and $O_2^-$, and then the capture of the $O_2^-$ by the $H^+$ to give finally $Fe^{3+}$ plus the $HO_2$ radical. Right? Now what would this be? My suspicion is that it is somewhat unfavorable. This is the problem I was referring to earlier of the marked unfavorableness from the thermodynamic point of view of getting oxygen to accept its first electron.

KING: Yes, as you just said, reaction 4 is actually composed of two steps:

$$FeO_2^{2+} \rightarrow Fe^{3+} + O_2^- \tag{4a}$$

and

$$O_2^- + H^+ \rightarrow HO_2^{\cdot} \tag{4b}$$

I have also thought that reaction 4a is slightly unfavorable. But, thermodynamically, reaction 4b is very favorable.

Now, let me inject a side question, if I may. You say in your paper, "It can be very fairly objected, however, that the free energy changes for the steps generating a radical are misleading because the subsequent more favored steps in which the radical reacts can serve to pull the reaction through." I don't understand what you really mean.

GEORGE: What I was referring to is that if, in addition to a reaction like equation 4, one has a follow-up reaction in which $HO_2^{\cdot}$ is reduced further to hydrogen peroxide, the second part of the over-all two-equivalent change is so much more favorable that it counterbalances the unfavorableness of the first part, making the over-all two-equivalent reaction favorable. It would seem, for instance, that this has an important bearing on the strange kinetics that one gets for the oxidation of simple ferrous ions in aqueous solution with the nitrate or perchlorate salts.

Rather than having kinetics that would suggest the simple radical pathway via $HO_2^{\cdot}$ or $O_2^-$ and then peroxide and $OH$ radical and so on, one gets kinetics where the rate of oxidation is proportional to the square of the ferrous iron concentration times the partial pressure of oxygen,

$$(Fe^{2+})^2 \cdot pO_2$$

The simple kinetics that would come from the straightforward pathway,

$$(Fe^{2+}) \cdot pO_2$$

should be proportional to the first power in ferrous iron concentration times the oxygen pressure. Here it would seem that the underlying reaction mechanism is in all probability something like the reaction between a free $Fe^{2+}$ (or I should say the water molecule attached to a free $Fe^{2+}$) and oxygen combined with another $Fe^{2+}$, so that one gets hydrogen atom transfer in this way from the bound water and electron transfer from the other ferrous ion. Thus there is a sort of cooperative two-equivalent reduction process giving $FeO_2H^{2+}$, in other words, the peroxide complex of ferric ion plus $FeOH_2^+$, which is just the hydroxide complex of ferric ion.

$$Fe—O^{2+} + (H_2O)Fe^{2+} \rightarrow FeO_2H^{2+} + FeOH^{2+}$$

KING: My final question concerns the last reaction, which is what I have been driving at. I realize that reaction 4a is somewhat thermodynamically unfavorable. But we have very favorable reaction 4b as well as the first three reactions. The last reaction is this:

$$Fe^{2+} + O_2 \rightarrow Fe^{2+}O_2 \qquad (5)$$

Now if $Fe^{2+}$ stands for the reduced form of cytochrome oxidase, then it is feasible that the oxidation of reduced cytochrome oxidase by molecular oxygen follows this sequence of reactions.

CHANCE: It might be relevant in this context to underline Philip's statement that unfavorable thermodynamics in one step need not prevent the completion of the reaction because of later favorable steps, and to refer to the properties of peroxidase and cytochrome oxidase. Peroxidase, on the one hand, forms highly stable peroxide intermediates. Cytochrome oxidase, on the other hand, shows a reluctance to react obviously with peroxides. I make that as an oblique statement, but surely it has meaning to those who have attempted to study peroxide intermediates of cytochrome oxidase. Yet we know that cytochrome oxidase reacts rapidly with oxygen and forms no intermediates having lifetimes of less than fractions of a millisecond. Also, the reaction of ferroperoxidase with oxygen, which I don't want to dwell on at this point in detail but will refer to later (see p. 504), is also extremely rapid. So perhaps it isn't useful, actually, to expect that the ability of ferrihemoproteins to form peroxide compounds will be a determining factor in the reactions of ferrohemoproteins with oxygen.

# The Mechanisms of Some Electron-Transfer Reactions in Solution

... N. SUTIN*

## I. INTRODUCTION†

Some electron-transfer reactions involving metal ions and their complexes are considered in this article. Studies of these reactions have shown that they are of two types, which have been called inner-sphere and outer-sphere reactions (1–3). No bonds are made or broken during the course of outer-sphere electron-transfer reactions. The calculation of the rates of such reactions therefore presents less difficulty, at least in principle, than the calculation of the rates of ordinary chemical reactions. A theory of outer-sphere reactions is described in section II of this article.

In contrast to outer-sphere electron transfers, inner-sphere reactions require the formation and rupture of bonds. Consequently it is very difficult to treat the rates of inner-sphere electron transfers theoretically, although various aspects of these reactions have been considered by a number of authors (4–6). Inner-sphere reactions are of particular interest because extensive and important molecular rearrangements may accompany the electron transfer in such systems; these processes are outlined in section III of this article. Section IV contains a discussion of some reactions involving oxygen.

## II. OUTER-SPHERE ELECTRON TRANSFERS

For convenience, oxidation-reduction reactions which involve the transfer of one or more electrons between two oxidation states of a single element will

* Visiting Fellow, The Weizmann Institute of Science, Rehovoth, Israel.

† Among the abbreviations used in this article are the following: cyt-$c$ (ferrocytochrome $c$); EDTA (ethylenediaminetetraacetate); Hb($H_2O$) (ferrohemoglobin); phen (1,10-phenanthroline).

be considered first. Such oxidation-reduction reactions are called electron-exchange reactions. Since the reactants and products of exchange reactions are identical, the over-all free energy change accompanying the electron transfer is zero.

## A. Electron-Exchange Reactions

Rate constants for a number of electron-exchange reactions are presented in Table 1 (7-14). It is evident that despite the formal similarity of the processes their rates vary by a factor of more than $10^{14}$.

Most theories of electron-transfer reactions are based upon the Franck-Condon principle (15–17). According to this principle, internuclear distances and nuclear velocities do not change during an electronic transition. Since

### TABLE 1

#### Second-Order Rate Constants for some Electron-Exchange Reactions

| Reaction | $T$, °C | $k$, $M^{-1} \text{sec}^{-1}$ | Reference |
|---|---|---|---|
| $V^{2+} + V^{3+}$ | 25 | $1.0 \times 10^{-2}$ | (7) |
| $Cr^{2+} + Cr^{3+}$ | 25 | $\leqslant 2 \times 10^{-5}$ | (8) |
| $Fe^{2+} + Fe^{3+}$ | 25 | 4.2 | (9) |
| $Fe(phen)_3^{2+} + Fe(phen)_3^{3+}$ | 0 | $> 10^5$ | (10) |
| $Co^{2+} + Co^{3+}$ | 25 | ~5 | (11) |
| $Co(NH_3)_6^{2+} + Co(NH_3)_6^{3+}$ | 64.5 | $< 10^{-9}$ | (12) |
| $Co(en)_3^{2+} + Co(en)_3^{3+}$ | 50 | $1.4 \times 10^{-4}$ | (13) |
| $Co(phen)_3^{2+} + Co(phen)_3^{3+}$ | 0 | 1.1 | (14) |

the equilibrium configurations of the inner coordination shells of a reactant, as well as the polarization of the surrounding solvent, depend upon its charge, the equilibrium configurations of the reactants and the products of an electron exchange reaction will be different. Therefore, if electron transfer between the reactants were to occur without the prior reorganization of their coordination shells, the products would be formed with distorted configurations and energy would not be conserved in the over-all process. Energy conservation thus requires that the coordination shells of the reactants (including the polarization of the surrounding medium) rearrange to some common, non-equilibrium configuration before the electron transfer takes place.

It is possible to rationalize some of the exchange rates presented in Table 1 in terms of the above model. Thus the slowness of the $Cr^{2+}$-$Cr^{3+}$ in comparison to the $Fe^{2+}$-$Fe^{3+}$ and $Co^{2+}$-$Co^{3+}$ exchanges could arise from the stable $(t_{2g})^3$ electron configuration of $Cr^{3+}$, which effectively increases the difference in the geometries of the coordination shells of $Cr^{2+}$ and $Cr^{3+}$, resulting in larger reorganization energies. In a similar manner, the slow rate of the $Co(phen)_3^{2+}$-$Co(phen)_3^{3+}$ exchange, as compared to the $Fe(phen)_3^{2+}$-$Fe(phen)_3^{3+}$ exchange, is thought to arise from the stable $(t_{2g})^6$ configuration of $Co(phen)_3^{3+}$. It should be noted that $Fe(phen)_3^{2+}$ also possesses a $(t_{2g})^6$ configuration; however, in the $Fe(phen)_3^{2+}$-$Fe(phen)_3^{3+}$ exchange it is the lower rather than the upper oxidation state which is stabilized. Unfortunately, the appropriate distances and force constants required for the calculation of the energy necessary to reorganize the coordination shells of the reactants are not known for the above systems. Fairly good agreement of calculated and observed rates is obtained when reasonable values of these quantities are assumed (3, 18).

The cobalt(II)-cobalt(III) exchanges require additional comment. These exchanges involve not only the transfer of an electron, but also the rearrangement of the other $d$ electrons of the two reactants. The electron transfer is thus partially spin-forbidden and should proceed slowly (19). There will be no spin multiplicity restriction if the exchange can occur between two spin-free or two spin-paired configurations. This may be the case in the $Co^{2+}$-$Co^{3+}$ and $Co(phen)_3^{2+}$-$Co(phen)_3^{3+}$ exchanges, respectively (14). Similarly, the relatively slow rates of the $Co(en)_3^{2+}$-$Co(en)_3^{3+}$ and $Co(NH_3)_6^{2+}$-$Co(NH_3)_6^{3+}$ exchanges may reflect the large multiplicity restrictions and inner-shell reorganization energies expected with ligands of intermediate field strength.

While the $Co^{2+}$-$Co^{3+}$ and $Co(phen)_3^{2+}$-$Co(phen)_3^{3+}$ exchanges proceed at comparable rates, the $Fe(phen)_3^{2+}$-$Fe(phen)_3^{3+}$ exchange is much faster than the $Fe^{2+}$-$Fe^{3+}$ exchange. This comparison suggests that, in contrast to the cobalt(II)-cobalt(III) exchanges, the rates of the iron(II)-iron(III) exchanges increase with the field strength of the ligands (at least for ligands in the water to phenanthroline range), or, put another way, the comparison suggests that the iron(II)-iron(III) exchange rates increase as the iron(II) and iron(III) go from spin-free to spin-paired configurations (provided exchanges involving octahedral complexes of the same charge type are compared, and specific chemical effects are absent).

## B. Electron Transfer Involving Two Different Couples

The problem is more complicated when the oxidation-reduction involves two different couples. It then becomes necessary to consider the atomic configurations, etc., of four species, instead of only two, as well as to take into account the standard free energy change of the reaction. The rates of electron-transfer reactions generally increase as their standard free energy changes become more negative (20–24). This increase in rate arises from the fact that, when $\Delta G° < 0$, it is not necessary to reorganize the coordination shells of the reactants to the same extent as in exchange reactions ($\Delta G° = 0$), since the vibrational excitation energy of the products can be liberated as part of the standard free energy change of the reaction.

Provided that the interaction between the redox orbitals of the reactants is neither too large nor too small (i.e., the interaction is small enough so that it can be neglected in calculating the free energy of activation, but large enough so that electron transfer occurs with unit probability in the activated complex), a given couple might be expected to behave in a similar manner in all electron-transfer reactions in which it is involved. Indeed Marcus [25] has derived a relatively simple relation between the rates of outer-sphere electron transfers which is applicable when the above condition is satisfied, and when correction has been made for any differences in the work required to bring the various pairs of reactants together. According to Marcus,

$$k_{12} = (k_1 k_2 K_{12} f)^{1/2} \tag{1}$$

where

$$\log f = \frac{(\log K_{12})^2}{4 \log (k_1 k_2 / Z^2)} \tag{2}$$

$k_{12}$ and $K_{12}$ are the rate and equilibrium constants, respectively, for the electron transfer involving two different couples, and $k_1$ and $k_2$ are the appropriate exchange rate constants, For example, if $k_{12}$ and $K_{12}$ refer to the reaction

$$\text{Ce(IV)} + \text{Fe}^{2+} \rightleftharpoons \text{Ce(III)} + \text{Fe}^{3+} \tag{3}$$

then $k_1$ and $k_2$ refer to the exchange reactions:

$$\text{Ce(IV)} + \text{Ce(III)} \rightleftharpoons \text{Ce(III)} + \text{Ce(IV)} \tag{4}$$

and

$$\text{Fe}^{2+} + \text{Fe}^{3+} \rightleftharpoons \text{Fe}^{3+} + \text{Fe}^{2+} \tag{5}$$

respectively.

The rate constants for a number of oxidation-reduction reactions are presented in Table 2, which also includes values calculated from equation 1. The agreement of the calculated and observed rates is encouraging. Exceptions are the $\text{Co}^{3+}\text{-Fe}^{2+}$ and $\text{Co}^{3+}\text{-Fe(phen)}_3^{2+}$ reactions, which proceed much more slowly than predicted [22, 24]. The reason for this discrepancy is not known. There is no evidence, though, that reactions such as $\text{Fe}^{2+}\text{-Fe}^{3+}$, $\text{Co}^{2+}\text{-Co}^{3+}$, and $\text{Fe}^{2+}\text{-Co}^{3+}$, which involve one or more substitution-labile species, proceed via outer-sphere mechanisms.

Equation 1 does appear to have some value in predicting and correlating the rates of a number of electron-transfer reactions. For example, equation 1 predicts that the oxidation of spin-paired iron(II) complexes by a given oxidizing agent will proceed more rapidly that the oxidation of spin-free complexes, when allowance is made for any difference in the free energy changes of the reactions. This is found in practice; the $\text{Fe}^{2+}\text{-Ce(IV)}$ reaction is slower than the $\text{Fe(phen)}_3^{2+}\text{-Ce(IV)}$ reaction at comparable standard free energy changes [22]. Similarly, it is evident from Table 2 that the oxidation of ferrocytochrome $c$ by ferricyanide proceeds much more rapidly than the

## TABLE 2

**Comparison of Observed and Calculated Rate Constants for some Electron-Transfer Reactions at 25.0°**

| Reaction | $k_{obs.}$, $M^{-1} sec^{-1}$ | $k_{calc.}$,[a] $M^{-1} sec^{-1}$ | Reference |
|---|---|---|---|
| $Fe^{2+} + Ce(IV)$ | $1.3 \times 10^6$ | $6 \times 10^5$ | (22) |
| $Fe(CN)_6^{4-} + Ce(IV)$ | $1.9 \times 10^6$ | $6 \times 10^6$ | (24) |
| $W(CN)_8^{4-} + Ce(IV)$ | $>10^8$ | $6 \times 10^8$ | (24) |
| $Mo(CN)_8^{4-} + Ce(IV)$ | $1.4 \times 10^7$ | $1 \times 10^7$ | (24) |
| $W(CN)_8^{4-} + Mo(CN)_8^{3-}$ | $5.0 \times 10^6$ | $1 \times 10^7$ | (24) |
| $Fe(CN)_6^{4-} + Mo(CN)_8^{3-}$ | $3.0 \times 10^4$ | $3 \times 10^4$ | (24) |
| $W(CN)_8^{4-} + Fe(CN)_6^{3-}$ | $4.3 \times 10^4$ | $5 \times 10^4$ | (24) |
| $Hb(H_2O) + Fe(CN)_6^{3-}$ | $7.0 \times 10^4$ | ... | (26) |
| $Cyt$-$c + Fe(CN)_6^{3-}$ | $1.6 \times 10^7$ | ... | (27) |

[a] The rate constant for the $W(CN)_8^{3-}$-$W(CN)_8^{4-}$ exchange used in the calculation is a fitted value, which lies above the lower limit established for the exchange.

oxidation of ferrohemoglobin. Although many factors are involved in this comparison, part of the difference in oxidation rates is probably due to the fact that the iron atoms in hemoglobin are spin-free whereas those in cytochrome $c$ are spin-paired, or, in simpler terms, the water molecule coordinated to the iron in hemoglobin protects it from oxidation by ferricyanide.

## C. Chemical Effects of Outer-Sphere Electron Transfers

The immediate effect of an outer-sphere electron transfer is, of course, the change in the charge on the reactants. This change has important consequences, some of which have been discussed by Taube (28). The dependence of the configuration of the coordination shells and the polarization of the solvent on the charge of the central metal ion has already been mentioned in connection with the barrier this presents to electron transfer. These polarizations also have important chemical consequences. Thus the oxidized species tends to compensate for its loss of electrons by withdrawing electrons from the ligands, leading to an increase in the acidity of ligands containing dissociable protons. In the case of $Fe(phen)_3^{3+}$ this electron withdrawal may lead to the dissociation of a proton from the 4-position, a position which tends to be negatively charged in $Fe(phen)_3^{2+}$. Similarly, the change in acidity produced on the oxidation of $Fe(H_2O)_6^{2+}$ is also very great, the hydrolysis constants of $Fe(H_2O)_6^{2+}$ and $Fe(H_2O)_6^{3+}$ being about $10^{-8}$ and $10^{-3}$, respectively.

The arrangement and number of $d$ electrons also markedly affect the substitution lability of a complex. For example, $Fe(H_2O)_6^{2+}$, $Cr(H_2O)_6^{2+}$, and

$Co(NH_3)_6^{2+}$ are about $10^3$, $10^8$–$10^9$, and $10^{11}$–$10^{12}$ times more substitution labile than the corresponding oxidized forms, respectively (28, 29). Thus in the above cases complexes of the higher oxidation states can be formed much more rapidly by oxidation of the lower oxidation states than by direct synthesis from the ligands. This is even more striking when thermodynamic factors determine the formation of a complex. For example, $Fe(phen)_3^{3+}$ cannot be made by mixing $Fe^{3+}$ and phenanthroline; instead, a dimer of the bisphenanthroline complex is obtained. It can readily be prepared, however, by oxidizing $Fe(phen)_3^{2+}$ with a variety of oxidizing agents. This is a rather obvious example of how the electron transfer itself can be used for synthetic purposes. More complex cycles, in which the free energy change accompanying oxidation-reduction is used to synthesize a compound containing an energy-rich bond, have been considered by George and Griffith (5).

## III. INNER-SPHERE ELECTRON TRANSFERS

Inner-sphere reactions will be discussed only insofar as they provide a framework for the treatment of reactions involving oxygen.

The activated complex in inner-sphere reactions contains a group which is bonded directly to both metals. The electron transfer is thus preceded by substitution of a ligand attached to one of the metals (usually the reducing agent). These reactions have been studied mainly by Taube and co-workers (4, 30–33). A typical reaction is

$$Cr^{2+} + (NH_3)_5Co^{III}X + 5H^+ \rightarrow Cr^{III}X + Co(II) + 5NH_4^+ \qquad (6)$$

where $X = H_2O$, $OH^-$, $F^-$, $Cl^-$, $Br^-$, $I^-$, $SO_4^{2-}$, $PO_4^{3-}$, $OAc^-$, etc. In each case $X$ is found in the inner shell of the chromium(III). Since both chromium(III) and cobalt(III) are substitution-inert, it follows that the electron transfer occurs in the bridged intermediate

$$(NH_3)_5Co^{III}-X-Cr^{II}(H_2O)_5$$

in which $X$ is bonded to both the cobalt and the chromium. Bridging by the pyridine carboxylato group has also been demonstrated (34). When $X$ is the methyl half-ester of fumarate, or terephthalate,

$$\left[ (NH_3)_5Co \overset{O}{\underset{O}{\diagup\diagdown}} C - \bigcirc - C \overset{O}{\underset{O}{\diagup\diagdown}} CH_3 \right]^{2+}$$

but not succinate or isophthalate, hydrolysis of the ester occurs, and the methyl alcohol produced is found in the inner shell of the newly formed chromium(III) (32, 33). Moreover, the ester hydrolysis proceeds by rupture of the alkyl-oxygen bond, rather than by acyl-oxygen rupture, which normally occurs in ester hydrolysis.

With maleate as a bridging ligand, some isomerization to fumarate and exchange of ethylenic hydrogens with the solvent occur during the lifetime of the activated complex (35). Enolization appears to be associated with the electron transfer with maleate as the bridging group (36).

These chemical changes are some examples of how the free energy change accompanying inner-sphere oxidation-reduction reactions can be utilized. The ester-hydrolysis reaction, in particular, has been proposed as a model for oxidative phosphorylation (37).

Until recently, $Cr^{2+}$ was the only aquo ion for which inner-sphere mechanisms had definitely been established. However, by the use of flow techniques, it has now been shown that $Fe^{2+}$ is also capable of reacting via an inner-sphere mechanism (38).

A particular type of bridging mechanism involves the transfer of a hydrogen atom between the hydration shells of the reactants. Such a hydrogen atom transfer was first proposed to account for the rapid rate of the $Fe^{2+}$-$FeOH^{2+}$ reaction (39, 40). It may be represented as follows:

$$(H_2O)_5Fe^{II}\!\!-\!\!\overset{\overset{\displaystyle H}{|}}{\underset{\underset{\displaystyle H}{|}}{O}} + \overset{\overset{\displaystyle H}{|}}{O}\!\!-\!\!Fe^{III}(H_2O)_5 \rightarrow \left[ (H_2O)_5Fe\!\!-\!\!\overset{\overset{\displaystyle H}{|}}{O} \underset{\underset{\displaystyle H}{|}}{\diagdown} \overset{\overset{\displaystyle H}{|}}{O}\!\!-\!\!Fe(H_2O)_5 \right]^{4+}$$

$$\downarrow \tag{7}$$

$$(H_2O)_5Fe^{III}\!\!-\!\!\overset{\overset{\displaystyle H}{|}}{\underset{\underset{\displaystyle H}{|}}{O}} + \overset{\overset{\displaystyle H}{|}}{O}\!\!-\!\!Fe^{II}(H_2O)_5$$

The hydrogen atom transfer may proceed via intervening solvent molecules, in a manner proposed for the migration of protons in water. This model has been extended by several authors (41–44). The essential feature of the extended models is that the electron transfer occurs via the hydration shells of the reactants, and that net transfer of a hydrogen atom does not necessarily occur. Whether it takes place depends on the relative proton affinities of the products of the electron transfer. Electron conduction via hydrogen bonds may well be important in proteins, where electron transfer over large distances, often in the absence of conjugated groups, may be necessary. It is conceivable that in some instances hydrogen atom or hydride ion transfer to $O_2$, forming $HO_2$ and $HO_2^-$, respectively, occurs via such a "long-range" mechanism.

## IV. REACTIONS OF METAL COMPLEXES WITH OXYGEN

Metal complexes which are oxidized by oxygen more rapidly than they undergo substitution presumably react by outer-sphere mechanisms. Equation 1 predicts that the rates of a series of outer-sphere reactions should increase as their free energy changes become more negative, and that, for a given free energy change, the oxidation of a system which undergoes rapid electron exchange should be faster than the oxidation of one which undergoes slow electron exchange. Unfortunately, kinetic data on outer-sphere oxidations by oxygen are lacking at the present time. The free energy dependence has been found for a series of organic reactions of the type

$$QH^- + O_2 \rightleftharpoons QH + O_2^- \tag{8}$$

where $QH^-$ is an ionized leucoindophenol, and $QH$ the corresponding semiquinone (45–47). However, a hydrogen atom transfer mechanism is also consistent with the data.

Dipyridine-ferrohemochrome is diamagnetic and presumably undergoes substitution relatively slowly. It might therefore be expected to undergo oxidation by an outer-sphere mechanism. However, a preliminary report indicates that its reaction with oxygen is complicated (48).

The oxidation of spin-paired $Cr(CN)_6^{4-}$ by oxygen (as well as by hydrogen peroxide) produces $Cr(CN)_6^{3-}$ (49, 50). The absence of oxygen atoms in the inner coordination shell of the chromium(III) produced is strong evidence that the oxidation proceeds via an outer-sphere mechanism. This behavior contrasts with the oxidation of ammoniacal solutions of chromium(II), in which the oxygen is incorporated into the product $[(NH_3)_5Cr—O—Cr(NH_3)_5]^{5+}$. Joyner and Wilmarth (49) propose that the binuclear peroxide:

$$[(NH_3)_5Cr^{III}—O—O—Cr^{III}(NH_3)_5]^{4+}$$

formed by the reaction of molecular oxygen and two chromium(II)-ammonia complex ions, is an intermediate in the oxidation. Similarly, the oxidation of aqueous chromium(II), which produces a dimer of chromium(III), probably also proceeds via a binuclear peroxide complex (51). It is interesting to speculate about the reasons for the difference in the mechanism of the oxidation of the chromium(II)-cyanide complex, on the one hand, and the chromium(II)-aquo and ammino complexes, on the other. One factor may be the different "electron conductivities" of the ligands. A cyanide group is probably a better electron conductor than a water or ammonia molecule; it should therefore be easier for an electron to be conducted through the inner coordination shell of the chromium(II) in the cyanide complex than in the aquo and ammino complexes (50). However, the difference in the configurations of the inner coordination shells of chromium(II) and chromium(III) is probably a more important factor in determining the oxidation mechanism. Thus, $Cr(CN)_6^{4-}$ is a spin-paired complex, while the aquo and ammino complexes are spin-free. The configurations of the coordination shells of chromium(II) and chromium(III) are probably more similar in the cyanide complexes than in the aquo and ammino complexes (50) [cf. the slow electron exchange between the aquo complexes of chromium(II) and chromium(III), Table 1].

The oxidation of $Co(CN)_5^{3-}$ by oxygen produces the binuclear peroxide:

$$[(CN)_5Co^{III}—O—O—Co^{III}(CN)_5]^{6-}$$

The complex decomposes to cobalt(III) and $H_2O_2$ in acid solution, whereas the peroxide

$$[(NH_3)_5Co^{III}—O—O—Co^{III}(NH_3)_5]^{4+}$$

decomposes to cobalt(II) and oxygen (50). Several other binuclear complexes of cobalt, some of which carry oxygen reversibly, are known. The oxidation state of the cobalt in these complexes is believed to be between 2 and 3 (52).

The rate of oxidation of $Fe^{2+}$ by oxygen is very dependent on the nature of the anions present (53, 54). The rates increase with the affinity of the anion for iron(III) and undergo a change in reaction order. The rate law is

$$-d[Fe^{II}]/dt = k_1[Fe^{II}]P_{O_2} \tag{9}$$

in pyrophosphate and phosphate media and

$$-d[Fe^{II}]/dt = k_2[Fe^{II}]^2P_{O_2} \tag{10}$$

in sulfate, chloride, and perchlorate media at room temperature. The following structures have been proposed for the activated complex (55):

$$(X—Fe^{II}—O_2) \rightleftharpoons (X—Fe^{III}—O_2^-) \tag{11}$$

The above equilibrium lies over to the left-hand side in perchlorate media $[X = (H_2O)_5]$. Ions which form strong complexes with iron(III), e.g., pyrophosphate and phosphate, displace this equilibrium to the right, thereby bringing about the oxidation by a path which is first order with respect to iron(II). The reaction in sulfate and chloride media also becomes first order with respect to iron(II) at higher temperatures. In the absence of complexing ions the intermediate is attacked by another iron(II), possibly forming the binuclear peroxide:

$$[(H_2O)_5Fe^{III}-O-O-Fe^{III}(H_2O)_5]^{4+}$$

which rapidly decomposes to iron(III) and hydrogen peroxide (54–56). On the other hand, ligands which complex iron(II) very strongly will displace equilibrium 11 far to the left, thus stabilizing the iron(II)-oxygen complex. Under suitable conditions this complex can act as an oxygen carrier, as occurs, for example, when X = dimethylglyoxime (plus pyridine) or in hemoglobin (57). Factors influencing the stability of these oxygen carriers have been discussed by Williams (58–60) and by Fallab and co-workers (61–63).

To summarize, the inner-sphere reactions with oxygen proceed via mononuclear (containing one metal ion and one oxygen molecule) and binuclear (containing two metal ions and one oxygen molecule) intermediates. Several structures may be written for the mononuclear intermediates:

$$XM(II) + O_2 \rightleftharpoons XM^{II}O_2 \tag{12}$$

$$XM^{II}O_2 \rightleftharpoons XM^{III}O_2^- \rightleftharpoons XM^{IV}O_2^{2-}, \text{ etc.} \tag{13}$$

The stabilities of the various structures depend upon the relative electron affinities of X, M, and oxygen. If the mononuclear intermediate is sufficiently long-lived, it may react with another molecule of XM(II) to form a binuclear intermediate as follows:

$$XM^{II}O_2 + XM^{II} \rightleftharpoons XM^{II}\text{---}O{=}O\text{---}M^{II}X \tag{14}$$

$$XM^{II}\text{---}O{=}O\text{---}M^{II}X \rightleftharpoons XM^{III}-O-O-M^{III}X, \text{ etc.} \tag{15}$$

This type of two-equivalent, intramolecular oxidation-reduction may also occur in other systems of interest to biochemists. For example, disulfide bond formation may proceed via such a mechanism. Thus Leussing and Neumann (64) have proposed that dimers of ferric cysteinate and ferric thioglycolate undergo an intramolecular electron transfer to form the corresponding disulfides as follows:

$$
\left[
\begin{array}{c}
H \\
| \\
O \\
\diagup \quad \diagdown \\
(RS^{2-})_2Fe^{III} \qquad Fe^{III}(RS^{2-})_2 \\
\diagdown \quad \diagup \\
O \\
| \\
H
\end{array}
\right]^{4-} \rightarrow 2Fe(II) + RSSR^{2-} \tag{16}
$$

Here two sulfur atoms in the same complex "simultaneously" transfer one electron each to a ferric ion, thereby producing two RS radicals very close together. These radicals rapidly combine to form the corresponding disulfide.

Similar binuclear intermediates may also play a role in the oxidation of a copper(I)-cysteine complex, which has been reported to carry oxygen reversibly (63, 65). This oxidation may proceed via the binuclear intermediate:

$$(RS^{2-})Cu^{I} \cdots O = O \cdots Cu^{I}(RS^{2-})$$

In systems of this type, and there are undoubtedly many others, the formal oxidation state of the metal may not be a particularly meaningful quantity. The metal ion conducts electrons (or hydrogen atoms) from the organic residue to the oxygen and does not necessarily undergo any net change in oxidation state during the process.

## V. CONCLUSION

Some inner-sphere and outer-sphere reactions involving metal complexes have been considered. Substitution-labile complexes react with oxygen via an inner-sphere mechanism in which the oxygen is bonded directly to the metal. Inner-sphere reactions are favored when the electronic interaction between the reactants is very small (as occurs, for example, when the electron transfer is accompanied by a change in spin multiplicity) or when the energy required to reorganize the coordination shells of the reactants is very large.

The reactions with oxygen proceed via mononuclear and binuclear complexes, in which an oxygen molecule is bonded to one and two metal ions, respectively. The reduction of oxygen to hydrogen peroxide can be brought about in the binuclear complex by the "simultaneous" transfer of electrons (or hydrogen atoms) by each of the metals to which it is bonded. For this reason binuclear intermediates may be quite common in reactions between a two-equivalent oxidizing agent and a one-equivalent reducing agent, and vice versa.

### ACKNOWLEDGMENTS

I wish to thank I. Pecht for helpful discussions.

This research was performed under the auspices of the United States Atomic Energy Commission.

### REFERENCES

1. H. Taube, in H. J. Emeléus and A. G. Sharpe, Eds., *Advances in Inorganic Chemistry and Radiochemistry*, Vol. I, Academic Press, New York, 1959, p. 1.

2. J. Halpern, *Quart. Revs. (London)*, **15**, 207 (1961).
3. N. Sutin, *Ann. Rev. Nuclear Sci.*, **12**, 285 (1962).
4. H. Taube and H. Myers, *J. Am. Chem. Soc.*, **76**, 2103 (1954).
5. P. George and J. S. Griffith, in P. D. Boyer, H. Lardy, and K. Myrbäck, Eds., *The Enzymes*, Vol. I, Academic Press, New York, 1959, p. 347.
6. J. Halpern and L. E. Orgel, *Discussions Faraday Soc.*, **29**, 32 (1960).
7. V. K. Krishnamurty and A. C. Wahl, *J. Am. Chem. Soc.*, **80**, 5921 (1958).
8. A. Anderson and N. A. Bonner, *J. Am. Chem. Soc.*, **76**, 3826 (1954).
9. J. Silverman and R. W. Dodson, *J. Phys. Chem.*, **56**, 846 (1952).
10. M. W. Dietrich and A. C. Wahl. *J. Chem. Phys.*, **38**, 1591 (1963).
11. N. A. Bonner and J. P. Hunt, *J. Am. Chem. Soc.*, **82**, 3826 (1960).
12. D. R. Stranks, *Discussions Faraday Soc.*, **29**, 73 (1960).
13. F. P. Dwyer and A. M. Sargesen, *J. Phys. Chem.*, **65**, 1892 (1961).
14. B. R. Baker, F. Basolo, and H. M. Neuman, *J. Phys. Chem.*, **63**, 371 (1959).
15. W. F. Libby, *J. Phys. Chem.*, **56**, 863 (1952).
16. R. J. Marcus, B. J. Zwolinski, and H. Eyring, *J. Phys. Chem.*, **58**, 132 (1954).
17. R. A. Marcus, *Discussions Faraday Soc.*, **29**, 21 (1960).
18. N. S. Hush, *Trans. Faraday Soc.*, **57**, 557 (1961).
19. L. E. Orgel, *Report of the 10th Solvay Conference on Chemistry, Brussels, 1956*, p. 329.
20. P. George and D. H. Irvine, *J. Chem. Soc.*, **1954**, 587.
21. M. H. Ford-Smith and N. Sutin, *J. Am. Chem. Soc.*, **83**, 1830 (1961).
22. G. Dulz and N. Sutin, *Inorg. Chem.*, **2**, 917 (1963).
23. H. Diebler and N. Sutin, *J. Phys. Chem.*, **68**, 174 (1964).
24. R. J. Campion, N. Purdie, and N. Sutin, *Inorg. Chem.*, **3**, 1091 (1964).
25. R. A. Marcus, *J. Phys. Chem.*, **67**, 853 (1963).
26. N. Sutin, *Nature*, **190**, 438 (1961).
27. N. Sutin and D. R. Christman, *J. Am. Chem. Soc.*, **83**, 1773 (1961).
28. H. Taube, in "Enzyme Models and Enzyme Structure," *Brookhaven Symposia in Biol.*, No. 15, 1 (1962).
29. T. J. Swift and R. E. Connick, *J. Chem. Phys.*, **37**, 307 (1962).
30. A. Zwickel and H. Taube, *J. Am. Chem. Soc.*, **83**, 793 (1961).
31. R. T. M. Fraser, *J. Am. Chem. Soc.*, **83**, 4920 (1961).
32. R. T. M. Fraser and H. Taube, *J. Am. Chem. Soc.*, **83**, 2239 (1961).
33. D. K. Sebera and H. Taube, *J. Am. Chem. Soc.*, **83**, 1785 (1961).
34. E. S. Gould and H. Taube, *J. Am. Chem. Soc.*, **85**, 3706 (1963).
35. R. T. M. Fraser and H. Taube, *J. Am. Chem. Soc.*, **83**, 2242 (1961).
36. G. Svatos and H. Taube, *J. Am. Chem. Soc.*, **83**, 4172 (1961).
37. L. E. Orgel, in J. E. Falk, R. Lemberg, and R. K. Morton, Eds., *Haematin Enzymes*, Pergamon Press, Oxford, 1961, p. 1.
38. T. J. Conocchioli, G. Nancollas, and N. Sutin, *J. Am. Chem. Soc.*, **86**, 1453 (1964).
39. R. W. Dodson, *J. Phys. Chem.*, **56**, 852 (1952).
40. R. W. Dodson and N. Davidson, *J. Phys. Chem.*, **56**, 866 (1952).
41. W. L. Reynolds and R. W. Lumry, *J. Chem. Phys.*, **23**, 2460 (1955).
42. D. R. Stranks, in J. Lewis and R. G. Wilkins, Eds., *Modern Coordination Chemistry*, Interscience, New York, 1960, p. 78.
43. J. Hudis and A. C Wahl. *J. Am. Chem. Soc.*, **75**, 4153 (1953).
44. R. A. Horne, *J. Phys. Chem.*, **64**, 1512 (1960).
45. E. S. G. Barron, *J. Biol. Chem.*, **97**, 287 (1932).
46. J. H. Baxendale and S. Lewin, *Trans. Faraday Soc.*, **42**, 126 (1946).
47. R. A. Marcus, *J. Chem. Phys.*, **26**, 872 (1957).
48. J. H. Wang and O. H. W. Kao, paper presented at the 145th meeting of the American Chemical Society, New York, September 1963.

49. J. B. Joyner and W. K. Wilmarth, *J. Am. Chem. Soc.*, **83**, 516 (1961).
50. A. Haim and W. K. Wilmarth, *J. Am. Chem. Soc.*, **83**, 509 (1961).
51. R. W. Kolaczowski and R. A. Plane, *Inorg. Chem.*, 3, 322 (1964).
52. L. H. Vogt, H. M. Faigenbaum, and S. E. Wilberley, *Chem. Revs.*, **63**, 269 (1963).
53. P. George, *J. Chem. Soc.*, **1954**, 4349.
54. F. E. Huffman and N. Davidson, *J. Am. Chem. Soc.*, **78**, 4836 (1956).
55. J. Weiss, *Experientia*, **9**, 61 (1953).
56. J. Weiss, *Nature*, **202**, 83 (1964).
57. J. F. Drake and R. J. P. Williams, *Nature*, **182**, 1084 (1958).
58. R. J. P. Williams, *Chem. Revs.*, **56**, 299 (1956).
59. R. J. P. Williams, in P. D. Boyer, H. Lardy, and K. Myrbäck, Eds., *The Enzymes*, Vol. I, Academic Press, New York, 1959, p. 391.
60. R. J. P. Williams, in J. E. Falk, R. Lemberg, and R. K. Morton, Eds., *Haematin Enzymes*, Pergamon Press, Oxford, 1961, p. 41.
61. S. Fallab, *Helv. Chem. Acta*, **45**, 1957 (1962).
62. O. Bekâroğlu and S. Fallab, *Helv. Chim. Acta*, **46**, 2120 (1963).
63. L. Graf and S. Fallab, *Experientia*, **20**, 46 (1964).
64. D. L. Leussing and L. Newman, *J. Am. Chem. Soc.*, **78**, 552 (1956).
65. L. L. Ingraham, *Biochemical Mechanisms*, Wiley, New York, 1962, p. 68.

*Discussion*

ORGEL: To what range of reactions do you consider the theory to apply?

SUTIN: The theory is applicable to outer-sphere electron-transfer reactions, i.e., to reactions in which the inner coordination shells of the reactants remain intact. This probably occurs, for example, in rapid electron-transfer reactions involving $Fe(phen)_3^{2+}$–$Fe(phen)_3^{3+}$, $Fe(CN)_6^{4-}$–$Fe(CN)_6^{3-}$, $IrCl_6^{3-}$–$IrCl_6^{2-}$, $MnO_4^{2-}$–$MnO_4^{-}$, and similar couples. These reactants undergo substitution relatively slowly. Another condition is that the electron transfer occur with unit probability in the activated complex.

ORGEL: I should like to continue with that question if I may. Suppose that the outsides of the molecules were very different. Suppose that one had water molecules outside, and another had aromatic groups. Do you still think that the approximations would work?

SUTIN: We have tested this. For example, the $Fe^{2+}$–$Fe(phen)_3^{3+}$ reaction occurs between a species which has hydrogen-bonding ligands and one with an aromatic ligand. The observed rates are about one hundred times slower than predicted by the square-root relationship. This has been ascribed to the fact that the work terms, which now also contain non-coulombic contributions, are different for the cross reactions and for the simple exchange reactions and thus no longer cancel [R. A. Marcus, *J. Phys. Chem.*, **67**, 853, 2889 (1963)].

MASON: You say that electronic conduction by hydrogen bonds may well be important in proteins where electron transfer over large distances may be necessary, and then you go on to state that conceivably in some instances hydrogen atom or hydride ion transfer to oxygen occurs by such long-range mechanisms. I wonder whether you would specify which instances you have in mind.

SUTIN: This is purely speculative. There have been some experiments by Dr. Ralph Horne on the ferrous-ferric exchange in ice media. Dr. Horne found that the exchange still proceeded at a measurable rate, even though the reactants were about 100 Å apart on the average. He interpreted this in terms of a hydrogen atom-transfer mechanism. Similar "long-range" mechanisms could conceivably operate in more complex systems.

ROSENBERG: The mechanism that you have mentioned here, involving the Franck-Condon principle in the ferric-ferrous changeover, is quite similar to that which occurs in optical transitions. In that case some fairly extensive work has been done on changing the solvent environment of the atoms to investigate the blue and red shifts as a function of the solvent dielectric constant. Can you do the same kind of experiments on the ferric-ferrous couple by using different dielectric constant media, say mixed solvents, and look for similar changes?

SUTIN: There have been a number of studies of electron-transfer reactions in non-aqueous media. For example, the ferrous-ferric exchange has been studied in alcohol-water mixtures. The rates become very slow in the absence of water. It is difficult to interpret these effects, since many factors are involved in a solvent change. Thus if water in the inner coordination shells of the reactants is replaced by alcohol, one has now to consider the reorganization of an alcohol coordination sphere. In addition, the work required to bring the two reactants together will be different in water and in alcohol. It would be desirable to have more information on the effect of solvent change on electron-transfer reactions involving substitution-inert reactants.

INGRAHAM: I think that a corollary of this work, which perhaps is obvious to everyone but nevertheless should be brought out, is that really fast electron transfer requires a very rigid structure. An example, of course, is the rigid structure of the porphyrin ring in the cytochromes used in the electron-transport chain.

# A Kinetic Theory of Electron and Ion Transport in Particulate and Membranous Systems, with Applications to the Cytochrome Oxidase, Melanin Free Radical, and Pyruvate Carboxylase Reactions, and to Control of Enzymes by Hormones and Radiation

... FREEMAN W. COPE

## I. INTRODUCTION

Various investigators, starting with Szent-Györgyi in 1941 (1), have suggested that electron conduction within particulate and membranous structures of cells may play an important role in metabolic processes. This idea, applied in a specific and quantitative way, has led to a new type of enzyme kinetics, based on the hypothesis of electron conduction across an enzymatic particle. The new theory predicts rate equations which are in agreement with experimental data for reactions catalyzed by various particulate biochemical systems and for some reactions which are catalyzed by inorganic semiconductor particles. A special case of the theory provided a new derivation of the Elovich equation, which often has been used empirically by physicists to describe inorganic electron-transport processes in semiconductor solids. Because of the analogous behavior of charge carriers in liquid and solid systems, a similar analysis was found applicable to experimental data on ion transport across cell membranes.

These investigations on the quantitative application of the concepts of solid-state physics to biology began with attempts to analyze kinetically the experimental concentration-time curves of free-radical decay in eye melanin (2). Since the conventional equations of mass-action kinetics did not well describe this data, various unconventional approaches were tried.

In particular, I was impressed by the point that the free-radical reaction seemed to occur in or on a *particle*, suggesting that the reactants might be tethered to the particle, thus invalidating mass-action theories, which assume free and random motion of all molecules in a solution.

Therefore, it seemed logical to try a new kinetic approach based on the solid-state properties of the melanin particle. Since the decay of free radicals implied the pairing of previously unpaired electrons, it was reasonable to postulate electron conduction within the solid particle as the rate-limiting process. The development of such a theory was stimulated by theoretical predictions that melanin should be a conductor of electrons (3, 4) and by the feeling that such a theory also should be applicable to particulate *enzyme* systems, since electron conduction in *proteins* has been reported [reviewed by Eley (5) and Cope (7)].

A preliminary mathematical analysis (6) of a simple model based on the electron-conduction hypothesis led to a better understanding of the nature of the problem, although not to an experimentally useful solution. More detailed studies (7–11), however, did lead to rate equations which described not only free-radical decay in eye melanin but also the kinetics of some particulate enzyme reactions, and in addition provided a new explanation of the kinetics of various phenomena from the field of solid-state and surface physics. Because of analogies between the behavior of electrons in solids and of ions in solution, a similar theory was applied to ion transport across cell surfaces (10) and to group transport across particulate fragments of membranes (11).

The present paper describes these theories, with the emphasis on the nature and significance of the postulates and on the correlation of the results with experimental data. Mathematical detail has been omitted except when necessary for an understanding of the experimental basis and logical structure of the theory.

## II. A SIMPLE MODEL OF AN ELECTRON-TRANSPORT ENZYME AND GENERALIZATIONS THEREOF. CYTOCHROME OXIDASE

Let us postulate the existence of a melanin or protein particle with a site for enzymatic oxidation-reduction of substrate molecules of type $X$ at one end and a site for oxidation-reduction of substrate molecules of type $Y$ at the other end, with electron conduction through the particle between the two sites (Fig. 1). In other words, we postulate that the electrons of substrates $X$ and $Y$ are in free equilibrium with the particle at, but only at, their respective sites, and that electrons can travel from one site to the other only by passing through the electrical resistance of the particle. The two enzymatic sites may be considered analogous to two electrodes, immersed in two different solutions, while electron conduction between the two sites (or electrodes) occurs through a resistor, which is analogous to the transparticle electrical resistance.

If the two redox reactions are as shown in Fig. 1, we may calculate the potential experienced by the $X$-site by using the electrode equation in the form

$$E_x = E_x^0 - \frac{kT}{F} \log_e \left[ \frac{x_r}{x_{ox}} \right] \tag{1}$$

where $E_x$ is the electrical potential at the $X$-site on the particle, $x_r$ and $x_{ox}$ are, respectively, the concentrations of reduced and oxidized forms of substrate $X$, $T$ is absolute temperature, $F$ is the Faraday, $k$ is the gas constant, and $E_x^0$ is a constant. If we define the total concentration of oxidized plus reduced substrate to be $C_x$, then it is obvious that

$$x_r + x_{ox} = C_x \tag{2}$$

Combining equations 1 and 2, we obtain

$$E_x = E_x^0 - \frac{kT}{-F} \log \left[ \frac{x_r}{C_x - x_r} \right] \tag{3}$$

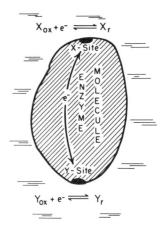

One might develop a similar equation for the potential $(E_y)$ experienced by the $Y$-site on the enzymatic particle. For simplicity, however, we shall assume here that $E_y = Y = $ constant. The potential difference $(V)$ across the enzymatic particle between the two sites may then be written

$$V = E_x - Y \tag{4}$$

Fig. 1. Diagrammatic representation of the postulated model of a particulate redox enzyme.

*Our purpose is to set up a differential rate equation in terms of the concentration of reduced substrate $(x_r)$ and time $(t)$.* To derive this equation, we note that the potential drop $(V)$ across the enzymatic particle may be expressed also in terms of transparticle resistance $(R)$ and transparticle current $(i)$ by the use of Ohm's law,

$$V = iR \tag{5}$$

Since the passage of 1 mole of electrons across the particle results in the oxidation (or reduction) of 1 mole of substrate, we may write

$$i = F \frac{dx_r}{dt} \tag{6}$$

We may now derive the differential rate equation of the reaction by equating the two expressions for transparticle potential difference $(V)$ as given by equations 4 and 5, and then substituting for $E_x$ and $i$ as given by equations 3 and 6, resulting in

$$RF \frac{dx_r}{dt} = -\frac{kT}{F} \log \left[ \frac{x_r}{C_x - x_r} \right] + (E_x^0 - Y) \tag{7}$$

Equation 7 is the basic differential rate equation describing the kinetics of a particulate enzyme that is rate-limited by conduction of electrons across the particle (6). Unfortunately, because of the log term, it cannot be integrated by any exact method. One might, however, test experimental data for electron-conduction kinetics by plotting a graph of $dx_r/dt$ vs. $\log [x_r/(C_x - x_r)]$, although this is rather inconvenient (6). Linearity of such a plot would indicate conformity of the data to equation 7.

When some cytochrome oxidase data of Smith and Conrad (12) were plotted in this manner, linearity was obtained, suggesting that electron conduction occurred across the cytochrome oxidase molecule. It was most disconcerting to discover that the same cytochrome oxidase data also gave a positive test for first-order kinetics and were therefore describable also by an equation of the form

$$- \frac{dx_r}{dt} = K x_r \qquad (8)$$

where $K$ is a constant.

Only much later was it realized that this pair of observations indicated a mathematical fact which provided the key to the convenient analysis of equation 7. That the same data conformed to both equations 7 and 8 could mean only that the function $\log [x_r/(C_x - x_r)]$ may be closely approximated by a linear function of $x$, which leads to a general, although approximate, solution of differential equation 7.

When this observation was pursued in mathematical detail (equation 7), it was shown that the differential rate equation of an electron-conduction enzyme (equation 7), could be closely approximated by an equation of the form

$$- \frac{dx_r}{dt} = \left[ \frac{\alpha}{C_x} \right] x_r + \delta \qquad (9)$$

where $\alpha$ and $\delta$ are constants. This approximation is accurate within a few per cent between 10 and 90% reduction of substrate (7). The striking feature of equation 9 is the inverse proportionality, or hyperbolic relationship, between the first-order rate constant ($k'$) and the concentration ($C_x$) of oxidized plus reduced substrate. Since the cytochrome oxidase data of Smith and Conrad (12) and of Minnaert (13) showed hyperbolic relationships between $k'$ and $C_x$, it was felt that the theory was close to being in a useful form, even though the axes of the hyperbolas derived from the data were displaced from those predicted by theory.

To obtain a more realistic theory of particulate enzyme kinetics, it seemed reasonable to take account of diffusion of substrate up to the surface of the enzyme particle, as well as electron conduction across the particle. This seemed especially important for the case of cytochrome oxidase, which is a very active enzyme acting on large, slowly diffusing substrate molecules. A voltage drop across the layer of solution adjacent to an electrode caused by substrate diffusion is well known in the field of polarography. The postulation of such a process at the surface of an enzyme particle seems a natural extension of the analogy that has already been made between an enzymatically active surface and an electrode.

Also, it seemed desirable to generalize the theory by eliminating the restrictive special postulate used in equation 4, which is that the percentage reduction of the second substrate ($Y$) remains constant over the course of the reaction. This generalization would be in accord with an experiment which allowed a significant change in the concentration of $O_2$, as well as of reduced cytochrome $c$, during the operation of cytochrome oxidase.

Hence, the model shown in Fig. 1 was refined to include a voltage drop across the layer of solution immediately adjacent to the enzymatic surface due to substrate diffusion as well as the voltage drop across the body of the particle due to electron conduction (7). In addition, the postulate of the constancy of percentage reduction of $Y$ was eliminated (11). A straightforward analysis (11) led to a differential rate equation of the form

$$-\frac{dx_r}{dt} = \left[\frac{\alpha}{C_x + \beta} + \gamma\right]x_r + \epsilon \qquad (10)$$

where $\beta$ is a constant that is a function of the diffusion constant of substrate $x_r$, $\gamma$ is a positive constant, and $\epsilon$ is a constant. Hence, like equation 9 for the simpler model, the refined theory predicts a hyperbolic relationship between the first-order rate constant ($k'$) and $C_x$, but of a more complicated form as follows:

$$k' = \frac{\alpha}{C_x + \beta} + \gamma \qquad (11)$$

This predicts exactly the form of the experimental data on cytochrome oxidase of Minnaert (13) and of Smith and Conrad (12). It also describes kinetic data on cytochrome *peroxidase* reported by Beetlestone (14).

A modified form of the theory applicable to coupled reactions predicts a negative value for $\gamma$ (11).

## III. EYE MELANIN, THE TAFEL EQUATION, AND THE ELOVICH EQUATION

Despite its success in the analysis of cytochrome oxidase kinetics, the theory of electron-conduction enzymes still had not fulfilled the purpose for which it was created, which was to explain the shape of eye-melanin free-radical decay curves. The success with cytochrome oxidase served, however, as the stimulus to further development of the theory. The key to additional progress was found in another extension of the analogy of the enzymatically active surface of the biochemical particle to an electrode surface (7).

Besides potential drops due to substrate diffusion and to the resistance of oxide films, detailed studies of metal and semiconductor electrodes in solution have frequently shown the existence of potential drops caused by an activation energy requirement for transferring the electron across the liquid-solid interface. The magnitude of the voltage drop due to activation has been shown experimentally to be dependent on electrode current, in accordance with the following equation, which also may be derived from a simple statistical-mechanical argument (15):

$$V = e - \frac{kT}{Fa} \log_e \left[ -\frac{i}{A'} \right] \tag{12}$$

This is known as the Tafel equation. $V$ is the voltage drop across the electrode surface, $i$ is electrode current, $A'$ is electrode surface area, and $e$ and $a$ are constants characteristic of the electrode material.

To develop further the theory of particulate electron-conduction processes, one may continue to use the model represented by Fig. 1, with the postulate that the *only* voltage drop in the system is caused by an activation energy requirement for transfer of electrons across the liquid-solid interface at the $X$-site on the particle (7). The transparticle driving potential (given by equation 4) may then be set equal to the voltage drop at the surface of the $X$-site, which is given by the Tafel equation (equation 12). If, as before, equations 3 and 6 are used also, one may derive

$$-\frac{kT}{F} \log \left[ \frac{x_r}{C_x - x_r} \right] = -\frac{kT}{Fa} \log \left[ -\frac{F}{A'} \frac{dx_r}{dt} \right] + (e - E_x^0 + Y) \tag{13}$$

which may be converted easily to

$$-\frac{dx_r}{dt} = \frac{A'}{Fg} \left[ \frac{x_r}{C_x - x_r} \right]^a \tag{14}$$

where $g$ is a new constant. If $a = 1$, as is theoretically the case for an ideal electrode (7), and if reaction velocity ($v$) is defined as $v = -dx_r/dt$, then equation 14 may be written in the form

$$\frac{1}{v} = \frac{Fg}{A'} \left[ \frac{C_x}{x_r} - 1 \right] \tag{15}$$

which may be compared with the rate equation of Michaelis-Menten kinetics (in the usual notation),

$$\frac{1}{v} = \frac{1}{V} \left[ \frac{K_s}{s} + 1 \right] \tag{16}$$

It is apparent from equations 15 and 16 that activation-limited particulate kinetics gives a linear double reciprocal plot like Michaelis-Menton kinetics, with the important difference that the $1/v$ axis intercept is negative instead of positive (7). Equation 15 proved to describe well our eye-melanin free-radical decay curves. Thus the original search for an explanation of eye-melanin kinetics in terms of solid-state concepts finally proved successful.

The development of the theory of particulate kinetics remained at this state until it was realized that an important correlation with the field of experimental solid-state physics was at hand.

By using the approximate linear relationship between $\log [x_r/(C_x - x_r)]$ and $x_r$ that was described in section II, it was easy to show (9, 10) that equation 14 in describing activation-limited particulate kinetics may be written (to close approximation) as

$$-\frac{dx_r}{dt} = me^{nx_r} \tag{17}$$

where $m$ and $n$ are constants. An empirical rate equation of essentially this form has been used widely to describe data from the field of solid-state and surface physics and is generally known as the Elovich equation. The Elovich equation has been used by many investigators to describe data on the kinetics of gas (especially oxygen) adsorption by inorganic and semiconductor solids (16) and data on the decay of surface charge from semiconductor solids (17). In addition, some cases of heterogeneous catalysis by semiconductor particles have been observed to obey the Elovich rate equation (18). Since the Elovich equation was proved to be equivalent to equation 15, eye-melanin kinetics of course conformed to it (8, 9). Later, the Elovich equation was found also to describe the decay of photogenerated free radicals in a photosynthetic system (36). These seem to represent the first applications of the Elovich equation to biological data.

## IV. APPLICATIONS TO ION AND GROUP TRANSPORT BY MEMBRANES

Although the previous discussion has dealt with electron conduction in biological *solids*, similar considerations may be applied to ionic conduction in biological *solutions* and *gels*, because of the marked similarities in the behavior of charge carriers in solids and liquids.

Similarities between electron conduction in solids and ionic conduction in liquids have been noted by a number of investigators (19–22). The analogy was extended (10) with the suggestion that ion conduction across liquid-liquid or liquid-gel interfaces at cell surfaces might obey the Tafel equation. The voltage-current behavior of the squid axon surface proved to be fairly well described by the Tafel equation under at least one set of conditions (10). The conformity of a variety of kinetic data on ion transport to the Elovich equation demonstrated a further correspondence of ionic transport to activation-limited electron transport. To complete the analogy between the two processes, it remained only to find similar equations for the driving potentials of the two processes. To do this required only the postulates that most of the inorganic ions within the cell were associated with cellular proteins, and that only the associated form of the ion was available for membrane transport (10). This allowed the construction of a theory predicting Elovich kinetics for ion transport across a cell surface, as sometimes observed experimentally (8, 10).

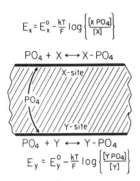

$$E_x = E_x^0 - \frac{kT}{F} \log \left\{ \frac{[X \, PO_4]}{[X]} \right\}$$

$$PO_4 + X \longleftrightarrow X\text{-}PO_4$$

$$PO_4 + Y \longleftrightarrow Y\text{-}PO_4$$

$$E_y = E_y^0 - \frac{kT}{F} \log \left\{ \frac{[Y \, PO_4]}{[Y]} \right\}$$

**Fig. 2.** Diagrammatic representation of a postulated fragment of a phosphate transfer membrane. One surface of the particle is assumed to have enzymatic activity capable of maintaining an equilibrium of intraparticle phosphate with phosphorylated and unphosphorylated substrate $X$. The opposite surface of the particle is assumed to have similar enzymatic activity with regard to substrate $Y$. It is supposed that phosphate is driven across the particle by the difference in phosphate potentials between its two surfaces as established by the concentrations of phosphorylated and unphosphorylated substrates.

The applicability of the theory of electron-conduction enzymes to ion transport suggests a similar application to chemical group transport reactions involving, for example, phosphate or carbonate. Let us postulate the existence of a cellular membrane whose two surfaces have the enzymatic ability to transfer phosphate to and from two phosphorylated substrates, in the manner that an electrode surface can exchange electrons with a redox substrate (Fig. 2). Specifically, let us suppose that the membrane surface can exchange phosphate ion from the *inside* of the membrane with a phosphorylated substrate *outside* the membrane. Fragmentation of such a membrane would yield à *particulate* preparation which should show phosphotransferase activity between substrates $X$ and $Y$. Such a particle is shown diagrammatically in Fig. 2. The driving force for phosphate transport across such a particle should be given by the difference in phosphate potentials at its two surfaces. Conductance of phosphate across the surface and through the bulk of the particle could reasonably be expected to obey equations like those for electrons in solids. Hence, the kinetics of particulate enzyme preparations catalyzing chemical group transfer might conform to the same rate equations that were originally derived for electron-transport enzymes.

A possible example of carboxyl group transfer by the above mechanism is yeast pyruvate carboxylase (11), which was studied kinetically by Eadie and Gale (24). This enzyme showed a hyperbolic relation between first-order rate constant and the sum of substrate plus product (11, 24). The negative sign of one of the constants in the hyperbolic equation indicated the likelihood of coupled transport (11). It appears likely that other particulate group transfer enzymes also will be found to conform to the rate equations given in this paper.

## V. APPLICATIONS TO CONTROL OF ENZYMES BY HORMONES OR RADIATION

If the reaction rate of a particulate enzyme is governed by the electrical resistivity of the enzyme protein, it follows that factors controlling resistivity will thereby control reaction rate. By analogy with the physics of inorganic semiconductors, one may expect protein resistivity to be markedly influenced by adsorbed impurities, suggesting that reaction rates of electron-conduction enzymes may be controlled by the adsorption of hormones and drugs. The hormone would not be consumed during control of substrate oxidation by this mechanism, but would be effective for as long as it remains adsorbed on the protein and for as long as it is not destroyed by side reactions. Small concentrations of hormones would be expected to produce large changes in the rate of substrate oxidation.

The effects of adsorbates on the conductivity of inorganic semiconductors are often presumed to be due to the transfer of electrons between adsorbate and semiconductor, thus altering the concentrations of electrons and holes available to serve as charge carriers within the solid. It seems reasonable to expect similar processes to occur when a particulate enzyme interacts with adsorbed small molecules, especially those which are able to participate easily in redox reactions (e.g., epinephrine) or to form charge-transfer complexes [e.g., serotonin (25)]. In a further analogy to inorganic and semiconductor processes, one might expect to find some hormones and drugs that could donate charge carriers to the enzyme when adsorbed, thus increasing conductivity and reaction rate, while other hormones and drugs might have the opposite effect. Simultaneous adsorption of different hormone and drug molecules should have synergistic or antagonistic effects on enzyme reaction rates, since the total effect on enzyme charge-carrier concentration should be the sum of the effects of the individual adsorbates.

Radiation, both light and ionizing, is frequently capable of changing charge-carrier concentration in inorganic semiconductor solids (26). Similar effects of radiation might be expected in the particulate enzymes of living organisms, which could be responsible for some of the photochemical processes of vision or for some of the pathological events of radiation sickness. Radiation effects produced by this mechanism should be influenced synergistically or antagonistically by adsorbates which change protein charge-carrier concentration, especially by small organic molecules which are easily oxidized and reduced. It is well known that some such compounds can alleviate or intensify the symptoms of radiation sickness (27).

## VI. DIRECT MEASUREMENT OF INTRAPARTICLE ELECTRON CONDUCTANCE

That the hypothesis of electron conduction across a biological particle has led in several instances to correct predictions of reaction kinetics may be considered as evidence for the correctness of the hypothesis. However, one would gain additional confidence in this theory if a direct measurement of the resistance of the particle to electron conduction could be made.

If one were working with a heterogeneous reaction catalyzed by particles of an inorganic semiconductor, this information might be obtained by measuring the electrical resistance of a large piece of the semiconductor, after which it might be ground up into particles for use as a catalyst. If the semiconductor were available only in the form of particles, one might compress a quantity of particles into a larger pellet whose resistance could be measured. Although this procedure is sometimes followed by experimental solid-state physicists, the value of such measurements is always in doubt, because the resistances across the solid-solid interfaces between particles are sometimes far larger than the resistances *within* the particles. Hence, an estimate of particle resistance by this method may be much too large.

A further source of error is also likely to appear. If the original large chunk of semiconductor is ground to a powder of sufficient fineness, electrical conduction within the particles will mostly occur very near the particle surfaces. The resistance to electron conduction in the surface layer of a semiconductor is in general quite different from that in the bulk of the semiconductor. In addition, surface conductivity is usually changed markedly by adsorption of minute quantities of water or of other impurities. Hence, a knowledge of the bulk resistivity of the semiconductor does not usually allow one to predict the conductivity of minute particles of the same material. These experimental problems have been discussed by Garrett (28).

Biological particles, such as proteins or melanin, are not available in large pieces of homogeneous structure, so that bulk conductivities are obtainable only by unreliable measurements on compressed pellets, and the smallness of such particles leads one to suspect that surface effects, especially the changes due to adsorption of water and ions, may be large. The direct experimental measurement of the electrical resistance within biological particles under *physiological* conditions is, therefore, a problem of the greatest difficulty.

Numerous measurements of compressed pellets of dried proteins have been made (5). It has been demonstrated that conduction in dried hemoglobin is electronic rather than ionic (29). Although most measurements on dried proteins have yielded extremely high values of resistance, small degrees of hydration have produced large decreases in resistance (30), suggesting that a completely hydrated protein may have a very much lower resistance. Direct experimental confirmation of this suspicion seems impossible because the wetting of the protein provides low-resistance pathways of ionic conduction in parallel with the electron-conduction pathways within the protein molecules, so that the conductances of the latter cannot be estimated.

Similar problems arise in the measurement of electrical resistance within melanin particles. My attempts to determine the resistance of a *dried* film of eye-melanin particles revealed only that it is too high to be measurable by a

TABLE 1

Estimates of Resistivities within Individual Protein Molecules
Compared with Those of Common Materials

| Material | Temp., °C | Resistivity, ohm × cm | Reference |
|---|---|---|---|
| Copper | 20 | 1.7 | (32), p. 1845 |
| Brass | 0 | 7 | (32), p. 1844 |
| Germanium | 13 | $10^2$ | (33), p. 10-9 |
| Carbon | 0 | $3.5 \times 10^3$ | (32), p. 1844 |
| Protein in solution | | $10 \times 10^3$ | (31), p. 189 |
| Bakelite #190 | 25 | $10^{11}$ | (32), p. 1862 |
| Glass | 20 | $9 \times 10^{13}$ | (32), p. 1862 |
| Most dry proteins | 30 | $>10^{18}$ | (5), p. 362 |

vacuum-tube ohmmeter. Indirect evidence, based on ESR studies (2) of the decay of light-generated free radicals, had already suggested that the electrical resistance of the melanin particle is far higher in the dry than in the wet state, since the reversibility of radical production (probably reflecting electron conductivity) was present in the wet state but was lost in the dry state. However, no direct method for measuring resistance within wet melanin particles has been discovered.

The only experiments known to me which may measure resistivity within fully hydrated biological particles are those described by Schwan (31). The electrical properties of aqueous solutions of protein were measured at high frequencies. Calculations by Schwan (31, p. 189) from such measurements estimated resistivity within the protein molecule to be approximately $10^4$ ohms × cm, which is roughly the resistivity of solid carbon. These values are compared with those of some other common materials in Table 1. The value for wet protein resistivity is certainly compatible with the concept that electron conduction within the protein plays a role in biochemical processes. Unfortunately the data used by Schwan (31) may be interpreted also in terms of mechanisms other than conduction within the protein, so that this method may lack applicability.

## VII. GRAPHICAL METHODS FOR KINETIC ANALYSIS OF PARTICULATE SYSTEMS

Four different graphical methods have been found useful for testing data for conformity to electron-conduction kinetics:

1. A plot of reaction rate ($dx_r/dt$) vs. substrate concentration ($x_r$).
2. A Lineweaver-Burk double reciprocal plot.
3. A plot of log ($-dx_r/dt$) vs. $x_r$.
4. A plot of the reciprocal of reaction rate vs. time.

Although the first two of these tests are superficially like those of mass-action kinetics, the postulates and structure of the theory of electron-conduction kinetics are totally different from those of mass-action kinetics, so that the methods of interpretation of the graphical tests are also entirely different. Some of the areas of possible confusion between mass-action kinetics and electron-conduction kinetics will be indicated. I have applied the methods described here to several particulate biochemical systems and to cellular ion transport. It seems likely that they may prove useful also in the analysis of some data of heterogeneous catalysis and of solid-state and surface physics.

When a reaction is rate-limited solely by the $iR$ drop across the enzyme particle, by substrate diffusion alone, or by both simultaneously, the basic differential rate equation has the following form (7, 11):

$$ -\frac{dx_r}{dt} = k'x_r + \delta \tag{18} $$

where $k'$ and $\delta$ are constants. If one should test data conforming to equation 18 for reaction order by plotting $\log(-dx_r/dt)$ vs. $\log(x_r)$, a first-order reaction would be indicated only if $\delta$ happens to be zero, which seems to be the case for cytochrome oxidase. Since the integrated form of equation 18 shows a linear relationship of $\log(x_r + \delta/k)$ vs. $t$, a test for first order by a semilog plot of $x_r$ vs. $t$ will in general give non-linearity, unless $\delta$ happens to be zero. It would perhaps be wise, therefore, to avoid the term "reaction order" when dealing with particulate electron-conduction enzymes.

One may test graphically for conformity to equation 18 by a plot of reaction rate ($dx_r/dt$) vs. substrate concentration ($x_r$) (method 1). A positive test is indicated by a linear plot, from which the values of the constants $k'$ and $\delta$ can be obtained. When the reaction is rate-limited by the $iR$ drop alone, or simultaneously by $iR$ and substrate diffusion, then hyperbolic relationships between the rate constant ($k'$) and $C_x$ (the concentration of substrate plus product) will be observed [see equations 9, 10, and 11 in this paper; also equations 65 and 71 of (7) and equation 19 of (11)], which may serve as criteria of reaction type. This implies hyperbolic relationships between the first-order rate constant ($k'$) and the initial substrate concentration at the start of the reaction. Data from such reactions may be expected, therefore, to have the general appearance shown in Fig. 3. When dealing with reactions rate-limited by $iR$ alone, $iR$ plus diffusion, or diffusion alone, both $k'$ and $\delta$ will be found proportional to enzyme concentration ($N$) [(7), equations 71, 65, and 64]. This fact may be used as a method of enzyme assay for such systems.

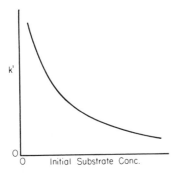

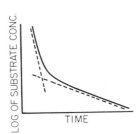

Fig. 3. Sketch of relationship of first-order rate constant ($k'$) to initial substrate concentration that is predicted by electron-conduction kinetics. Initial substrate concentration may of course be replaced by the sum ($C_x$) of substrate plus product. The relationship is hyperbolic. Either axis may be shifted from zero, depending on conditions (see text).

Fig. 4. Sketch of time course of a reaction that is rate-limited by an activation barrier at the surface of a particle plotted on semilog paper. Dotted lines show how such a reaction may be confused with a pair of simultaneous first-order processes having different rate constants.

Where substrate diffusion is the sole rate-limiting process, both $\delta$ and $k'$ will be found proportional to the substrate diffusion constant $D$, and $\delta$ will be found proportional to $C_x$ [(7), equation 64].

A process rate-limited by *electron activation* may be suspected if the data appear to show stepwise decreases in first-order rate constant as the reaction proceeds. Such reactions are often described empirically by equations of the form (10)

$$x_r = ae^{-bt} + ce^{-ft} \tag{19}$$

where $a$, $b$, $c$, and $f$ are constants.

Plotted on semilog paper, data from these reactions show curves like the sketch in Fig. 4. Such data have been observed fairly frequently in various processes involving electron transport across the surfaces of inorganic semiconductor solids (9). Some physicists at first considered that these curves probably should be approximated by two or three straight lines on the semilog plot, and only later was it realized that this sort of kinetics, as indicated by conformity to the Elovich equation, was of frequent occurrence and probably represented some common underlying physical principle.

As a graphical test for electron activation kinetics, one may use the Lineweaver-Burk double reciprocal plot (method 2). A linear plot, with a *negative* intercept on the $1/v$ axis, constitutes a positive test (see equation 15), although the derivation of this theory has nothing in common with that of Michaelis-Menten kinetic theory (see equation 16). Method 2 sometimes gives a false negative result due to inaccurate experimental measurement of the zero value of substrate concentration $(x_r)$, which causes the plot to become curved. False negative tests will occur also if the constant $a$ in the Tafel equation (equation 12) is *un*equal to 1. Hence, if method 2 gives a negative test, methods 3 and 4, which are susceptible to neither of the foregoing difficulties, should always be tried.

Since reactions conforming to electron activation kinetics are describable (to a close approximation) by the Elovich equation, conformity to equation 17 may be used as a criterion. When logarithms of both sides of equation 17 are taken, it is quickly evident that a plot of the logarithm of reaction rate $[\log(-dx_r/dt)]$ vs. substrate concentration $(x_r)$ should give a straight line (method 3). It has been shown (9) by direct mathematical analysis that a linear plot of the reciprocal of reaction rate $(dx_r/dt)^{-1}$ vs. time $(t)$ (method 4) also indicates conformity to the Elovich equation and hence can serve as a graphical criterion of electron activation kinetics (9).

Although two situations were described in which methods 3 and 4 are preferable to method 2, there is one situation where the opposite is true. When the reaction has gone less than $10\%$ or more than $90\%$ to completion, the approximation used in the derivation of the Elovich equation becomes inaccurate (7), so that methods 3 and 4 also become inaccurate. For this reason, one may sometimes observe that the last point on the end of a plot of method 3 or 4 may be far off the straight line through the other points, if the last point represents more than $90\%$ completion of the reaction. Method 1 also becomes inaccurate at the very beginning and the very end of a reaction, when it must be replaced by a less convenient criterion presented in an earlier publication (6).

From an analysis of the behavior of the enzyme-substrate complex, *mass-action* kinetic theory leads to simple mathematical expressions for initial velocities. Therefore, measurements of initial velocity as a function of substrate concentration may be interpreted conveniently in terms of mechanism. In *electron-conduction* kinetic theory, however, the analysis of initial velocities is usually not profitable, since the rate equations underlying graphical methods 1, 3, and 4 become inaccurate when the reaction has gone less than 10% to completion because of the nature of the approximation used in their derivation. Hence, for this type of study, it is necessary to analyze an individual reaction throughout most of its time course, rather than initial velocities (7).

## VIII. THE FUTURE

The application of some concepts of solid-state physics to biology has led to some interesting kinetic predictions that are in accord with the experiment. The hypothesis of electron conduction within the biological particle provides an explanation of data on cytochrome oxidase and peroxidase kinetics and also of data on eye-melanin free radicals.

Skeptics will say that this evidence is inadequate to prove the hypothesis of the electron-conduction enzyme, and that direct measurements should be made before indulging in such excessive speculation. Unfortunately, the prospects for direct experimental measurement of the resistivity within enzyme molecules seem dim for the immediate future, because of the technical problems discussed in section VI. However, before dismissing the value of the electron-conduction enzyme hypothesis and its kinetic theory, let us consider a parallel from recent history.

A kinetic theory based on the hypothesis of the enzyme-substrate complex was formulated in 1913 by Michaelis and Menten (34). Over the succeeding years this theory was found useful for the description of many enzyme systems, so that the enzyme-substrate complex became a fundamental concept in enzyme kinetics, despite the complete absence of direct evidence for its existence until the late 1930's and early 1940's [reviewed by Chance (35)]. Today, the enzyme-substrate complex is a widely used and widely useful concept in enzyme kinetics, even though it has been demonstrated directly in very few systems.

So let us not become discouraged if direct evidence for electron conduction in enzymes is not immediately at hand. The concept and the theory may nevertheless prove useful.

## SUMMARY

It has been suggested in the past by Szent-Györgyi and others that electron conduction within semiconductive particulate and membranous solid structures in cells may play a role in metabolic processes. The quantitative formulation of this hypothesis has led to a kinetic theory of electron-conduction enzymes or particles, which has been found to describe experimental data on cytochrome oxidase, cytochrome peroxidase, and the decay of light-generated free radicals in eye-melanin particles and in a photosynthetic system. One special case of this theory leads to a derivation of the Elovich equation, which is known to describe various phenomena of inorganic semiconductors, such as gas adsorption and the decay of surface charge. Because of the analogous behavior of charge carriers in liquid and solid systems, a similar theory was developed for the kinetics of ion transport across liquid-liquid or liquid-gel interfaces and was found to predict various experimental data on ion transport across cell surfaces. A similar theory seems likely to be applicable to reactions involving chemical group transport (e.g., phosphate or carbonate) across fragmented membranes in particulate form. This theory describes well the data of Eadie and Gale on pyruvate carboxylase.

## REFERENCES

1. A. Szent-Györgyi, *Science*, **93**, 609–611 (1941).
2. F. W. Cope, R. J. Sever, and B. D. Polis, *Arch. Biochem. Biophys.*, **100**, 171–177 (1963).
3. H. C. Longuet-Higgins, *Arch. Biochem. Biophys.*, **86**, 231–232 (1960).
4. A. Pullman and B. Pullman, *Biochim. et Biophys. Acta*, **54**, 384–385 (1961).
5. D. D. Eley, "Semiconductivity in Biological Molecules," in M. Kasha and B. Pullman, Eds., *Horizons in Biochemistry*, Academic Press, New York, 1962.
6. F. W. Cope, *Bull. Math. Biophys.*, **25**, 165–176 (1963).
7. F. W. Cope, *Arch. Biochem. Biophys.*, **103**, 352–365 (1963).
8. F. W. Cope, *Federation Proc.*, **23**, 113 (1964).
9. F. W. Cope, *J. Chem. Phys.*, **40**, 2653 (1964).
10. F. W. Cope, *Bull. Math. Biophys.*, **27** (in press).
11. F. W. Cope, *Bull. Math. Biophys.*, **27** (in press).
12. L. Smith and H. Conrad, *Arch. Biochem. Biophys.*, **63**, 403–413 (1956).
13. K. Minnaert, *Biochim. et Biophys. Acta*, **50**, 23–24 (1961).
14. J. Beetlestone, *Arch. Biochem. Biophys.*, **89**, 35–40 (1960).
15. G. Kortüm and J. O. Bockris, *Textbook of Electrochemistry*, Vol. 2, Elsevier, Amsterdam, 1951.
16. F. S. Stone, "Chemisorption and Catalysis on Metallic Oxides," *Advances in Catalysis*, **13**, (1962).
17. S. R. Morrison, *Phys. Rev.*, **102**, 1297–1301 (1956).
18. N. Thon and H. A. Taylor, *J. Am. Chem. Soc.*, **75**, 2747–2750 (1953).
19. W. H. Brattain and C. G. B. Garrett, *Ann. N.Y. Acad. Sci.*, **58**, 951–958 (1954).
20. C. S. Fuller, *Record Chem. Progr.*, **17**, 75–93 (1958).
21. M. Green, "Electrochemistry of the Semiconductor-Electrolyte Interface," in J. O. Bockris, Ed., *Modern Aspects of Electrochemistry*, Vol. 2, Butterworths, London, 1959.
22. A. Mauro and A. Finkelstein, "Principles of Ionic Physics Related to Physiological Membranes and Solid State Devices," in *Proceedings of the 16th Annual Conference on Engineering in Medicine and Biology, Baltimore, 1963*.
23. G. N. Ling, *A Physical Theory of the Living State*, Blaisdell, New York, 1962.
24. G. S. Eadie and G. R. Gale, *Arch. Biochem. Biophys.*, **93**, 37–42 (1961).
25. A. Szent-Györgyi, *Introduction to a Submolecular Biology*, Academic Press, New York, 1960.
26. R. H. Bube, *Photoconductivity of Solids*, John Wiley, New York, 1960.
27. Z. M. Bacq and P. Alexander, *Fundamentals of Radiobiology*, Butterworths, London, 1955.

28. C. G. B. Garrett, "Organic Semiconductors," in N. B. Hannay, Ed., *Semiconductors*, Reinhold, New York, 1959.
29. B. Rosenberg, *Nature*, **193**, 364–365 (1962).
30. B. Rosenberg, *J. Chem. Phys.*, **36**, 816–823 (1962).
31. H. P. Schwan, "Electrical Properties of Tissue and Cell Suspensions," *Advances in Biol. and Med. Phys.*, **5** (1957).
32. C. D. Hodgman and H. N. Holmes, *Handbook of Chemistry and Physics*, 25th ed., Chemical Rubber Publishing Co., Cleveland, Ohio, 1941.
33. L. P. Hunter, *Handbook of Semiconductor Electronics*, McGraw-Hill, New York, 1956.
34. L. Michaelis and M. L. Menten, *Biochem. Z.*, **49**, 333 (1913).
35. B. Chance, "Reaction Kinetics of Enzyme-Substrate Compounds," in S. L. Friess, and A. Weissberger, Eds., *Investigation of Rates and Mechanisms of Reactions*, 1st ed., Interscience, New York, 1953.
36. F. W. Cope, *Proc. Natl. Acad. Sci. U.S.*, **51**, 809 (1964).

## *Discussion*

COPE: It is my privilege to present for your consideration a completely new type of kinetic theory based on solid-state and electrode physics rather than on mass action. All postulates of the theory are based on phenomena observed frequently in electrode and solid-state processes. No extra postulates of mysterious or uncertain origin are used. The mathematical development of the theory is straightforward except for an approximation whose accuracy would not be guessed but which can be verified by a very simple graphical method. The rate equations predicted by the new theory are quite different from those predicted by the usual mass action approaches, but they describe data from such diverse fields as enzymology, photobiochemistry, heterogeneous catalysis, ion transport, and solid-state physics. It is my hope and expectation that this theory will prove a powerful tool both for the general understanding and for the detailed analysis of charge transport in those biological systems where *structure* adds new characteristics above and beyond the mass action principle.

CHANCE: I should like to raise a question with respect to the enzyme systems which you have used as models. Why do you think electron conductivity is involved in the reactions of soluble cytochrome and solubilized cytochrome oxidase or in the case of soluble cytochrome and soluble peroxidase plus $H_2O_2$? In neither case is it clear that collision theory is inadequate to account for the kinetics. In fact, the very point that Beetlestone added to our earlier studies of peroxidase reactions was that collisions were adequate and that collision areas of a few angstrom units were large enough to account for the observed rates. Thus, while your theoretical reasoning is of great interest to this meeting, the physical basis to invoke electron conductivity theory in the reactions of *soluble* oxidases and peroxidases is not obvious to me. The systems where biological structure may hinder or prevent collision processes are much more relevant to your proposed mechanism.

COPE: I have to admit that my evidence is entirely kinetic. I cannot produce direct measurements of electron conductivity in cytochrome oxidase or indeed in any other enzyme. It is true, of course, that any set of data can be approximated by many kinds of equations and that the same kind of equation can often be derived from different postulates. I should mention that Minnaert [*Biochim. et Biophys.*

*Acta*, **50**, 23–34 (1961)] proposed a number of mass action schemes which can account for cytochrome oxidase kinetics. The fact that these schemes are multistage and require the assumption of equality of the rate constants for the first and last steps makes them less attractive. On the positive side, I can say that the new theory of electron conduction enzymes does give an accurate prediction of the kinetics observed for cytochrome oxidase and peroxidase. Other developments in the theory predict kinetics seen in a variety of other particulate and membranous systems. One can derive these kinetics from a consistent and rather simple set of postulates followed by a rather simple train of logic. I hope that people will consider this new method at the same time that they consider the usual mass action approaches. I also hope that over the course of time more evidence will accumulate to clarify the validity of the theory. This evidence can consist partly of the finding of more systems that are of a particulate or membranous nature which conform to the predicted equations. In addition, someone may find a good way of measuring protein conductivity directly.

A lot of minor points and side issues that arise in connection with this theory are rather interesting in that they fit in a general way with what one would expect. I will mention at the moment just one of these. It relates to the idea that an enzyme has in general the function of speeding up a reaction by lowering its activation energy. Those systems to which I have applied this theory which are enzymes in the conventional sense, namely, cytochrome oxidase and peroxidase, are predicted by the theory to be rate-limited by electron conduction across the enzyme and by diffusion of substrate up to the enzyme, but the activation energy for the transfer of the electrons from the enzyme to the substrate is predicted to be zero. On the other hand, the processes which according to the criteria of the theory are rate-limited by the activation of an electron across an interface turn out to be those that are probably non-enzymatic, physical processes, namely, the decay of photogenerated free radicals in melanin and in a particular photosynthetic system.

CHANCE: May I make the point that I don't think your mechanism leads to a new kinetic equation? Figure 1 compares your electron-conductivity model with my protein-mobility model in terms that are more readily understood by workers in this field. The over-all reaction is that of electron transport in the respiratory chain, namely, the reduction of cytochrome $a$ and the oxidation of cytochrome $c_1$ (equations 5 and 10, Fig. 1). The electron-transfer reactions are the same, namely, cytochrome $c$ donates an electron to cytochrome $a$, equations 2–4 and 6–9. The difference here is how the electron is transported from the point where it is donated to cytochrome $c$ (equations 1 and 6) to the point where cytochrome $c$ donates it to cytochrome $a$ (equations 4 and 9). Dr. Cope is in favor of immobile proteins and an electron conductivity of the protein that carries the electron from the iron atom of $c$ to the iron atom of $a$ (equation 3).

It should be noted that this equation involves a transport velocity constant designated as $k_t$. In our model of electron transport by protein mobility, the velocity constants by which the proteins turn from an unfavorable to a favorable orientation are indicated by $k_r$, which may not be identical for $c$ and $a$. The model points out, however, that both mechanisms have a kinetic aspect, and for most purposes the models are kinetically identical. This is why I stated that your model does not have kinetic novelty. In your case, the transport velocity constant is $k_t$. In my case it is

$k_r$. In both cases, a step which may or may not be rate-determining has been interposed between the electron-donating site and the electron-accepting site. Of course, the mechanisms can ultimately be distinguished by studying the influence of physical factors upon $k_t$ or $k_r$. The kinetic requirements on $k_r$ were put forward as early as 1952 (B. Chance and P. K. Maitra, in B. Wright, Ed., *Control Mechanisms in Respiration and Fermentation*, The Ronald Press, New York, 1963, p. 307). In summary, then, I don't really see that the idea of electron transport through a

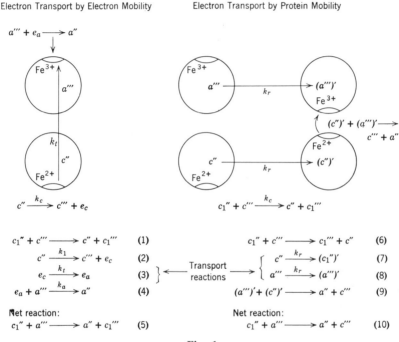

Fig. 1

solid medium has introduced any new kinetic aspects that were not implicit in a chemical mechanism.

COPE: In other words, you are saying that one can derive the same equation through different processes.

CHANCE: Yes, it has nothing to do with the question of electron conductivity.

COPE: I am sure that one can also think of other mechanisms which will give similar equations. The more complicated the mechanisms are allowed to become, the more such mechanisms can be concocted. However, I have gained additional confidence in the electron conduction approach because it also predicts correct rate equations for a number of biological systems that are entirely different from cytochrome oxidase. Of special interest is the melanin free-radical system of the eye.

First, I should describe what eye melanin is. The black pigment which lies immediately behind the retina was previously thought to serve the same function as the black paint in the camera to prevent scattered light. We found that if we extract this material from the eye, make an aqueous suspension thereof, and irradiate it with visible light, free radicals which decay in the dark are generated. The half-life of decay is of the order of 1 or 2 sec. The eye-melanin particle is a dense black pigment particle about the size of mitochondrion. It is a very stable particle. Its free-radical-generating properties are unimpaired even after 15 min of boiling, which means the free-radical process must be non-enzymatic. The melanin particle is a quinone polymer and may be considered to be a chunk of organic semiconductor. We have then a system very close to that which the solid-state physicists study, even though it comes from a living organism. When we find that the kinetics obeyed by free-radical decay in this biological organic semiconductor system is the same as has been observed by solid-state physicists for inorganic semiconductor systems, our interest in the application of solid-state concepts to other biological systems is stimulated.

SUTIN: I was very much interested in the model proposed by Dr. Cope. However, I am unhappy about the validity of some of the equations. I have discussed this point with Dr. R. A. Marcus, who is well known for his work on electron-transfer theory. He made the following comments:

1. It is apparent that the reaction rate predicted by equation 7 tends to infinity as the percentage of reaction tends to zero. Since the observed rate does not become infinite at zero reaction, equation 7 cannot be correct. The fact that it is subsequently approximated by equation 9, which agrees with it from 10–90% reaction and which is itself well behaved at zero reaction, can in no way justify the use of equation 7.

2. In addition, Dr. Cope has not interpreted the Tafel equation (equation 12) correctly, so that equations 13, 14, 15, and 17 are wrong. The error stems from the fact that the quantity $e$ in equation 12 is constant only with respect to variation in the electrode-solution potential difference and not with respect to variations in the concentrations.

COPE: Let me comment first on this matter of equation 7. The point seems to be that actual enzymatic reactions do not have infinite rates at zero times. In fact, in any real enzyme system, when the reaction becomes sufficiently fast, substrate diffusion will take over as the rate-limiting process, which prevents an infinite reaction rate from ever being reached. Equation 7 refers only to an idealized model which one would never encounter experimentally. The theory was presented here in this way to make the train of logic clear. The extra refinements were added later in the paper to include the more nearly real case with the actual complication of substrate diffusion. In my original publication, I did it the other way because it was more elegant, although considerably more difficult to follow.

Do you raise another question regarding the validity of the use of the Tafel equation?

SUTIN: No, no. My point is that you've misinterpreted the Tafel equation. I am referring to $e$ in equation 12.

COPE: You say that $e$ is dependent on concentration?

SUTIN: Yes.

COPE: Is your statement based on actual electrode experiments?

SUTIN: Yes.

COPE: Would you care to elaborate on this?

SUTIN: May I just raise one question first? In equation 12 as written, is your $V$ in fact $V_{activation}$ as used in your previous papers?

COPE: Yes, I changed my terminology.

SUTIN: Let me write down some equations:

$$i = i_+ - i_- = k_+ C_+ - k_- C_-$$

I'll define the terms: $i_+$ is the current in one direction and $i_-$ the current in the opposite direction at a particular electrode, and we have assumed that the forward and reverse reactions at the electrode are first order. I'm referring to a reaction of the type

$$Fe^{3+} + e \underset{k_-}{\overset{k_+}{\rightleftharpoons}} Fe^{2+}$$

where $C_+$ is the concentration of the reactant in the forward step, $C_-$ is the concentration of the reactant in the reverse step, and $k_+$ and $k_-$ are the rate constants in units of current. Then you have the well-known equations for the electrode-solution potential difference which are the Tafel-like equations:

$$k_+ = A_+ e^{-\alpha n E F/kT}$$

$$k_- = A_- e^{(1-\alpha)n E F/kT}$$

In these expressions $A_+$, $A_-$, and $\alpha$ are constants, and $n$ is the number of electrons transferred from $C_-$ to the electrode to make $C_+$. Then from these equations one can show that

$$V_{activation} = e - \frac{kT}{\alpha nF} \ln i_+$$

and

$$e = \frac{kT}{\alpha nF} \ln (A_+ C_+)^{1-\alpha} (A_- C_-)^{\alpha}$$

So your $e$ is an expression of this form and is a function of concentration. This is the Tafel equation and $\alpha$ is the Tafel coefficient, usually about 0.5 for simple electron transfers.

COPE: Under certain conditions this might hold, and under other conditions it might not. Also, again we may be dealing with a pure solid-state event. In this case we are not dealing with the Tafel equation; we are dealing with a diode equation which has approximately the same logarithmic form, but the nature of the constant $e$ would have a different derivation and I could not say exactly at this moment how that would work.

# Some Problems in the Electrical Conductivity of Proteins

. . . BARNETT ROSENBERG

## I. INTRODUCTION

It now appears possible that a number of biological problems may in their solutions involve the electrical conductivity of proteins. These are problems that have proved most refractory to normal biochemical approaches. This situation justifies searching out more "exotic"—or better—more unfamiliar mechanisms. The difficulty in the case of the electrical conductivity of proteins is that we know so little about it, and at this stage it is hard to say whether the potential values will justify the efforts needed to learn more. However, apart from its applicability to biology, it represents a fascinating and complex physical problem.

The solid-state electrical properties of proteins have been fairly extensively investigated. From this work, a quite interesting and novel picture is beginning to emerge. Some results have been well established and are reliable. Most, however, must be taken as tentative and subject to future modification. I should like to try to develop some aspects of this picture here.

In the dry state, crystalline and amorphous proteins are semi-conductors (1); that is, the temperature dependence of the conductivity follows the operational definition of a semiconductor:

$$\sigma(T) = \sigma_0 \exp\left(-E/2kT\right) \tag{1}$$

where $E$ is an activation energy, $k$ is Boltzmann's constant, and $T$ is the temperature (in degrees Kelvin). For a wide variety of proteins $E$ has the approximate value 2.4 ev, and $\sigma_0$ has the value of about $10^3$–$10^4$ (ohm-cm)$^{-1}$ (2).

There is nothing unique in these characteristics. Almost every non-metallic or organic solid is a semiconductor. Moreover, all large biomacro-molecules that have been tested so far seem to have the same dry-state value for $E$ of about 2.4 ev. This group includes, in addition to the proteins, DNA (3) and polysaccharides (4). If this continues, it will be necessary to nominate 2.4 ev for status as a "magic number" in biophysics. At present, it does not appear that various proteins have "specific" electrical properties. This is in marked contrast to their very specific biochemical properties.

## II. CONDUCTIVITY IN HYDRATED PROTEINS

When water or another solvent of high dielectric constant is adsorbed by the proteins at a constant temperature, the conductivity increases enormously, by about a factor of $10^8$ for 8% by weight of water adsorbed. Experiments have shown that this is due entirely to a decrease in the value of the activation energy $E$ in equation 1 from its dry-state value of 2.4 ev to a minimum value in a highly hydrated condition of about 1.1 ev. Interestingly, the value of $\sigma_0$ does not change at all with hydration (2). A theoretical mechanism has been developed which is capable of describing the effect of water adsorption on the conductivity process. It depends upon the increasing effective dielectric constant of the protein as more water is adsorbed; this decreases the amount of work which must be done to separate electrical charges (because of the increasing stabilization of the charge centers by the polarization of the medium). The mechanism is a quite general one and is independent of both the nature of the charges (electronic or ionic) and the nature of the medium. Again here I must point out the lack of "specificity" in this phenomenon, and indeed its complete generality. The water effect is similar in DNA (5), polysaccharides (4), paper, glass, etc., as the theory requires. The theory leads to the following equation to describe the dependence of the conductivity on the temperature and the effective dielectric constant $K'$:

$$\sigma(T, K') = \sigma_0 \exp(-E_D/2kT) \cdot \exp[(e^2/2kTR)(1/K - 1/K')] \qquad (2)$$

where, for the case of proteins, $E_D$ equals the dry-state value of 2.4 ev, $R = 2.8$ Å, and K is the dry-state dielectric constant of the protein. Equation 2 predicts that the current will increase exponentially as more water is adsorbed until finally a saturation value will be reached (when $1/K'$ is small compared to $1/K$). The second exponential term becomes a constant equal to about $10^{10}$. This leads to the minimum value of $E$ of 1.1 ev, as mentioned above. All these results are in agreement with experiment. It is known, for example, for hemoglobin that the saturation occurs when the water adsorption reaches a value of about 10% by weight (6).

The nature of the charge carriers in this water-enhanced current has been a subject of speculation for many years. The variety of suggestions made includes electrons, holes, adventitious ions, and protons. Three experiments (7, 8, 9) have now given direct evidence that the charge carriers are, for a water adsorption below the current saturation level, electronic (electrons or holes) and not ionic. All these experiments involve solid-state electrolysis measurements which lead to the evolution of hydrogen. This is the major distinguishing characteristic between an electronic and an ionic conduction process.

It is quite obvious that for a large amount of water present (i.e., proteins in solution) the charge carriers are mainly ions or protons. Somewhere

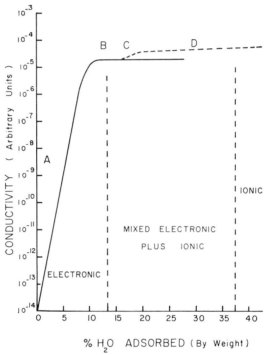

**Fig. 1.** A schematic representation of the electrical conductivity in proteins as a function of the per cent of water adsorbed (by weight). The regions where the different types of charge carriers predominate are roughly indicated.

between the dry and the very wet state of the protein there is a changeover from predominantly electronic conduction to predominantly ionic conduction. The present picture is illustrated schematically in Fig. 1. Here the conductivity on a logarithmic scale is plotted vs. the percentage of water adsorbed by the system. The different regions of the curve are roughly demarcated as $A$, $B$, $C$, and $D$. In region $A$, the conductivity is electronic and increases exponentially with the amount of adsorbed water. Equation 2 is valid. In region $B$, the conduction is still electronic but has entered the saturation region as discussed before, and equation 2 is still valid. In region $C$, the transition to an ionic mechanism occurs, and the two types of charge carriers are mixed in about equal proportions. In region $D$, the conduction is mainly by the ionic mechanism with electronic charge carriers diminishing in importance as the water adsorption increases. In regions $C$ and $D$, equation 2 should no longer be valid; an additional ionic term must be added to the equation. Region $D$ is shown with a slight slope. The data in this region are not yet reliably established. Our measurements at greater than 30% water adsorbed indicate that the charge carriers are about 50% electronic and 50% ionic (roughly 50% electrolysis current efficiency) (8). Maricic, Pifat, and Pravdic (9) have found electrolysis current efficiencies ranging from 26 to 112% at 18% water adsorption, and 30–80% current efficiency at 40.6% water adsorption.

It is of interest to consider such a curve for hemoglobin in terms of the BET (Brunauer, Emmett, and Teller) monolayer coverage of the molecular surface. Cardew and Eley established that the first monolayer occurs at a hydration value of about 5.7%. Therefore, with somewhat less than two monolayers of water formed, the conductivity is still predominantly electronic. Only when three or more monolayers have formed does ionic conductivity predominate.

A second point of interest is that most of the novel electrical changes have occurred in the region where the electronic processes predominate. In this region, $A$, the conductivity is extremely sensitive to the water content; small changes in water content cause large changes in electronic conductivity.

These results enable us to establish a rough criterion for judgment of the involvement of *electronic* conductivity processes in the function of a biological system. To put this argument in its simplest terms, if we are interested in controlling a current flow, we may vary the applied potential or the conductivity of the material. Biological potentials normally arise from biochemical reactions or membrane potentials due to concentration gradients or both. Changes in such potentials during a controlled reaction may cover one or two decade units. If we wish these potentials to be the current controls, it is obvious that the variations of current due to the second mechanism, the change in conductivity of the material, should be of a much lower order. Since the variation in the conductivity of proteins is exponential with changes in water content for hydration values below 10%, it must be required that the water content of the protein be constant to a high order. For example, using data known for hemoglobin, if we require that the conductivity not change by more than a factor of 2 because of the water mechanism, then the per cent water on the protein must be held constant to less than 0.25%. Thus, if we have one BET monolayer of water on the protein surface—which corresponds to about 319 molecules of water attached to the polar side chains—the loss or gain of 15 water molecules will be sufficient to change the conductivity by the factor of 2.

In region *B*, somewhere between 10 and 18% hydration, the current is independent of the water content. This special region is therefore of great interest, since the conductivity is maximal and independent of small changes in hydration value. The difficulty in this region is that it requires the presence of a large amount of water, about 2 BET monolayers, and yet the third monolayer, which introduces the proton conduction mechanism, must be restricted. These requirements appear to be almost contradictory.

An obvious and biologically successful device to restrain the free interactions of proteins and water is to provide a lipid environment about the protein. This protective environment may or may not completely exclude water. One can imagine circumstances where a controlled, but non-zero, amount of water on the protein may be advantageous. The rough criterion of judgment can be stated as follows: *In a biological function, if the potentials are to be the controlling factor in the current flow, then the protein must be in a predominantly lipid environment for the electronic charge carriers to play a role.*

Since lipids by themselves are excellent insulators and do not adsorb water, it is probable that they will electrically insulate the proteins if they form a protective sheath. This insulation of course will make the electrical conductivity of the system so small as to be insignificant. Fortunately two pieces of experimental evidence indicate that this is not the case in at least two examples of lipid-protein lamellar organelles. The electrical conductivity of extracted chloroplasts (11) and rods (12) has been measured. In general, these organelles conform to the characteristics of proteins described above. They are semiconductors; for dried chloroplasts the activation energy is 2.1 ev; for dried rods it is 2.3 ev. In the case of the rods, the presence of water increases the conductivity by many orders of magnitude. Thus, this organelle has electrical properties similar to those of its protein constituent, and the presence of lipids in such membranous structures does not contraindicate the applicability of electronic conductivity concepts to their function. This, of course, begs the question of whether the lipids *in vivo* function at all to limit the access of water to the proteins. There is as yet no direct evidence bearing on this question. One indirect piece of evidence is that the final stage of bleaching of metarhodopsin, which is known to occur *in vivo*, requires the presence of water (13). Unfortunately, we do not know how much water is needed and where the water molecules are required to be. If the water is needed simply to reverse the Schiff base condensation, then only one molecule is required at the site of the bonding of the retinene to the protein. How many molecules of water need to be adsorbed to guarantee this site being occupied is again unknown.

One further point can be made safely and is a corollary to the criterion of judgment. If electronic conduction is occurring in a lipid-protein system in a water ambient, and this is the biological function of that system, then if the lipids are removed and water has free access to the protein, the functioning of the system will cease. This point is, of course, consistent with the role of phospholipid in the enzymatic functioning of the electron-transfer system in mitochondria (14). However, nothing more definite can be stated at present.

These considerations lead to the most crucial question, at present unanswerable, concerning the electrical conductivity of proteins in the function of organelles: Does water have free access or limited access to the proteins in the lamellae?

## III. FURTHER EXPERIMENTS;
## THE HALL EFFECT IN PROTEINS

The conductivity of a substance (assuming charge carriers of one sign only) is the product of the density of charge carriers ($n$), the charge on each ($e$), and the mobility of the carriers ($\mu$),

$$\sigma = ne\mu \tag{3}$$

The exponential temperature dependence of the conductivity may be due to an exponential temperature dependence of $n$ or $\mu$ or both, that is:

$$n(T) = n_0 \exp\left(-E_n/kT\right) \quad \text{and/or} \quad \mu(T) = \mu_0 \exp\left(-E_\mu/kT\right) \tag{4}$$

It is essential, for a deeper understanding of the conductivity processes in proteins, to be able to evaluate $n$ and $\mu$ separately. This cannot be done from

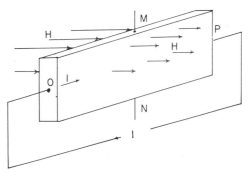

Fig. 2. A schematic representation of the method of measuring a Hall effect.

pure conductivity measurements. An independent measurement of one or both is necessary. The most useful physical effect which makes it possible to evaluate these variables separately is the Hall effect.

The Hall effect utilizes an experimental arrangement shown in Fig. 2. A constant voltage (or current) is impressed across the two end electrodes ($O$ and $P$), and current flows through the solid. Under these conditions there is no voltage drop between electrodes $N$ and $M$ in the direction perpendicular to the current flow. If, now, a steady magnetic field is applied in the third perpendicular direction, the moving charges will be deflected in a direction perpendicular to both the electric field and the magnetic field, and a potential will develop between electrodes $N$ and $M$. This is the Hall potential, $V$. This potential is proportional to the strength of the current and the magnetic field and is inversely proportional to the thickness of the solid in the magnetic field direction. We can therefore write:

$$V = \frac{RIH}{t} \times 10^{-8} \qquad (5)$$

where the units of $I$ are amperes, $H$ is in gauss, $t$ is in centimeters, $V$ is in volts, and $R$, the constant of proportionality (called the Hall coefficient), is in cubic centimeters per coulomb. Thus a measurement of $V$, $I$, $H$, and $t$ makes is possible to evaluate $R$. From electromagnetic theory is it simple to show that $R$ is given by

$$R = \frac{\pm 1}{ne} \qquad (6)$$

where $n$ is the density of the single type of charge carriers, and $e$ is the electronic charge ($= 1.6 \times 10^{-19}$ coulomb). If the sign of the Hall coefficient is negative, then the predominant charge carriers are negative (electrons or negative ions); if the sign of the Hall coefficient is positive, the predominant charge carriers are positive (holes or positive ions).

If the current is measured and the dimensions of the solid are known, we can calculate $\sigma$ (equal to the current density divided by the electric field strength). Then from equations 3 and 6 we see that

$$R \cdot \sigma = \mu \qquad (7)$$

Thus we have separately evaluated $n$ (equation 6) and $\mu$ (equation 7). In actuality, equation 7 defines a "Hall mobility." In practice, this is generally equal to the "drift (conduction) mobility." From the temperature dependence of $R$ and $\sigma$, we can then determine the temperature dependence of $n$ and $\mu$ separately. From the sign of $R$, we can determine the sign of the charge carriers. From the value of the mobility, we may with a fair degree of certainty be able to determine the nature of the charge carriers, i.e., whether they are electronic or ionic. If the mobility is very high, we can reasonably expect electronic processes. If it is low, we cannot specify their nature. The value of the mobility also sets bounds on the type of model we can apply to the system. If $\mu$ is high ($\gg 1$ in units of square centimeters per volt $\times$ second), a band model is reasonable; if it is low ($\ll 1$), a hopping model is more reasonable. If $\mu$ is on the order of 1, no clear choice can be made. In well-developed crystals, the anisotropy of the mobility in different crystallographic directions can be measured.

It is obvious from this discussion that the detection and measurement of a Hall effect in hydrated proteins will be of great value in furthering our understanding of the electrical conductivity of these substances. At this time my colleagues and I are attempting to secure such measurements in our laboratory.

## ACKNOWLEDGMENTS

I am very grateful to Professor Maricic *et al.* for permitting me to see the manuscript of their article before publication.

This work has been supported by Research Grant GB-1057 from the National Science Foundation.

## REFERENCES

1. D. D. Eley, G. D. Parfitt, M. J. Perry, and D. H. Taysum, *Trans. Faraday Soc.*, **49**, 79 (1953).
2. B. Rosenberg, *J. Chem. Phys.*, **36**, 816 (1962).
3. D. D. Eley and D. Spivey, *Trans. Faraday Soc.*, **58**, 405, 411 (1962).
4. W. L. Peticolas, *Nature*, **197**, 898 (1963), and personal communication.
5. C. Y. Liang and E. G. Scalco, *J. Chem. Phys.*, **40**, 919 (1964), and J. Drobnik, unpublished results in our laboratory.
6. D. D. Eley in M. Kasha and B. Pullman, Eds., *Horizons in Biochemistry*, Academic Press, New York, 1962, p. 367.
7. B. Rosenberg, *Nature*, **193**, 364 (1962).
8. B. Rosenberg, *Biopolymers, Symposia No. 1*, 453 (1964).
9. S. Maricic, G. Pifat, and V. Pravdic, *Biochim. et Biophys. Acta*, **79**, 293 (1964).
10. M. H. Cardew and D. D. Eley, in *Fundamental Aspects of the Dehydration of Foodstuffs*, Macmillan, New York, 1958, p. 24.
11. W. Arnold and H. K. Sherwood, *Proc. Natl. Acad. Sci. U.S.*, **43**, 105 (1957).
12. B. Rosenberg, *Arch. Biochem. Biophys.*, **93**, 395, (1961).
13. G. Wald, J. Durrell, and R. C. C. St. George, *Science*, **111**, 179 (1950).
14. S. Fleischer, G. Brierley, H. Klouwen, and D. B. Slautterback, *J. Biol. Chem.*, **237**, 3264 (1962).

### *Discussion*

ORGEL: It is extremely hard to understand how there would be electronic conduction in this type of system. I want to ask some questions in an effort to see whether there is any possible way out of the conduction mechanism being electronic. It's just that I personally can see no explanation, and when a theoretician can't see any way of explaining things he's likely to look for other possibilities. Now I'd like to ask, Is there any alternative? As far as I can see, the evidence for electronic conduction is really that one fails to isolate certain chemical products or to show the carrying through of certain chemical reactions which would be expected if the conducting species were protons and hydroxyl ions or some other ion in the solution. Have I understood this right?

ROSENBERG: I don't know that I fully understand your question, but there is a possibility that these electrolysis experiments would not give the correct answer if you could involve something like Lingane's mechanism for hydrogen peroxide generation at the electrodes. This would therefore be a factor which would decrease the electrolytic efficiency of the current.

But this involves an even worse assumption, namely, that the hydrogen peroxide can move freely through the protein, crystalline lattice, and not be the rate-limiting step in the conduction process.

ORGEL: I do not wish to propose the peroxide mechanism, but I understood that the chemical efficiency of electronic transport is lower than you would anticipate if the process were electrolysis rather than conduction. If we are to find an alternative explanation, the only direction in which we can look is toward some way of transporting current by ions but not allowing this to have its normal effect on the production of water or whatever it may be.

Now, it does seem to me that we conceivably have such a mechanism, in the reaction of the oxidizing and reducing species with the protein. You would expect this mechanism to become more and more important if the amount of protein became larger and larger. Let me be specific. Suppose that there were an S-S link in a protein, which got reduced at one electrode and oxidized at the other, and meanwhile used some of the charge which is being carried. You can exclude this if the experiments have been carried on for sufficient time to say with absolute firmness that there is no possibility at all, and that you've recovered the protein and shown that it was unchanged.

ROSENBERG: This has been tried. The conductivity does not change as a function of time under conditions where you would expect it to decrease if you were utilizing some process which was not completely reversible. You see, the hydrogen peroxide mechanism of Lingane is a reversible process. Nothing is being utilized except the water. The protein does not change with time. Therefore this is a conceivable alternative to electronic conduction, but any other process which utilizes a change in the protein structure, at the electrode perhaps, cannot be considered very seriously because long-term experiments do not show any change with time.

ORGEL: How do you know that the chemical change which occurs at the electrode cannot diffuse through the material? And the apparent conductivity is really not a measure of the diffusion rate of the reaction of linked S-S with, let's say, opened SH.

ROSENBERG: As I say, the only mechanism which has been fairly well developed as reversible is the Lingane, as far as I know. You would have to suggest a complete reversible mechanism before I'd seriously consider it.

ORGEL: I'm suggesting, just to try it out on you and see the way you'd react, that proteins, most of them, contain S-S bridges.

ROSENBERG: The processes I'm talking about here are not restricted to proteins. The general work that has been done on this phenomenon shows that it occurs in DNA, it occurs in a polysaccharide, it occurs in paper, it occurs in glass and many other substances. So you cannot pick any kind of specific structural element within the proteins themselves to hang your arguments on; you must pick something within the water, and this is, of course, what Lingane has done. Because of the generality of these concepts you should not argue from the S-S bond type of thing or anything specific to the protein structure.

ORGEL: Let me ask you one further question, if I may. Do they occur in substances which clearly contain no oxidizing and reducing groups? I mean, for example, the silk type, where you have polyamide structure.

ROSENBERG: Yes, this process occurs in nylon—just pure polyamide. I don't know whether it has very many oxidizing and reducing groups.

CHANCE: But you have not done the tritium experiment on nylon, have you?

ROSENBERG: No, the tritium experiment was not done on nylon, but the mechanisms are generally the same in nylon as they are in the other materials. No, Dr. Chance is quite right; we have not done the tritium experiments nor has Maricic done his experiments on nylon.

I don't quite understand why a theoretician should have any great difficulty in assuming that you can get electronic conduction mechanisms in these materials. After all, in an aromatic hydrocarbon crystal you do have roughly the same kind of characteristics as you would have in the aromatic elements of a protein chain; a purely saturated substance is similar to the non-aromatic parts of the protein. You do get electronic conduction in these substances; they are electronic semiconductors. So the extension to a protein should not necessarily lead to any theoretical difficulty. What does seem to be a theoretical difficulty is to explain what this activation energy of 2.4 ev means. Where do the charges come from? How are they transported? What is the mobility of the charges? What are the signs of the charges? These are questions we cannot as yet answer. We are attempting in our laboratory to investigate the Hall effect to answer some of these questions. When we can answer some of the fundamental questions, we can then go on to look at these things from the theoretical point of view and see whether it makes sense or not.

COPE: I don't think Dr. Orgel needs to be disturbed that he can't lay his hand on a good theoretical explanation of why and how protein should conduct electrons. I was at a conference on organic semiconductors at Stanford two or three weeks ago, and it was evident that the whole theory of conduction in organic semiconductors is in confusion. At least a half-dozen different conduction mechanisms have been suggested. People are usually quite unsure which, if any, may be operative or whether they all may be. The whole field is still in an experimental phase. I don't think that we need to be disturbed if we can't predict that a protein ought to be a conductor or how good a conductor it should be, because nobody else can do it very well with any other organic semiconductor either.

CHANCE: My questions, I hope, are independent of whether or not electron or ion mobility is involved; they have to do with the effect of temperature on mobility. I presume that you would still get an energy gap of 2.4 ev in the intact biological system.

ROSENBERG: We have measured the energy gap in extracted rods from eyes, and we find it's about 2.3 ev. A rod is, after all, a very complex lamellar structure involving lipids. The energy gap has also been measured in chloroplasts by Arnold, and he finds about 2.1 ev.

CHANCE: I should like to infer from this that the temperature coefficient of electron mobility as measured in proteins is very much greater than that measured kinetically for electron transport in the cytochrome chain. I think we can agree that the values are orders of magnitude different. Is that right?

ROSENBERG: Well, no, I cannot argue that because we don't as yet have any figures on the mobility of the charges.

CHANCE: Essentially you are saying that you have no data which would bear on any biological system conducting electrons.

My second question is about the rate law that you might expect in electron conductivity. How would you expect the transit time, say through a protein, to vary with the diameter of the protein?

ROSENBERG: If I had figures on the mobility of the charges in the protein, I could perhaps say something.

CHANCE: I think that you can estimate the ratio of the transit time in cytochromes $c$ and $c_1$, which have very different molecular weights. Would they have the same or different transit times?

ROSENBERG: Well, I would assume that if you put the electron into a conduction state, the transit time would be proportional to the length, assuming that the field strength is the same in both cases. It may be that a square is involved.

CHANCE: Well, I agree that the transit times would differ considerably. But we do not find anything in the steady states or kinetics of these components that would suggest a relationship between path length of electron mobility and the rate of electron transfer. The rates appear independent of molecular size.

ROSENBERG: May I make one further comment? This is a somewhat tenuous argument because of the difficulty of knowing the path of the electron within the structure of the molecule. After all, a complex molecule such as hemoglobin has sections which are helical coiled structures and other sections which are not. Where do the electrons move in the molecule? Do they move on or near the surface, as I believe they do, or do they move along the surface of the convolution, or do they make jumps, or what? We have no ideas concerning these questions as yet. As I tried to point out, the art is in a primitive state right now, and we cannot answer these.

CHANCE: Yes, but then maybe we can agree that our kinetic data on electron transfer confine your conductivity mechanism to cytochrome orientations such that the electronic path length from molecule to molecule or through molecule to molecule is constant. It is unlikely that such a structure exists.

ROSENBERG: Well, let me make it clear that I disassociate myself from the work of Dr. Cope if that's his work. I have no direct suggestion in my work that electron conduction is involved in enzymatic reactions. I merely state that the experimental evidence makes reasonable at least the first requirement for it, namely, that there be electronic conduction in a protein. That's all I have so far suggested.

COPE: I should like to emphasize that it is very difficult to extrapolate from the relatively simple experiments that have been reported so far to the real biological situation. It's quite evident from a great deal of work on solid-state physics that when you get adsorption of small amounts of impurities on surfaces you change surface conductivity by many orders of magnitude. Furthermore, the theory of these effects is very poor so that most studies are entirely empirical. Therefore I don't think that we should worry too much at this point about whether or not the measurements on the purified simple proteins agree quantitatively with what is going on in complex enzymes, because it is reasonable to expect that the conductivities in the two situations might differ very widely.

Rosenberg: There is a dangerous element in what you say, Dr. Cope, in the sense that you seem to be willing to accept the experimental evidence that electronic conduction may occur in a protein but you are not willing to accept the limitations that our experiment set upon the value of the electronic conduction.

Cope: I don't think that your present experiments set very many limitations.

Estabrook: In his paper Dr. Rosenberg has posed what I believe is a most provocative question, which goes to the heart of electron-transfer reactions in biological systems. This question is stated on p. 77: "Does water have free access or limited access to the proteins in the lamellae?" This could apply to oxidation-reduction catalysts in the mitochondrial membrane. Dr. David D. Tyler [D. Tyler and R. W. Estabrook, "The Influence of Deuterium Oxide and Organic Solvents on the Interaction of Respiratory Chain Components" (in preparation) and R. W. Estabrook, J. Gonze, and D. Tyler, *Federation Proc.*, **23**, 322 (1964)] in our laboratory has attempted to answer this question by determining the influence of various organic solvents on the succinate and DPNH oxidase activity of respiratory catalysts in particles of heart muscle. You will recall the high lipid content of this system, as shown by the extensive studies of Dr. Fleischer [S. Fleischer, "The Role of Lipids in Mitochondrial Structure and Function," Sixth International Congress of Biochemistry, New York, July 1964] in Dr. Green's laboratory. These studies indicate the role of phospholipids in cytochrome reaction. I must add at this time also that our thinking on this problem has been guided by the very elegant paper by Dr. Malmstrom [E. W. Westhead and B. G. Malmstrom, *J. Biol. Chem.*, **228**, 655 (1957)] and his work on the solvent effects on enolase activity, as well as the studies of Laser and Slater [H. Laser and E. C. Slater, *Nature*, **187**, 1115 (1960)] on $D_2O$ effects and of Chance and his co-workers on glycerol effects [B. Chance and E. L. Spencer, Jr., *Discussions Faraday Soc.*, **27**, 259 (1959)]. Briefly, two basic observations have emerged from Dr. Tyler's studies. Using solvents such as dimethyl formamide, dimethyl sulfoxide, and glycerol, he found that respiration was impeded in a reversible manner. By studying the influence of varying concentrations of these solvents on DPNH oxidation, it was apparent that a relationship existed between the degree of water replacement and the percentage of inhibition observed. The data obtained are shown in Fig. 1. If one plots per cent of inhibition of the over-all reaction as a function of per cent of water replacement, the points for all the solvents fall very nicely on a curve which indicates 100% inhibition at about 50% replacement of the water (Fig. 2).

The second observation in this study concerns the locus of inhibition by these solvents in such a system. Measurements on the cytochrome steady state under the various conditions of solvent addition show that there is little or no modification of the steady-state reduction of the cytochromes when one obtains up to 80% inhibition of the over-all respiratory activity. The inability to observe any crossover point for inhibition indicates that solvent replacement of water results in a non-specific inhibition; that is, there are multiple-site inhibitions occurring. As an aside, it might be added that use of such solvents without modification of the steady-state reduction is comparable to using a slow-motion camera on the whole process of electron transfer.

These studies have led to the conclusion that the respiratory carriers, that is, the cytochromes, are accessible to solvents as well as water. The mechanism of

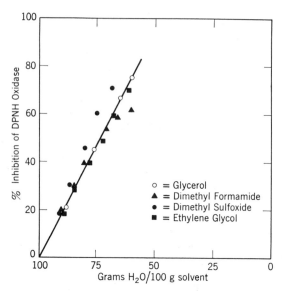

**Fig. 1.** The effect of replacement of water by various solvents on the DPNH oxidase activity of heart muscle particles (D. D. Tyler, J. Gonze, and R. Estabrook, manuscript in preparation.)

inhibition occurring during water replacement is obscure, with possibilities such as modification of the hydration shell of the protein, alteration of the tertiary structure, or alternatively a direct role of water in the electron-transfer reaction itself. The basic question still remains to be answered, but the meager evidence which I have described here leads tentatively to a conclusion against conduction in a non-aqueous environment during mitochondrial oxidation.

ROSENBERG: In the development of the theoretical explanation that we have proposed for the effect of water on the electronic conduction mechanism we have

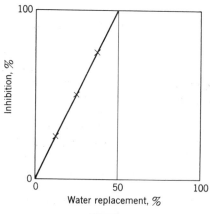

**Fig. 2**

involved the dielectric constant of the medium as the determining factor. This is what decreases the activation energy for conduction. In that sense, therefore, any material with a fairly high dielectric constant absorbed on the protein would increase the electronic conductivity. I should like to know whether there is any kind of correlation of this inhibition effect and the dielectric constant of the solvents that you are using.

ESTABROOK: We have not been able to see any obvious correlation between dielectric constant and solvent inhibition. Some solvents have a high dielectric constant, some low, and they all seem to have very much the same effect.

CAUGHEY: Increased insight into the mechanisms for these electron-transfer processes may well come from experiments on contact shifts observed in nuclear magnetic resonance spectra of compounds with paramagnetic metal ions, such as those studied by the Du Pont workers [D. R. Eaton, A. D. Josey, W. D. Phillips, and R. E. Benson, *J. Chem. Phys.*, **37**, 347 (1962)]. It is of particular interest to explore the mechanisms for transmission of contact shift effects along a peptide chain. Li, Becker, and others have observed the effects of bound paramagnetic and other metal ions on proton chemical shifts of amino acids and peptides [N. C. Li, R. L. Scruggs, and E. D. Becker, *J. Am. Chem. Soc.*, **84**, 4650 (1962); R. M. Mathur and N. C. Li, *ibid.*, **86**, 1289 (1964); P. Tang and N. C. Li, *ibid.*, **86**, 1293 (1964)]. Also, in Kowalsky's studies on the NMR spectra of cytochrome *c*, some of the protons at very high and very low fields may well be experiencing contact shift effects [A. Kowalsky, *Federation Proc.*, **23**, 222 (1964)]. In our own laboratory, we have been studying the very marked shifts experienced by protons at the periphery of the porphyrin ring in porphyrins with central paramagnetic metal ions; our results are consistent with the partial delocalization of unpaired electrons associated with the metal ion through the porphyrin $\pi$-system to loci at the periphery of the molecule.

ROSENBERG: Can you explain to me, please, what the contact shift is?

CAUGHEY: A contact shift is a large shift in the usual normal chemical shift of a proton due to the fact that it is close to a paramagnetic metal ion or a paramagnetic center in the molecule. This shift generally falls off with distance rather markedly; it's usually a factor of $1/r^3$ relationship, but in a conjugated system and in peptides it seems to extend far beyond $1/r^3$.

ROSENBERG: The structure and conformation of the protein do not seem to markedly affect the conduction mechanisms; therefore, even in denatured protein, you would still get the same kind of responses that we have measured in a natural protein. In this sense, I don't think that the phenomenon you describe could be involved as a determining factor of the electron conduction.

I should like to make one more point here. We have been disturbed for some time now because all proteins tested seem to show roughly similar properties in semiconduction measurements. In other words, if we consider the conductivity chamber as a black box in which we can vary the electric field, the relative humidity, and the temperature, the measured results do not allow us to guess the protein in the chamber. Now, in most biological systems, the action of a protein is highly specific. These two considerations would seem to be antithetical. However, Dr. Cope has indicated a way of removing this antithesis. In his considerations, he uses the specific nature of the active sites of the protein to establish a unique electric field across the protein. The electronic conduction across the protein will then be proportional to this specific voltage gradient. Thus the conduction mechanism may be the same in all proteins, but the electrical driving field is specific for each protein. I think that this is a major clarification of the application of conductivity to biological activity.

HEMMERICH: I cannot accept the conclusions of Dr. Estabrook that it follows from his experiments that in the respiratory chain water should be accessible to all the electron carriers. I think it may be possible that an unfolding or any alteration of tertiary structures accompanied by the addition of unpolar solvents to the water may give the changes he observes, but I cannot accept the idea that the electron carrier of the active site of any electron-carrying complex itself is accessible to water.

ESTABROOK: Perhaps I misunderstand, but you should consider the electron carriers as proteins. If you are going to use the solvent to modify the tertiary structure, you have in turn modified the electron carrier, because it is a protein with tertiary structure.

HEMMERICH: When I am speaking of electron carriers, I speak about the active site, about the coenzymes involved, about the active centers; I mean a part of the protein and not the whole protein.

JACOBS: Throughout this type of work (I think the problem was initially discussed by Arnold when he was doing his studies on the semiconduction of the dry films of chloroplasts), the problem of whether, in the case of dry crystalline powders, etc., or of dry films of amorphous configuration, the measured number represents the inter- or intra- particle or molecular barrier has never quite been resolved. Can you say whether any advances have been made in suggesting that the measured number represents the inter- or intra- barrier to the electron flow?

ROSENBERG: About the only thing I can suggest along this line from the experimental point of view is that we have worked with crystalline powder pressed together and that pressure does not seem to affect the conductivity at all. In this sense, large crystalline surface barriers to conduction do not seem to be operating. A second piece of experimental evidence we have is that, if we take a flake which may be amorphous or a polycrystalline mass but which is a fairly uniform mass of hemoglobin and apply electrodes to it, we find exactly the same effects as with the powdered material. Again, this is not a direct piece of evidence that would perhaps satisfy you, but it is an item of evidence along the lines which show that intercrystalline barriers do not dominate the electrical conduction mechanism in these materials. I hope that some day we can work with single crystals of protein, but so far we have not been able to get the necessary micromanipulative techniques to do this.

COPE: You are still left with the problem that the energy required to transfer the electron from one single molecule to the next, be it in a crystal or not, may be far higher than the energy required to get the electron across the individual molecule. I can see no way to get at that problem directly.

ROSENBERG: You were talking about there being an activation energy barrier between the molecules.

COPE: Yes.

ROSENBERG: So far as we know, there is no experimental evidence in protein work to suggest this barrier.

COPE: Do you have a way of telling?

ROSENBERG: Not directly, no. What we should like to do, of course, is to put two microelectrodes into a protein molecule, but this is obviously ridiculous. Until that can be done we cannot directly answer your question. But by indirect means we can show that an energy barrier between molecules is not a dominant feature in conduction.

COPE: How do you know it is not by indirect means?

ROSENBERG: By pressure experiments for one thing, and the fact that there does not seem to be any difficulty in making ohmic contacts to a protein substance.

WINFIELD: In much of the discussion this morning on electron transport the possibility seems to have been neglected that in the living cell there could be a corresponding proton transport. This may seem a little farfetched to many of you, but it bears thinking about. I think that in the cytochrome system or part of the cytochrome system there may be a proton current which is carried at the inter-face between the lipid and the water phase. If this is true, replacement of the water by a solvent whose p$K$ is appreciably different from that of water would inevitably affect the rate of transport of protons.

INGRAHAM: It is clear that whatever this energy band may be that is empty it is at least 50 or 60 kcal above the filled band below, so that we are talking about large energies, and I am not aware of any biological system, not photochemical, that has any activation energies anywhere near 50–60 kcal. I think it is certainly true that there is no comparison directly between this and the energies involved in electron transport, but I would certainly guess that particularly in electron transport the activation must be very much lower than anything involved here.

ROSENBERG: Let me point out that the value of 2.4 ev refers to the dry-state activation energy of the protein. When you hydrate the protein, the only effect that occurs is that the activation energy decreases. According to the theoretical work we have done, this energy would reach a minimum value of about 1 ev or 23 kcal/mole. This is still a large figure, and I agree with Dr. Ingraham that it poses a difficulty. There may be other mechanisms involved, such as attaching other substances to the protein, as Eley has done with chloranil attached to a protein. This does increase its conductivity enormously. But there are some grounds to believe that the mechanism is the same that we have talked about and that therefore it would be subject to the same limitation and would reach a minimum of about 1 ev and not go below that. If that figure, 1 ev, is too big, then electronic conduction is, as Szent-Györgyi once said, "a dead duck" in relation to enzyme action.

# A Theoretical Study of the Structure
# of Oxygen-Metallic Ion Complexes

... GERALD M. MAGGIORA, RICHARD O. VIALE,

and LLOYD L. INGRAHAM

## I. INTRODUCTION

The structure of the iron-oxygen complex in hemoglobin and other oxygen-carrying metalloproteins has occupied the interest of scientists for many years. Oxygen-metallic ion complexes are important not only in oxygen transport in organisms, but also in oxygen "activation" in many oxygenase

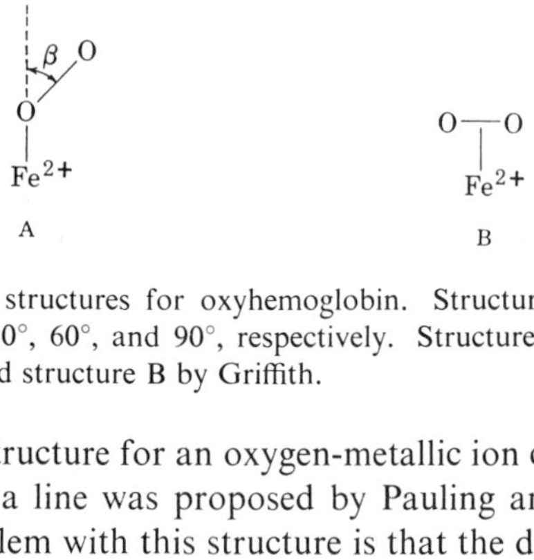

Fig. 1. Two proposed structures for oxyhemoglobin. Structures $A_1$, $A_2$, $A_3$, and $A_4$ correspond to $\beta = 0°$, $30°$, $60°$, and $90°$, respectively. Structures $A_1$ and $A_3$ have been proposed by Pauling, and structure B by Griffith.

enzymes. The first structure for an oxygen-metallic ion complex, $A_1$ (Fig. 1), with three atoms in a line was proposed by Pauling and Coryell (1) many years ago. The problem with this structure is that the diamagnetism of oxy-hemoglobin becomes very difficult to explain. Later Pauling (2) proposed structure $A_3$ with a $60°$ angle between the molecular oxygen axis and the iron-oxygen bond, which more readily explains the diamagnetism observed.

Oxygen in hemocyanin and in certain copper oxygenase enzymes is probably bound by two metal ions (cuprous) instead of one as in hemoglobin. Mason (3) has extended the Pauling structure, $A_3$, to propose the possible structures $A_{3a}$, $A_{3b}$, and $A_{3c}$ shown in Fig. 2 for the binding of oxygen by two metal ions.

More recently Griffith (4) pointed out that structure B (Fig. 1) may be a more likely structure for the iron-oxygen complex. In this structure the $\pi$-electrons of oxygen-oxygen are donated to the metal instead of the $sp^2$-electrons. The $\pi$-electrons should be more easily donated because of their lower ionization potential. The tendency in more recent years has been to accept Griffith's structure B as the proper structure for all metallic ion-oxygen complexes. The extension of this structure to the hemocyanin problem has been discussed (5).

Wang (6) has pointed out that the stability of the complex would depend not only upon the ionization potential of the electrons donated but also upon

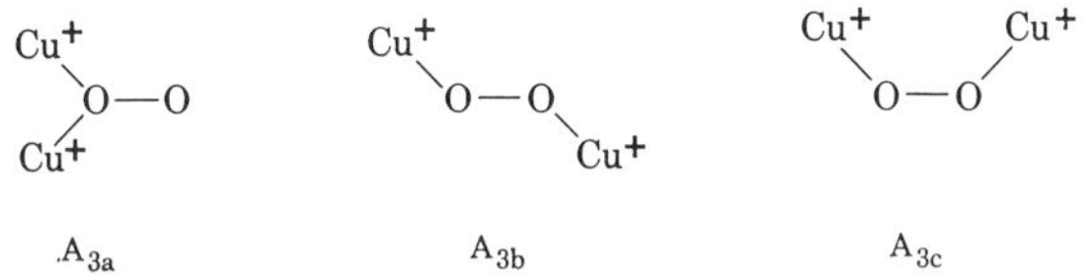

Fig. 2.   Three structures for oxyhemocyanin as proposed by Mason.

the strength of the bond formed. Therefore a molecular orbital calculation is required to differentiate between the two possible structures, $A_3$ and B. This paper describes such a calculation. In order to make the survey of structures more complete, structures $A_2$ and $A_4$ were also considered in which the angle between the molecular oxygen axis and the iron-oxygen bond, $\beta$, is 30° and 90°, respectively. These calculations have not been completed at this time.

## II. GENERAL ASSUMPTIONS AND METHODS

A total of eight oxygen orbitals was considered in the calculation, one $2s$ and three $2p$ on each oxygen atom. Nine iron orbitals were considered. These are the five $3d$, one $4s$, and three $4p$ orbitals. A total of 18 electrons was placed in the resulting molecular orbitals, 12 from the oxygen and 6 from the ferrous iron. The ionization potentials $(H_{ii})$ for the $2s$ and $2p$ electrons of the oxygen were taken from the atomic values given by Moore (7), and the corresponding coulombic integrals for iron were taken from the work of Pullman, Spanjard, and Berthier (8). A list of all $H_{ii}$ values is given in Table 1.

Some of the atomic orbitals of interest for the A structures are shown in Fig. 3. The orbitals $t_1$ to $t_6$ (trigonal) are $sp^2$ hybrids. Point group symmetry $C_s$ divides the atomic orbitals into the irreducible representations listed in Table 2. Some of the atomic orbitals of interest for structure B are shown in Fig. 4. These orbitals were not hybridized before use. Point group symmetry $C_{2v}$ divides these orbitals into the irreducible representations shown in Table 3.

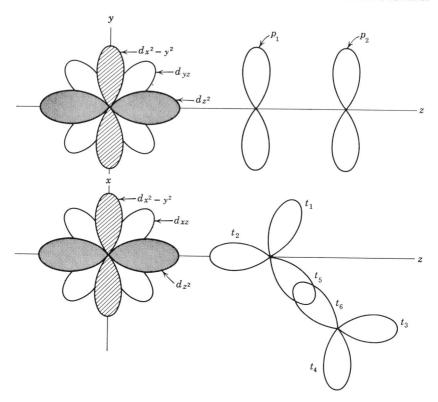

**Fig. 3.** Two views of the orbitals of interest in the $A_3$ structure of oxyhemoglobin proposed by Pauling.

All calculations were performed on an IBM 7040 computer. The atomic overlaps were computed by the method of Mulliken *et al.* (9) and Jaffe (10), using Slater's (11) radial wave functions for an oxygen-oxygen distance of 1.0 Å and an oxygen-iron distance of 1.78 Å (12). Atomic overlap integrals involving the fourth-shell electrons on iron were obtained by solving for

**TABLE 1**

**Values of $H_{ii}$ Integrals**

| Atom | Orbital | Energy, electron volts |
|------|---------|------------------------|
| Ferrous iron | $3d$ | −9.73 |
|  | $4s$ | −8.66 |
|  | $4p$ | −7.66 |
| Oxygen | $2s$ | −33.7 |
|  | $2p$ | −14.4 |

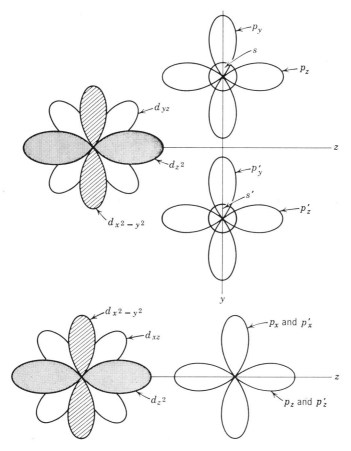

**Fig. 4.** Two views of the orbitals of interest in the B structure of oxyhemoglobin proposed by Griffith. The oxygen molecular axis in the lower diagram is perpendicular to the plane of the paper.

## TABLE 2

**Irreducible Representations to Which Orbitals of Structure A Belong for Point Group $C_s$**

| Irreducible Representation | Metal | Oxygen |
|---|---|---|
| $A'$ | $3d_{xz}$, $3d_{x^2-y^2}$, $3d_{z^2}$, $4s$, $4p_z$, $4p_x$ | $t_1$, $t_2$, $t_3$, $t_4$, $t_5$, $t_6$ |
| $A''$ | $3d_{yz}$, $3d_{xy}$, $4p_y$ | $p_1$, $p_2$ |

## TABLE 3

### Irreducible Representations to Which Orbitals of Structure B Belong for Point Group $C_{2v}$

| Irreducible Representation | Metal | Oxygen |
|---|---|---|
| $A_1$ | $3d_{z^2}, 3d_{x^2-y^2}, 4s,$ $4p_z$ | $(p_z + p'_z)$ $(s + s')$ $(p_y + p'_y)$ |
| $A_2$ | $3d_{xy}$ | $(p_x - p'_x)$ |
| $B_1$ | $3d_{xz}, 4p_x$ | $(p_x + p'_x)$ |
| $B_2$ | $3d_{yz}, 4p_y$ | $(s - s')$ $(p_z - p'_z)$ $(p_y - p'_y)$ |

$n - \delta = 3$ and $n - \delta = 4$ and approximating the value for $n - \delta = 3.3$ ($\delta = 0.7$ for $n = 4$) by linear interpolation. The exchange integrals $H_{ij}$ were approximated by equation 1 (13),

$$H_{ij} = K_x S_{ij} \frac{H_{ii} + H_{jj}}{2} \tag{1}$$

where $S_{ij}$ is the group overlap integral, and $K_x$ is a parameter equal to 1.67 for σ-bonds and 2.00 for π-bonds (14).

The secular determinate $|H - SE| = 0$ was solved by inverting* the matrix $S$ and premultiplying by $S^{-1}$, giving (15)

$$|S^{-1}H - S^{-1}SE| = 0$$
$$|S^{-1}H - IE| = 0 \tag{2}$$

where $I$ is the identity matrix. The characteristic equation and the eigenvectors of the resulting product matrix, $S^{-1}H$, were obtained by the method of Fettis (16), and the eigenvalues of the characteristic equation were found by the bisectional root searching method.

## III. RESULTS AND DISCUSSION

The energy levels of the $A_3$ and B structures are shown in Tables 4 and 5, respectively.

The difference in the energy of structures $A_3$ and B, $-313$ ev and $-290$ ev, respectively, is large enough that it can be considered sufficient, within the

* The matrix inversion routine was programmed by Ross Brown of the Computer Center at the University of California.

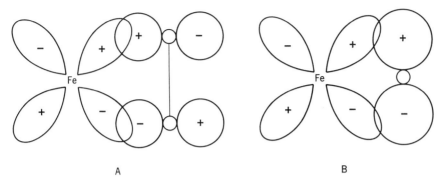

A                                    B

**Fig. 5.** Types of bonding in the B structure of oxyhemoglobin. Bonding in A is by donation of electrons from a filled $d\pi$ orbital of iron into a partially filled $\pi_g$ orbital of oxygen. Bonding in B (the oxygen molecular axis is perpendicular to the plane of the paper) shows strong interaction between a filled $d\pi$ orbital of iron and a filled $\pi_u$ orbital of oxygen, leading to instability of the complex.

## TABLE 4
### Energy Levels of Structure $A_3{}^a$

| Irreducible Representation | Energy, electron volts | Number of Electrons in M.O. |
|:---:|:---:|:---:|
| A' | −40.35747 | 2 |
|  | −25.00933 | 2 |
|  | −17.73628 | 2 |
|  | −15.70438 | 2 |
|  | −12.27501 | 2 |
|  | −9.73150 | 2 |
|  | −9.31369 |  |
|  | −8.16644 |  |
|  | −8.05194 |  |
|  | −5.89038 |  |
|  | 10.08935 |  |
|  | 38.02716 |  |
| A″ | −17.37500 | 2 |
|  | −10.68660 | 2 |
|  | −9.72651 | 2 |
|  | −8.87154 |  |
|  | −6.00551 |  |

$^a$ Values are significant to only three figures but are reported in a computer output format.

## TABLE 5
### Energy Levels of Structure B[a]

| Irreducible Representation | Energy, electron volts | Number of Electrons in M.O. |
|:---:|:---:|:---:|
| $A_1$ | −43.08962 | 2 |
| | −18.17305 | 2 |
| | −13.43043 | 2 |
| | −9.72865 | 2 |
| | −9.15659 | |
| | −7.22821 | |
| | 44.08621 | |
| $A_2$ | −10.26324 | 2 |
| | −8.67076 | |
| $B_1$ | −18.36703 | 2 |
| | −9.36145 | 2 |
| | −3.47965 | |
| $B_2$ | −10.03544 | 2 |
| | −9.67289 | 2 |
| | −8.33283 | |
| | −6.93865 | |
| | −0.08469 | |

[a] Values are significant to only three figures but are reported in a computer output format.

assumptions made, to show that Pauling's $A_3$ structure is to be preferred over structure B. In the light of the present calculations Mason's $A_{3a}$, $A_{3b}$, $A_{3c}$ structures for oxygenated hemocyanin appear to be quite probable at this time.

The B structure has been compared with a metal-olefin complex in which the $\pi_u$-electrons of oxygen are donated into an empty $3d\sigma$ orbital of iron while there is back donation from the $d\pi(d_{xz})$ electrons of iron into the partially filled $\pi_g$ orbital of oxygen as shown in Fig. 5a. However, oxygen should not be compared to an olefin. Oxygen has filled $\pi_u$ orbitals in both the $x$ and $y$ directions, and the filled $d_{yz}$ orbital of iron is also strongly interacting with the filled $\pi_u$ orbital of oxygen as shown in Fig. 5b—an energetically unfavorable situation.

Weiss (17) has suggested from a consideration of (a) magnetic properties, (b) absorption spectrum, and (c) the acid dissociation constant of oxygenated hemoglobin that the iron is in the +3 (ferric) state. The charge on the iron atom may be obtained from the equation (18):

$$q_j = \sum_r \sum_j n_r C_{rj}^2 - \sum_r \sum_j \sum_{i \neq j} n_r C_{rj} C_{ri} S_{ji}*$$

$$q_{\text{atom}} = Q - \sum_j q_j$$

where $q_{\text{atom}}$ = signed charge of the atom in question.

$Q$ = number of electrons on the unperturbed atom.

$q_j$ = electron density in the $j$th atomic orbital.

$n_r$ = number of electrons in the $r$th filled energy level.

$C_{rj}$ = wave function coefficient of the $j$th atomic orbital in the $r$th energy level.

$S_{ji}$ = overlap integral value between the $i$th and $j$th orbitals of the system.

The result of our calculation is $q_{\text{iron}} = +2.02$ for the Pauling structure $A_3$, in excellent agreement with the Weiss suggestion that $q$ is $+3$.

Although calculations have not been completed for $A_1$, $A_2$, and $A_4$, we believe that $A_1$ and $A_2$ are very unlikely structures. However, $A_4$, the $90°$ structure, does have merit and cannot be ruled out at this time.

Metal-oxygen complexes are important not only in binding oxygen but also a complex III in many enzymic reactions requiring activation of oxygen (17). In order to activate oxygen it is necessary to facilitate the addition of an electron to oxygen. Therefore, it is of interest to compare the energy of the lowest empty molecular orbital of the complexes studied with that of the partially filled $\pi_g$ orbital of oxygen. The value for structure $A_3$ is $-9.50$ ev and for structure B is $-9.13$ ev, as compared with $-9.75$ ev for the calculated $\pi_g$ orbital of oxygen, using the same parameters as were used for the complexes. Therefore, there is no evidence from these calculations that either structure A or B will "activate" oxygen. However, these are small energy differences compared with the errors inherent in the difference of the values for the complexes compared with that of oxygen. For this reason, we can make no predictions as to whether structures $A_3$ and B would activate oxygen or not. Three serious errors contribute to this difference:

1. No correction was made for singlet-triplet splitting, and structure B is a singlet, whereas the oxygen molecule is a triplet.

2. In calculations where configuration interaction is neglected, the higher energy levels are notoriously poor.

3. The calculated energy levels are dependent upon the iron parameters for $H_{ii}$ that were used.

These arguments either do not apply or are second-order effects in comparison of the energies of structures $A_3$ and B.

* The index $j$ is over the orbitals of the atom in question, whereas the index $i$ is over all the orbitals of the system. The index $r$ denotes only the filled energy levels.

Chemical intuition enables one to predict that the complex is "activated." If an electron is donated from iron to oxygen, the oxygen is of the very active form $O_2^-$.

## IV. CONCLUSIONS

Molecular orbital calculations have shown that the Pauling $A_3$ structure for oxygenated hemoglobin is to be preferred over the Griffith B structure. The iron is essentially ferric iron, and the oxygen is $O_2^-$. These calculations are not accurate enough to make predictions as to whether structure $A_3$ or structure B will enzymically "activate" oxygen. However, chemical intuition tells one that the oxygen must be "activated" if it has gained an electron. Calculations for structure $A_4$, the 90° structure, are in progress but have not been completed at this time.

## ACKNOWLEDGMENTS

We wish to acknowledge financial support of this project by United States Public Health Service Grants FR-00009 and RG-08285.

Richard O. Viale received financial support from a National Science Foundation Graduate Fellowship.

## REFERENCES

1. L. Pauling and C. D. Coryell, *Proc. Natl. Acad. Sci. U.S.*, **22**, 210 (1936).
2. F. J. W. Roughton and J. C. Kendrew, *Haemoglobin*, Interscience, New York, 1949, p. 57.
3. H. S. Mason, *Nature*, **177**, 79 (1956).
4. J. S. Griffith, *Proc. Roy. Soc. (London)*, A235, 23 (1956).
5. L. L. Ingraham, *J. Chem. Educ.*, **41**, 66 (1964).
6. J. H. Wang, in J. E. Faulk, R. Lemberg, and R. K. Morton, Eds., *Haematin Enzymes*, Pergamon Press, Oxford, 1961, p. 103.
7. C. E. Moore, "Atomic Energy Levels," *Circ. Natl. Bur. Standards*, No. 467, Vol. 1, Washington, D.C.
8. B. Pullman, C. Spanjard, and G. Berthier, *Proc. Natl. Acad. Sci. U.S.*, **46**, 1011 (1960).
9. R. Mulliken, C. Rieke, S. Orloss, and H. Orloff, *J. Chem. Phys.*, **17**, 1248 (1949).
10. H. Jaffe, *J. Chem. Phys.*, **21**, 258 (1953).
11. J. Slater, *Phys. Rev.*, **36**, 57 (1930).
12. L. Pauling, *Nature of the Chemical Bond*, Cornell University Press, New York, 1945, pp. 164, 182.
13. H. Gray and C. Ballhausen, *J. Am. Chem. Soc.*, **85**, 260 (1963).
14. M. Wolfsberg and L. Helmholtz, *J. Chem. Phys.*, **20**, 837 (1952).
15. H. O. Pritchard and F. H. Sumner, *Proc. Roy. Soc. (London)*, A235, 126–143 (1956).
16. D. H. E. Fettis, *Quart. Appl. Math.*, **8**, 206 (1950).
17. H. S. Mason, *Advances in Enzymol.*, **19**, 79 (1957).

### Discussion

*This paper is discussed jointly with the paper of Drs. Caughey, Alben, and Beaudreau on pp. 107–114.*

# Structure and Medium Effects
## on the Reactions of $Fe^{2+}$ Porphyrins
## with Oxygen and Carbon Monoxide

. . . WINSLOW S. CAUGHEY, JAMES O. ALBEN,
and CHARLES A. BEAUDREAU

## I. INTRODUCTION

The influence of both structure and medium on the properties and reactions of $Fe^{2+}$ porphyrins can be rather marked. As an example of this fact, during an isolation of heme $a$ from beef-heart muscle, the protoheme isolated was much more readily oxidized than was the heme $a$ (1). Heme $a$ was isolated as a solid in an $Fe^{2+}$ oxidation state, although no reducing agent such as sodium dithionite was added nor was oxygen excluded; in solution, the heme appeared capable of reversible oxygenation. The protoheme usually experienced oxidation during its isolation under the same conditions used for heme $a$. Several other $Fe^{2+}$ porphyrins have also been prepared in our laboratory, and in this paper some general observations on the importance of structure and medium on the reactions of these compounds with oxygen and carbon monoxide are considered.

## II. PREPARATIONS OF $Fe^{2+}$ PORPHYRINS

In only a few cases have $Fe^{2+}$ porphyrins been prepared as solids, although the possibility of their preparation has long been known (2–7). Probably the first preparation was a complex containing ammonia reported by von Zeynek in 1898 (2). The ready autoxidation of these compounds, under many conditions, has complicated their preparation and characterization as solids to the extent that the usual practice has been to prepare $Fe^{2+}$ porphyrins only *in solution* from $Fe^{3+}$ porphyrins [frequently prepared in doubtful purity (8)] and reducing agent.

Now a convenient method has been found for the preparation of a variety of $Fe^{2+}$ porphyrins with pyridine ligands. In this method the $Fe^{3+}$ chloride or methoxide of a porphyrin (esters of the acidic porphyrins are used) is reduced in aqueous pyridine with excess sodium dithionite, benzene is added, the excess dithionite and water-soluble products are extracted from a pyridine-benzene-water solution with water, the water is removed from the washed solution with sodium sulfate, and the product is isolated as a solid from the dried benzene-pyridine solution. No special apparatus for the exclusion of oxygen is required, as the reduced compound is maintained throughout the procedure in a solvent environment in which it is inert toward autoxidation.

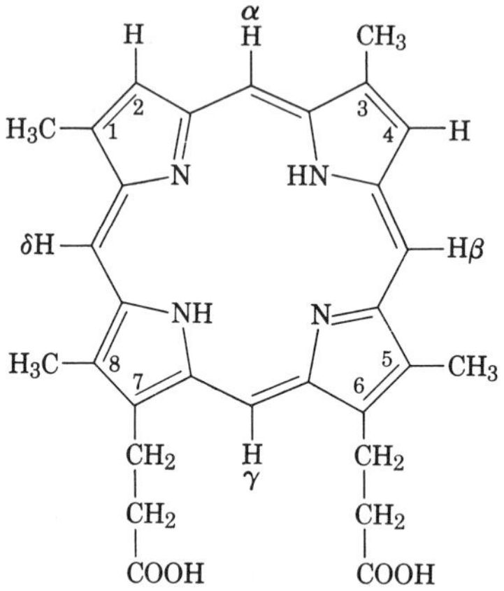

Fig. 1.   Deuteroporphyrin IX.

The bispyridino-$Fe^{2+}$ porphyrins obtained, mainly $Fe^{2+}$-2,4-substituted deuteroporphyrin IX dimethyl esters (Fig. 1), were stable in the presence of air as solids and exhibited typical hemochromogen spectra, gave elemental analyses (carbon, hydrogen, nitrogen, and iron) in close agreement with calculated values, and bound CO reversibly in pyridine-benzene solutions. Their NMR spectra have shown they are diamagnetic (consistent with low spin) $Fe^{2+}$ compounds and have also provided confirmation of structure (Fig. 2).

### III. STRUCTURAL EFFECTS ON CARBON MONOXIDE AND PYRIDINE BINDING

The relative effects of ethyl, hydrogen, vinyl, and acetyl groups as 2,4-substituents in $Fe^{2+}$ deuteroporphyrin IX dimethyl esters on the competition between CO and pyridine as ligands have been examined in benzene solutions. In 1925 Hill reported evidence that hemochromogens contain two pyridine ligands and that one pyridine ligand can be reversibly replaced with one CO

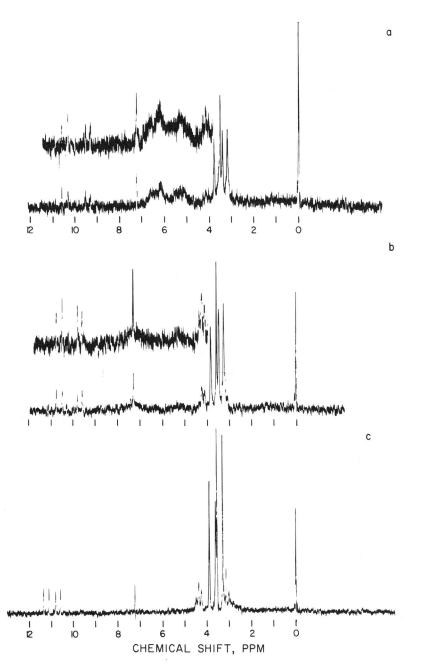

CHEMICAL SHIFT, PPM

**Fig. 2.** NMR spectra. (a) Bispyridino-Fe$^{2+}$-2,4-diacetyldeuteroporphyrin IX dimethyl ester, 20 mg in 0.4 ml CDCl$_3$. (b) As in (a) with the solvent saturated with CO before the addition of heme. (c) 2,4-Diacetyldeuteroporphyrin IX dimethyl ester, 20 mg in CDCl$_3$ containing 2.5% trifluoroacetic acid.

ligand; the relative amounts of bispyridino and carbonyl species are dependent on the relative concentrations of pyridine and CO (9). He also noted in alkaline aqueous media association phenomena which have complicated interpretations in several studies carried out in such media (10). With the $Fe^{2+}$ porphyrins available as esters it has been possible for us to carry out studies in non-aqueous media where association phenomena have been avoided more readily than in aqueous media. Also non-aqueous media may well resemble more closely the environment experienced by the heme moiety in many heme proteins. The extent of conversion to the carbonyl complex in pyridine-benzene solutions was readily followed via visible spectra. Carbon monoxide was bound less effectively, as compared with pyridine, as the electron-withdrawing character of the 2,4-substituents increased. For example, with benzene solutions at 20° with $3.5 \times 10^{-5}$ $M$ heme, 1.3 $M$ pyridine, $4.5 \times 10^{-4}$ $M$ CO, the bispyridinohemes were 77, 60, 56, and 17% converted to the carbonyl complex for the ethyl, hydrogen, vinyl, and acetyl compounds, respectively.

Carbonyl complexes of these hemes have been studied also by observing structural effects on the C-O stretching frequency of bound CO (11). Effects of structural differences in both the porphyrin and the pyridine moieties were observed; $\nu_{CO}$ increased with increasingly electron-withdrawing substituents in either the 2,4-positions of the porphyrin or the 4-position of the pyridine (12, 13). Thus, in bromoform with 0.1 $M$ pyridine, $\nu_{CO}$ was 1973 and 1984 cm$^{-1}$ for the diethyl and diacetyl hemes, respectively. With the diacetyl heme, $\nu_{CO}$ values of 1979 and 1989 cm$^{-1}$ were found in the presence of 0.1 $M$ 4-amino- and 4-cyanopyridine, respectively. Both infrared and NMR evidence support the presence of the carbonyl species as monocarbonyl mono-4-substituted pyridinohemes under these conditions. Among compounds as similar as these, relative C-O stretching frequencies can be expected to demonstrate relative degrees of triple-bond character in the C-O bond; the larger $\nu_{CO}$, the greater the triple-bond character. As the triple-bond character of CO increases, a concomitant weakening of the metal-carbon bond can be expected. A reciprocal relationship between the carbonyl and metal-carbon force constants has been demonstrated with nickel carbonyls by Bigorgne (14). For free CO, $\nu_{CO}$ is about 2155 cm$^{-1}$. On this basis the carbon-metal bond strength appears sensitive to changes in substituents on either porphyrin or pyridine rings with the strength of binding of CO to iron decreasing as the electron-withdrawing character of the substituents increases.

That pyridine binding to nickel in similarly substituted deuteroporphyrin IX nickel complexes is markedly dependent upon the nature of 2,4-substituent has also been demonstrated (15). The more electron withdrawing is the substituent, the greater is the strength of pyridine binding. Similarly, for equilibria between the stronger base piperidine and the nickel porphyrins in chloroform at 25°C, the equilibrium constants corresponding to equation 1 for the 2,4-hydrogen and 2,4-diacetyl compounds are 2.2 and 62.0 times greater, respectively, than the constants for the diethyl compound (16).

Thus, among the substituents used, which cover a range of structural differences less great than is found among the heme moieties of heme proteins, ligand binding at the metal atom can be markedly affected by substituent type. As substituents become more effectively electron-withdrawing, nitrogen basicity decreases, and low-spin $Fe^{2+}$ can be expected to participate *less* effectively in $\pi$-bonding, which involves the participation of a filled $t_{2g}$ orbital (as a $\pi$-donor), and to participate *more* effectively in $\sigma$-bonding, which involves the empty $d_{z^2}$ orbital (as a $\sigma$-acceptor). Our results with carbonyl hemes are consistent with an important role for $\pi$-bonding in the bond between the very weak base CO and iron, with the CO acting as $\pi$-acceptor and the iron as $\pi$-donor (12, 13), a finding fully in accord with current views of bonding in transition metal carbonyls (11). On the other hand, substituent effects on pyridine binding are quite the opposite of those found with CO bonding, and are consistent with strong participation of $\sigma$-bonding, wherein iron acts as an acceptor and the pyridine nitrogen as the donor. The relative thermal stabilities of bispyridino compounds can also be interpreted on this basis; on heating the solid bispyridino 2,4-substituted deuteroheme dimethyl esters under vacuum, pyridine was lost at a lower temperature the less electron-withdrawing were the 2,4-substituents.

## IV. STRUCTURE AND MEDIUM EFFECTS ON REACTIONS OF BISPYRIDINOHEMES UNDER AEROBIC CONDITIONS

As solids, bispyridinohemes appear stable indefinitely to exposure to air at room temperature or below (several such compounds have now been stored in this fashion for years). However, as mentioned above, at higher temperatures pyridine ligands can be removed—the more basic the porphyrin, the lower the temperature at which this can occur. Bispyridino compounds heated under vacuum, cooled, and exposed to oxygen have given products whose elemental analyses are consistent with a loss of pyridine and an uptake of oxygen. At lower temperatures compounds with analyses consistent with one pyridine per heme, and no other ligand, have been obtained; Fischer *et al.* have reported such a compound for mesoheme (4). Monopyridino compounds after standing exposed to air for long periods (months) have exhibited elemental analyses consistent with uptake of oxygen. Corwin and co-workers have studied the reversible uptake of oxygen in solid hemes (6, 7).

In solution, changes in solvent, porphyrin structure, and oxygen concentration were found to affect markedly the stabilities of bispyridinohemes, as well as the spectra and products which resulted. Different spectra were obtained on dissolving bispyridino-2,4-diacetyldeuteroporphyrin IX dimethyl

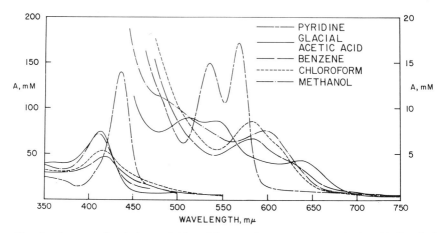

**Fig. 3.** Spectra of solutions of bispyridino-2,4-diacetyldeuteroporphyrin IX dimethyl ester Fe²⁺.

ester $Fe^{2+}$ in different solvents (Fig. 3). In all cases the solutions were open to air. With pyridine the hemochromogen spectrum of the original compound was obtained, whereas a variety of altered products was secured with the other solvents. The stability of hemes in pyridine has been observed previously (1, 5, 17).

Solvent effects on the rate of disappearance of the hemochromogen spectra have also been studied by observing the reactions in various (1:1) pyridine-solvent mixtures. These studies were carried out with 2,4-diethyl-, 2,4-divinyl-, and 2,4-diacetyldeuteroheme dimethyl ester. The stability of the hemochromogens was essentially unchanged upon dilution of a pyridine solution of heme with an equal volume of benzene, bromoform, or dimethyl formamide. Similar dilutions with certain other solvents led to a decrease in hemochromogen spectrum; thus, the rate of loss of hemochromogen spectrum increased in the following order: ethanol, acetone, methanol, $n$-butylamine $< 0.38$ $M$ aqueous potassium hydroxide $<$ water $\ll$ acetic acid. Similarly, for one-hundredfold dilutions of pyridine with benzene no measureable rate of decrease in hemochromogen spectrum was detected, although with methanol as diluent the rate of decrease was extremely rapid.

In the foregoing experiments, the solutions were saturated with air. The influence of oxygen concentration on the rates of these transformations was observed in several cases, although oxygen concentrations were not determined. Thus, when solid bispyridino-2,4-diacetyldeuteroporphyrin IX dimethyl ester $Fe^{2+}$ was dissolved in degassed benzene, where air was displaced by argon or nitrogen, a stable hemochromogen-type spectrum was obtained. Upon exposure to air the spectrum gradually changed to one like that for the benzene solution shown in Fig. 3. Analogous differences between degassed and oxygen-saturated solvents were also noted in NMR spectra. The spectrum in Fig. 2a was obtained in $CDCl_3$ which had not been degassed; however, after standing for 1 hr, it was much weakened. In degassed or CO-saturated $CDCl_3$, NMR spectra were quite stable (Fig. 2b).

Although these preliminary observations by no means permit a detailed description of the oxygenation, oxidation-reduction, and/or other ligand-exchange processes which occur in the observed reactions, several features of these reactions deserve comment. The influence of 2,4-substituents on the rate was uniformly one in which the more electron-withdrawing the substituent, the slower the rate of change from the hemochromogen, as was the case for the relative rates of autoxidation of heme $a$ and protoheme (1). Such an order of substituent effects is consistent with more stable pyridine binding in complexes of less basic porphyrins. Since the $\pi$-donor character of the iron will be less effective the less basic the porphyrin, weaker oxygen binding could also be expected (see below). Thus, both pyridine dissociation and oxygenation reactions (which could well be successive steps in these reactions) would be favored by increased porphyrin basicity. It is apparent also that the effect of solvent type on the rates of these reactions cannot be related in any direct way with solvent polarity *per se*. The protic character of the solvent does seem to be very important. Pyridine will certainly appear less effective as a ligand in solutions where the pyridine nitrogen experiences protonation via hydrogen bonding, or proton donation, from a protic solvent. Thus, with nickel porphyrin complexes, pyridine binding to nickel is greatly reduced in the presence of water or alcohols; these solvents do not appear to act as ligands themselves, but rather strongly solvate the pyridine (15, 16). Similar findings have been reported for alkylamine complexes of nickel (18). Thus, observed effects of protic solvents on pyridinohemes need not be ascribed to the direct participation of these solvents in oxygenation or oxidation steps.

## V. OXYGEN BONDING IN RECONSTITUTED HEMOGLOBINS AND MYOGLOBINS AND IN OTHER HEME PROTEINS

The structural effects on CO bonding found here can be compared to the order and magnitude of substituent effects described for reconstituted myoglobins and hemoglobins. In reconstituted myoglobins, Rossi-Fanelli and

Antonini found deuteromyoglobin to have three times greater oxygen affinity than protomyoglobin (19). With reconstituted hemoglobins, deutero-hemoglobins and mesohemoglobins bound oxygen two and six times, respectively, more firmly than reconstituted protohemoglobin, the oxygen affinity of which was identical to that of native hemoglobin (20). Thus, oxygen affinity increased as the 2,4-substituents changed from vinyl to hydrogen to ethyl groups. The order and the extent of the effects observed on changing these substituents can be reasonably ascribed to the difference in electron-withdrawing character of the substituents, as was the case in the CO-bonding studies described in section III. An increased oxygen affinity as porphyrin basicity increases is consistent with an important participation of $\pi$-bonding via a filled $t_{2g}$ orbital of $Fe^{2+}$ and an antibonding $\pi$ orbital of the oxygen. Such bonding is expected in the proposed models for oxygen binding of Pauling (21) and of Griffith (22).

Pauling model                    Griffith model

Strong $\pi$-donation by iron can contribute polar character to the metal-oxygen bond, and as a consequence oxygen binding could be appreciably stabilized by interactions (e.g., hydrogen bonding) between the distal histidine and oxygen. In x-ray structure studies on metmyoglobin azide, Struyer, Kendrew, and Watson interpreted their results in terms of hydrogen bonding between the distal histidine and azide (23). These authors also discussed the probable influence of pH on such hydrogen bonding in relation to the Bohr effect. Also of interest is the report by Corwin and Bruck that imidazole promotes the reversible oxygenation of hemes in pyridine solutions (7).

The differences in relative affinities for CO and oxygen observed among various heme proteins require explanation. These differences could be ascribed to differences in stereochemistry on the basis of the C-O bond being perpendicular to the heme plane, whereas the O-O bond is either bent from the perpendicular (Pauling model) or parallel to the heme plane (Griffith model). Such differences in stereochemistry become particularly important if rather specific interactions, such as hydrogen bond formation with a distal histidine, occur between the ligand and a group on the protein.

That structural differences can affect oxygen binding and CO bonding to a different extent is expected from comparisons of models of CO bonding with the Griffith model for oxygen bonding. The latter model closely resembles currently accepted descriptions for olefin-metal bonding. Here a filled iron

$t_{2g}$ orbital "back-bonds" to the acceptor antibonding $\pi$ orbital of oxygen, whereas the filled $\pi$ orbital of oxygen "donates" to a vacant $d_{z^2}$ orbital of the iron. Oxygen was shown bound to iridium in this fashion in an x-ray structure determination by Ibers (24) of the oxygenated form of chloro-carbonyl-bis(triphenylphosphine) iridium (1), a reversible oxygen carrier prepared by Vaska (25).

Since it is known that in at least one case oxygen can bind in the fashion described in the Griffith model, speculations involving this model seem particularly appropriate. For example, one can suggest that compounds with strongly electron-withdrawing substituents could achieve significant bond strength with oxygen by virtue of the iron acting as a good $\sigma$-acceptor of the filled $\pi$ orbital of oxygen, despite the fact that in this instance iron would be a poor $\pi$-donor. Such bonding would be facilitated by the absence of a strong (or any) back-side ligand, since in that event the iron could be a better $\sigma$-acceptor, and distortion of the iron from the porphyrin plane could also be more readily achieved. Oxygen binding of this type is expected to be stronger with the iron out of the porphyrin plane (24). Such deviations from planarity have now been shown in metmyoglobin (26), protohemin chloride (27), and mesoporphyrin IX dimethyl ester $Fe^{3+}$ methoxide (28), with the iron atom out of the mean plane of the heme group by $\sim$0.25, 0.475, and 0.49 Å, respectively.

Using the Griffith model, one can speculate also on possible mechanisms for reactions of oxygenated heme intermediates in oxidases, catalases, peroxidases, etc. Thus, in the reduction of heme-bound oxygen to hydrogen peroxide or to water, a mechanistically simple scheme is one where pro-tonation (by water) of the iron-bound oxygen proceeds either at the same time as, or immediately following, the passage of electrons from iron to oxygen. The number of electrons obtained from the iron atom, two or four, would determine the nature of the product, peroxide or water. The move-ment of oxygen atoms from the iron atom other than in the fully reduced state as hydroxyl or water would not be required. In these terms cytochrome oxidase could contain a reductive unit consisting of hemes $a$, and probably copper as well (with the possibility of copper participating in the linkage between heme $a$ molecules), in sufficient number to provide four electrons to oxygen via the iron of one of the heme $a$ groups (heme $a_3$). Here the oxygen molecule would be bonded to iron parallel to the heme plane and would remain bound until fully reduced and protonated to yield two molecules of water. These suggestions appear consistent with observations on the oxidase, for example, the interpretations of Gibson and Greenwood on the composition of the "reductive unit" (29) and on the number of iron atoms (one) which take part in the primary reactions with oxygen (30).

Oxygen binding as proposed by Griffith and found in Vaska's oxygenated iridium compounds is perhaps a better description of bonding in oxygenated heme *a* and the oxygenated species associated with oxidases, peroxidases, and catalases than it is for the oxygen carriers hemoglobin and myoglobin. Certainly, in hemoglobin and myoglobin with back-side histidine ligands, the $Fe^{2+}$ atom would not be expected to function as a good $\sigma$-acceptor or to exist very far out of the porphyrin plane in the oxygenated species. As an alternative, the Pauling structure could be considered more (or equally) acceptable. Another alternative is suggested by the bonding of oxygen

proposed by Vlcek (31) and found by studies of crystal structure by Vannerberg and Brosset (32) for decammine-$\mu$-peroxodicobalt pentanitrate, where two cobalt atoms are linked through a bridging peroxide group and held together in a $\pi$-complex. Here the ammonia molecules were found but slightly distorted from octahedral symmetry. In hemoglobin and myoglobin it would thus seem possible for the back-side histidine and porphyrin nitrogens to exist in an essentially octahedral environment with an oxygen molecule parallel to the heme plane. We suggest that such a configuration is achieved through interaction between the bound oxygen and a group on the protein, presumably the distal histidine as mentioned above. The resulting structure would appear fully compatible with the known properties of oxyhemoglobin and oxymyoglobin.

## ACKNOWLEDGMENT

This work was supported by Grant HE-06079-04 of the United States Public Health Service.

## REFERENCES

1. W. S. Caughey and J. L. York, *J. Biol. Chem.*, **237**, PC 2414 (1962).
2. R. von Zeynek, *Z. Physiol. Chem.*, **25**, 492 (1898).
3. H. Fischer and K. Schneller, *Z. Physiol. Chem.*, **128**, 230 (1923).
4. H. Fischer, A. Treibs, and K. Zeiler, *Z. Physiol. Chem.*, **195**, 1 (1931).
5. A. H. Corwin and J. G. Erdman, *J. Am. Chem. Soc.*, **68**, 2473 (1946).
6. A. H. Corwin and Z. Reyes, *J. Am. Chem. Soc.*, **78**, 2437 (1956).
7. A. H. Corwin and S. D. Bruck, *J. Am. Chem. Soc.*, **80**, 4736 (1958).
8. K. G. Paul, *Acta Chem. Scand.*, **12**, 1611 (1958).
9. R. Hill, *Biochem. J.*, **20**, 419 (1926).
10. M. H. Smith, *Biochem. J.*, **73**, 90 (1959).
11. E. W. Abel, *Quart. Revs.*, **17**, 133 (1963).
12. J. O. Alben and W. S. Caughey, *Federation Proc.*, **21**, 46 (1962).

13. W. S. Caughey, J. O. Alben, and B. D. McLees, *Proceedings of the 7th International Conference on Coordination Chemistry, Stockholm and Uppsala, 1962*, p. 136.

14. M. Bigorgne, in S. Kirschner, Ed., *Advances in the Chemistry of the Coordination Compounds*, Macmillan, New York, 1961, p. 199, and later papers.

15. W. S. Caughey, R. M. Deal, B. D. McLees, and J. O. Alben, *J. Am. Chem. Soc.*, **84**, 1735 (1962).

16. B. D. McLees and W. S. Caughey, unpublished work.

17. R. Hill, *Biochem. J.*, **19**, 341 (1925).

18. R. S. Drago, D. W. Meek, R. Longhi, and M. D. Joesten, *Inorg. Chem.*, **2**, 1056 (1963).

19. A. Rossi-Fanelli and E. Antonini, *Arch. Biochem. Biophys.*, **72**, 243 (1957).

20. A. Rossi-Fanelli and E. Antonini, *Arch. Biochem. Biophys.*, **80**, 299, 308 (1959); A. Rossi-Fanelli, E. Antonini, and A. Caputo, *ibid.*, **85**, 37 (1959).

21. L. Pauling, in F. J. W. Roughton and J. C. Kendrew, Eds., *Hemoglobin*, Interscience, New York, 1949, p. 60.

22. J. S. Griffith, *Proc. Roy. Soc. (London)*, **A235**, 23 (1956).

23. L. Struyer, J. C. Kendrew, and H. C. Watson, *J. Molecular Biol.*, **8**, 96 (1964).

24. J. A. Ibers, *Abstracts of Papers, 147th Meeting, American Chemical Society, Philadelphia, 1964*, p. 20L.

25. L. Vaska, *Science*, **140**, 809 (1963).

26. J. C. Kendrew, *Science*, **139**, 1259 (1963).

27. D. F. Koenig, Ph.D. thesis, The Johns Hopkins University, Baltimore, 1962.

28. M. T. Hamor, T. A. Hamor, J. S. Hoard, and W. S. Caughey, unpublished work.

29. Q. H. Gibson and C. Greenwood, *Biochem. J.*, **86**, 51 (1963).

30. Q. H. Gibson and C. Greenwood, *J. Biol. Chem.*, **239**, 586 (1964).

31. A. A. Vlcek, *Trans. Faraday Soc.*, **56**, 1137 (1960).

32. N. G. Vannerberg and C. Brosset, *Acta Cryst.*, **16**, 247 (1963).

## Discussion

*Joint discussion of the papers by Drs. G. M. Maggiora, R. O. Viale and L. L. Ingraham, and by Drs. W. S. Caughey, J. O. Alben, and C. A. Beaudreau.*

SUTIN: I should like to comment on Dr. Caughey's paper and also on Dr. Ingraham's paper.

When comparing the effects of different substituents in the porphyrin ring on the rate of oxidation of the $Fe^{2+}$ complexes, it is also necessary to consider their effect on the standard free-energy changes for the reaction. Thus electron-withdrawing substituents will stabilize $Fe^{2+}$ relative to $Fe^{3+}$, thereby tending to make a standard free-energy change for the oxidation of $Fe^{2+}$ less negative. Provided that all other factors are equal, this would decrease the rate of the oxidation reaction. I believe that this can also account for the effect of substituents on the oxidation rate reported by Dr. Caughey. Incidentally, we have observed similar substituent effects on the rate of oxidation of a variety of $Fe^{2+}$-phenanthroline complexes by $Mn^{3+}$, $Ce^{4+}$, and $Co^{3+}$.

CAUGHEY: Of course, I agree completely with Dr. Sutin's comment on the expected effects of substituent type on the rates of oxidation of $Fe^{2+}$ porphyrins and on the free-energy changes. However, it is quite clear that these reactions of bispyridino-$Fe^{2+}$ porphyrins can involve several steps and can also lead to a variety of products. The rate of decrease in hemochromogen spectrum is not necessarily a rate of an oxidation reaction but may well reflect the rate of a ligand exchange or oxygenation process or the sum of several competing processes.

SUTIN: I have discussed Dr. Ingraham's paper with Dr. Max Wulfsberg, who with Dr. Helmholtz developed the procedures used by Dr. Ingraham and co-workers in their calculations. Dr. Wulfsberg made the following comments:

1. The semiempirical molecular orbital method does not take into account all the electron-electron, electron-nucleus, and nucleus-nucleus interactions. One would therefore tend to distrust energy differences calculated for different geometries.

2. The calculations should be self-consistent. Thus the ionization potentials (which should be valence-state ionization potentials) and the overlap integrals should correspond to the final charge distribution. If the final charge on the iron corresponds to ferric, then the ionization potential $H_{ii}$ should also correspond to a charge of $+3$. Similar arguments also apply to the charge on the coordinated oxygen atoms.

3. Overlap integrals calculated with Slater orbitals are notoriously unrealistic, especially for $3d$ orbitals. Hartree-Fock functions should be used.

4. The use of trigonal hybrids as a starting point for the A structure while $s$ and $p$ orbitals are used in the B structure seems somewhat strange. Why were the calculations done in this manner?

INGRAHAM: The first point about the repulsion between the nuclei is certainly valid. This is very difficult to take into account, and all we can say is that our calculation is a big step further than any arguments that have been made in the past. It is very true that this effect should be taken into account; I would expect it to be larger in structure B.

The second point about the self-consistency of the calculation is not as incriminating as it seems at first because $Q$ is $+2$ as a result of strong pi back-donation. Therefore our $H_{ii}$ integral that we start with is essentially the same one that we should use in the final calculation.

The third point is well taken, too. Again, I can only make the same comment as before; this is a further approximation. This sort of thing is unlimited until you get the perfect calculation. I should like to point out in regard to both points 1 and 3 that very large energy differences are involved between the A and B structures, whereas small energy differences are involved between the $A_1$, $A_2$, $A_3$, and $A_4$. It is my feeling that our approximations are all the amount of energies that are involved between these structures.

As for the fourth point, involving $sp^2$ hybrids in the A structure, when we started, we first looked at the $A_3$ structure and it seemed to us that the calculations would be easier if we hybridized it to start with the $sp^2$ hybrid because it would be pointed directly at the iron. However, it shouldn't make any difference what the original vectors are because you can start with any set of vectors. Actually, we have done the same thing by using both unhybridized $s$ and $p$ orbitals, and the calculations are very similar. I might point out that one of the matrices in the A structure is a 12 by 12. I was not aware of the errors you could incur just by solving a 12 by 12 matrix, even on a computer, so that there was a difference of fractions of an electron volt between using the hybridized and the unhybridized orbitals as a starting point.

ORGEL: I should like to be devil's advocate and ask some general questions about the paper by Dr. Ingraham. What worries me really is the accuracy of calculations of this type. Do you know of anyone who has computed energies and compared them with experiment? If you don't, why should we believe that these results are sufficiently accurate to be interesting?

INGRAHAM: All I can do is present the fact that this is the difference found in this calculation—whether you have to find 1 electron volt difference or 10 or 100 electron volts to make the difference significant, I don't really know. Thirty-three electron volts is a large energy.

ORGEL: Maybe one could say that the more electron volts one finds, the less likely the difference is to be significant. We can't seriously believe that the A and B structures would differ by 33 electron volts, 759 kcal, because both structures must surely be stable and neither of them would have a heat of formation in excess of 100 kcal. Therefore the fact that the calculations for the two differ by 759 seems to me to argue against rather than for the accuracy of the method.

INGRAHAM: Well, I don't think it is necessarily true that both of them have to be stable. It may be that the B structure is never formed in the first place and may even have a positive free energy of formation from oxygen and ferrous ion.

ORGEL: Well, that would merely give us 0; it can't be antistable. I don't see how you could have 759 kcal difference between the heats of formation and have two types of complex. You know that this is exactly the problem which we faced when we worked with ferrocene. I am sure that some of the things we said were not right.

INGRAHAM: Well, my only answer is that this is what this calculation says, and I think it will have to be taken on the basis of the type of calculation that is made.

CAUGHEY: Would you discuss the choice of an oxygen-oxygen distance of 1 Å? I raise this point because in the x-ray structure determination of the oxygenated iridium compound the distance turns out to be 1.30 Å. In molecular oxygen I believe that this distance is about 1.20 Å, and in a typical peroxide about 1.48 Å. I am wondering whether there is a problem here.

INGRAHAM: Well, we took 1.0, which is probably a low value. I can't say offhand which way the calculations would be changed if we took a larger distance between the oxygen atoms.

CAUGHEY: It is of interest that in the oxygenated iridium compound an oxygen-oxygen distance of 1.30 is consistent with oxygen being present as $O_2^-$; it doesn't necessarily mean that this is exactly the situation, however.

INGRAHAM: I think that our distance probably is too short. There is less bonding between the oxygen, and therefore the distance probably should be slightly longer than the one that we've taken. This is perhaps a similar criticism to the criticism of the self-consistent field. We should go back again and correct the overlap for the new distance, corresponding to the new bond order.

MORRISON: Dr. Caughey, I was wondering about the validity of your statement concerning the differences in the heme $a$ isolated by the two procedures. Is this a real difference in the chemistry of heme $a$, or a difference in the ligands that are extracted with the different procedures? If it is a real difference in the chemistry of the heme $a$, where do we stand in terms of the chemistry of heme $a$?

CAUGHEY: I don't recall saying that the heme $a$ we isolated was different but indeed it is.

MORRISON: I thought you implied a difference by indicating that the extraction procedure you use gives a type of heme compound different from the one obtained by the acid extraction procedure that most of us use.

CAUGHEY: Isolation of heme $a$ in the manner we have reported [*J. Biol. Chem.*, **237**, P.C. 2414 (1962)], in which we use pyridine-chloroform solutions to extract the heme, gives a product of somewhat different structure from that reported by others for products obtained by acidified acetone extraction. It does not correspond in all respects to the structure recently proposed by Lynen and co-workers [M. Grassl, G. Augsberg, E. Coy, and F. Lynen, *Biochem. Z.*, **337**, 35 (1963)]. We have not found a compound with such a structure among our products. Our product as isolated has a long alkyl side chain of about 17 carbon units, and in addition elemental analyses are consistent with a hexosamine grouping in the molecule. We have reason to believe that this hexosamine unit, if it is indeed that, is attached to the long alkyl side chain. The nitrogen of this extra group is bound to iron. So we isolate a compound in which there is one pyridine ligand and one nitrogenous ligand of another type.

MORRISON: Is that other nitrogenous group covalently bound to the heme?

CAUGHEY: All our evidence would point to that, yes. It is covalently bound to the heme and bound as a ligand to the iron.

KING: In relation to this question, perhaps the pyridine extraction method of Dr. Caughey is more mild. However, recently Dr. Takemori and I used the acid-acetone extraction with our modifications, and we have demonstrated a functional activity of heme $a$. In other words, we don't think heme $a$ is grossly altered as far as the functional activity is concerned. (See the discussion on pp. 736–737 of Volume Two.)

ORGEL: I should like to run through the elementary theory of the electronic structure of oxygen, but it is convenient to start with a brief description of nitrogen. The usual chemist's formula shows two nitrogen atoms joined by a triple bond. The electronic interpretation of this formula is shown in the diagram. Two of the ten valence electrons form a $\sigma$-bond, and four form two unshared $\sigma$-pairs; the

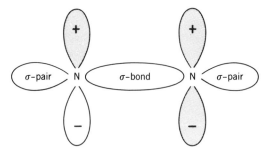

remaining four electrons go into the two $\pi$ orbitals. In the diagram only one of these is shown (shaded); there is another, identical in shape, at right angles to it.

You will notice that the upper lobes of the $\pi$ orbitals are both marked with a + sign. This indicates that the orbital is bonding; the two $\pi$-bonding orbitals each containing two electrons are responsible for two of the three bonds between the nitrogen atoms.

Now the $\pi$ orbitals on the nitrogen atoms can be combined to form a molecular orbital in a different way:

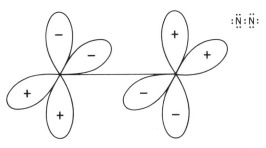

Here I have included both components in the diagram. An orbital of this kind is antibonding, and electrons in it tend to push the bonded atoms apart. In nitrogen this antibonding orbital is empty, but in oxygen it must contain the extra two electrons. Note that there are only two extra electrons, but there is room for four in the two components of the $\pi$-antibonding orbital. A rule of quantum mechanics covers this situation and tells us that one electron goes into each component orbital and that the spins remain parallel. The differences between nitrogen and oxygen are due to the presence of these two unpaired electrons in the antibonding orbital.

The presence of two antibonding electrons has at least four important consequences:

(*a*) The bond is weakened and is perhaps best represented as a double bond, or more correctly as a one and two-halves bond.

(*b*) The molecule is in a triplet state; this is important in connection with the kinetics of reactions involving oxygen. Reactions converting a triplet system to a singlet are often abnormally slow.

(*c*) The antibonding $\pi$ orbital forms a reservoir for electrons; for example, the ions $O_2^-$ and $O_2^{2-}$ are well known in superoxides and peroxides. Recently the $O_2^+$ ion has been obtained as a salt, $O_2^+PtF_6^-$.

(*d*) The antibonding electrons are rather loosely held and are the ones most easily used in further bonding. Since they are on the "side" of the molecule, this favors sideways-on bonding of the type suggested by Griffith for oxyhemoglobin and more recently discovered in a number of simple transition-metal complexes and peroxides.

NICHOLLS: I'd like to ask both Dr. Orgel and Dr. Ingraham whether they believe that the CO complex of the iron has a similar structure to the oxygen complex and, if not, why the visible absorption spectra are so similar.

ORGEL: First of all, only psychologically do I believe that they are the same. I don't believe that they are the same structurally. Why then are the visible spectra the same if the geometrical structure is different? Well, I don't see any reason to believe that there should be a strong correlation between geometrical structure and absorption spectra. I think that there should be a strong correlation between electronic structure and absorption spectrum, but that the same sort of electronic structure may be consistent with two different geometric structures. This is just what happens in the case of oxygen; it is a good acceptor sideways-on and that gives the same sort of electronic structure that you get with CO end-on.

NICHOLLS: I think that the question can still be asked of Dr. Ingraham because he proposed an ion somewhat in a ferric state, which would imply different electronic structure as well as geometrical.

INGRAHAM: We are implying different electronic structures. I think that there certainly must be strong $\pi$-electron donations from iron to CO, much as there is from iron to oxygen. It is very likely that the CO complex is linear, whereas this doesn't have to have the same structure as the oxygen.

ESTABROOK: I should like to ask Dr. Ingraham whether Dr. Perutz has done x-ray crystallography of oxyhemoglobin and, if so, whether he can tell from this the orientation of the oxygen to the plane of the heme in the iron.

INGRAHAM: I have looked over Perutz's article in *Nature* about oxyhemoglobin, and I see no mention of the actual oxygen-iron structure.

CHANCE: Stryer, Kendrew, and Watson report [*J. Molecular Biol.*, **8**, 96 (1964)] on the azide compound, where indeed the orientation is most accurately determined.

INGRAHAM: What is the azide-iron structure?

CHANCE: Figure 1 is from the article of Stryer, Kendrew, and Watson. The

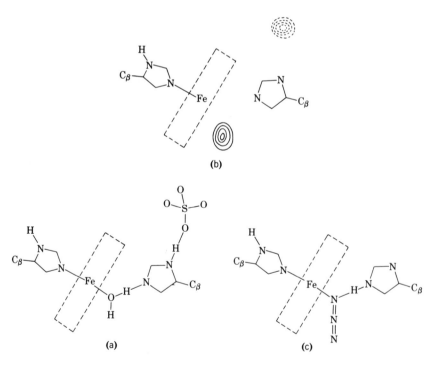

**Fig. 1**   [Reproduced from *J. Molecular Biol.*, **8**, 96 (1964) by permission].

angle between the plane of the heme and the direction of the hydrazoic acid right above the angle and intercepted by the small letter $c$ is $111°$.

INGRAHAM: The angle $B$ would be about $70°$, very similar to the $A_3$ structure. I haven't thought enough about azide to know whether that should be the same as oxygen or not.

ORGEL: I really don't know. This is a matter of a detailed and difficult computation. I don't really see how one can expect to know intuitively which of these structures would be more stable to 2 or 3 kcal.

CHANCE: Surely the hemoglobin can distinguish between azide and oxygen even if we can't.

ROSENBERG: Dr. Orgel, if one more electron is put into the antibonding orbitals of the oxygen molecule, can you say anything about what would happen to the next electron coming in?

ORGEL: Well, this is a question that has to be considered rather carefully. I think that we can say two different things: one if we are dealing with an isolated oxygen molecule in a gas phase and a quite different sort of thing if we are dealing with oxygen in a condensed phase—for example, a crystal or an aqueous solution. Now I suppose that for oxygen in the gas phase there is no reasonable doubt that it is much harder for the second electron than the first. There is no doubt also that the first-electron affinity of the oxygen molecule will be positive, and I suspect that the second-electron affinity will be either negative, zero, or positive, very slightly positive. But it is a very different matter indeed when you consider the oxygen molecule in an aqueous environment or an ionic crystal, and this again seems to me to be a detailed quantitative problem which you can't make any great generalizations about. However, it does seem to be true—and I think that this is mainly what you are getting at—that the $O_2^-$ tends to disproportionate into $O_2^{2-}$ fairly rapidly. It is easier to isolate compounds containing $O_2^{2-}$ than those with $O_2^-$ for many but not all of the alkali metals. The answer is that it depends on the environment in the gas phase, where the first electron goes easily, the second one with difficulty. In a crystal or aqueous solution the environment could alter that, and it could happen that it would be much easier to put the two on, thermodynamically. But the intermediate might be readily reduced.

ROSENBERG: The reason I asked the question was that I recently came across some evidence that in zinc oxide there can be electron traps which are positively charged and double positively charged. It is more difficult for the electron to get in if there is a double positive charge than a single positive charge. The suggestion was made that this has to do not so much with the increased depth of the trap as with the fact that the Coulomb barrier begins to get very narrow so that tunneling into the trap occurs much more readily the stronger the charge repulsion is. It seems to me that whereas that suggestion ordinarily would be somewhat difficult to understand, the same thing may be true here in the case of the oxygen.

ORGEL: Yes, but I hate to have to distinguish carefully between effects which are essentially kinetic and those which are essentially thermodynamic. What you have just described is the kinetic evidence as to how easily an electron can get into a trap, but this doesn't reveal too much about the equilibrium situation which tells you how many traps are filled with electrons. These are two quite different things. The kinetics might behave differently from the thermodynamics, so that you could have a trap being stable but filling slowly, or a trap being relatively unstable but nontheless filling rapidly.

CAUGHEY: The significance of drawing an analogy between the type of bonding between histidine and azide in myoglobin as suggested by the x-ray studies and possible function of this so-called distal-histidine and oxygen in oxygen binding is certainly of interest. There is also an interesting finding by Perutz and co-workers which suggests that no change in distance between iron and the distal-histidine occurs upon oxygenation. Thus the distal-histidine in hemoglobin appears to be in just the right position to hydrogen-bond with oxygen upon oxygenation, with the hemoglobin molecule undergoing kinetical structural change in the sense proposed for hydrogen bonding with azide in the case of myoglobin. Unfortunately the crystal structure of oxymyoglobin is not yet available.

# Mechanisms of Oxygen Uptake:
# The Autoxidation of Myoglobin
# and of Reduced Cyanocobaltates
# and Their Significance to Oxidase Reactions

... M. E. WINFIELD

## I. INTRODUCTION

Material drawn from studies of the action of $O_2$ on myoglobin (1), of $H_2O_2$ on metmyoglobin (2), and of free radicals formed by oxidation of amino acids and peptides (3, 4) is used to derive the probable mechanism of myoglobin autoxidation. Several of the reactions described are indicative of the types of processes we should expect to find in the functioning of hemoprotein oxidases and peroxidases. By use of certain of the reaction types, a possible mechanism is deduced for the reduction of $O_2$ to water in the presence of cytochrome oxidase. Our knowledge of the peroxo complexes which can be formed by reaction of $O_2$ with $[Co^{2+}(CN)_5]^{3-}$ (5), or $[HCo^{3+}(CN)_5]^{3-}$ (6), provides information on how hydrolysis of the peroxide intermediate in the oxidase mechanism can be avoided.

## II. MYOGLOBIN AUTOXIDATION

### A. Rate Equation

The symbols $Mb^{2+}$, $Mb^{2+}O_2$, $Mb^{3+}$, and $Mb^{4+}$ are used to denote, respectively, myoglobin, oxymyoglobin, metmyoglobin, and ferrylmyoglobin. The amino acid units phenylalanine, tyrosine, dopa, and the free radicals formed from them by removal of a hydrogen atom are referred to as p, t, d, and ṗ, ṫ, ḋ, respectively. An internal phenylalanine unit near the iron atom of the hemoprotein is referred to as $p_i$, whereas one on the exterior or periphery of the protein is designated as $p_e$.

From the kinetics of myoglobin autoxidation described by George and Stratmann (1) it is clear that both $Mb^{2+}$ and $Mb^{2+}O_2$ enter into the autoxidation mechanism, and also that 2–3 times as much $O_2$ is taken up as can be accounted for by oxidation of the iron atoms to the ferric state. Long ago, Lemberg and others had realized that part of the protein must enter into the process, as well as the iron (7). But which part, and how, could not be studied until the structure of the protein in the vicinity of the iron atom was known and a technique was available for distinguishing between the seven kinds of amino acids close to the metal.

In an earlier paper (2) King and I showed that peroxide brought near the iron of $Mb^{3+}$ reacts rapidly with the metal atom while almost simultaneously extracting a hydrogen atom from a nearby amino acid, to give a free radical. Also, we demonstrated that oxygen uptake occurred by addition of $O_2$ to the free radical. If the stoichiometry of $O_2$ absorption during $Mb^{2+}$ autoxidation, the participation of $Mb^{2+}O_2$, and the net removal of one electron from the iron atom are kept in mind, it is clear that the autoxidation is a chain reaction in which most of the oxygen uptake occurs by direct addition of $O_2$ to an amino acid free radical, and that the oxygenated product is able to generate another free radical capable of reacting with $O_2$. From the stoichiometry it is concluded that each cycle which increases by one the number of ferric protein molecules present, generates on the average nearly three free radicals that combine with $O_2$.

**Chain Initiation.** Because of the high electronegativity of oxygen, the group $Fe^{2+}$—$O$=$O$ in $Mb^{2+}O_2$ is to be regarded as usually electron accepting during collisions with other protein molecules; it is less likely to act as electron donor than is $Mb^{2+}$. The main significance of the latter to the kinetics is that $Mb^{3+}$ (the product whose rate of formation is being measured) can be formed by removal of an electron from the iron atom of non-oxygenated $Mb^{2+}$. For chain initiation there is no alternative to the $Fe^{2+}$—$O$=$O$ group as the reaction site. Studies of the one-equivalent oxidation of $Mb^{3+}$ and of amino acids indicate that the first-formed free radical will be $\dot{p}$, and that the most stable radical which can be formed in the vicinity of the iron atom is $\dot{t}$ (3, 4). If initiation is intramolecular, the resulting oxidation state of the iron is necessarily ferric, and there is no obvious alternative to the reaction

$$p_i Fe^{2+}\text{—}O\text{=}O \rightarrow t_i Fe^{3+} \qquad (1)$$
$$(Mb^{2+}O_2)$$

That there are no stable intermediates is made apparent by writing the likely reaction sequence, e.g.,

$$Fe^{2+}\text{—}O\text{=}O \qquad H \quad \rightarrow \quad \left[ Fe^{3+}\text{—}O\text{—}OH \qquad \cdot \quad \right] \qquad (2)$$

$$\left[ \text{Fe}^{3+}\text{—O—OH} \quad \cdot \right] \rightarrow \left[ \text{Fe}^{4+}\!\!=\!\!\text{O} \quad \text{H—O} \right] \tag{3}$$

$$\left[ \text{Fe}^{4+}\!\!=\!\!\text{O} \quad \text{H—O} \right] \rightarrow \text{Fe}^{3+}\text{—OH} \quad \overset{\cdot}{\text{O}} \tag{4}$$

It will be seen later that intermolecular chain initiation is not in harmony with the over-all kinetics of myoglobin autoxidation.

**Propagation.** Chain propagation will be considered under three conditions of oxygen pressure. At "very low" pressures the concentration of dissolved $O_2$ is much less than the concentration of $MbO_2$. Any oxygen which adds to a free radical is therefore taken to be oxygen attached to $Mb^{2+}$. The only propagation reactions would then be steps by which the free-radical site migrates from the interior to the exterior of the protein molecule, and thence to the exterior of a second molecule, i.e.,

$$\dot{t}_i\text{Fe}^{3+} \rightleftharpoons \dot{t}_e\text{Fe}^{3+} \tag{5}$$

and the bimolecular processes

$$\dot{t}_i\text{Fe}^{3+} + t_e\text{Fe}^{2+} \overset{*}{\rightleftharpoons} t_i\text{Fe}^{3+} + \dot{t}_e\text{Fe}^{2+} \tag{6}$$

$$\dot{t}_e\text{Fe}^{3+} + t_e\text{Fe}^{2+} \rightleftharpoons t_e\text{Fe}^{3+} + \dot{t}_e\text{Fe}^{2+} \tag{7}$$

At "low" pressures (approximately 0.1–4 mm Hg partial pressure of $O_2$) equilibrium 5 could well be influenced by dissolved $O_2$ which penetrates within the protein molecules, addding to free-radical carbon atoms and thus altering the rate at which radical transfer occurs. On the one hand the greater stability of the oxygenated radical could slow migration, while on the other hand the larger size of the amino acid radical which results could increase the frequency of collision with hydrogen atoms of nearby amino acid residues. The second-order propagation is therefore a combination of equilibria 6 and 7 and

$$O_2 + \dot{t}_e\text{Fe}^{3+} \rightleftharpoons \dot{O}Ot_e\text{Fe}^{3+} \tag{8}$$

$$\dot{O}Ot_e\text{Fe}^{3+} + t_e\text{Fe}^{2+} \rightarrow \dot{d}_e\text{Fe}^{3+} + d_e\text{Fe}^{2+} \tag{9}$$

* This reaction is possible only if a peripheral tyrosine unit can penetrate to the vicinity of the iron atom of another protein molecule. Kendrew's (8) tyrosine residue HC-3 has the appropriate location.

and

$$O_2 + \dot{t}_iFe^{3+} \rightleftharpoons \dot{O}Ot_iFe^{3+} \tag{10}$$

$$\dot{O}Ot_iFe^{3+} + t_eFe^{2+} \rightarrow \dot{d}_iFe^{3+} + d_eFe^{2+} \tag{11}$$

accompanied by a smaller amount of reaction 12,

$$\dot{O}Ot_iFe^{3+} + t_eFe^{2+} \rightarrow d_iFe^{4+} + d_eFe^{2+} \tag{12}$$

The latter is in effect a propagation, because the reversion of $d_iFe^{4+}$ to the ferric state must proceed via a free-radical intermediate.

At "high" pressures the amount of unoxygenated $Mb^{2+}$ present is negligible. In reactions 9 and 11, $Mb^{2+}$ is entirely replaced by $MbO_2$. Reactions 6 and 7 are likely to be less important than 8, 9, 10, and 11.

**Termination.** Termination of the radical chains at "very low" pressures may be represented by

$$\dot{t}_eFe^{3+} + \dot{t}_eFe^{3+} \longrightarrow t_eFe^{3+} + d_eFe^{3+} \tag{13}$$

$$p_iFe^{2+} + \dot{t}_eFe^{3+} \longrightarrow p_iFe^{3+} + t_eFe^{3+} \tag{14}$$

$$\dot{t}_iFe^{3+} + t_eFe^{2+} \xrightarrow{\;\;*\;\;} t_iFe^{2+} + d_eFe^{2+} \tag{15}$$

During autoxidation the concentration of free radicals is too low to permit appreciable contribution by mechanism 13, even though a mechanism of this type appears to be involved in the loss of free radicals during oxidation of $Mb^{3+}$ by $H_2O_2$ (2). Considerably lower still is the probability of collisions favorable to those termination reactions in which an externally located free radical of one molecule penetrates to the vicinity of an internal free radical of a second protein molecule.

At "low" oxygen pressures the following reaction will be important as well as reactions 14 and 15:

$$\dot{t}_iFe^{3+} + t_eFe^{2+}\!-\!O\!=\!O \rightarrow t_iFe^{3+} + d_eFe^{2+}\!-\!O\!=\!O \tag{16}$$

That is, $Mb^{2+}$ and $Mb^{2+}O_2$ are regarded as equally satisfactory hydrogen donors in the type 15 reaction.

At "high" pressures the free radical which is to undergo the termination reaction is largely $\dot{d}_iFe^{3+}$:

$$\dot{d}_iFe^{3+} + t_eFe^{2+}\!-\!O\!=\!O \rightarrow d_iFe^{2+} + d_eFe^{2+}\!-\!O\!=\!O$$

---

* A protruding $t_e$ of $Mb^{2+}$ penetrates through the surface of the molecule $\dot{t}_iFe^{3+}$ to the vicinity of the iron atom and its neighboring free radical. As a result of reaction 6, the invading $t_e$ becomes a free radical, which is expected to have a high probability of losing a hydrogen atom to $Fe^{3+}$, since such a process would be irreversible as well as thermodynamically favored. It will be seen later that a reaction of this kind is required to satisfy the observed kinetics of myoglobin autoxidation.

The concentration of $Mb^{2+}$ is so low that reaction 14 becomes negligible. It is possible that $MbO_2$ can act in a type 14 reaction, but more slowly than does $Mb^{2+}$:

$$p_iFe^{2+}\!-\!O\!=\!O + \dot{d}_eFe^{3+} \xrightarrow{-O_2} p_iFe^{3+} + d_eFe^{3+}$$

**Low-Pressure Kinetics.** In kinetic studies of myoglobin autoxidation the rate of disappearance of iron which is in the ferrous state has been measured as a function of time, over the range of oxygen pressures from 0.3 to 760 mm Hg (1). At "low" pressures the rate proves to be proportional to

$$[M^{2+}]\alpha(1 - \alpha)$$

where $[M^{2+}]$ = the concentration of total ferrous iron;

$[M^{2+}]\alpha$ = the concentration of ferrous iron which is present in the free form;

$[M^{2+}](1 - \alpha)$ = the concentration of the ferrous iron which is present as $Mb^{2+}O_2$.

In an analysis of the kinetics, George and Stratmann (1) point out that in all probability the rate equation contains $[M^{2+}]$ in the denominator, thus accounting for the apparent first-order behavior, in spite of the implication of both $Mb^{2+}$ and $Mb^{2+}O_2$ as reactants. In other words, the rate equation is expected to be of the form

$$\frac{-d[M^{2+}]}{dt} = \frac{const. \; [Mb^{2+}] \cdot [Mb^{2+}O_2]}{f[M^{2+}]}$$

The presence of $[M^{2+}]$ in the denominator is reasonably interpreted to indicate the influence of a reaction involving $M^{2+}$ which causes an increase rather than a decrease in $[M^{2+}]$.

A rate expression of the appropriate form is obtained if we choose the following set of reactions as having the principal influence on the rate of disappearance of ferrous iron:

$$p_iFe^{2+}O_2 \xrightarrow{k_1} \dot{t}_iFe^{3+} \tag{1}$$

$$(Mb^{2+}O_2)$$

$$\dot{t}_iFe^{3+} \underset{}{\overset{K}{\rightleftharpoons}} \dot{t}_eFe^{3+} \tag{5}$$

$$p_iFe^{2+} + \dot{t}_eFe^{3+} \xrightarrow{k_3} p_iFe^{3+} + t_eFe^{3+} \tag{14}$$

$$(Mb^{2+})$$

$$\dot{t}_iFe^{3+} + t_eFe^{2+} \xrightarrow{k_4} \dot{t}_iFe^{2+} + d_eFe^{2+} \tag{15, 16}$$

$$(M^{2+})$$

where $k_1$, $k_3$, and $k_4$ are the rate constants of reactions 1, 14, 15, and 16, while $K$ is the equilibrium constant for reaction 5. It will first be assumed that the rate of attainment of equilibrium in reaction 5 is sufficiently high that, under steady-state conditions of autoxidation, near equilibrium prevails for this reaction. In reaction 15, 16 either of the ferrous forms of the protein may participate, while in reaction 14 the non-oxygenated form is required, and in 1 the oxygenated.

If $r_1$, $r_3$, and $r_4$ are the rates of the steps 1, 14, 15, 16 in the steady state, we have

$$\frac{-d[M^{2+}]}{dt} = r_1 + r_3 - r_4$$

Since the rate of formation of free radicals is equal to the rate of loss,

$$r_1 = r_3 + r_4$$

$$= k_3[Mb^{2+}] \cdot [t_eFe^{3+}] + \frac{k_4[M^{2+}][t_eFe^{3+}]}{K}$$

$$\therefore [t_eFe^{3+}] = \frac{r_1}{k_3[Mb^{2+}] + \frac{k_4}{K}[M^{2+}]}$$

Putting $k_4/K = k_5$,

$$\frac{-d[M^{2+}]}{dt} = 2r_3$$

$$= \frac{2k_3[Mb^{2+}]k_1[MbO_2]}{k_3[Mb^{2+}] + k_5[M^{2+}]}$$

i.e.,

$$\text{Rate} = \frac{2k_1k_3[M^{2+}]\alpha(1-\alpha)}{k_3\alpha + k_5} \tag{17}$$

It can now be seen that intermolecular initiation would lead to second-order autoxidation rates (i.e., the rate equation would contain $[M^{2+}]^2$ in the numerator), which would be contrary to the observed behavior (1).

To test the suitability of expression 17 for describing the experimental results of George and Stratmann (1) it is rewritten, using $k_{obs}$ to represent their first-order rate constant:

$$k_{obs} = \frac{2k_1k_3\alpha(1-\alpha)}{k_3\alpha + k_5} \tag{18}$$

A plot of $(1-\alpha)/k_{obs}$ against $1/\alpha$ is shown in Fig. 1. From the intercept and the slope of the straight line obtained we have

$$k_1 = 1.85 \text{ hr}^{-1}, \quad \frac{k_5}{k_3} = 0.78$$

Since $k_3$ and $k_5$ are of comparable value, neither of the terms in the denominator of expression 18 can be neglected (except at "high" oxygen pressures, but different reactions then govern the rate, as already indicated).

A more detailed description of autoxidation, accounting for all oxygen uptake, results in a kinetic scheme little different from the set of reactions 1, 5, 14, and 15, 16. The resulting rate equation is unchanged.

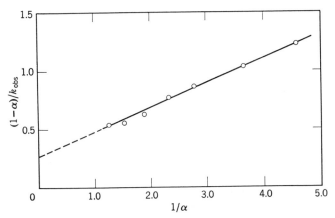

**Fig. 1.** Experimental results of George and Stratmann (1) for the net rate of metmyoglobin formation during autoxidation of myoglobin, replotted according to rate equation 18.

## B. Alternative Rate Equations

If equilibrium 5 is assumed to be slow of attainment, the rate equation for autoxidation becomes

$$\frac{-d[M^{2+}]}{dt} = \frac{2k_1[M^{2+}]\alpha(1-\alpha)}{\alpha + \dfrac{Ak_4[M^{2+}]\alpha^2}{k_2'(1-\alpha)}}$$

which cannot describe the observed kinetics $\left( k_2' \right.$ is the rate constant of the reaction

$$t_iFe^{3+} + O_2 \rightarrow d_eFe^{3+}$$

and $A$ is a constant given by

$$A = \left. \frac{[MbO_2]}{[O_2][Mb^{2+}]} \right).$$

Several other alternative rate equations have been derived, making use of reactions 1, 5, 8, 9, 10, 11, 14, 15, 16. None fits the experimental results as well as does equation 17. Reaction 6 can be important only at very low oxygen pressures, since $O_2$ can reach the vicinity of the iron atom, and therefore of the nearby free radical, with ease. In reaction 7 there is even readier access of the oxygen to the free radical, which is external. Neither process would have an influence on the kinetics which have been observed. Reaction 12, occurring as an alternative to reaction 11, makes little difference to the over-all kinetic scheme, since $Fe^{4+}$ should function in much the same way as $\dot{d}_i$ in subsequent reactions.

## C. Significance of the Autoxidation Mechanism

That reaction 5 is reversible and relatively rapid indicates ready electron transport, to a $\dot{p}$ or $\dot{t}$ unit which is near the iron atom, from a related amino acid unit at the periphery of the molecule. Achievement of the equilibrium by means of the sterically difficult bimolecular process 6 is unlikely to be rapid.

It seems necessary to accept the occurrence of reaction 15, 16, in spite of the stringent steric requirements. The same over-all result cannot be achieved without penetration by part of one protein molecule into the region near the iron atom of a second molecule.

Reduction of the ferric ion by a free radical should be kept in mind as a possible step in certain oxygenase reactions. The insertion of an amino acid unit of a hemoprotein molecule into the restricted space near the heme of another molecule suggests a way in which cytochrome molecules may interact.

## III. AUTOXIDATION OF CYANO COMPLEXES OF COBALT

Combination of $O_2$ with the metal atom of a coordination complex can be envisaged in the following ways:

$$M + O_2 \qquad\qquad \rightarrow M\text{—}O\text{=}O \tag{19}$$

$$M + O_2 \qquad\qquad \begin{array}{c} \rightarrow \\ M \cdots \| \\ O \end{array} \overset{O}{} \tag{20}$$

$$M + O_2 \qquad\qquad \rightarrow M\text{—}O\text{—}\dot{O} \tag{21}$$

$$M^- + O_2 \qquad\qquad \rightarrow M\text{—}O\text{—}O^- \tag{22}$$

$$M\text{—}R + O_2 \qquad\qquad \rightarrow M\text{—}O\text{—}O\text{—}R \tag{23}$$

$$M + O_2 + M \qquad\qquad \rightarrow M\text{—}O\text{—}O\text{—}M \tag{24}$$

$$M + O_2 + M \qquad\qquad \rightarrow M \overset{O}{\underset{O}{\diamond}} M \tag{25}$$

$$M\text{—}O\text{—}O\text{—}M + O_2 \qquad \rightarrow M\text{—}O\text{—}\dot{O} + M\text{—}O\text{—}\dot{O} \tag{26}$$

in which M represents the metal ion in one of its common reduced states (e.g., $Fe^{2+}$) while $M^-$ is an uncommon, highly reduced state (e.g., $Fe^{1+}$ or $Fe^0$). R is an anionic ligand such as $H^-$.

Experimental evidence for the occurrence of mechanism 24 has been obtained by Haim and Wilmarth (10) and by Bayston, Beale, King, and Winfield (5), for mechanism 26 by Bayston, Looney, and Winfield (11), and for mechanism 23 by Bayston and Winfield (6), by studying $O_2$ uptake by $[Co^{2+}(CN)_5]^{3-}$, $[(CN)_5Co^{3+}-O-O-Co^{3+}(CN)_5]^{6-}$, and $[(CN)_5Co^{3+}H]^{3-}$, respectively.

The product of the type 23 reaction is the hydroperoxo complex, $[(CN)_5Co^{3+}OOH]^{3-}$, which has a p$K$ of 12 (for dissociation of the proton). It hydrolyzes at an appreciable rate at 0° at neutral pH, and rapidly at pH 5.

The dinuclear peroxo complex obtained in the type 24 reaction is $[(CN)_5Co^{3+}-O-O-Co^{3+}(CN)_5]^{6-}$, which is stable in strongly alkaline solution. It hydrolyzes via its conjugate acid at a pH value 4–5 units higher than that for hydrolysis of the mononuclear hydroperoxide at the same rate (6).

$$[(CN)_5Co^{3+}-O-O-Co^{3+}(CN)_5]^{6-} \underset{}{\overset{+H^+}{\rightleftharpoons}}$$

$$\left[ \begin{array}{c} \qquad\qquad H \\ \qquad\qquad \backslash \\ \qquad\qquad O-Co^{3+}(CN)_5 \\ \qquad\qquad / \\ (CN)_5Co^{3+}-O \end{array} \right]^{5-}$$

$$\left[ \begin{array}{c} H \\ \backslash \\ O-Co^{3+}(CN)_5 \\ / \\ (CN)_5Co^{3+}-O \end{array} \right]^{5-} \xrightarrow{+H_2O} \left[ \begin{array}{c} OH \\ / \\ (CN)_5Co^{3+}-O \end{array} \right]^{3-} + [H_2OCo^{3+}(CN)_5]^{2-}$$

The considerable change in absorption spectrum and reactivity (6, 5) when a proton adds to $[(CN)_5Co^{3+}-O-O-Co^{3+}(CN)_5]^{6-}$ suggests that protonation involves loss of the linear peroxo bridge, with its greater resonance possibilities.

Since the very strong reductant $[Co^{2+}(CN)_5]^{3-}$ will not reduce the binuclear peroxo complex in 1 $M$ aqueous KOH, but will do so readily under mildly alkaline conditions (5, 10), it is concluded that the conjugate acid is the reactive species in reduction as well as in hydrolysis.

The type 26 reaction is rare, and in the one instance studied it required strongly alkaline conditions (11). It cannot occur simultaneously with reaction 24 (i.e., while any M ions remain unreacted) but can account for a second phase of $O_2$ uptake.

Under mildly alkaline conditions (or neutral or acid conditions if hydrolysis could be circumvented), $[(CN)_5Co^{3+}—O—O—Co^{3+}(CN)_3]^{6-}$ is oxidized by $O_2$ to the much more stable peroxo complex written

$$[(CN)_5Co^{3+}—O—O—Co^{4+}(CN)_5]^{5-}$$
or
$$[(CN)_5Co^{3+}—O—\dot{O}—Co^{3+}(CN)_5]^{5-}$$

which resists hydrolysis even in strongly acid solution. The p$K$ for proton uptake is probably near 1. Addition of the proton requires bending of the peroxo bridge and consequent loss of a large amount of resonance energy [ESR spectrometry shows that the unpaired electron spends time at each of the oxygen and cobalt atoms (11)].

It has been pointed out (6) that reduction of a hydroperoxo or peroxo complex, without appreciable hydrolysis to $H_2O_2$, should be possible if electrons are supplied rapidly and if the pH of the environment is little less than the p$K$ of the conjugate acid of the complex to be reduced. In oxidases in which $O_2$ is reduced to water, we may expect to find devices for feeding electrons to the oxygen atoms in quick succession, for preventing the local pH from rising too high for rapid reduction, and for promoting the rupture of the O-O bond.


## IV. MODE OF ACTION OF CYTOCHROME OXIDASE

### A. Copper-free System

**Hypothetical Mechanism.**   The cytochrome oxidase of *Pseudomonas* apparently consists of an *a*-type cytochrome permanently linked to cytochrome *c* (12). Copper ions are not required (12). From a considerable body of information it is evident that $O_2$ combines with cytochrome $a_2$, and that four reducing equivalents supplied by cytochrome *c* convert the first-formed oxygen complex to water via a hydroperoxo complex. The over-all result is

$$O_2 + 4e + 4H^+ \rightarrow 2H_2O$$

with no detected liberation of peroxide except under certain abnormal conditions (12, 6). The reduction of $O_2$ to a hydroperoxo complex is taken to be analogous to that shown for myoglobin autoxidations:

$$Fe^{2+} + O_2 \xrightarrow{+H} Fe^{3+}—O—OH$$

Studies of the oxidation of $Mb^{3+}$ by $H_2O_2$ indicate that, when $H_2O_2$ approaches the iron atom, there is rapid peroxide decomposition, provided that a phenylalanine type of amino acid unit is close enough to readily donate a hydrogen atom. The metal atom is regarded as initiating the breaking of the O-O bond, the process being facilitated by addition of $\dot{H}$ to the $O\dot{H}$ which is splitting off. In cytochrome oxidase, we may consider that once $O_2$ has taken up two reducing equivalents the resulting hydroperoxo complex will have a very short lifetime in the presence of the iron atom and a conveniently placed hydrogen donor.

In a previous hypothesis for the mode of action of cytochrome oxidase all four electrons needed for the reduction of $O_2$ were fed in via the iron atom (13). It is now suggested that there is less likelihood of $H_2O_2$ being formed if the splitting of the O-O bond is effected by the simultaneous supply of an electron and a proton in the form of a hydrogen atom, rather than by first providing a proton to give the conjugate acid which is susceptible to reduction by an electron. In effect an electron from cytochrome $c$, and a proton from the solvent, are assembled on the phenyl group of the donor amino acid unit to form a hydrogen atom which is ready to be added to the —OH of the hydroperoxide without "waiting" for an electron to be supplied via the metal ion.

Next we wish to know whether hydrogen atom donation by a phenyl group is also involved during formation of the hydroperoxide, as in the autoxidation of myoglobin. The number of reducing equivalents supplied as hydrogen atoms, per molecule of $O_2$ reduced to water, is likely to be equal to the number of phosphorylations (14). This is believed to be two (15) for mammalian cytochrome oxidase and is taken to be the same for *Pseudomonas*. It is assumed therefore that one hydrogen atom is donated by the protein during hydroperoxide formation and one atom during its decomposition.

The complete reaction mechanism can now be written as follows:

$$Fe^{2+} \quad d \quad d \quad O{=}O{-}Fe^{2+} \longrightarrow Fe^{2+} \quad d \quad \dot{d} \quad HOO{-}Fe^{3+}$$

$$\downarrow \begin{array}{l} +2e \\ +H^+ \end{array}$$

$$Fe^{2+} \quad d \quad \dot{d} \quad HO{-}Fe^{3+} \xleftarrow[-H_2O]{+H^+} Fe^{2+} \quad d \quad d \quad HOO{-}Fe^{2+}$$

$$\downarrow \begin{array}{l} +2e \\ +2H^+ \end{array}$$

$$Fe^{2+} \quad d \quad d \quad H_2O{-}Fe^{2+}$$

The hypothetical arrangement which permits electrons to be fed toward oxygen via the iron atom of cytochrome $a_2$, and hydrogen atoms via an aromatic amino acid unit, is shown in more detail in Fig. 2. A description of the means by which electrons may pass from the iron atom of cytochrome $c$, via a largely conjugated system of oxidized amino acids, to the heme of cytochrome $a_2$ is given elsewhere (14).

**Structure of the Hydrogen-Donating Amino Acid of Cytochrome c.** At the end where it approaches $O_2$, the electron-transport pathway is taken to be as oxidized as it is possible for a polypeptide to be in the presence of $H_2O_2$, within limits imposed by steric effects. The long sequence of reactions by

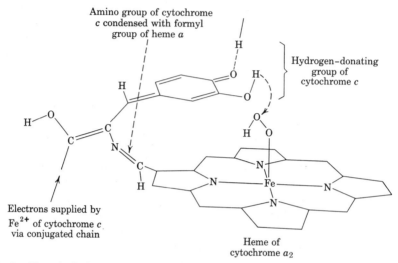

**Fig. 2.** Hypothetical structure near the heme $a_2$ of *Pseudomonas* cytochrome oxidase. A conjugated aromatic amino acid unit of cytochrome *c* is shown as the hydrogen donor which participates in the reduction of the peroxo complex of cytochrome $a_2$.

which "free" tyrosine can be progressively oxidized (16) will apply for two or three 2-equivalent steps, at most, if the tyrosine is bonded to other amino acids. When the steric restraints imposed by neighboring amino acid units prevent indole formation, the oxidation of dopaquinone must take place thus:

If the tyrosine unit we have been considering is linked by a conjugated group to a second tyrosine, the oxidation will not necessarily proceed via dopaquinone (14). The product could retain one or more phenolic groups, e.g., structure III:

(III)

which is the hydrogen donor shown in part in Fig. 2.

To recapitulate, as an electron passes from cytochrome $b$ toward $O_2$, it moves along a progressively more conjugated path, because the environment becomes increasingly dehydrogenated. Since the supply of electrons from the cytochrome $b$ end of the chain is unlikely to be continuous, any phenylalanine, tyrosine, or tryptophan near heme $a_2$ is expected to be oxidized at least as far as it can be oxidized by ferricytochrome $a_2$. To what extent hydrogenation of the products will occur on resumption of the supply of electrons has not yet been determined. Preliminary oxidation-reduction experiments with amino acids and peptides suggest that the equilibrium situation may correspond to the oxidizing potential of dopaquinone.

**Additional Notes on the Mechanism.** It is clear from what has been said about the need to reduce Fe—OOH before it can be hydrolyzed that there must be no delay in supplying electrons once the hydroperoxo complex has been formed. We may assume therefore that cytochrome $c$ is chemically bonded to cytochrome $a_2$ not far from its active site, so that electron transfer does not have to await an appropriate collision between the two cytochromes. On the same grounds, we may deduce that the free energy of activation for electron transport must be small. For this reason $Fe^{3+}$—OOH is shown receiving an electron into the iron atom before peroxide decomposition begins.

To avoid ferryl ion formation during peroxide decomposition, and to increase the speed of the decomposition, it is necessary to supply reducing equivalents to both ends of the hydroperoxide. To do so requires the electron-transport path from the iron atom to cytochrome $c$ to be attached to the heme of cytochrome $a_2$ while a hydrogen donor attached to the same pathway is held near the Fe—OOH group.

## B. Mammalian Cytochrome Oxidase

In the mammalian enzyme there is one atom of copper per heme (excluding loosely held copper), and all bonds between cytochromes $c$ and $a$ are weak

(17, 12). The copper is so difficult to remove that it has not been possible to determine whether it is an essential component of the catalyst proper or its role is that of a promoter. The properties of copper compounds which seem to have a bearing on the problem are as follows:

(*a*) Copper forms stronger complexes with α-amino acids than do most other metals (18). The structures are usually of type IV.

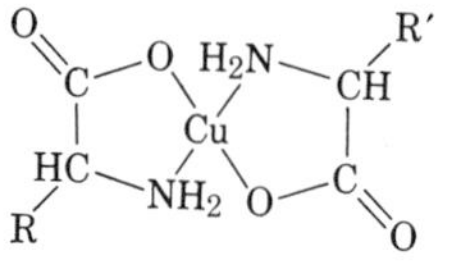

(IV)

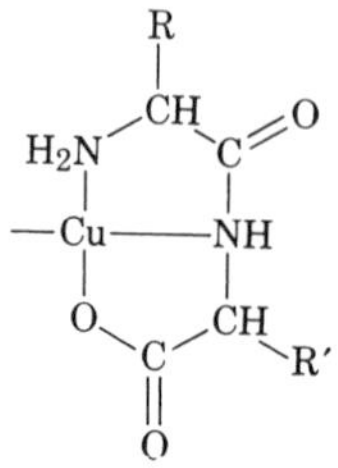

(V)

(*b*) Tridentate copper complexes are known whose analogs within a protein would have structures of type V.

(*c*) Complexes of $Cu^{1+}$ are tetrahedral; those of $Cu^{2+}$ are usually planar but can be tetrahedral.

(*d*) Copper promotes the decomposition of $H_2O_2$, which is catalyzed by ferric ion. Kremer (19) has shown that the promotion is related to the decomposition of one of the intermediates in the catalysis. He suggests that approach of the $Cu^{2+}$ ion to $Fe^{3+}$—O—OH facilitates the movement of charge away from the iron atom, resulting in detachment of OH—$Cu^{2+}$ from the binuclear complex $Fe^{3+}$—O—OH—$Cu^{2+}$. No change in valance of the copper ion is required.

The most obvious conclusion to be drawn regarding the role of copper in mammalian cytochrome oxidase is that the copper ion takes over part of the function of the hydrogen donor which we have shown participating in the reduction of $O_2$ by *Pseudomonas* cytochrome oxidase. The scheme on p. 129, which is only one of several which could be written, illustrates the kinds of dinuclear peroxo complex which could occur in biological autoxidations and their expected behavior.

The copper atom is assumed to be held in three of its four coordination positions by cytochrome *a* or $a_3$ or both, with its fourth position available for bonding to —OOH, which can receive electrons from cytochrome *c* via cytochrome *a*. Although all reducing equivalents are supplied to $O_2$ via heme *a*, hydrolysis is limited by the effect of copper in straightening the bonds to oxygen and in facilitating rupture of the O—O bond. Other canonical forms of structure VII are $Fe^{3+}$—Ȯ—O—$Cu^{2+}$, $Fe^{4+}$—O—O—$Cu^{2+}$, and $Fe^{3+}$—O—O—$Cu^{3+}$; and of VIII are $Fe^{2+}$—Ȯ—O—$Cu^{2+}$, $Fe^{3+}$—O—O—$Cu^{2+}$, $Fe^{3+}$—O—Ȯ—$Cu^{1+}$, and $Fe^{3+}$—Ȯ—O—$Cu^{1+}$. There is reason to believe that

$$\text{Fe}^{2+}\!\!-\!\text{O}\!\!=\!\!\text{O} \quad \text{Cu}^{2+} \quad \longrightarrow \quad \text{Fe}^{3+}\!\!-\!\text{O}\!\!-\!\dot{\text{O}}\!\!-\!\text{Cu}^{2+}$$
$$\text{(VI)} \qquad\qquad\qquad\qquad \text{(VII)}$$

$$\left[ \begin{array}{c} \text{H} \\ | \\ \text{O} \\ \text{Fe}^{2+} \diagdown \quad \diagup \text{Cu}^{2+} \\ \text{O} \\ \end{array} \right] \quad \xleftarrow[+\text{H}^+]{+e} \quad \text{Fe}^{2+}\!\!-\!\text{O}\!\!-\!\dot{\text{O}}\!\!-\!\text{Cu}^{2+}$$

(IX) (VIII)

with $+e,\ +\text{H}^+$ addition to (IX), and $+e$ from (VII) to (VIII).

$$\text{Fe}^{3+}\!\!-\!\text{O} \diagup^{\text{H}} \quad \text{O}\!\!-\!\text{Cu}^{2+} \quad \xleftarrow[-\text{H}_2\text{O}]{+e,\ +2\text{H}^+} \quad \text{Fe}^{2+}\!\!-\!\text{O} \diagup^{\text{H}} \diagdown_{\text{H}} \quad \text{Cu}^{2+}$$

the resonance-stabilized (electron-deficient) peroxo complexes will be resistant to hydrolysis. Thus it is not until complex IX is formed that the danger of hydrolysis becomes pronounced. If the third electron addition is made quickly, little or no $H_2O_2$ should result.

Okunuki's oxygenated mammalian cytochrome oxidase (12) could be a mixture of forms VI and VII. If the equilibrium favors the latter, its ESR signal may show informative hyperfine structure. As judged from experience with cobalt peroxo complexes, the temperature for detection of maximum hyperfine structure could well be critical, possibly in the range 0 to —15° (11). Detection of complex IX may be difficult because the contribution of canonical forms other than $Fe^{3+}$—O—O—$Cu^{2+}$ is expected to be small.

Both Okunuki (12) and Morrison et al. (20) have demonstrated that the firmly bound copper can change its valence state, but there does not appear to be complete proof that a valance change is necessary to the mechanism in vivo. There is little doubt that the efficiency of peroxide decomposition can be increased by donation of an electron to the peroxide by the copper ion.


## V. SUMMARY

A mechanism is described for the autoxidation of myoglobin, based on the known kinetics, interpreted with the aid of recent studies of amino acid free radicals and of metmyoglobin oxidation. From the nature of two of the principal steps it is concluded that the following apparently improbable mode of interaction between cytochrome molecules should be considered seriously. A protruding aromatic amino acid unit (e.g., tyrosine) of one cytochrome molecule is inserted into a cavity near the heme of a second protein molecule. The aromatic group can donate a hydrogen atom to the ferriheme of the second protein molecule and can then receive an electron (via the polypeptide of which it is part) from a related amino acid unit which is close to the heme of the first cytochrome molecule.

It is suggested that hemoprotein enzymes which deal with peroxides (e.g., peroxidase, and cytochrome oxidase in the latter half of $O_2$ reduction) generally act as follows: the iron atom initiates peroxide decomposition; it is aided by a nearby aromatic group which donates a hydrogen atom to the decomposing peroxide; the aromatic group, now a free radical, withdraws an electron from a more remote aromatic group, to which it is connected by a largely conjugated system of double bonds; the more remote group is appropriately situated for interaction with the substrate, from which it removes a hydrogen atom. In the highly oxidizing environment near the iron atom we may expect to find at least one aromatic amino acid unit which is more unsaturated than is common in other proteins. The unsaturation could facilitate electron transport from substrate to heme.

On the basis of the reactions of myoglobin and the chemistry of $O_2$ reduction by cyanocobaltates, a mechanism is proposed for the action of cytochrome oxidase.

## REFERENCES

1. P. George and C. J. Stratmann, *Biochem. J.*, **51**, 418 (1952).
2. N. K. King and M. E. Winfield, *J. Biol. Chem.*, **238**, 1520 (1963).
3. N. K. King, F. D. Looney, and M. E. Winfield, *Biochim. et Biophys. Acta*, **88**, 235 (1964).
4. N. K. King, F. D. Looney, and M. E. Winfield (to be published).
5. J. H. Bayston, R. N. Beale, N. K. King, and M. E. Winfield, *Australian J. Chem.*, **16**, 954 (1963).
6. J. H. Bayston and M. E. Winfield, *J. Catalysis*, **3**, 123 (1964).
7. R. Lemberg and J. W. Legge, *Hematin Compounds and Bile Pigments*, Interscience, New York, 1949, p. 395.
8. J. C. Kendrew, *Sci. American*, **205**, 96 (1961).
9. N. K. King, unpublished work.
10. A. Haim and W. K. Wilmarth, *J. Am. Chem. Soc.*, **83**, 509 (1961).
11. J. H. Bayston, F. D. Looney, and M. E. Winfield, *Australian J. Chem.*, **16**, 557 (1963).
12. K. Okunuki, in O. Hayaishi, Ed., *Oxygenases*, Academic Press, New York, 1962, p. 409.
13. N. K. King, and M. E. Winfield, *Australian J. Chem.*, **12**, 47 (1959).
14. M. E. Winfield (to be published).
15. J. D. Judah, *Biochem. J.*, **49**, 271 (1951).
16. J. C. Wertz, D. C. Reitz, and F. Dravnieks, in M. S. Blois, Jr., H. W. Brown, R. M. Lemmon, R. O. Lindblom, and M. Weissbluth, Eds., *Free Radicals in Biological Systems*, Academic Press, New York, 1961, p. 183.
17. B. Eichel, W. W. Wainio, P. Person, and S. Cooperstein, *J. Biol. Chem.*, **183**, 89 (1950).
18. J. C. Bailar, Jr., and D. H. Busch, in J. C. Bailar, Jr., and D. H. Busch, Eds., *The Chemistry of Coordination Compounds*, Reinhold, New York, 1956, p. 37.
19. M. L. Kremer, *J. Catalysis*, **1**, 351 (1962).
20. M. Morrison, S. Horie, and H. S. Mason, *J. Biol. Chem.*, **238**, 2220 (1963).

# Mechanisms of Aromatic Hydroxylation and Ring-Opening Reactions

... R. O. C. NORMAN and J. R. LINDSAY SMITH

## I. INTRODUCTION

Both the hydroxylation and the ring cleavage of aromatic compounds are of widespread occurrence in nature, whereas such processes are relatively uncommon in the laboratory and are of little value in synthesis. Nevertheless, a number of chemical systems which bring about these reactions are now known, together in some cases with detailed information about their mechanisms. It is our purpose in this paper to discuss these reactions with particular respect to their mechanisms in the hope that the conclusions may help to throw light on the natures of the corresponding biological processes.

## II. AROMATIC HYDROXYLATION

### A. Fenton's Reagent

The best-known and most extensively studied system which brings about the hydroxylation of aromatic compounds is Fenton's reagent, which consists of ferrous ion and hydrogen peroxide. The system is complex, but there is now strong evidence that the hydroxylating species is the hydroxyl radical, ·OH.

Haber and Weiss (1) suggested that the ferrous ion-catalyzed decomposition of hydrogen peroxide is described by equations 1–4:

$$Fe^{2+} + H_2O_2 \rightarrow Fe^{3+} + \cdot OH + OH^- \tag{1}$$

$$\cdot OH + Fe^{2+} \rightarrow OH^- + Fe^{3+} \tag{2}$$

$$\cdot OH + H_2O_2 \rightarrow H_2O + \cdot O_2H \tag{3}$$

$$\cdot O_2H + H_2O_2 \rightarrow O_2 + H_2O + \cdot OH \tag{4}$$

Later, it was concluded (2) that equation 4 plays no part in the process, and equations 5 and 6 were introduced to account for the ferric ion-catalyzed decomposition of the peroxide:

$$Fe^{3+} + H_2O_2 \rightarrow Fe^{2+} + \cdot O_2H + H^+ \qquad (5)$$

$$\cdot O_2H + Fe^{3+} \rightarrow O_2 + H^+ + Fe^{2+} \qquad (6)$$

The essential feature of the modified scheme is that the metal ion takes part in one-electron redox changes with the production of free radicals; and, although it has been suggested as a result of $^{18}O$-fractionation experiments that the main pathway involves two-electron transfers (3), there is strong evidence for the intermediacy of radicals in the reactions of Fenton's reagent with organic compounds.

(i) The system initiates a radical-chain polymerization (4).

(ii) Biphenyl and bibenzyl, which are among the oxidation products of benzene and toluene, respectively (5, 6), are typical products of free-radical dimerization.

(iii) Radicals are observed by electron spin resonance (ESR) spectroscopy when ferrous ion, EDTA, and hydrogen peroxide interact either alone or in the presence of various organic compounds (7).

(iv) The isomer distributions of the phenolic products obtained by the oxidation of monosubstituted benzenes (8) can be understood in terms of homolytic reactions (see below).

The conclusion in (iv) that aromatic hydroxylations by Fenton's reagent are effected by a radical raises the question or whether this is the hydroxyl ($\cdot OH$) or perhydroxyl ($\cdot O_2H$) radical, for according to the modified Haber-Weiss mechanism both are intermediates. The following evidence is relevant.

(i) The ratios of the amounts of the nuclear-substituted phenolic products obtained from the reactions of anisole, fluorobenzene, and benzoic acid with Fenton's reagent are similar to those obtained when the attacking radicals are generated by the irradiation of hydrogen peroxide, indicating that there is a common hydroxylating entity (8, 9). Hydroxyl radicals are likely to participate in the latter reaction.

(ii) The interaction of ceric ion with hydrogen peroxide is reported to give the perhydroxyl radical (10), identified by ESR spectroscopy (11), whereas the hydroxyl radical is not formed because of the weak reducing power of cerous ion. We have found this system to have a negligible effect in oxidizing benzene.

(iii) The hydroxyl radical has been observed by ESR spectroscopy during the decomposition of hydrogen peroxide by titanous ion (12), and this system hydroxylates chlorobenzene, fluorobenzene (6), and anisole in a manner essentially similar to that of Fenton's reagent. It is therefore concluded that aromatic hydroxylation by Fenton's reagent is brought about by $\cdot OH$ and that $\cdot O_2H$, if present, is either destroyed too rapidly by further oxidation or is much less reactive than ·OH toward aromatic carbon, just as it is less reactive toward olefinic monomers (2).

Two possible ways in which an aromatic compound may react with ·OH are the hydrogen-exchange process, equation 7, and the addition-elimination process, equation 8.

$$H_2O + Ar\cdot \xrightarrow{\ \cdot OH\ } ArOH \qquad (7)$$

$$\cdot OH + Ar{-}H$$

$$Ar \xrightarrow{\quad} ArOH + (H\cdot) \qquad (8)$$

Evidence that the latter path is followed is derived from the finding that there is no isotope effect when benzene and hexadeuterobenzene are oxidized with Fenton's reagent (6). Moreover, the radical (I) has been identified by ESR spectroscopy as an intermediate during the oxidation of benzene by the titanous-peroxide system (13), and there is also evidence for the intermediacy of (I) in the radiolysis of benzene-water mixtures (14). Studies have shown (6) that (I) gives phenol by further oxidation by a second radical, ferric ion, or oxygen, and that biphenyl is formed by the dimerization of (I)

(I)

and subsequent dehydration.

Fenton's reagent has been employed for the hydroxylation of both benzenoid (5, 6, 15) and heteroaromatic (16) compounds. Much of the earlier work was of a qualitative or semiquantitative nature, but spectrophotometric and gas chromatographic techniques (17) are in many cases suitable for the accurate estimation of isomeric phenols. We have investigated the hydroxylation of four monosubstituted benzenes, using Fenton's reagent in aqueous acetone, in the presence of EDTA, a phosphate buffer, and ascorbic acid (8). The isomer distributions (Table 1) were determined by gas chromatography and infrared spectrophotometry, and the problem of further oxidation was avoided by keeping the extent of hydroxylation low: no dihydroxy products were detected.

The conditions used in this work represent a modification of Fenton's system, but the nature of the attacking agent is unaltered, for anisole gives the same isomer distribution when hydroxylated in the absence of EDTA, ascorbic acid, and acetone. EDTA increases the efficiency of the hydroxylation, and a study of the oxidation of benzoic acid (15) has shown that a ratio of $Fe^{2+}$ to EDTA of 1:1 provides the optimum conditions. Ascorbic acid also increases the yield, and in the oxidation of quinoline (18) both the extent of conversion of quinoline and the amount of 3-hydroxyquinoline formed are increased about fivefold by the addition of ascorbic acid. This has been attributed to the fact that ascorbic acid regenerates ferrous ions by the reduction of the ferric ions formed.

TABLE 1

Hydroxylation of Benzenoid Compounds by Fenton's Reagent

| Compound | Isomer Distribution, % | | |
|---|---|---|---|
| | $o$ | $m$ | $p$ |
| Anisole | 84 | ... | 16 |
| Chlorobenzene | 42 | 29 | 29 |
| Fluorobenzene | 37 | 18 | 45 |
| Nitrobenzene | 24 | 30 | 46 |

The results in Table 1 are characteristic of homolytic aromatic substitutions (19) in that, with the exception of the products from anisole, the distribution of isomers is relatively unspecific. There are, nevertheless, marked differences between this pattern and that for the homolytic phenylation of the same compounds. For example, nitrobenzene in the latter reaction gives the three nitrobiphenyls (20) in the ratio $o:m:p = 62.5:9.8:27.7$, and the corresponding ratio for anisole (21) is 67:18:15. Now, the relative reactivities for benzenoid compounds toward ·OH, determined (8) under the same conditions as the results in Table 1, are:

$$\text{Ph—OMe} : \text{Ph—H} : \text{Ph—Cl} : \text{Ph—NO}_2$$
$$\phantom{xx}6.35 \phantom{xxxxx} 1 \phantom{xxxxx} 0.55 \phantom{xxxxx} 0.14$$

This order is different from that for phenylation, for most monosubstituted benzenes are more reactive than benzene toward the free phenyl radical, regardless of the polar properties of the substituent (22); it is in fact the same as that in typical electrophilic substitutions, although the *spread* of reactivities in the latter reactions is usually far greater (23). Both the reactivity order and the pattern of products are consistent with the view (8) that the hydroxyl radical has *electrophilic character*.

Other examples of this phenomenon are known. For example, electron-releasing substituents accelerate, and electron-withdrawing substituents retard, the rate of the free-radical side-chain chlorination of substituted toluenes, and this has been attributed to the fact that, because the attacking

atom (Cl·) is strongly electronegative, ionic canonicals of type (II) contribute
to the transition state (24). The effect of (II) in lowering the energy of the

$$X-\langle\bigcirc\rangle-\overset{+}{C}H_2\ \overset{\cdot}{H}\ Cl^-$$

(II)

transition state is determined by the polar character of X, being greater when
X is electron-releasing than when it is electron-withdrawing. Evidence has
been obtained that the hydroxyl radical displays electrophilic character in its
reactions with both styrenes (25) and saturated aliphatic compounds (26).

It is therefore understandable that the order of reactivities of benzenoid
compounds toward ·OH is the same as that toward electrophiles. The
predominance of *ortho*-substitution in the hydroxylation of anisole can be
ascribed to the importance of the ionic structure (III) in determining the
energy of the transition state (III–V, etc.) for the rate-determining step. The
analogous structure for *para*-substitution involves greater separation of unlike
charges, while for *meta*-substitution there is no such contributing canonical.
It is likewise reasonable that nitrobenzene should give a higher proportion of
the *meta*-derivative with ·OH than with the phenyl radical, just as it does with
the electron-deficient *p*-chlorophenyl and *p*-nitrophenyl radicals (27).

Attention has been focused on the electrophilic characteristics of the
hydroxyl radical because of the possible relevance of the general principle
to biological hydroxylations. It has been noted that the patterns of phenolic
metabolites derived from benzenoid compounds foreign to animal organisms
are in general non-specific and characteristic of free-radical processes, but
certain results, such as the exclusive hydroxylation of acetanilide by a microsomal system in the *ortho*- and *para*-positions (28, 29), have led to the
suggestion that an electrophile such as $OH^+$ may be involved (30). The
results for the hydroxyl radical show that the two sets of observations are
compatible: if an oxygen-containing free radical is responsible for biological
hydroxylation, it may be expected to show some of the discriminating properties of an electrophile.

Finally, the isomer distribution in the hydroxylation of anisole is the same,
within the limits of accuracy of the measurements, when cuprous ion is used
instead of ferrous ion (8), and for chlorobenzene, fluorobenzene (6), and
anisole the distribution is essentially the same when titanous ion is used

instead of ferrous ion. We conclude that the attacking hydroxyl radical is *free* and not complexed with a metal ion, for in the latter event different metals would be expected to give hydroxylating entities of different selectivity.

In summary, the evidence indicates that the hydroxylation of aromatic compounds by Fenton's reagent is brought about by the free hydroxyl radical, that this radical shows some of the discriminating power of an electrophile, and that reaction occurs through the formation of an adduct of this radical with the benzene ring.

## B. Peracids

It has long been known that aromatic compounds are oxidized by peracids, but because oxidation usually proceeds to quinones it has not always been recognized that the first reaction is a hydroxylation. For example, several phenols and naphthols are oxidized by peracetic acid to *o*- and *p*-quinones (31). However, oxidation to the quinone level is not always complete, and in a study of the oxidation of *m*-xylene by trifluoroperacetic acid the 2,4- and 2,6-dihydroxy products were obtained in 15 and 35% yield, respectively, together with 20% of *m*-xyloquinone (32).

That these processes involve electrophilic attack on the ring was first suggested by Roitt and Waters (33), who observed that polycyclic aromatic hydrocarbons are oxidized by perbenzoic acid at their nucleophilic centers rather than at those which are most reactive to "double-bond" reagents, and their view has received confirmation (34). This fact can be attributed to the tendency of the peroxy bond to undergo heterolysis, the hydroxyl cation being the electrophilic reagent:

$$\text{R—CO—O—OH} \rightarrow \text{R—CO}_2^- + \text{OH}^+ \tag{9}$$

and would account for the greater effectiveness of trifluoroperacetic acid in comparison with other peracids in effecting these oxidations (32), since the trifluoroacetate ion is relatively stable. However, two aspects of the evidence must be considered. The first is that tracer experiments show that neither peracetic nor performic acid forms $\text{OH}^+$ to a detectable extent, even in acid solution (35), and it is therefore probable that the oxidations are initiated by nucleophilic displacement by the aromatic compound on an oxygen atom of the peracid, equation 10.

$$\text{ArH} \quad \text{O—OCOR} \rightarrow \text{Ar}\overset{+}{\underset{\text{OH}}{\big\langle}}\overset{\text{H}}{} \quad \xrightarrow{-\text{H}^+} \text{Ar—OH} \tag{10}$$

The second and more fundamental question is whether the peroxy bond undergoes heterolysis or homolysis in these reactions, for in the light of our findings about the behavior of the hydroxyl radical, the observations about the electrophilic nature of aromatic oxidation by peracids could be interpreted as well in terms of the reagent's being an *electrophilic* radical (i.e., ·OH) as of its being an *electrophile* (i.e., OH$^+$, or covalently bound hydroxyl from which OH is abstracted without its bonding pair). We have therefore determined the characteristics of trifluoroperacetic acid as an aromatic hydroxylating agent (36).

Isomer distributions and relative reactivities for the reactions of this peracid with three benzenoid compounds in methylene chloride solution are listed in Table 2. Since the introduction of one hydroxyl group activates the

### TABLE 2
**Isomer Distributions and Relative Reactivities for Hydroxylation by Trifluoroperacetic Acid**

| Substituent in PhX | Isomer Distribution, % | | | Reactivity Relative to Benzene |
|---|---|---|---|---|
| | *o* | *m* | *p* | |
| OMe | 73.7 | ... | 26.3 | 530 |
| Me | 78.2 | 2.3 | 19.5 | 11.7 |
| F | 17.2 | ... | 82.8 | 0.2 |

compounds toward further reaction, these values were obtained by extrapolating the results from experiments, using decreasing proportions of the peracid, to zero concentration of peracid.

The characteristics of trifluoroperacetic acid as a hydroxylating agent are clearly different from those of the hydroxyl radical. In particular, fluorobenzene gives an appreciable proportion of the *meta*-derivative with the hydroxyl radical, whereas this could not be detected with the peracid, and the spread of relative reactivities is far greater for the peracid than for the radical. In general, the results for the peracid fit well into the general pattern established for electrophiles of comparatively low selectivity (23).

Two other reactions of trifluoroperacetic acid are of particular interest. First, it effects the conversion of chalcone into the 3-hydroxyflavylium cation (VI), the product being isolated as its stannichloride in low yield (37), equation 11.

$$(11)$$

(VI)

Second, it has been used to bring about the oxidative cyclization of the

4-arylbut-1-ene compounds (VII; R = H and R = OMe) to the tetralols (VIII), equation 12 (36).

(12)

In each case, hydroxylation is accompanied by ring closure, thereby demonstrating the feasibility of these processes being concurrent in the biosynthesis of lanosterol from squalene, as suggested by Ruzicka (38).

### C. Hamilton's System

Hamilton and Friedman (39) have reported that anisole is hydroxylated to its *ortho-*, *meta-*, and *para*-derivatives (in the ratio 64:3:33) by hydrogen peroxide, in aqueous solution at pH 4, in the presence of catalytic quantities of ferric ion and catechol. Conversions are up to about 50% based on the hydrogen peroxide used, and quinol can replace catechol without much loss of efficiency. Initially, it was reported that the system fails to oxidize chlorobenzene, and since this compound is much less reactive than anisole toward electrophiles but is normally either weakly activated or not strongly deactivated toward radicals, it was suggested that the hydroxylating reagent is electrophilic. More recently, however, independent studies (40) have shown not only that chlorobenzene gives chlorophenols but also that the reagent is relatively unselective. Thus, we have found that anisole is less than twice as reactive as benzene, and chlorobenzene and benzene are of closely comparable reactivity. Neither this small selectivity nor the isomer distributions for chlorophenols ($o:m:p$ = 46:15:39), nitrophenols (30:41:29), and cresols (51:17:32) is consonant with the reagent's being electrophilic, but rather each is indicative of a radical reaction. The free hydroxyl cannot be responsible, since the pattern of phenolic products is different from that obtained with Fenton's reagent.

The following results of our investigations are relevant to the elucidation of the mechanism of hydroxylation by Hamilton's system. (i) Ferric ion can be replaced by ferrous or, less effectively, cupric ion. (ii) Oxygen cannot be substituted for hydrogen peroxide. (iii) Reaction is inhibited by EDTA. (iv) Catechol can be replaced by a number of phenols or enols, although in each case the hydroxylating efficiency is impaired. The following compounds are arranged in decreasing order of efficiency, as estimated by the conversion of toluene into the cresols (percentage conversion for the same reaction time in parentheses): catechol (11), quinol and 2,6-dihydroxynaphthalene (6–7), 3,4-dihydroxytoluene, 2,6-dimethoxyphenol, and pyrogallol (2.5–5), thiophenol and ascorbic acid (0.8), *p*-aminophenol and *p*-methoxyphenol (0.3–0.4), protocatechualdehyde and guaiacol (0.2). A possible explanation for the activity of the monophenols might be that these compounds are first hydroxylated, perhaps by a Fenton mechanism, to *ortho*- or *para*-diols, which then catalyze hydroxylation in a manner similar to catechol or quinol, but the fact that phenol and resorcinol are ineffective in the system while thiomesitol is effective argues against this speculation. The effective compounds all readily undergo one-electron oxidation, but the relative ease with which they do so is not correlated with their efficiencies as catalysts in this oxidation system.

In the light of these results, the following mechanistic scheme for hydroxylation is suggested:

$$Fe^{3+}(X)_x + zP \rightleftharpoons Fe^{3+}(X)_{x-y}(P)_z + yX$$

Complex I

Inactive oxidation products of P

$$Fe^{3+}(X)_{x-y}(P)_z \begin{cases} H_2O_2 + PhX \\ H_2O + PhX\text{—}OH \end{cases}$$

where X = any ligand, e.g., $H_2O$, $Cl^-$, other than a phenol; and P = the phenol or enol used as catalyst.

According to this scheme, the hydroxylating efficiency of a given system should depend on both the position of the first equilibrium and the effectiveness of complex I to take part in the cyclic hydroxylating step compared with its ease of oxidation to inactive products. Now, when guaiacol was used as the catalyst and the concentrations of ferric alum and guaiacol were varied, the yield of the cresols changed as follows:

| Experiment | Volume of Solution, ml | Yield, % |
| --- | --- | --- |
| 1 | 500 | 0.2 |
| 2 | 50 | 2.5 |
| 3 | 10 | 0.5 |

In the first two experiments guaiacol was detected in appreciable amounts at the end of the reaction, whereas in the third experiment it had been completely consumed.

These results are consistent with the proposed reaction scheme. In experiment 1, the low yield is attributed to the fact that guaiacol is a poor ligand for ferric ion, so that the first equilibrium is unfavorable. Increase in the concentration of both ferric and guaiacol moves the first equilibrium in the direction of complex I, and the yield is increased (experiment 2). The decrease in yield on further increase in concentration (experiment 3) is ascribed to the rapid oxidation of complex I to quinones before the hydrogen peroxide is added, and consistently with this view there was a fourfold increase in yield when, in the condition of experiment 3, the peroxide was added in one batch instead of over a period of 1 min. With catechol as catalyst, there was no detectable change in the yield when the volume of the solution was reduced from 500 to 100 ml. We conclude that complex I is essentially completely formed, even in the dilute solution, because catechol is a much better ligand than guaiacol for ferric ion. The inhibition of the catechol-catalyzed reaction by EDTA is then due to the displacement of the first equilibrium to the left by the EDTA ligands; and, in agreement with this, the characteristic green of the ferric-catechol complex is replaced by the pale yellow color of the ferric-EDTA complex.

The hydroxylation effected catalytically by complex I consists over-all of the reduction of hydrogen peroxide by the aromatic undergoing oxidation ($ArH + H_2O_2 \rightarrow ArOH + H_2O$), and apparently this reduction is facilitated by the ability of the catalyst to provide one electron which it subsequently regains. This donation may occur across a ferric bridge, to give in essence a complexed radical which reacts with the aromatic to give (IX), from which electron transfer regenerates the catalyst and yields the product. Possibly the formation and reaction of (IX) are concerted, thereby accounting both for the unselectivity of the hydroxylation (for radical-stabilizing influences within the aromatic would not then be involved) and for the non-formation of biphenyls, which would be expected if the adduct ·ArH(OH) became free (6). In the latter context, it has been established that such adducts are oxidized to phenols by ferric ion (6).

This mechanism may account for the fact that, e.g., protocatechualdehyde is far less effective than catechol in the hydroxylating system, although it forms a more stable complex with ferric ion, for the electron-attracting aldehydic group, by stabilizing the phenoxide ion from protocatechualdehyde relative to the corresponding radical, would render the initial electron transfer more difficult. The nature of the other ligands on ferric ion is also important: e.g., the replacement of alum by chloride in the conditions of experiment 2 causes a fourfold increase in the yield of cresols.

## D. Oxidation by Cupric-Amine-Oxygen

Phenol is oxidized by a system consisting of cupric ion, oxygen, and morpholine (MH) to the *ortho*-quinone derivative (X) (41). The induction period which precedes reaction has been traced to the necessity for hydrogen peroxide to be formed, and this brings about an initial hydroxylation for which equation 13 has been proposed. Subsequent oxidation of the catechol to o-quinone regenerates hydrogen peroxide, and nucleophilic attack by the amine and further oxidation lead to (X). Only cupric ion of the metal ions studied is effective in this oxidation, and this has been ascribed to the unique valence structure of the ion. The system may be regarded as a model for tyrosinase.

$$(13)$$

The mechanism for the hydroxylation, equation 13, has a formal similarity to that considered for Hamilton's system. Essentially, it is suggested that in both cases the high activation energy barrier for the reaction $ArH + H_2O_2 \rightarrow ArOH + H_2O$ is by-passed by incorporation of the transition metal ion which provides, in effect, a medium for electron flow.

## E. Udenfriend's and Related Systems

Udenfriend and his co-workers (42) found that aromatic compounds are hydroxylated by a system consisting of ferrous ion, EDTA, ascorbic acid, and oxygen. They reported also that oxygen can be replaced by hydrogen peroxide and suggested that oxygen is first reduced to hydrogen peroxide by ascorbic acid. It is then reasonable to suggest that hydroxylation is brought about by the hydroxyl radical which is formed by interaction of the hydrogen peroxide with ferrous ion (43). However, there are differences in the distribution of isomers when monosubstituted benzenes are hydroxylated by

Fenton's and Udenfriend's systems, so that hydroxyl radicals appear not to be involved in the latter (8).

Work in our laboratory has shown that Udenfriend's system is unexpectedly complex, and we shall therefore discuss first the simpler system in which ascorbic acid is omitted, together with the related system in which ferrous is replaced by titanous ion.

**Ascorbic Acid Omitted.**    Nofre *et al.* (44) showed that ascorbic acid is not essential for hydroxylation by Udenfriend's system. We have extended their work, and that of Dewhurst and Calcutt (45), by examining the isomer distributions of the phenolic products obtained when this system is used, with the aim of deriving evidence about the nature of the attacking reagent from its selectivity. Our investigations have revealed a surprising feature: the pattern of phenolic products varies markedly with the initial concentration of ferrous ion, and, in particular, the proportion of the *meta*-derivative formed by the three substrates we have so far studied (toluene, anisole, and fluorobenzene) increases with increase in ferrous ion concentration (e.g., for anisole, from 10 to 50%). One explanation might be that, on further oxidation (which becomes more important as $[Fe^{2+}]$ is increased), the *ortho*- and *para*-derivatives are preferentially removed, but there is strong evidence to the contrary which can be summarized as follows. (i) The isomer distribution from the hydroxylation of anisole did not vary significantly when increasing *amounts* (as opposed to *concentrations*) of ferrous sulfate were used. (ii) When the same concentrations of ferrous sulfate and EDTA were employed in two experiments, in one of which this solution was dripped slowly into aqueous anisole and in the second of which the entire solution was present initially, the yield of monohydroxylated products remained constant, but the proportion of the *meta*-derivative increased from 27 to 50%. We therefore conclude that at least two distinct hydroxylating mechanisms occur concurrently, one being more strongly dependent than the other on $[Fe^{2+}]$.

Further information was obtained by extrapolating the $o:m:p$ ratios obtained at various ferrous ion concentrations to zero $[Fe^{2+}]$ (e.g., Fig. 1). Similar experiments were carried out with titanous instead of ferrous ion. In every case a small amount of phenol was also formed.

If the reaction which predominates at low metal ion concentrations gave a hydroxylating intermediate, such as $HO_2 \cdot$, which was common to both ferrous and titanous ion systems, the extrapolated isomer distributions might be expected to be the same for the two systems. The distributions are sufficiently different, however, to suggest that, even at low metal ion concentrations, a metal ion is itself involved in the hydroxylating entity. Now, George (46) has shown that in perchloric acid the reaction of ferrous ion with oxygen, which leads to hydrogen peroxide, is second order in $[Fe^{2+}]$ and has suggested that this reaction consists of a rapid reaction between

### TABLE 3
**Extrapolated $o:m:p$ Ratios Obtained by Hydroxylation by Metal Ion-$O_2$**

| Substituent in PhX | Metal Ion | | | | | |
|---|---|---|---|---|---|---|
| | Ferrous-EDTA | | | Titanous | | |
| | Isomer Distribution, % | | | | | |
| | $o$ | $m$ | $p$ | $o$ | $m$ | $p$ |
| OMe | 56 | 8 | 36 | 54 | 0 | 46 |
| Me | 41 | 23 | 36 | 61 | 16 | 23 |
| F | 2 | 45 | 53 | 2 | 33 | 65 |

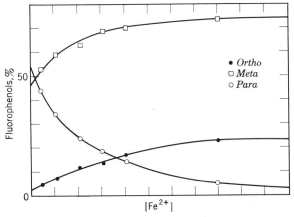

**Fig. 1.** Variation in distribution of fluorophenols with [$Fe^{2+}$].

ferrous ion and oxygen to give $Fe^{2+}O_2$, which then reacts slowly with a second ferrous ion, leading ultimately to the production of hydrogen peroxide. More recently, Hammond (47) has obtained evidence that the sequence

$$FeCl_2 \xrightarrow{O_2} Cl_2FeO_2 \xrightarrow{FeCl_2} Cl_2FeO_2FeCl_2 \longrightarrow 2Cl_2FeO \quad (14)$$

is followed in the oxidation of ferrous chloride with oxygen, and that both species, $Cl_2FeO$ and $Cl_2FeO_2$, are capable of bringing about oxidations of the type $DH_2 \rightarrow D$, where $DH_2$ may be, for example, an enediol.

It is therefore possible that, at low [$Fe^{2+}$] or [$Ti^{3+}$], the hydroxylating species is the complex $Fe^{2+}O_2$ or $Ti^{3+}O_2$, while at higher concentrations one or both of the species $Fe^{2+}O_2Fe^{2+}$ and $FeO^{2+}$ may also be involved. It is difficult, nevertheless, to account for the predominance of *meta*-substitution at higher metal ion concentrations, and we suggest tentatively that this arises from some form of complexing between the electron-rich *para-* (or *ortho-*) positions of the aromatic ring and the hydroxylating entity, followed by intramolecular transference of oxygen to the *meta*-position, as in equation 15:

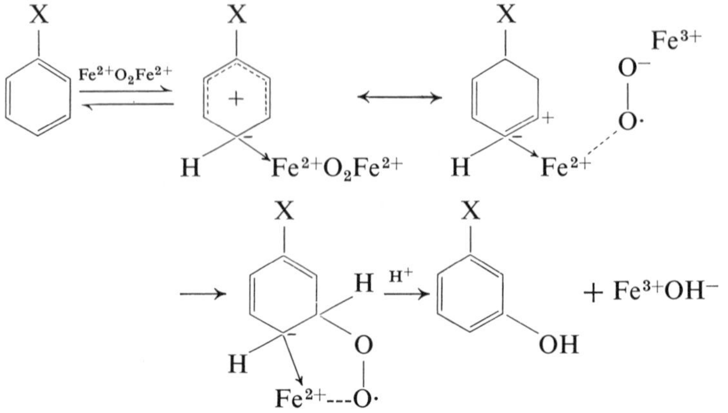

$$+ Fe^{3+}OH^-  \quad (15)$$

One other observation requires comment: even at very low metal ion concentrations, fluorobenzene, unlike toluene and anisole, gives a very high proportion of the *meta*-derivative (Table 3). Correspondingly, significant yields of catechol and quinol, but no resorcinol, are obtained, but these do not arise from further oxidation of phenol or *o*- and *p*-fluorophenol. We believe that these properties are related and that catechol and quinol arise from intermediates which might otherwise give *o*- and *p*-fluorophenol; e.g., for quinol:

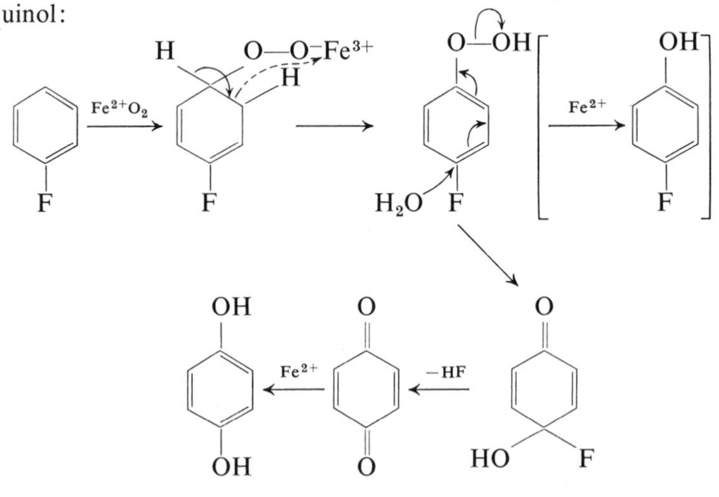

The formation of catechol could occur in a similar manner. This mechanism is analogous to that established for the acid-catalyzed rearrangement of N-phenylhydroxylamine. The unique property of fluorobenzene, according to this scheme, resides in the stability of fluoride ion as a leaving group.

**Ascorbic Acid Present.** The addition of ascorbic acid to the $Fe^{2+}$-$O_2$-EDTA system increases the hydroxylating efficiency (45), but its mode of operation is not clear. It has been suggested that its role is to reduce oxygen to hydrogen peroxide (18), but there is evidence that hydrogen peroxide is not an intermediate in the oxidation of either aromatic (8) or aliphatic (48) compounds by Udenfriend's system, although Grinstead (49) found that the addition of catalase to Udenfriend's system does partially inhibit hydroxylation. Another possible role for ascorbic acid is to regenerate ferrous ion by

### TABLE 4

Isomer Distributions Obtained with Udenfriend's System,
$[Fe^{2+}]:[EDTA]:[ascorbic acid] = 1:1:6$

| Substituent in PhX | Isomer Distribution, % | | |
|---|---|---|---|
| | $o$ | $m$ | $p$ |
| OMe | 46 | 22 | 32 |
| Me | 26 | 25 | 49 |
| F | 35 | 63 | 2 |

reducing the ferric ion formed (18). However, our studies (50) show that ascorbic acid functions in a more complicated manner: the pattern of hydroxylation effected by Udenfriend's system depends, for constant initial concentrations of the other components, on the concentration of ascorbic acid. For a 1:1 ratio of $[Fe^{2+}]$ and [EDTA], the pattern changes continuously with increase of [ascorbic acid] until this is present in greater than about sixfold excess; typical isomer distributions in these conditions are shown in Table 4.

These results indicate that the hydroxylating entity in Udenfriend's system is different from the entities present when ascorbic acid is omitted.

The role of EDTA in Udenfriend's system is probably to reduce the oxidation potential of the ferrous-ferric couple (49). Other complexing agents have been used in its place, but none is as effective. Some ligands, notably $F^-$ and $CN^-$, partially inhibit hydroxylation (51), while $o$-phenanthroline inhibits completely (45). The function of the metal ions is not well established. One report (45) asserts that ferric ion cannot replace ferrous ion, at least at 95°, but this is at variance with other research (42, 51), and it has been suggested (51) that ferric is the active species, reacting with ascorbic acid to give the semiquinone radical. We have found, however, that ferric ion, oxygen, and ascorbic acid in the absence of EDTA constitute a comparatively ineffectual oxidizing agent. Since in these conditions the autoxidation of ferrous to ferric ion occurs much less readily than when EDTA is present, we conclude that the active entity in hydroxylation by Udenfriend's system is derived from a ferrous ion-EDTA complex. The discovery (47) that $Cl_2FeO_2$ reacts with enediols leads us to suggest that the complex $Fe^{2+}O_2$ generates a hydroxylating entity by reacting with ascorbic acid. The following scheme is a possible representation, the salient features of which are that an initial electron flow from ascorbic acid through ferrous ion activates the complexed oxygen (XI) and that reversal of the direction of this electron movement (XII) leads to the ferryl ion, $FeO^{2+}$, which is known to oxidize ascorbic acid (47).

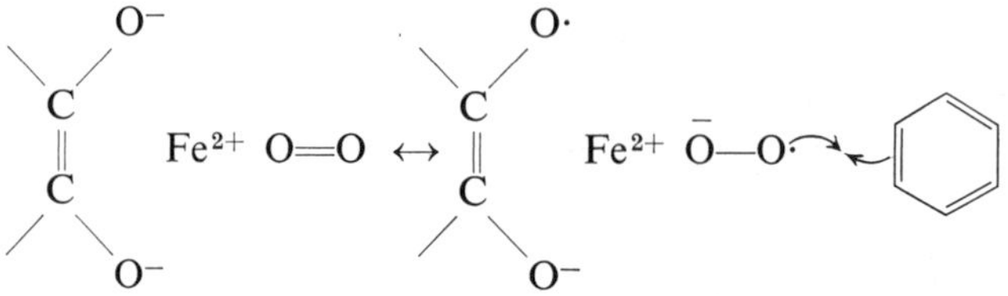

(XI)

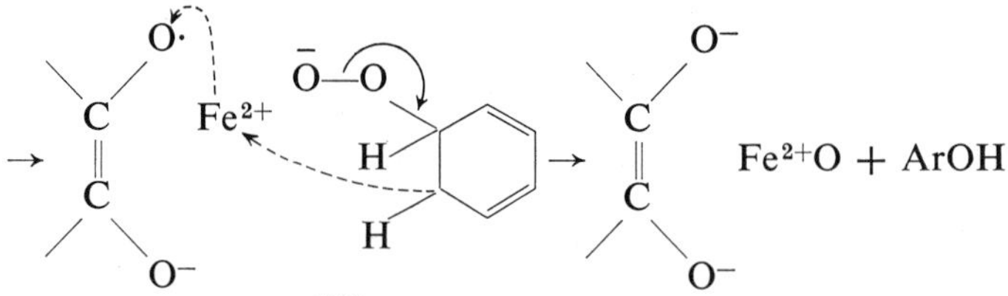

(XII)

An alternative mechanism has been put forward by Hamilton (52) in which the complex (XIII) undergoes cleavage to oxene, $:\overset{..}{O}:$, an analog of carbene, while at the same time ascorbic acid undergoes oxidation.

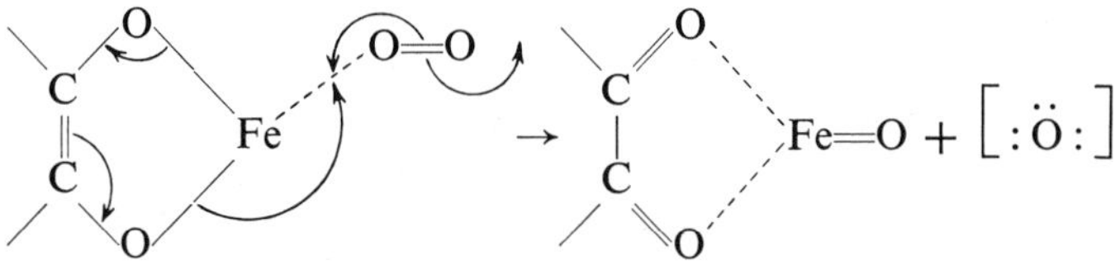

(XIII)

In support of this proposal it has been found that the system brings about the insertion reactions typical of carbene, such as the formation of cyclo-hexanol from cyclohexane and cyclohexene oxide from cyclohexene (48). This novel suggestion merits further examination, although the isomer distributions in hydroxylation by Udenfriend's system are difficult to account for in terms of oxene: thus, if this were to effect hydroxylation by epoxidation followed by hydrolysis, isomer ratios typical of those in electrophilic sub-stitution would be expected, while direct insertion into an aromatic C-H bond would probably be as unselective as the insertion of carbene.

## F. Summary

It is pertinent to summarize our discussion with particular reference to the facts at present available about the biological hydroxylation of aromatics. The *in vivo* processes fall into two groups: first, those which are part of established metabolic processes, of which the best known and most fully understood is the hydroxylation of L-phenylalanine to L-tyrosine (53, 54), and, second, those which occur with many aromatic compounds which are foreign to the organism.

The first group of processes have the following characteristics (55, 56):

(i) The source of the hydroxylic oxygen introduced is almost invariably molecular oxygen. One exception which has been documented is the hydroxylation of nicotinic acid to 6-hydroxynicotinic acid by *Pseudomonas fluorescens*, where the source of the hydroxylic oxygen is water (57), and this difference in behavior may be a result of the susceptibility of pyridine systems, unlike benzenes, to nucleophilic attack.

(ii) Transition metal ions, notably ferrous, have been implicated in many cases.

(iii) An electron donor is required: e.g., DPNH is essential for the hydroxylation of imidazoleacetic acid by *Pseudomonas*.

The same generalities appear to apply also to the second group of hydroxylations. Thus, in the liver microsomal hydroxylating system (28) molecular oxygen is incorporated into the phenol, TPNH is required, and ferrous ions are involved (55). This group differs from the first primarily in that the hydroxylations are less positionally specific: whereas, for example, the enzymatic oxidation of L-phenylalanine yields specifically L-tyrosine, most "foreign" monosubstituted benzenes yield all three monohydroxylated derivatives.

Of the chemical reactions which we have discussed, Udenfriend's system clearly comes nearest to being a suitable model for the biological processes: it requires molecular oxygen, utilizes an electron donor (ascorbic acid), and involves a transition metal ion. Moreover, we note the following further points:

(i) Ascorbic acid may be replaced by a pteridine derivative (48) of basically similar type to that established as the cofactor for phenylalanine hydroxylase (54). In this respect it is also of interest that aromatic hydroxylation is brought about by $FMNH_2$ and oxygen, even in the absence of added ferrous ion (58); this may be of significance in connection with the finding that FAD is essential for the activity of the hydroxylase obtained from a soil bacterium which converts salicylate into catechol (59).

(ii) The reaction of Udenfriend's system with monosubstituted benzenes leads invariably to the formation, *inter alia*, of phenol, paralleling our finding that, for example, anisole gives phenol in the rat and the cat. It is particularly interesting that Udenfriend's reagent so readily leads to the displacement of fluorine from fluorobenzene, for 4-fluorophenylalanine is converted into tyrosine by phenylalanine hydroxylase (53).

(iii) Udenfriend's system effects the epoxidation of aliphatic compounds (48). Evidence is accumulating at present that certain biological hydroxylations occur via epoxides (60): e.g., naphthalene is converted into its 1,2-dihydrodiol in rat liver (61), and the enzymatic oxidation of kynurenic acid in the presence of oxygen and DPNH or TPNH gives the 7,8-dihydrodiol (62).

(iv) The variations of the positional selectivity of Udenfriend's reagent with the concentration of the individual components of that system noted in section IIE are of interest with respect to the finding that the *in vivo* selectivity in the hydroxylation of foreign compounds by animals depends on the age, sex, and species of the animal. If the *in vivo* process involves a system analogous to Udenfriend's, we should expect the isomer distribution of phenolic products to depend both on the structure of, for example, the electron donor and on the concentrations of the components in the immediate environment of the benzenoid compound undergoing reaction.

(v) Finally, the fact that the hydroxyl radical has been found to exhibit a quite marked positional selectivity indicates that the comparatively specific orientations observed for certain *in vivo* hydroxylations are by no means incompatible with the reagent's being a radical.

It is clear that a chemical hydroxylating reagent which utilizes atmospheric oxygen is a more suitable model for the biological processes than one which utilizes peroxide. On the other hand, since an electron donor is required by the *in vivo* systems, it is in principle possible that oxygen is first reduced to (formally) the peroxidic level. Certainly the observations which we have described above, both for the reagents which incorporate oxygen and those which involve peroxide, suggest that the function of the metal ion is to enable electrons more freely to move through a complexed system, and it is not possible at present to say whether or not the oxygen-utilizing systems achieve the peroxidic state before bonding to the aromatic takes place. Indeed, if the metal ion, the electron donor, the aromatic, and oxygen are all involved in the complex through which hydroxylation occurs, a concerted movement of electrons could lead to hydroxylation without the participation of any other discrete oxidation level.

## III. RING-OPENING REACTIONS

There have been comparatively few investigations of the mechanisms involved in the cleavage of benzenoid systems. Benzene itself can be split under fairly vigorous conditions, e.g., by catalytic oxidation in the vapor phase to maleic anhydride, and naphthalene can be opened by a molybdate-catalyzed reaction with hydrogen peroxide (63). Phenolic compounds can be cleaved under much milder conditions: e.g., phenol gives *cis,cis*-muconic acid with peracetic acid at room temperature (64), and since the well-studied biological ring openings involve phenols, discussion will be focused on these reactions.

The conversion of phenol into *cis,cis*-muconic acid might be expected to proceed via catechol and *o*-benzoquinone, equation 16. It was originally argued that catechol is not an intermediate in the peracetic acid oxidation, since catechol is oxidized to *cis,cis*-muconic acid in lower yield than phenol (65), but this deduction may be discounted in the light of our finding that catechol reacts with the next intermediate, *o*-benzoquinone, to divert it from further oxidation with ring cleavage (66). This diversion is more significant when catechol is the substrate than when phenol is used, for in the latter case the stationary-state concentration of catechol is likely to be small. There is evidence, in fact, of the occurrence of an intermediate between phenol and the *o*-quinone, and this is likely to be catechol in view of the known capacity of peracids to effect electrophilic hydroxylation.

$$\text{(16)}$$

$$\text{(17)}$$

The oxidation of catechol to *o*-benzoquinone by peracetic acid may well be a two-electron process, equation 17, but such oxidations can be brought about also by one-electron oxidizers: e.g., 3-aminocatechol and protocatechuic acid have been oxidized to the corresponding *o*-quinones with silver oxide (67, 68). The peracid oxidation of *o*-quinones to muconic acids may follow the path established for the cleavage of benzils (69), equation 18; R = alkyl or acyl.

$$\text{(18)}$$

The oxidation of 3-aminocatechols to 6-hydroxypicolinic acids may be effected in two stages: the first, oxidation to the *o*-quinone, is accomplished conveniently by silver oxide, and the second may be brought about by a peracid. The latter step probably involves cleavage to the *cis,cis*-muconic acid, which, after isomerization to the *trans,trans*-isomer, undergoes ring closure to the picolinic acid (67). These conversions resemble those involved in, e.g., the biological transformation of 3-hydroxyanthranilic acid to quinolinic, nicotinic, and picolinic acids, in that ring opening and ring closure are apparently involved in the conversion of benzenoid into pyridinoid systems (70).

Except for this resemblance, the oxidation of catechols to muconic acids described above is an unsatisfactory model for biological ring opening for two reasons. First, in all the cases in which the biological ring cleavage of phenols has so far been characterized by $^{18}O$ experiments, two atoms of molecular oxygen are incorporated into the substrate, and the enzymes may be classified as *oxygenases* (56). Thus, a model system in which the oxygen is introduced as a peroxy compound lacks one established characteristic of the enzymic system, although the latter may have the property of reducing molecular oxygen formally to the peroxide level before introducing it into the substrate. Second, in the conversion of catechol into *cis,cis*-muconic acid by pyrocatechase all attempts to detect *o*-benzoquinone as an intermediate have been unsuccessful (55, 71). These facts have led to the suggested mechanism for the pyrocatechase reaction shown in equation 19 (72).

$$(19)$$

Ferrous ion is present in the enzyme protein and may act as a carrier for the molecular oxygen (56). The above mechanism involves a spin conversion (oxygen being a triplet), and the function of the iron may be connected with this requirement.

Apart from the lack of direct evidence for the mechanism in equation 19, there is also no chemical analogy. We therefore suggest an alternative formulation, equation 20, based on two more firmly established *in vitro* reactions. The first step is written as an electrophilic attack by oxygen on the

$$(20)$$

activated aromatic by analogy with the mechanism for the aerial oxidation of resorcinol and orcinol (73). This leads to an intermediate which, by protropic shift, gives the same species as would be obtained by peroxide attack on *o*-benzoquinone, and this is then postulated to undergo cleavage in the manner established for benzils (69). Thus, the *o*-quinone is not an intermediate; in effect, the system (catechol + oxygen), which is at the same oxidation level as (*o*-quinone + peroxide), is reacting in the same way.

The asymmetric catechol oxidases such as protocatechuic oxygenase, which effects the transformation shown in equation 21, have no *in vitro* counterparts. Mechanistic discussion is necessarily speculative, but we call attention to the following.

$$\tag{21}$$

Many phenols give phenoxy radicals both with one-electron oxidizers (e.g., ferric ion) and in basic solution in the presence of oxygen. These are delocalized species, the unpaired spin being associated with the *ortho*- and *para*-carbons as well as with oxygen, and subsequent reaction usually occurs at carbon. For a highly hindered phenol, reaction with oxygen can occur to give hydroperoxides, as shown for 2,4,6-tri-*t*-butylphenol, equation 22, but when the *ortho*- or *para*-positions are not so hindered, dimerization occurs instead [e.g., *p*-cresol gives Pummerer's ketone with potassium ferricyanide (74)]. If in an enzymic reaction the relatively unhindered phenoxy radicals were constrained from dimerizing, hydroperoxides might be obtained which could undergo cleavage as in equation 23.

$$\tag{22}$$

$$\tag{23}$$

The feasibility of the mechanism in equation 23 is supported by two observations. First, there is spectroscopic evidence that the radical (XIV, equation 24) formed by the pulse radiolysis of a benzene-water mixture, reacts with oxygen (75). Second, x-irradiation of benzene in the presence of oxygen gives mucondialdehyde as well as phenol, and evidence for the following mechanism has been obtained (76, 77):

(24)

(XIV)

It is interesting that tryptophan gives formylkynurenine under the same conditions (76).

As this discussion indicates, our ideas of the mechanisms involved in ring opening are not so far advanced as those for hydroxylation. As in the latter reactions, however, it is probable that the function of the metal ion is to activate molecular oxygen, while in ring opening the phenolic substrates may simultaneously be activated through their ready capacity for electron donation. Once more, therefore, it is tempting to visualize a mechanism in which the metal ion acts as an intermediary for the repairing of electrons.

## REFERENCES

1. F. Haber and J. Weiss, *Proc. Roy. Soc. (London)*, **A147**, 332, (1934).
2. W. G. Barb, J. H. Baxendale, P. George, and K. R. Hargrave, *Trans. Faraday Soc.*, **47**, 462 (1951).
3. A. E. Cahill and H. Taube, *J. Am. Chem. Soc.*, **74**, 2312 (1952).
4. J. H. Baxendale, M. G. Evans, and G. S. Park, *Trans. Faraday Soc.*, **42**, 155 (1946).
5. J. H. Merz and W. A. Waters, *J. Chem. Soc.*, **1949**, 2427.
6. J. R. Lindsay Smith and R. O. C. Norman, *J. Chem. Soc.*, **1963**, 2897.
7. A. L. Buley and R. O. C. Norman, unpublished observations.
8. R. O. C. Norman and G. K. Radda, *Proc. Chem. Soc.*, **1962**, 138.
9. A. M. Downes, *Austral. J. Chem.*, **11**, 154 (1958).
10. S. Baer and G. Stein, *J. Chem. Soc.*, **1953**, 3176.
11. E. Saito and B. H. J. Bielski, *J. Am. Chem. Soc.*, **83**, 4467 (1961).
12. W. T. Dixon and R. O. C. Norman, *J. Chem. Soc.*, **1963**, 3119.
13. W. T. Dixon and R. O. C. Norman, *Proc. Chem. Soc.*, **1963**, 97.
14. L. M. Dorfman, R. E. Bühler, and I. A. Taub, *J. Chem. Phys.*, **36**, 549 (1962).
15. A. Cier and C. Nofre, *Bull. soc. chim. France*, **1959**, 1523.
16. R. O. C. Norman and G. K. Radda, "Free-Radical Substitutions of Heteroaromatic Compounds," in A. R. Katritzky, Ed., *Advances in Heterocyclic Chemistry*, Vol. 2, Academic Press, New York, 1963, p. 167.

17. J. R. Lindsay Smith, R. O. C. Norman, and G. K. Radda, *J. Gas Chromatography*, **2**, 146 (1964).
18. R. Breslow and L. N. Lukens, *J. Biol. Chem.*, **235**, 292 (1960).
19. G. H. Williams, *Homolytic Aromatic Substitution*, Pergamon Press, 1960.
20. Ref. (19), p. 68.
21. T. Suehiro, *J. Chem. Soc. Japan, Pure Chem. Sect.*, **72**, 301 (1951).
22. Ref. (19), p. 57.
23. L. M. Stock and H. C. Brown, "A Quantitative Treatment of Directive Effects in Aromatic Substitution," in V. Gold, Ed., *Advances in Physical Organic Chemistry*, Vol. 1, Academic Press, New York, 1963, p. 35.
24. C. Walling and B. Miller, *J. Am. Chem. Soc.*, **79**, 4181 (1957).
25. F. Minisci and R. Galli, *Tetrahedron Letters*, **1962**, 533.
26. W. T. Dixon, R. O. C. Norman, and A. L. Buley, *J. Chem. Soc.*, **1964**, 3625.
27. Ref. (19), p. 71.
28. C. Mitoma, H. S. Posner, H. C. Reitz, and S. Udenfriend, *Arch. Biochem. Biophys.*, **61**, 431 (1956).
29. H. S. Posner, C. Mitoma, and S. Udenfriend, *Arch. Biochem. Biophys.*, **94**, 269 (1961).
30. S. Udenfriend, C. T. Clark, J. Axelrod, and B. B. Brodie, *Federation Proc.*, **11**, 300 (1952).
31. J. Böeseken and Jkv. M. L. von Konigsfeldt, *Rec. trav. chim.*, **54**, 313 (1935); J. Böeseken and C. F. Metz, *ibid.*, **54**, 345 (1935).
32. R. D. Chambers, P. Goggin, and W. K. R. Musgrave, *J. Chem. Soc.*, **1959**, 1804.
33. I. M. Roitt and W. A. Waters, *J. Chem. Soc.*, **1949**, 3060.
34. S. L. Freiss, A. H. Soloway, B. K. Morse, and W. C. Ingersoll, *J. Am. Chem. Soc.*, **74**, 1305 (1952); H. Davidge, A. G. Davies, J. Kenyon, and R. F. Mason, *J. Chem. Soc.*, **1958**, 4569.
35. C. A. Bunton, T. A. Lewis, and D. R. Llewellyn, *J. Chem. Soc.*, **1956**, 1226.
36. A. J. Davidson and R. O. C. Norman, *J. Chem. Soc.*, **1964**, 5404.
37. B. R. Brown, A. J. Davidson, and R. O. C. Norman, *Chem. & Ind.*, **1962**, 1237.
38. L. Ruzicka, *Experientia*, **9**, 357 (1953).
39. G. A. Hamilton and J. P. Friedman, *J. Am. Chem. Soc.*, **85**, 1008 (1963).
40. J. R. Lindsay Smith and R. O. C. Norman, unpublished observations; G. A. Hamilton, personal communication.
41. W. Brackman and E. Havinga, *Rec. trav. chim.*, **74**, 937, 1070, 1100, 1107 (1955).
42. S. Udenfriend, C. T. Clark, J. Axelrod, and B. B. Brodie, *J. Biol. Chem.*, **208**, 731 (1954).
43. R. C. Krueger, *Federation Proc.*, **15**, 294 (1956).
44. C. Nofre, A. Cier, and A. Lefier, *Bull. soc. chim. France*, **1961**, 530.
45. F. Dewhurst and C. Calcutt, *Nature*, **191**, 808 (1961).
46. P. George, *J. Chem. Soc.*, **1954**, 4349.
47. G. S. Hammond, personal communication.
48. G. A. Hamilton, L. Woo, and R. J. Workman, *146th American Chemical Society Meeting, Denver, Colorado*, 1964, p. 13A; *J. Am. Chem. Soc.*, **86**, 3390 (1964).
49. R. R. Grinstead, *J. Am. Chem. Soc.*, **82**, 3472 (1960).
50. C. R. E. Jefcoate, J. R. Lindsay Smith, and R. O. C. Norman, unpublished observations.
51. J. H. Green, B. J. Ralph, and P. J. Schofield, *Nature*, **198**, 754 (1963).
52. G. A. Hamilton, *J. Am. Chem. Soc.*, **86**, 3391 (1964).
53. S. Kaufman, "Phenylalanine Hydroxylation," in P. D. Boyer, H. Lardy, and K. Myrbäck, Eds., *The Enzymes*, Vol. 8, Academic Press, New York, 1963, p. 373.
54. S. Kaufmann, *Proc. Natl. Acad. Sci. U.S.*, **50**, 1085 (1963).
55. H. S. Mason, "Mechanisms of Oxygen Metabolism," *Advances in Enzymol.*, **19**, 79 (1957).

56. O. Hayaishi, "Direct Oxygenation by $O_2$, Oxygenases," in P. D. Boyer, H. Lardy, and K. Myrbäck, Eds., *The Enzymes*, Vol. 8, Academic Press, New York, 1963, p. 353.
57. A. L. Hunt, D. E. Hughes, and J. M. Lowenstein, *Biochem. J.*, **66**, 2P (1957).
58. R. Higgins and R. O. C. Norman, unpublished observations.
59. M. Katagiri, S. Yamamoto, and O. Hayaishi, *J. Biol. Chem.*, **237**, 2413 (1962).
60. E. Boyland and J. Booth, *Ann. Rev. Pharm.*, **2**, 129 (1962).
61. J. Booth and E. Boyland, *Biochem. J.*, **70**, 681 (1958).
62. S. Kuno, M. Tashiro, H. Taniuchi, K. Horibata, and O. Hayaishi, *Federation Proc.*, **20**, 3 (1961).
63. I. D. Raacke-Fels, C. H. Wang, R. K. Robins, and B. E. Christensen, *J. Org. Chem.*, **15**, 627 (1950).
64. J. A. Elvidge, R. P. Linstead, B. A. Orkin, P. Sims, H. Baer, and D. B. Pattison, *J. Chem. Soc.*, **1950**, 2228; J. Böeseken and R. Engelberts, *Proc. Acad. Sci. Amsterdam*, **34**, 1292 (1931).
65. J. Böeseken and R. Engelberts, *Proc. Acad. Sci. Amsterdam*, **35**, 750 (1932).
66. R. A. G. Marshall and R. O. C. Norman, unpublished observations.
67. J. H. Boyer and L. R. Morgan, *J. Am. Chem. Soc.*, **82**, 4748 (1960).
68. L. R. Morgan, *J. Org. Chem.*, **27**, 1208 (1962).
69. H. Kwart and N. J. Wegemer, *J. Am. Chem. Soc.*, **83**, 2746 (1961).
70. A. Miyake, A. H. Bokman, and B. S. Schweigert, *J. Biol. Chem.*, **211**, 391 (1954).
71. O. Hayaishi, A. A. Patchett, and B. Witkop, *Ann. Chem.*, **608**, 158 (1957).
72. O. Hayaishi, M. Katagiri, and S. Rothberg, *J. Am. Chem. Soc.*, **77**, 5450 (1955).
73. H. Musso, *Angew. Chem. (Intern. Ed.)*, **2**, 723 (1963).
74. D. H. R. Barton, A. M. Deflorin, and O. E. Edwards, *J. Chem. Soc.*, **1956**, 530.
75. L. M. Dorfman, I. A. Taub, and R. E. Bühler, *J. Chem. Phys.*, **36**, 3051 (1962).
76. M. Daniels, G. Scholes, and J. Weiss, *J. Chem. Soc.*, **1956**, 832.
77. I. Loeff and G. Stein, *J. Chem. Soc.*, **1963**, 2623.

## Discussion

HAYAISHI: I should like to ask you about equation 20 on p. 150 of your paper. In this scheme of the two oxygens added to catechol, one atom should be derived from water, whereas the other atom should come from the molecular oxygen, but our $^{18}O$ experiment shows that both atoms are derived from molecular oxygen. I wonder how you reconcile these two observations.

NORMAN: They can only be reconciled, I think, on the assumption that the hydroxide which is displaced at step 3 reacts in some intramolecular manner with the developing anhydride; in other words, this anhydride must be bypassed. I am glad that you called my attention to that, for clearly as the equation stands it is not a true representation.

DAWSON: You refer to the observation concerning a reaction between catechol and *o*-benzoquinone. Can you give us a little more information about the reaction?

NORMAN: Yes, one of the products is the cyclic ether, possibly formed by nucleophilic attack by the hydroxyl group of catechol on the *o*-quinone, followed by oxidation, ring closure, and a second oxidation.

DAWSON: Could nucleophilic reactions involving the *para* or *ortho* position to the hydroxyl occur?

NORMAN: It is conceivable that they could, but I believe that in some recent work [F. R. Hewgill, T. J. Stone, and W. A. Waters, *J. Chem. Soc.*, 408 (1964)] on a reaction which is either this one or something very close to it, Waters isolated a ring-closed product of that general structure which is actually analogous to the one obtained from *o*-phenylenediamine under one-electron oxidizing conditions.

DAWSON: Tetrahydroxydiphenols have been isolated as intermediates in this reaction system.

NORMAN: Yes.

ESTABROOK: Biological hydroxylating systems are generally known to contain sulfhydryl reactions. I wonder whether you have examined any of the iron sulfhydryl models for hydroxylation, and if so how they might differ from the other models.

NORMAN: No, we have not examined them. The nearest we got is to have two sulfhydryl compounds in this particular system which is, in fact, not a very good system for us, a biological model, but it starts at peroxide.

ESTABROOK: Are you aware of the paper published by T. Gerthsen [*Biochem. Z.*, **336**, 251 (1962)] on the conversion of phenylalanine to tyrosine by such a model?

NORMAN: No.

STAUDINGER: He did work concerning the role of SH groups in hydroxylation of tyrosine. He could detect an effect of SH, but the effect was very weak. You do not get good hydroxylation under these conditions, probably because SH groups will trap free radicals.

HEMMERICH: Do you have any evidence that $\cdot O_2H$ radicals are involved in the oxidation of $FMNH_2$?

NORMAN: No, we have none and are inclined to rule out the simple perhydroxyl radical as the reactive entity.

HEMMERICH: Yes, I would say that, according to our research, it is rather improbable that you have $\cdot O_2H$. It appears that a two-electron oxidation is involved and that the flavin radical is formed by disproportionation of the flavoquinone and the excess $FMNH_2$. This is formed in a secondary reaction.

NORMAN: This results from disproportionation, but I don't think that anyone has ever ruled out the possibility that this is also an intermediate in the ultra-stages.

HEMMERICH: There is no evidence so far, but the possibility hasn't been ruled out.

NORMAN: I agree. The conclusion one reaches, if the oxidation of $FMNH_2$ is a two-electron process, is that the hydroxylating agent results from a reaction between $FMNH\cdot$ and oxygen; in other words, oxygen is activated by the radical.

CAUGHEY: You mentioned the fact that chelating agents other than EDTA are not as effective in Udenfriend's system. In view of Hoard's crystallographic studies on EDTA complexes [J. L. Hoard, G. S. Smith, and M. Lind in *Advances in the Chemistry of the Coordination Compounds*, S. Kirschner, Ed., The Macmillan Co., N.Y., 1961, pp. 296–302; J. L. Hoard, M. Lind, and J. V. Silverton, *J. Am. Chem. Soc.*, **83**, 2770 (1961); J. L. Hoard, C. H. L. Kennard, and G. S. Smith, *Inorg. Chem.* **2**, 1317 (1963)], in which EDTA frequently proved unable to completely encompass the metal atom to form a true octahedral complex thereby leaving a coordination position exposed, can such structural considerations aid in correlations of structure with activity? Also, in your scheme where you consider electron flow from ascorbic acid through the ferrous ion to the complexed oxygen, is EDTA complexed at the time? If so, is not the environment about the metal ion a rather crowded situation?

NORMAN: EDTA is not a hexadentate ligand for ferrous ion in solution, and we have to presume, I think, that there is an equilibrium involving a species in which only, say, three of the six ligand positions of the ferrous ion are taken up by EDTA, the remainder being taken up by oxygen and ascorbic acid.

CAUGHEY: Is it not possible for ascorbic acid to react directly with the oxygen which is attached to the iron?

NORMAN: That is a possibility.

STAUDINGER: Pyrophosphate is nearly as good as EDTA, so the system is not very specific for EDTA.

The second comment I would make is that ascorbic acid can use oxygen by itself without a heavy metal, but not very well. It is not very active. It does much better with iron.

NORMAN: The rate of oxidation of ascorbic acid above the pH of about 5 in the absence of ferric ions is very slow, isn't it? It becomes very fast when a fair proportion of dianion is present, but it is pretty slow when you are dealing only with the monoanionized molecule.

# The Chemistry of Flavin-Metal Interaction

... P. HEMMERICH, F. MÜLLER,*

and A. EHRENBERG

## I. INTRODUCTION

### A. Biochemical Implications of Flavin-Metal Interaction

Metal-containing flavoproteins participate widely in biological oxidations, particularly in the mitochondrial apparatus of the animal cell and also in some microorganisms (1). The importance of metal ions incorporated in flavoproteins was controversial until advanced procedures for obtaining more intact soluble fractions of respiratory enzyme systems and physical methods for demonstrating metal valence changes in native enzymes became available (2). Bray, Palmer, and Beinert demonstrated beyond reasonable doubt the participation of flavoprotein-linked "non-heme iron" in electron transfer (3), as did Bray, Malmström, and Vänngård for molybdenum (4) in milk xanthine oxidase. In addition, Handler and his group (5) have shown that the optical absorption characteristics of metalloflavoproteins in the oxidized state, which are essentially different from those of metal-free flavoproteins, are due mainly to iron-protein coordination. Nevertheless, in the course of enzyme action, the protein-bound flavin has to be in direct contact with the protein-bound iron, as is also indicated by Beinert's spin relaxation studies (6) of enzyme-bound flavin free radical. Surprisingly, the chemical nature of this obligatory flavin-iron contact has seldom been considered.

But whatever differences there may be in the behavior of coenzyme or metal in the protein-linked and the free (hydrated) state, the roots for such differences must depend on the chemical nature of coenzyme and metal and thus will be reflected by the protein-free system under suitable conditions. This, we felt, might be worth while investigating.

* Abstracted in part from dissertation by F. Müller, Basel, 1964. IV. Communication in the series, "Zum Verhalten des Riboflavins gegen Metallionen"; cf. (8), (15), (17).

## B. Earlier Chemical Studies

Metal coordination chemistry of flavins was initiated in 1950 by Albert (7), who concluded from potentiometric data that flavin should be a strong metal-chelating agent under normal aerobic conditions. Re-examining these studies, Hemmerich and Fallab showed in 1958 (8) that in spite of a formal structural analogy to 8-hydroxyquinoline, I (Table 2), the redox-active heteroaromatic moiety (= isoalloxazine, II) of flavocoenzymes does not exhibit any measurable affinity whatsoever toward redox-inactive transition (d-) metal ions in dilute aqueous solution. Furthermore, the conclusions of Foye and Lange (9), who claimed the isolation of solid flavin-metal chelates by coprecipitation of riboflavin and metal hydroxides, were shown to be in error. In addition, solid suspension infrared spectra (10) cannot be used to obtain information on flavin-metal chelation, since simple salt formation, e.g., in the potassium salt of riboflavin, deletes absorption in the carbonyl region (11). Evidence supporting our findings was presented later by Baarda and Metzler (12), as well as by Radda and Calvin (13). On the other hand, a stable red silver complex of riboflavin had been known as early as 1933 (14). Baarda and Metzler (12) and, independently, Bamberg and Hemmerich (15) showed this to be a true chelate of the "oxinate" type, III.

In view of these facts, three questions had to be answered:

(*a*) What is the explanation for this unexpected lack of affinity of flavoquinones towards divalent Mn, Fe, Co, Ni, Cu, but not $Ag^+$?

(*b*) What other mechanisms are possible for interaction between flavin and metal ions?

(*c*) What may be the meaning of metals being associated with flavin *in vivo* (the "teleological" question)?

Studies on these problems utilizing protein-free model systems have been undertaken in our laboratory with gratifying results. A first part of these studies has been presented elsewhere (16, 17) and will be reviewed here only briefly. Additional information will be presented on the spectra and stability of flavoquinone (charge-transfer) chelates and on the spectra and paramagnetism of flavosemiquinone (radical) chelates.

## II. THE SPECIFIC METAL AFFINITY OF FLAVOQUINONE (OXIDIZED FLAVIN)

### A. Redox-Inactive Metal Ions

The molecular species occurring in flavin solutions, as they depend on pH and redox state, are given in Table 1. The three states of oxidoreduction are indicated as flavoquinone, flavosemiquinone, and flavohydroquinone. Furthermore, Table 1 refers to the optical absorption maxima of the isolated species, as given by Dudley *et al.* (18). A scheme for metal chelation under aerobic conditions has to allow for neutral flavoquinone (FlH) or flavo-quinone anion (Fl⁻) as ligands, leading to the reaction sequence

$$FlH + Me^{2+} \leftrightarrows (MeFlH)^{2+} \leftrightarrows (MeFl)^{+} + H^{+}$$

Since $K_{FlH}^{H^{+}}$ [terms $K_{AB}^{B}$ used throughout here mean thermodynamic constants for B associating to form AB (19)] is as high as $10^{10}$ (cf. Table 1), it follows that for slightly soluble FlH the activity of Fl⁻ can never be much higher than that of OH⁻ in non-alkaline aqueous solution. Thus, formation of $(MeFl)^{+}$ will not be observable unless the metal affinity of Fl⁻ exceeds that of OH⁻ appreciably. Therefore liberation of the ligand proton has to occur much earlier than metal-ion hydrolysis in the pH titration of FlH in the presence of metal. This is the case for Ag⁺ and Cu⁺ only (cf. IIB, and Fig. 1). Thus, log $K_{FlMe^{+}}^{Me^{2+}} \sim 2.5$ is an upper limit for non-reducing metal ions.

On the other hand, formation of $(MeFlH)^{2+}$ will not show up at all during pH titrations, because of the low log $K_{FlH_{2}^{+}}^{H^{+}}$ ($\sim 1.5$). This handicap can be overcome by introducing an additional basic function into the flavin nucleus as in 2-iminoflavins, flavin analogs of guanine-like shape, which we synthesized. In this way we found log $K_{FlHNi^{2+}}^{N;2+} = 1.8$; cf. Fig. 1. This can again be taken as an upper limit for non-reducing metal ions and unaltered flavoquinones.

Formation of flavoquinone chelates can be assayed directly by measuring spectrophotometrically the partition of a suitable flavoquinone, e.g., lumi-flavin (II, R = CH₃, R' = H), between CHCl₃ and water of constant ionic strength in the presence and absence of excess *d*-metal ions. Any disturbing factors brought about by the side-chain OH groups of natural flavins will be eliminated by this procedure. We found that, within the range of obtain-able solubility (up to $10^{-3}$ M in flavin), no change of partition occurs upon addition of *d*-metal ion at any pH below the point of metal-ion hydrolysis, when the pH was maintained by a pH-stat. This procedure again gives an upper limit of log $K_{FlHMe}^{Me} \sim 1$.

To explain the apparent lack of affinity toward metal ions of high co-ordination number, it had to be ascertained that there was no essential overcrowding effect in the metal coordination sphere caused by CH-6 of the heteroaromatic moiety (cf. III, Table 2). For this reason we investigated pteridine analogs of flavin, which lack this potential hindrance. We were able to confirm that 4-pteridone, IV, has a general, oxinate-type metal affinity (8), whereas the flavin analog 8-methyl-2,4-pteridinedione, V, has not. Instead, it forms another type of "covalently hydrated" chelates, VI, by accepting OH⁻ rather than releasing H⁺ (20). Again, Ag⁺ was an exception in that it stabilized an unhydrated chelate, VII, whereas VI could not be dehydrated without destruction in the case of, e.g., Ni²⁺. Thus, the weak

# TABLE 1
## The Flavin Redox System

**Quinoid state**

$(FlH_2^{\oplus})$   [390, 264, 222]$^a$

$(FlH)$   [446, 370, 270, 230]$^b$

$(Fl^{\ominus})$   [444, 350, 270, 230]$^c$

$pK_a \sim 0$    $pK_a \sim 10$

**Semiquinoid (Radical) state**

$(\dot{F}lH_3^{\oplus})$   [488, 358, 258]$^a$

$(\dot{F}lH_2)$   [622, 590 (S.)]$^d$ [570]$^b$

$(\dot{F}lH^{\ominus})$   [612 ? ]$^g$

$1 < pK_a < 3$    $pK_a \sim 6.5$

$[800]^b$

$\frac{1}{2}(FlH_2)_2$

**Hydroquinoid ("Leuco") state**

$FlH_4^{\oplus}$   [316, 250]$^a$

$(FlH_3)$   [400 (S.), 280 (S.), 250]$^e$

$(FlH_2^{\ominus})$   [350 (S.), 288, 256]$^f$

$pK_a < 0$    $pK_a \sim 6.2$

$e^{\ominus}$   $\frac{1}{4}O_2$

Numbers in [ ] give $\lambda_{max}$ in m$\mu$, S = shoulder, solvents indicated by indices in italics: *a*, 6N HCl; *b*, phosphate pH 7; *c*, 2N NaOH, *d*, CHCl$_3$, *e*, sulfate pH 2, *f*, borate pH 9, *g*, CHCl$_3$, 20 m$M$ in triethylamine.

electron affinity of flavoquinone has its origin in electronic and not steric effects.

Consequently, our attention was directed toward two other parameters for metal ion affinity in flavoquinone, namely, basicity of N-5 and prototropic energy of 3-HN—CO-4 → 3-N=COH-4. This last parameter is reflected by the ease of hydrolytic cleavage of the corresponding iminol ester, VIII

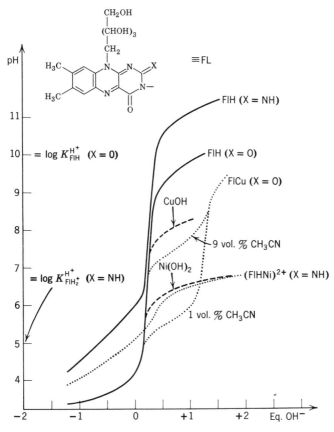

**Fig. 1.** Bjerrum titrations of flavoquinones. ——, ligand blank, – – –, metal blank (hydrolysis); . . ., ligand (2.0 $mM$) + metal (0.8 $mM$ Cu$^+$, 0.1 $M$ Ni$^{2+}$, respectively).

(R = alkyl). Having synthesized such esters, we found that they hydrolyzed quite rapidly without catalyst even at pH 7, while the same esters, when reduced, are rather stable (18, 21). On the other hand, the locus at which flavoquinone is protonated could be shown to be N-1, not N-5 (18); cf. Table 1. Flavoquinone does not exhibit any basicity at N-5, whereas flavosemiquinone does. Flavoquinone has a high 3,4-prototropic energy; flavosemiquinone, a low one.

## TABLE 2

### Chelate Formation and Structure

Thus, it was to be expected that flavoquinone only acquires metal affinity by taking up one electron.

## B. Metal-Ligand Charge Transfer

The potentiometric and extraction methods had been adopted, since it was clear that any spectral changes observed upon addition of metal ions to aqueous flavoquinone solutions were due to ionic strength changes, except at very high metal concentrations (*ca.* 1 *M*), as can be seen from Fig. 2. In that case $Zn^{2+}$ gave a slight bathochromic shift of the first absorption band

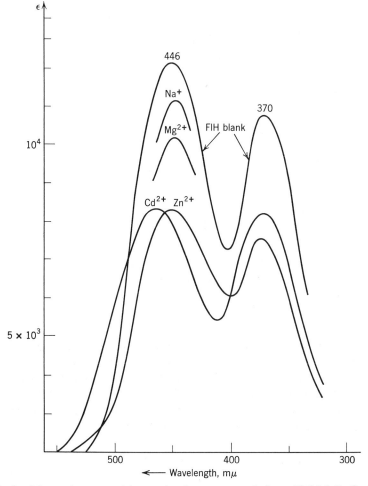

**Fig. 2.** Flavoquinone-metal interaction in aqueous solution. $10^{-3}$ *M* riboflavin, 1.0 *M* metal perchlorate; pH 5, no pH drop observed upon adding the ligand.

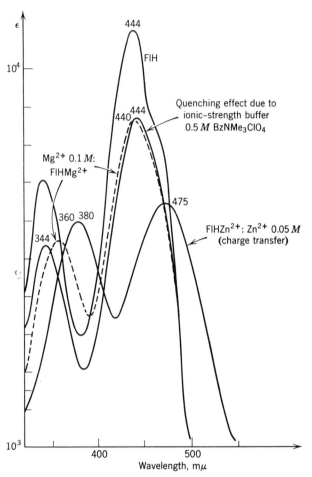

**Fig. 3.** Spectra of $10^{-3}$ $M$ tetraacetylriboflavin in acetone. Metals added as hydrated acetates.

and $Cd^{2+}$ a larger one, although saturation could not be obtained. Since, quite generally, $Cd^{2+}$ is a much weaker complexing ion than isoelectronic $Zn^{2+}$, the stronger shift found with $Cd^{2+}$ has clearly to be explained by charge transfer due to delocalization of electrons from a filled metal $d$ orbital to the ligand-acceptor $\pi$ orbital. This transfer should be facilitated in $Cd^{2+}$ by its lower $(d^{10}\text{-}d^9s)$-transition energy. The complex formed should thus be written as

$$FlH + Me^{2+} \rightleftarrows [FlH\ Me^{II} \leftrightarrow \dot{F}lH^- \ Me^{III}]^{2+}$$

Since FlH accepts one $\pi$-electron, and two lone pairs are blocked by $\sigma$-bonds to the metal, this "charge-transfer" chelate should be iso-$\pi$-electronic with the flavosemiquinone cation, $\dot{F}lH_3^+$. This is indeed true, as shown by spectral comparison (18).

To study this type of metal-ligand interaction more closely, we have looked for conditions to allow complete formation of metal-flavin complex and to compare the spectral effect of $Mg^{2+}$ and $Zn^{2+}$. This has been found possible in water-free acetone, the ionic strength of which was maintained by excess of benzyltrimethylammonium perchlorate. The spectra thus obtained are shown in Fig. 3: although $Mg^{2+}$ had no distinct effect on the first band (450 m$\mu$), but only on the second one (350 m$\mu$), $Zn^{2+}$ shifted the two bands equally. This red shift is practically independent of whether the ligand nucleus is alkylated in position 3 or not. The same is not true for $Hg^{2+}$; here the complex formation, as revealed by saturation of the spectral shift, needs very high metal concentration, when R = H, while a much more stable red complex is formed with R = $CH_3$. This indicates that, under the conditions present, 3-unsubstituted flavoquinone first forms a digonal complex with $Hg^{2+}$ 3-N—Hg—N-3, without substantial change of the ligand spectrum. This situation had been verified earlier (15) for $Ag^+$.

Adding triethylamine ($NEt_3$) to the acetone solution described above does not liberate a proton from $(FlHMe)^{2+}$, but displaces the flavin from the metal. Therefore, since $Fl^-$ and $NEt_3$ are of similar basicity, flavoquinone cannot have much stronger general metal affinity than do tertiary monoamines.

## C. Redox-Active Metal Ions

Upon addition of water (cf. Table 2) all "charge-transfer chelation" of flavoquinone is completely reversed regardless of pH, with the exception of $Ag^I$, $Cu^I$, $Fe^{II}$, and $Mo^V$ chelates. As described (15), AgFl is stable at pH > 6. In the absence of air, CuFl is stable at pH > 5. Upon addition of water, $FeFl^+$ and $MoOFl^{2+}$ undergo irreversible oxidoreduction. This is shown by anaerobic pH-titration of excess FlH in the presence of $Fe^{2+}$. At the equivalence point (pH 8) 2.6 $H^+/Fe^{2+}$ are liberated and a red precipitate is formed. Spectrophotometric analysis shows 90% of total flavin to be present as flavoquinone in the supernatant after aeration. Thus, the precipitate has to consist of nearly pure $Fe(OH)_3$, while the over-all reaction has to be formulated as oxidoreduction.

$$FlH + Fe^{2+}$$
$$\Updownarrow$$
$$[Fl\dot{F}e^{II} \leftrightarrow \dot{F}lFe^{III}]^+ \qquad\qquad + H^+$$
$$\downarrow H_2O,\ pH\ 8$$
$$Fe(OH)_3 \downarrow + \begin{cases} \dot{F}lH^- & + 3H^+ \\ \quad \uparrow\downarrow \\ \frac{1}{2}(FlH + FlH_2^-) & + 2.5H^+ \end{cases}$$

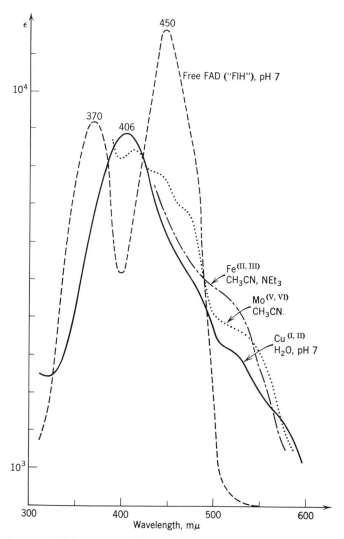

**Fig. 4.** Spectra of "charge-transfer" chelates of flavoquinone. Solutions obtained as mentioned in the text.

This reaction sequence is irreversible as long as precipitation of $Fe(OH)_3$ is not prevented either by auxiliary ligands and/or by decrease of $H_2O$ activity. Both needs are met by protein as well as by much simpler model media, e.g., abs. $CH_3CN$ as solvent and $(NBzMe_3)_2Fe^{II}Cl_4$,* which exhibits $Cl^-$ as

---

* This complex is obtained in colorless crystals by adding $NBzMe_3^+Cl^-$ to $FeCl_2$ in anhydrous MeOH containing HCl.

auxiliary ligand. Under these conditions the iron-flavin "charge-transfer" chelate is stable and does not even react readily with air. The spectrum is shown in Fig. 4; high pH was simulated by addition of triethylamine ($NEt_3$). Although, in the case of iron, the base is needed for complex formation, $Mo^{5+}$ [as $NH_4Mo^VOCl_4$] in $CH_3CN$ forms a flavin chelate, presumably $MoOCl \cdot FlH$, which is dissociated by $NEt_3$. Thus, it seems that $Mo^{5+}$ and $Fe^{2+}$, when competing for FlH, have a pH optimum each, which is, for $Mo^{5+}$, slightly acid, for $Fe^{2+}$, slightly alkaline (Fig. 4).

This shows that, for any "charge-transfer" chelate, two independent dissociation reactions have to be considered, yielding oxidized metal plus reduced ligand and reduced metal plus oxidized ligand, respectively. At the same time the metal and the ligand valences in the complex are not distinguishable.

The stoichiometry and structure of these entities are best exemplified by CuFl; Fig. 1 shows the pH titration of $Cu^+$, stabilized (22) in aqueous solution by increasing amounts of $CH_3CN$ up to 1 $M$ in the presence of excess FlH. The apparent $K_a$ of proton release from $CuFlH^+$ depends on the square of $CH_3CN$ concentration, indicating that flavin acts as bidental ligand, displacing two $CH_3CN$ molecules from the copper simultaneously. Not more than one ligand is coordinated readily by the metal ion, a very unusual fact in the presence of excess ligand, which favors the formation of ternary complexes in the equilibrium

$$CuFl_2^- + CuX_2^+ \rightleftharpoons 2FlCuX$$

## III. THE LACK OF AFFINITY OF FLAVOHYDROQUINONE FOR METALS (REDUCED FLAVIN)

### A. Acid-Base Reactions and Prototropism of Flavohydroquinone

Michaelis and Schwarzenbach (23) found as early as 1938 that "leuco" flavin exhibits the remarkable acid strength of log $K_{FlH_3}^H = 6.2$. On the other hand, it is an extremely weak base, log $K_{FlH_4}^H < 0$, as may be seen from the work of Beinert (24). We have found the value 6.2 to be independent of alkyl substitution in position 3, but not position 1. Furthermore, we observed strong carbonyl absorption for $FlH_3$ in infrared (solid and solution) spectra (18). Thus, the most acid proton should be attached to N-1, although the iminol tautomer, IX (Table 3), might participate to some extent. This might be concluded from the fact that 3-$FlRH_2$ undergoes further alkylation at one of the oxygens, but not at N-1, to give iminol esters, XI, that are stable to hydrolysis as long as they are kept in the reduced state (18).

The fact that neutral flavohydroquinone, $FlH_3$, is not colorless has been

## TABLE 3
### Structure and Conformation of "Leuco" Flavins

known for a long time [cf. (23)] but is often ignored as a consequence of using the term "leucoflavin," which should be abandoned. On the other hand, $FlH_4^+$ is indeed colorless, and $FlH_2^-$ is nearly so. We found the long-wave end absorption (with broad shoulder of $E = 2000$ liters $\times$ mole$^{-1}$ $\times$ cm$^{-1}$ at 400 m$\mu$) of $FlH_3$ to exceed even the flavoquinone absorption in the region of 540 m$\mu$ (18). This makes a $10^{-2}$ $M$ flavin solution look more red in the reduced than in the oxidized state at pH 5–6, but not at pH 7.

## B. Molecular Coplanarity

Protonation of $FlH_3$, which necessarily occurs at N-5, must bend the molecule along the N-5, N-10-axis. Consequently, the drop in residual absorption reflects loss of molecular planarity. Dissociation of NH-1 has the same effect, since the negative charge generated diminishes delocalization of the N-5 lone pair. We tested this by synthesizing the alkylated analogs, X and XII (Table 3). The 1,10-dimethyl compound, X (R = H), was found, as expected, to have much lower end absorption than the 1,10-ethylene analog, XII. Both compounds can only differ in $\pi$-electron distribution by steric effects: the peri-dimethyl configuration causes steric overcrowding, which favors the bent state ("butterfly-wing conformation," Table 3, XIV $\rightleftarrows$ XV). The same situation is enhanced by alkylation of NH-5, e.g., in X (R = benzyl), through deletion of the H-tunneling effect. But even free $FlH_3$ is not perfectly flat in the ground state, as is indicated by the adenine moiety of FAD increasing the $FlH_3$ absorption at 400 m$\mu$ substantially by molecular charge transfer (18). Thus, flavohydroquinone can be more or less coplanar according to environmental conditions.

We have tested the influence of metal ions on totally reduced flavin pH-metrically in aqueous solutions, as well as spectrophotometrically in aprotic solutions. To do this, we ran pH titrations under $H_2$ in the presence of palladium-asbestos and $Zn^{2+}$, or we reduced CHCl$_3$-soluble flavins, e.g., riboflavin with fully acetylated side chain or 3-alkylated lumiflavins (II, R, R' = CH$_3$), by shaking with aqueous dithionite and then adding Zn(CH$_3$COO)$_2$ in CH$_3$CN to the CHCl$_3$ phase and a slight excess of triethylamine to bind protons liberated. No effect whatsoever was found, as compared with the metal-free blanks, when $O_2$ exclusion was perfect.

This result is in full agreement with what can be expected from structural considerations. Since there is no measurable acidity in NH-5, formation of a 4,5-chelate would imply the same extent of bending as protonation, eliminating any polycyclic resonance. Thus, since $FlH_3$ is about a thousand times less basic but about as acid as $FlH_2$ (cf. Table 1), chelates of the totally reduced flavin should be a thousand times less stable than flavosemiquinone chelates.

## IV. THE GENERAL METAL AFFINITY
## OF FLAVOSEMIQUINONE (FLAVIN RADICAL)

### A. pH Dependence of Flavosemiquinone Disproportionation

Free flavosemiquinone, $\dot{F}lH_2$, is the strongest base among the neutral flavin species (Table 1). Thus, below pH $= \log K_{\dot{F}lH_3^+}^{H^+} \sim 2.5$, the equilibrium

$$FlH + FlH_3 \overset{H^+,\ OH^-}{\underset{}{\rightleftarrows}} 2\dot{F}lH_2$$

will be displaced toward the right. In turn, flavoquinone, FlH, is the weakest acid among the neutral flavin species. Thus, above pH $= \log K_{FlH}^{H^+} \sim 10$, the

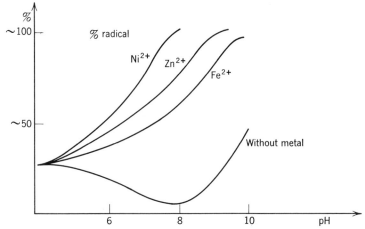

Fig. 5. pH dependence of flavosemiquinone disproportionation (schematic picture).

equilibrium will again be displaced toward the radical site (26, 27). In between, i.e., in the physiological range of pH, there is a minimum of radical concentration in solution, which is governed by the small but important difference between $K_{FlH_3}^{H^+}$ and $K_{\dot{F}lH_2}^{H^+}$, the acidities of flavohydroquinone and flavosemiquinone; cf. Table 1. This has been discussed in detail elsewhere (17, 26). The pH dependence of flavosemiquinone disproportionation is given schematically in Fig. 5.

The situation is still more complicated in more concentrated polar solutions, where associations of flavin species have to be taken into account. Principally, complexes can be formed between all species that are stable at a given pH and do not have the same charge (26, 27, 28), the most important being flavoquinhydrone $(FlH_2)_2$, which can be formulated as "radical dimer"

($\dot{F}lH_2$—$\dot{F}lH_2$) or as "charge-transfer complex" ($FlH$—$FlH_3$). These differ in the position of one proton and thus are simply tautomers, since the whole is one diamagnetic unit of $\pi$-electron delocalization. To differentiate between the tautomers, we synthesized $\dot{F}lR_2$ ($R$ = alkyl), XIII (Table 3), which corresponded in ESR and optical spectra perfectly with $\dot{F}lH_2$ but did not show a tendency to "dimerize," since no proton transfer was possible. Consequently, as proposed by Massey and Palmer (28), it is right to abandon the term "radical dimer" in favor of "charge-transfer complex" for flavoquinhydrone. While studying flavin-metal interaction, one can treat $(FlH_2)_2$, consequently, as $FlH + FlH_3$ in a good first approximation, as was done (17).

## B. Optical Spectra and Paramagnetism of Flavosemiquinone Chelates

Upon adding non-oxidizing $d$-metal ions to half-reduced flavin systems at physiological pH, the disproportionation is reversed (cf. Fig. 5), as was first shown (17) pH-metrically from the additional release of $0.5H^+/Me^{2+}$ according to

$$FlR + FlRH^- + 2Me^{2+} \rightleftarrows 2Me\dot{F}lR^+ + H^+$$

where R may be 3-alkyl or hydrogen but not 1-alkyl. This has been confirmed by the accompanying increase in ESR signal, when the $Me^{2+}$ was diamagnetic (29). In the case of $FlH = FAD$ or $FMN$, the radical chelates are insoluble through back-coordination of $>PO_2^-$ from the side chain:

When the metal is diamagnetic ($Zn^{2+}$ or $Cd^{2+}$), the precipitates show strong free-radical ESR absorption.

The complex formation goes along with a color change from light yellow to bright red, eventual precipitates being dark brown-red. This is shown in Fig. 6 for $Me^{2+} = 5\ mM$ and total $Fl = 1.25\ mM$ in $CHCl_3$, where the spectra in the presence and the absence of metal are given for 0, 25, 75, and 100% reduction. The special flavin derivative and $CHCl_3$ were chosen, because no precipitate is formed in $10^{-3}\ M$ solutions; in water there is no principal difference. The slight difference in the oxidized state reflects the change in ionic strength upon addition of $Me^{2+}$, but not $FlH$ chelation, since excess triethylamine ($2 \times 10^{-2}\ M$) is present.

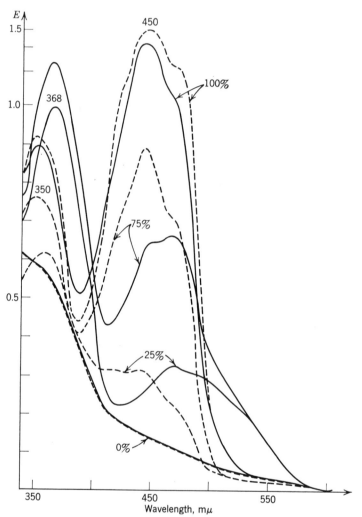

**Fig. 6.**   Reoxidation of FlH₂.   – – –, without Zn²⁺;  ——, with Zn²⁺.  Solutions obtained as mentioned in the text.

It is seen that the radical chelates MeF̣lH⁺ behave in optical absorption similar to the corresponding "charge-transfer" chelates MeFlH²⁺ (Fig. 3), although they are about 1000 times more stable (cf. Table 4).  But this spectral similarity extends only down to 600 m$\mu$:  the radicals MeF̣lH⁺ have one characteristic extra band in the near infrared, around 825 m$\mu$ (Fig. 7).  These bands can be differentiated from flavoquinhydrone "charge-transfer" type bands, which extend over 1000 m$\mu$ (28), by three features:  (*a*) their sharpness, (*b*) their obedience to Beer's law, and (*c*) their independence of solvent polarity. Furthermore, it has been ascertained that they reach their maximum intensity

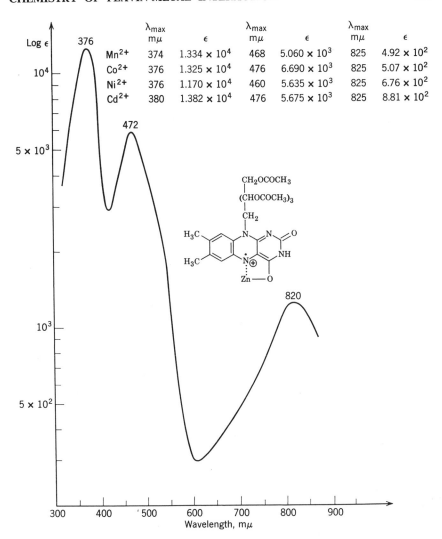

| | $\lambda_{max}$ m$\mu$ | $\epsilon$ | $\lambda_{max}$ m$\mu$ | $\epsilon$ | $\lambda_{max}$ m$\mu$ | $\epsilon$ |
|---|---|---|---|---|---|---|
| $Mn^{2+}$ | 374 | $1.334 \times 10^4$ | 468 | $5.060 \times 10^3$ | 825 | $4.92 \times 10^2$ |
| $Co^{2+}$ | 376 | $1.325 \times 10^4$ | 476 | $6.690 \times 10^3$ | 825 | $5.07 \times 10^2$ |
| $Ni^{2+}$ | 376 | $1.170 \times 10^4$ | 460 | $5.635 \times 10^3$ | 825 | $6.76 \times 10^2$ |
| $Cd^{2+}$ | 380 | $1.382 \times 10^4$ | 476 | $5.675 \times 10^3$ | 825 | $8.81 \times 10^2$ |

**Fig. 7.** Absorption characteristics of flavin radical chelates in CHCl$_3$.

at 50% reduction and are completely absent at 100% as well as 0% reduction. This type of absorption is found for NiMe$^{II}$, CoMe$^{II}$, ZnMe$^{II}$, MnMe$^{II}$, and CdMe$^{II}$. For FeMe$^{II}$, Cu$^{I}$, and Mo$^{V}$, measurement is complicated by the fact that, with these reducing ions, the "charge-transfer" chelate, which lacks one electron in comparison with the "radical" chelate, is also stable and absorbs at 800 m$\mu$. Attempts to differentiate quantitatively between these two valences are now being made by ESR as well as by optical means.

To obtain these spectra, the flavohydroquinone solutions described in section IIIB were oxidized by controlled addition of KI$_{3\ aq}$ or I$_2$ in CHCl$_3$.

In the latter case, the excess of triethylamine would not precipitate $Me^{2+}$ when water was efficiently excluded and metals were applied as dry acetates (except iron, which was applied as $FeCl_4^{2-}$; see above). Some three-fold excess of $Me^{2+}$ over flavin was always present in the sample as well as in the blank. The stability of the radical chelates follows the normal Irving-Williams (30) series, $Mn^{2+} < Fe^{2+} < Co^{2+} < Ni^{2+} > Zn^{2+} > Cd^{2+}$ (Table 4) (17).

## V. CONCLUSIONS

### A. Main Structural Features of Flavin in Its Three Valence States

To summarize the data we have given, the following can be said to differentiate the redox states of flavins:

1. Flavoquinone differs from both reduced states by its high prototropic energy; its iminol esters are very high in energy of hydrolysis.

2. Flavohydroquinone differs from both oxidized states by its tendency to bend, which makes the planar state vibrationally excited.

3. Flavosemiquinone is the only flavin redox state exhibiting general metal affinity, due to relatively high basicity at N-5 and low iminolization energy. Flavoquinone has in itself very low metal affinity but can acquire specific affinity by combining with electron-donating metal ions, thus accepting flavosemiquinone character. Flavohydroquinone has no metal chelation tendency whatsoever.

4. Since flavosemiquinone radical anion is the species of highest general metal affinity, equilibria are displaced from the disproportionated toward the radical (chelate) state at physiological pH in the presence of the metal.

5. Oxidized flavin gains metal affinity by adding just one electron to its lowest empty $\pi$ orbital, and it does not matter whether this electron comes from the chelating metal ion itself ($d,\pi$-charge transfer), from an external reducing agent (substrate), or, in the special case of "radical comproportionation," from reduced flavin ($\pi,\pi$-charge transfer). Thus, it follows that one might even take an electron from the highest filled $\pi$ orbital of flavoquinone and put it into the lowest empty orbital to obtain the same increase of metal affinity. In other words, flavoquinone should have general metal affinity in both excited states, singlet and triplet. Thus the energy of the excited states might be lowered in the metal-chelated state and the lifetimes altered according to the nature of the metal.

### B. Combination of Flavin and Secondary Redox System

Three secondary redox systems are known to occur in flavoproteins: $RSH \leftrightarrows RS \cdot$ in lipoic dehydrogenase (31), $Fe^{II}/Fe^{III}$ in mitochondrial flavoproteins, and—in addition—$Mo^V/Mo^{VI}$ in some flavoproteins of various

## TABLE 4
### Complex Stability Constants

Fl =  (structure)   R′ = ribityl

50% EtOH
0.1 $n$ NaClO$_4$

| Ligand | Metal | | log $K_{LMe}^{Me}$ | |
|--------|-------|--|--------------------|--|
| FlH | Ni$^{2+}$ | | < 1.0 | |
| FlR | Ag$^+$ | R = CH$_3$ | 1.3 | Flavoquinone chelates |
| | | R = H | 1.3 | |
| Fl$^{\ominus}$ | Ni$^{2+}$ | | < 2.3 | Charge-transfer chelates $t = 20°$ |
| | Cu$^{2+}$ | | < 3.0 | |
| | Ag$^+$ | | 8.5 | |
| | Cu$^+$ | | 10.0 | |
| FlR$^{\ominus}$ | Ni$^{2+}$ | R = CH$_3$ | 4.9 | Radical chelates $t = 50°$ |
| | | R = H | 4.3 | |
| | Co$^{2+}$ | R = CH$_3$ | 4.5 | |
| | | R = H | 4.0 | |
| | Fe$^{2+}$ | | 3.7 | |
| | Zn$^{2+}$ | R = CH$_3$ | 4.7 | |
| | | R = H | 4.6 | |
| | Cd$^{2+}$ | R = CH$_3$ | 4.1 | |
| | | R = H | 4.0 | |

other origins (5). All these cases have in common that no indications have been found for an interaction between flavin and secondary system in the totally oxidized or in the totally reduced state. This is reflected also by our chemical models in the "binary" case of flavin + metal. The more redox systems involved, the more intermediate states will have to be considered. Two other binary systems, i.e., metal + sulfur and flavin + sulfur, and the "ternary" system, flavin + metal + sulfur, demand further model studies, which are in progress in several laboratories. Theoretically, $n + 1$ "valence states" may exist for $n$ electrons that can be taken up per protein unit, e.g., as many as six in the ternary system flavin + 2S + Fe and seven in flavin + Mo + 2S + Fe, or even more if additional sulfur groups and iron atoms are involved. This is true if one assumes that none of these redox-active groups is constrained to stay apart from the others by steric forces. The system will be still much more complicated if mutual interaction is assumed between the two sets of flavins, i.e., the two active sites, that are present in most flavoenzymes per protein unit, and for all the atoms of non-heme iron present. Given that possibility, any kinetic evaluation of flavoprotein mechanisms seems to be doomed to inadequacy if all the possibilities of partial denaturation are considered. Therefore, the search for model systems simulating physical qualities of the enzymes seems to be urgently necessary. Thus one may hope to find the smallest and most simple unit representing the essential features of the enzyme active site.

On the other hand, if the different electron carriers in flavoproteins are assumed to exist without direct contact with each other, the main problem is not the structure of the active sites, but the conductivity between them. This possibility opens a quite different approach, which may be as promising as the one presented above but which cannot be included in this present discussion.

## C. Applications in Deducing the Structure of Flavoprotein Active Sites

Model studies can at best only disprove a proposed enzyme mechanism or structure of active site, but—in the positive sense—they may give to biochemists working hypotheses that are thermodynamically sound. Thus, they can give support for a theory, but no evidence concerning what may happen *in vivo*.

When this is taken into consideration, the following may be said as a consequence of our data:

1. There is always the question whether the enzymatically observed oxidized and substrate-reduced states correspond to the totally oxidized and reduced states of the free cofactor redox system like $Fl + Fe$. Our data are compatible with the $Fl + Fe$ system, upon hydride transfer from, say, NADH, shuttling not between flavoquinone (FlH) and flavohydroquinone (FlH$_3$) states, but between

$$\text{Oxidized state (non-chelated)}\ \ FlH + Fe^{3+} \xrightarrow[\ \ \ \ H^+\ \ \ \ ]{H^-} (\dot{Fl}HFe^{II})^+ \ \text{Radical chelate}$$

$$e^- \nearrow \qquad \qquad \searrow e^-$$

$$e^- \swarrow (\dot{Fl}HFe^{III} \leftrightarrow FlHFe^{II})^{2+} \ \substack{\text{"Charge-transfer"}\\ \text{chelate}}$$

2. As far as the potential connection between flavin electron transfer and oxidative phosphorylation is concerned, it follows from our data that a complex of flavin and the proposed energy-transfer agent X [cf., e.g., (32)] has to be written $Fl \sim X$ in the oxidized form ("high-energy flavin") and $Fl—X$ in the reduced form, and not in the reverse sense.

3. As Handler *et al.* (5) have shown, at least most of the long-wave residual absorption of metalloflavoproteins is due to non-heme iron linked to protein.

Surprisingly, iron-flavin chelates give a very similar spectrum. It follows that changes of absorption between 400 and 600 m$\mu$ may or may not reflect the degree of reduction.

4. From ESR kinetics (3) it is concluded that there is no significant time difference in the reduction of free flavin and iron; but in some enzymes the flavin radical signal fades out at complete reduction, whereas in others it does not; the iron signal never fades. In agreement with our data, this may be readily explained.

In the first case, e.g., in dihydroorotic acid dehydrogenase, reduction stops at the radical chelate level, the $g = 1.94$ signal being associated with flavosemiquinone-linked Fe. But, as we showed (29), this complex in itself if not sufficient to produce this characteristic signal. Thus one has to look out for ternary constituents, e.g., protein-bound or free ["acid labile," (5)] sulfur.

In the second case, e.g., in xanthine oxidase, the radical chelate is finally reduced to give free FlH$_3$ and Fe linked solely to protein. In both cases, direct interaction between flavin and iron would be confined to the semiquinone level, where in the steady state an equilibrium is established between chelated and uncomplexed flavin radical.

5. The fact that different metals, like iron and molybdenum, behave in different ways toward flavin may reflect only the difference in pH dependence of flavin-chelate stability. Thus, the apparent flow of electrons in xanthine oxidase from molybdenum to flavin and iron can be explained by actual H$_2$O activity being higher at the molybdenum site and lower at the iron site, when molybdenum is taken as really "carrying" electrons from the substrate to the flavin.

6. There are two possibilities, consistent with our data, to interpret the role of metals in flavoproteins in a "teleological" way, but both have to be regarded with great care and reservation. Metals might be used in nature to uncouple the H$^-$ electron pair accepted by flavin from the substrate and release two electrons in single steps of suitable potential. Or at least iron might be used as a link between electron transfer and energy conservation. These speculations are open to discussion. But certainly, whatever the function of flavoprotein metals may be, they stabilize flavosemiquinone, the intermediate valence of the flavin system, at the expense of oxidized and reduced flavin forms.

## ACKNOWLEDGMENTS

This research has been sponsored by the Swiss National Foundation for the Advancement of Scientific Research.

We acknowledge the co-operation of Dr. Helmut Beinert, Institute for Enzyme Research, Madison, Wisconsin, to whom one of us (P. H.) is indebted for providing support as a visiting scientist (United States Public

Health Service Grant AM-02512). Thanks are due also to Professor H. Erlenmeyer, Basel, for inauguration of this program and continuous encouragement.

## REFERENCES

1. P. D. Boyer, H. Lardy, and K. Myrbäck, Eds., *The Enzymes*, Vol. VII, Academic Press, New York, 1963.
2. H. Beinert, W. Heinen, and G. Palmer, in "Enzyme Models and Enzyme Structure," *Brookhaven Symposia in Biol.*, No. 15, p. 229 (1962).
3. R. C. Bray, G. Palmer, and H. Beinert, *J. Biol. Chem.*, **239**, 2657 (1964).
4. R. C. Bray, B. G. Malmström, and T. Vänngård, *Biochem. J.*, **73**, 193 (1959).
5. P. Handler, R. V. Rajagopalan, and V. Aleman, *Federation Proc.*, **23**, No. 1, Vol. I, 30 (1964).
6. H. Beinert, *Abstracts of the 6th International Congress of Biochemistry, New York, 1964*.
7. A. Albert, *Biochem. J.*, **54**, 646 (1953); **47**, xxvii (1950).
8. P. Hemmerich and S. Fallab, *Helv. Chim. Acta*, **41**, 498 (1958).
9. W. O. Foye and W. E. Lange, *J. Am. Chem. Soc.*, **76**, 2199 (1954).
10. J. T. Spence and E. R. Peterson, *J. Inorg. & Nuclear Chem.*, **24**, 601 (1962).
11. P. Hemmerich, *Habilitationsschrift*, Basel, 1963.
12. I. F. Baarda and D. E. Metzler, *Biochem. et Biophys. Acta*, **50**, 463 (1961).
13. G. K. Radda and M. Calvin, *Biochemistry*, **3**, 384 (1964).
14. R. Kuhn, T. György, and T. Wagner-Jauregg, *Ber. deut. chem. Ges.*, **60**, 576 (1933).
15. P. Bamberg and P. Hemmerich, *Helv. Chim. Acta*, **44**, 1001 (1961).
16. P. Hemmerich, in *Wirkungsmechanismen von Enzymen*, 14. Mosbacher Coll. deutsch. physiol. Gesellschaft, Springer-Verlag, Heidelberg, 1963, p. 183.
17. P. Hemmerich, *Helv. Chim. Acta*, **47**, 464 (1964).
18. K. H. Dudley, A. Ehrenberg, P. Hemmerich, and F. Müller, *Helv. Chim. Acta*, **47**, 1354 (1964).
19. J. Bjerrum, G. Schwarzenbach, and G. Sillen, Eds., "Stability Constants," *Chem. Soc. Spec. Publ.* No. 6, London, 1957.
20. P. Hemmerich, in *Proceedings of the 3rd International Symposium on Pteridines, Stuttgart, 1962*, Pergamon Press, Oxford, p. 143.
21. K. H. Dudley and P. Hemmerich (to be published).
22. P. Hemmerich and C. Sigwart, *Experientia*, **19**, 488 (1963).
23. L. Michaelis and G. Schwarzenbach, *J. Biol. Chem.*, **123**, 538 (1938).
24. H. Beinert, *J. Am. Chem. Soc.*, **78**, 5323 (1956).
25. H. Beinert, in P. D. Boyer, H. Lardy, and K. Mybäck, Eds., *The Enzymes*, Vol. II, Academic Press, New York, 1960, p. 358.
26. A. Ehrenberg, *Arkiv Kemi*, **19**, 97 (1962).
27. A. Ehrenberg, G. Eriksson, and P. Hemmerich, p. 179 of this book.
28. V. Massey and G. Palmer, *J. Biol. Chem.*, **237**, 2347 (1962).
29. P. Hemmerich, D. V. DerVartanian, C. Veeger, and J. D. W. van Voorst, *Biochim. et Biophys. Acta*, **77**, 504 (1963).
30. H. Irving and R. J. P. Williams, *Nature*, **162**, 746 (1948).
31. V. Massey and Q. H. Gibson, *Federation Proc.*, **23**, No. 1, Vol. I, 18 (1964).
32. M. Klingenberg, *Angew. Chem.*, **75**, 900 (1963).

# On the Nature
# of Flavin Free Radicals

... ANDERS EHRENBERG, GÖRAN ERIKSSON,
and PETER HEMMERICH

## I. INTRODUCTION

During the past few years evidence has accumulated to show that intermediates are formed in the enzymic redox reactions catalyzed by a number of flavoproteins. In some cases it has been proved by means of ESR* spectroscopy that the intermediates are free radicals. There are also cases where the available evidence rather suggests that no free radicals are formed in the course of the enzymic reaction, and in these instances the intermediates observed must be of a different nature, e.g., enzyme-substrate complexes. Some of the flavoproteins contain transition metal ions as a necessary component, whereas others seem to be independent of such ions. In order to make it possible to discuss, on the molecular and submolecular (electronical) level, the variety of compounds and reactions where flavin participates, it was found necessary to extend our knowledge about the properties of flavin coenzymes and model compounds in their free-radical form. This half-reduced state is often called the semiquinoid state, but since this name implies *a priori* certain features of the electronic structure we will in this paper use the more general label "free radical" for the half-reduced state. From investigations of the light absorption and the ESR absorption important information has been obtained concerning the molecular and electronic properties of flavin free radicals. In this context it is of special interest that these investigations offer a rather unique opportunity, in case of a complicated molecule of biological interest, to make a detailed comparison of part of the experimental results with those obtained by quantum-chemical calculations.

* The following abbreviations are used in this paper: ESR, electron spin resonance; LF, lumiflavin (6,7,9-trimethylisoalloxazine); RF, riboflavin; FMN, flavin mononucleotide; FAD, flavin adenine dinucleotide; concerning the notation of the various flavin species see Fig. 1.

## II. GENERAL PROPERTIES AND CHOICE OF EXPERIMENTAL CONDITIONS

Figure 1 defines the nomenclature used for the different forms of a typical flavin compound. It also shows schematically the relation between the protonation steps of the different states of oxidation. The general structure of an isoalloxazine derivative and the numbering of positions used are evident from the formula of the figure. Each protonation stage of the radical of a given derivative has its specific electronic structure, ESR, and light absorption spectra. A fourth radical form, the dianion $\cdot F^{2-}$, may possibly exist in a very alkaline milieu, but it has not yet been characterized.

In the first detailed investigation of the ESR absorption of FMN and FAD free radicals at neutral pH it was observed by Ehrenberg (1) that the spectrum had features indicating that it was composed of two portions. One portion had a complicated, partly resolved hyperfine structure, whereas the other was without any resolved hyperfine structure. Later investigations by Ehrenberg (2–4) and Gibson *et al.* (5) have revealed that, in certain pH ranges, complexes between the free radical and the oxidized or reduced form of flavin are present in appreciable amounts at the flavin concentrations used in the

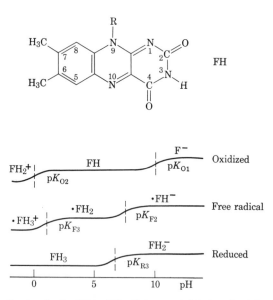

**Fig. 1.** Schematic diagram in the form of titration curves showing the approximate relative positions of the dissociations of the isoalloxazine moiety at the different oxidation levels of a flavin derivative. Lumiflavin: $R = CH_3$; riboflavin: $R = CH_2(CHOH)_3CH_2OH$; flavin mononucleotide: $R = CH_2(CHOH)_3CH_2OPO(OH)_2$. Modified from (2).

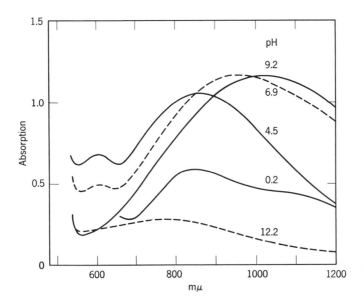

**Fig. 2.** Light absorption curves in the red and near infrared regions of 5 *mM* FMN, half-reduced with dithionite. Curve at pH 0.2 extrapolated from lower concentrations. pH solvent: 0.2/1 *N* HCl; 4.5/0.5 *M* acetate; 6.9/0.1 *M* phosphate; 9.2/0.2 *M* carbonate; 12.2/0.05 *N* NaOH (4).

experiments. Since the unpaired electron in these complexes is delocalized over two flavin molecules, the complexity of the hyperfine structure may preclude at present any resolution of the spectra. The complexes are of the charge-transfer type with light absorptions centered in the wavelength region of 700–1200 m$\mu$ (cf. Fig. 2). These bands are broad, and their positions and intensities are poorly defined because of overlap from the bands of the radical dimers. At present we cannot distinguish experimentally between the radical dimer, with the spins paired, and the complex between oxidized and reduced flavin. The disappearance of the radical absorption at about 600 m$\mu$ might be taken as indicating that a complex between the oxidized and reduced species is formed. However, a shift of the band some 50 m$\mu$ toward shorter wavelengths and/or a decrease in intensity would make it impossible to detect the absorption from the dimer (4); spectral shifts of this type have been reported in the case of dimerization of Wurster's blue perchlorate (6, 7).

The formation of radical dimers does not impair the study of the radical ESR spectra apart from decreasing the radical concentration somewhat. The presence of complexes between the free radical and the oxidized or reduced form, however, will seriously affect the ESR spectrum as described above. The conditions should therefore be chosen so as to minimize the formation of bimolecular complexes of this type.

Investigations of ESR and light absorption spectra have shown no such complications at pH 12.0–12.5 (4). Furthermore, the ESR spectrum of ·FH⁻ has a rather simple form. Unfortunately, the resolution of the ESR spectra of the radicals of FMN and FAD is not good enough to permit a detailed analysis. Such analysis has been possible, however, with LF and some related compounds (8); see section IIIA.

The neutral radical ·FH₂ is best studied at about pH 4.5, which is remote enough from $pK_{F2}$ and $pK_{F3}$. To avoid interference from the complex (·FH₂, FH₃) (4) it is necessary to use a low degree of reduction, low flavin concentration, high temperature, a solvent less polar than water, or a com-

## TABLE 1

**The Yield in Percentage of Free Radicals in 5 $mM$ Half-Reduced Aqueous FMN Solution of Various pH's (4)**

The value at pH 0.1 was extrapolated from lower FMN concentrations. Radical concentrations were determined by double integration of the recorded ESR spectra. Calibration was according to (2).

| pH:              | 0.1 | 4.8 | 7.1 | 9.2 | 12.3 |
|------------------|-----|-----|-----|-----|------|
| Free radicals, %: | 35  | 2.8 | 1.8 | 1.0 | 2.4  |

bination of these conditions. The present sensitivity of the instrumentation limits the use of low concentrations and low degrees of reductions. Especially when the solubility of the flavin derivative in aqueous medium is low, we have found useful a solvent mixture of 0.1 $M$ acetate buffer and cellosolve (1:1) at an increased temperature (9).

Also in acid aqueous medium there is interference from a radical complex (·FH₃⁺, FH₃) (4). The increased solubility and radical yield below pH 1 (see Table 1) make it easier than at pH 4.5 to meet the requirement of dilution (9). For certain compounds formic acid has been found to be a suitable solvent; see section IIIC.

All types of bimolecular complexes absorbing light in the near infrared seriously hamper a detailed investigation of the radical absorption in the region of about 600 m$\mu$. For a quantitative comparison of this absorption and the ESR intensity we have chosen to work with derivatives which do not form any bimolecular complexes in the solvent used; see section IV.

Various methods of reduction (or oxidation) have been used according to the experimental conditions. Most commonly we have applied dithionite as reducing agent; catalytic reductions (palladium, H₂) have also been used in alkaline solution, and in acid electrolysis, $SnCl_2$ or zinc has been employed. In no case have we observed any effect on the results of the mode of reduction. Reduced flavins have been oxidized with I₂ or O₂.

## III. ESR INVESTIGATIONS

### A. Anion Radicals

The coenzymes, as well as RF and LF at pH 12, all exhibit ESR spectra with an even number of hyperfine lines and an even spacing, but the resolution varies (2). A spectrum with 14 lines and with rather good resolution was afforded by LF. Eriksson and Ehrenberg (8) have investigated LF, using the technique of isotopic substitution in order to obtain an unambiguous interpretation of the spectrum. Nitrogen-15 and deuterium substitutions were carried out. Thus N-1, N-3, and N-10 have been exchanged for $^{15}$N, and H-5 and H-8 as well as $CH_3$-9 for D.

The isotropic hyperfine splitting arising from the Fermi contact term is proportional to the ratio $\mu/I$ (nuclear magnetic moment/nuclear spin). Hence, if $^{14}$N gives rise to three lines with a spacing between neighboring lines of $a^N(^{14}N)$, replacement by $^{15}$N in the same position will produce two lines with a spacing of $a^N(^{15}N) = -1.40a^N(^{14}N)$. Similarly, when protium is replaced by deuterium the doublet with a spacing of $a^H$ will transform into a triplet with the much smaller spacing $a^D = 0.154a^H$. As a practical consequence the hydrogen splitting will collapse when deuterium is introduced.

The effect of isotopic substitution upon the spectrum of LF radical anion is seen in Fig. 3. The main hyperfine splitting is not affected when N-1 and N-3 are substituted for $^{15}$N. The interaction from these nitrogens is a second-order effect increasing the resolution of the sublines within the main lines. The resolutions of these sublines were found to vary with the degree of reduction, but the reason for this is not yet understood. When N-10 is substituted the spectrum is strongly affected, showing that this nitrogen participates in the main hyperfine splitting. Deuterium substitution revealed that one, but only one, of the benzenoid hydrogens, H-5 or H-8, also contributes to the main splitting. However, it has not yet been possible to settle which of the positions contributes most. Also N-9 and the protons of the attached methyl group interact with a coupling close to the measured spacing. The anionic radical has one dissociable proton, which has been shown to be bound to N-3 (10). No effect on the ESR spectrum was observed when the LF radical was dissolved in alkaline $D_2O$. This may be due to a low spin density on N-3, or else the rate of exchange is too high.

The effect of the methyl groups in positions 6 and 7 was studied by means of a number of ethyl and chloro analogs of RF and LF. The influence of chloro substitution upon the spin-density distribution seems to be small, and no hyperfine interaction from the halogen itself was observed. Whereas substitution of methyl for chlorine is known to influence the redox potential (11, 12), it is interesting to note that the ESR evidence indicates that the

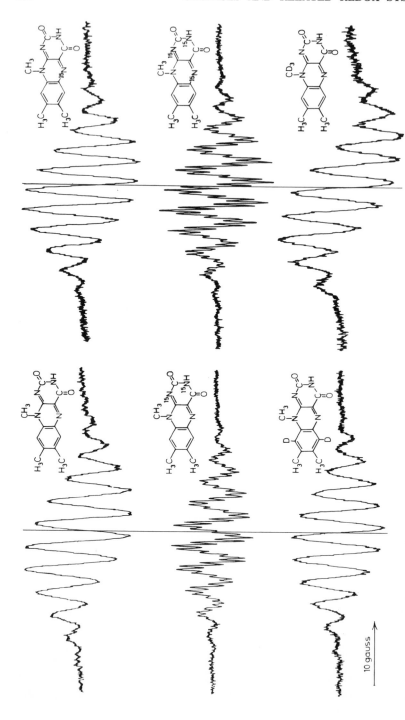

**Fig. 3.** ESR recordings of the free radicals of lumiflavin and isotopically substituted lumiflavin in aqueous solution at pH 12. Flavin concentration 10 m*M*, degree of reduction about 50% (8).

distribution of the unpaired $\pi$-electron remains essentially unaffected. A yellow non-paramagnetic precipitate was obtained when 6-chloro-7,9-dimethylisoalloxazine was reduced, even at rather low degree of reduction. The precipitate is probably the reduced form of the flavin. If the precipitate was partially reoxidized, the surface became greenish, and a weak unresolved ESR absorption was obtained. The precipitate dissolved upon reoxidation, and no change in the light absorption was observed.

All the 6-substituted derivatives (ethyl, methyl, and chloro) give rise to almost identical spectra; only the resolution varies slightly. This means that the spin density in the $2p_z$ orbital of C-6 is small. Investigation of 7-substituted derivatives revealed that the 7-methyl group of LF and RF takes part in the main hyperfine interaction of the radical. Thus 7-chloro-6,9-dimethylisoalloxazine afforded a spectrum with three lines less than for LF but with about the same spacing.

As we have mentioned, LF, RF, and the coenzymes all have spectra with an even number of lines. As found from the results by deuterium substitution, LF has three equivalent protons in the methyl group attached to N-9. This means that the two 1'-protons of the ribityl chain cannot be equivalent. One of the protons contributes with a coupling coinciding with the main spacing of the spectrum, whereas the other proton has a much weaker interaction. The total number of hyperfine lines for RF and the coenzymes has been difficult to settle experimentally. However, from the above-mentioned results we conclude that there are 12 lines. The asymmetry of the 1'-methylene group must be a consequence of the sterically hindered rotation of the ribityl chain. Whether the detailed mechanism should be expressed in terms of a positional time average or of a more fixed position, caused by a hydrogen bond from one of the ribityl hydroxyls to the pyrimidine moiety of the isoalloxazine, remains to be settled. In the latter case a rotational distortion and/or a bond angle distortion could take place.

The spectra of the various flavin radicals may be explained only by assuming that the hyperfine splittings of the nuclei participating in the interactions are multiples or fairly close to multiples of the measured spacing. The set of hyperfine coupling constants for the LF radical which fits the available experimental information is given in Table 2. It is not yet settled whether N-9 or N-10 gives the larger splitting. From theoretical relationships it is reasonable to assume that $a_9^N \sim a_9^H(NCH_3)$, and the larger splitting is therefore primarily assigned to N-10.

The spin densities at certain atoms have been calculated from the experimental coupling constants by means of the linear relations

$$a_i^H = Q_{CH}^H \rho_{C_i}^\pi; \quad a_i^H = Q_{XCH_3}^H \rho_{X_i}^\pi; \quad a_i^N = Q_N^N \rho_{N_i}^\pi$$

where $Q$ is the spin polarization parameter, and $\rho^\pi$ is the spin density in the $2p_z$ orbital of the trigonal intracyclic atom. The relationship for nitrogen

TABLE 2

**Main Isotropic Hyperfine Coupling Constants (in Gauss) for the Anionic Lumiflavin Free Radical**

Figures within brackets denote alternative possibilities (8).

| | |
|---|---|
| | $a_5^H = 3.5$ [small] |
| $a_9^N = 3.5$ [7.0] | $a_7^H(CCH_3) = 3.5$ |
| $a_{10}^N = 7.0$ [3.5] | $a_8^H = $ small [3.5] |
| | $a_9^H(NCH_3) = 3.5$ |

is a reasonable first approximation, since the contributions from the spin densities in the $p_z$ orbitals of nearest-neighbor atoms usually are small.

By means of the spin polarization parameters reported in the literature for other compounds and on the assumption that no negative spin densities occur, the values of the spin densities given in Table 3 were derived (8). Also included in the table are results from quantum-chemical calculations. Karreman (13) has applied the Hückel method, considering all the mobile

TABLE 3

**Comparison between Experimental Spin Densities and Theoretically Calculated Distributions of the Unpaired Electron in the Flavin Anion Radical**

The range of values stated for ESR is determined by the limits of the spin polarization parameters ($Q$) found in the literature. All values are in units of the negative electronic charge. Only positions relevant for the interpretation of the ESR spectra are included (8).

| | | | | Baudet | Grabe[a] | |
|---|---|---|---|---|---|---|
| | | | Karreman (13) | et al. (14) | | |
| | | | Keto | Keto | Keto | Enol |
| Position | Atom | ESR ($\rho^\pi$) | Form | Form | Form | Form |
| 1 | N | $\leqslant 0.025$ | 0.037 | 0.013 | 0.074 | 0.057 |
| 3 | N | $\leqslant 0.025$ | 0.001 | −0.007 | 0.000 | 0.094 |
| 5 | C | 0.130–0.167 | 0.097 | 0.158 | 0.044 | 0.037 |
| 6 | C | $\leqslant 0.025$ | 0.014 | −0.031 | 0.000 | 0.000 |
| 7 | C | 0.125–0.184 | 0.080 | 0.098 | 0.028 | 0.023 |
| 8 | C | $\leqslant 0.025$ | 0.037 | 0.015 | 0.011 | 0.008 |
| 9 | N | 0.123–0.189 | 0.096 | 0.107 | 0.036 | 0.027 |
| 10 | N | 0.246–0.378 | 0.282 | 0.427 | 0.343 | 0.321 |

[a] B. Grabe, personal communication, 1964. Calculations were made on UNIVAC 1105 at the Illinois Institute of Technology, Chicago, Ill.

electrons of the anionic radical in keto form. Baudet *et al.* (14) have used a self-consistent field method, calculating with separate orbitals for spin $\alpha$ and spin $\beta$. In this way also negative spin densities may be obtained. However, the type of wave function used in this calculation has been criticized (15). With the permission of Dr. B. Grabe, University of Stockholm, her unpublished self-consistent field calculations on the radical, explicitly considering the unpaired electron, are shown in Table 3. As seen from the table, the agreement between the experimental and theoretical spin densities is as good as could be expected when one considers the complexity involved in the calculations on the anion radical with not less than 23 $\pi$-electrons to account for.

## B. Neutral Radicals

Both RF and LF radicals give rather well-resolved ESR spectra in the acetate-cellosolve medium at $+65°C$ (9). A spectrum with 32 readily detectable lines was obtained for RF, confirming the observation made on the less well resolved spectra of FMN and FAD in aqueous phosphate or acetate buffer (1). Also in the case of LF there is an even number of lines. This suggests that the asymmetry of the 1'-protons of ribityl observed in alkaline solution persists also at neutral pH.

The spectrum of LF substituted with $^{15}N$ in position N-10 has an odd number of lines, demonstrating that N-10 has a strong hyperfine coupling also in the neutral radical. With $^{15}N$ substituted in positions 1 and 3, no effect whatsoever could be detected on the ESR spectrum. This shows that the hyperfine coupling to the pyrimidine nitrogens of the neutral radical is below detectability. In fact, the spin density distribution is very little affected also by 3-N-alkylation, as we have found from the close similarity between the spectra of LF and of 3-acetic acid-LF radicals. The same substituent, however, produces a profound change in the ESR spectrum of $\cdot FH^-$. This might be correlated with different $\pi$-electron conjugation with the pyrimidine moiety in $\cdot FH_2$ and $\cdot FH^-$.

## C. Cation Radicals

In acid solution the flavin radicals exhibit ESR spectra of about the same complexity as in neutral solution. The technique of isotopic substitution in LF shows again, as for the neutral radical, that there is no detectable hyperfine coupling to the pyrimidine nitrogens (9). Further support for this conclusion is obtained from the small, in some cases undetectable, effect on the ESR spectrum evoked by N-alkylation in the pyrimidine ring. This is illustrated in Fig. 4. In concentrated formic acid, LF, 3-acetic acid-LF, and 3-benzyl-LF all give identical radical spectra (Fig. 4a). As shown in Fig. 4c, 3-benzyl-1-methyl-LF yields a spectrum with an increased resolution in the center but with the wings unaltered. Similar results were obtained with 9-methylisoalloxazine and its 1,3-dimethyl derivative which gave practically super-posable radical spectra with 22 hyperfine lines (Fig. 4d). A comparison between Figs. 4a and 4b for LF radicals in concentrated formic acid and 10 $N$ HCl, respectively, shows that the change in solvent does not influence the main lines but merely affects the resolution of sublines.

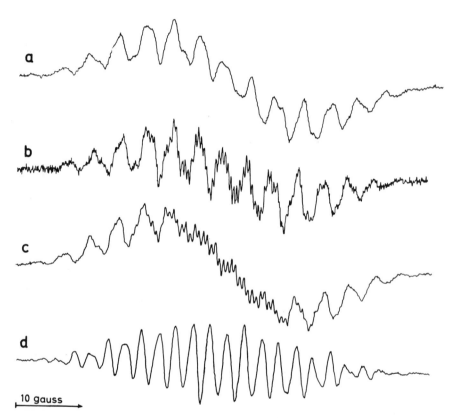

**Fig. 4.** ESR recordings of flavin free radicals in acid medium. (a) Lumiflavin in conc. HCOOH and SnCl$_2$ reduction. The spectra of 3-acetic acid- and 3-benzyl-lumiflavin are identical. (b) Lumiflavin in 10 $N$ HCl; electrolytic reduction to about 50% degree of reduction. (c) 3-Benzyl-1-methyl-lumiflavin in conc. HCOOH and SnCl$_2$ reduction. (d) 9-Methylisoalloxazine in conc. HCOOH and SnCl$_2$ reduction. This spectrum is almost identical with that for 1,3,9-trimethylisoalloxazine.

Furthermore, work with isotopic substitutions in the LF radicals has shown convincingly (9) that N-10, CH$_3$-9, and, consequently, also N-9, as well as at least one of the ring protons, H-5 and H-8, participate in the observed hyperfine splitting of the cation radical. Part of this finding is in contradistinction to other work giving no assignment of coupling to any of the ring protons (16) but suggesting a considerable hyperfine coupling to N-1 (16, 17).

Partially reduced LF, 6-chloro-7,9-dimethylisoalloxazine, and 7-chloro-6,9-dimethylisoalloxazine in formic acid give quite different ESR spectra. It is hence clear that both the 6- and 7-methyl groups contribute to the hyperfine structure with appreciable, but different, coupling constants. Consequently, the spin densities in positions 6 and 7 are more nearly equal in $\cdot FH_3^+$ than in $\cdot FH^-$.

Because of the complexity of the ESR spectra of $\cdot FH_3^+$ and the possible presence of more than one radical species (4) we are not yet able to give any definite assignments of hyperfine coupling constants and spin densities. It is evident, however, that in $\cdot FH_3^+$ the spin density in the pyrimidine ring is even smaller, and the spin density distribution over the pyrazine and benzene rings is more even, than in $\cdot FH^-$. The available quantum-chemical calculations (13, 14, 16) are in rough agreement with the latter conclusion.


## IV. LIGHT ABSORPTION

In the red and near infrared region, where the oxidized and reduced species have very weak or no absorption, half-reduced FMN in aqueous solution at various pH values gives light absorption spectra as shown in Fig. 2. The maximum in the neighborhood of 600 m$\mu$ at neutral pH was ascribed to the free radical by Beinert (18). We have been able to confirm this assignment completely. The yield of free radicals at half-reduction at the various pH values has been determined (4) from the ESR spectra as given in Table 1. The minimum at about pH 9 is consistent with the potentiometric results for RF obtained by Hemmerich (10).

The light absorption at about 600 m$\mu$ is much smaller at pH 12.2 than at pH 6.9. In the curve for pH 12.2 (Fig. 2) no peak, not even an inflection, is developed in this region; in spite of that at pH 12.2 the concentration of $\cdot FH^-$ is higher than the total radical concentration at the pH 6.9, i.e.,

$$[\cdot FH_2] + [\cdot FH^-] + [(\cdot FH_2, FH_2^-)]$$

This demonstrates that the absorption at 600 m$\mu$ is characteristic of $\cdot FH_2$, whereas the absorption of $\cdot FH^-$ in this region must be of much smaller magnitude.

In partially reduced solutions of tetraacetyl-RF and 3-ethyl acetate-LF in the comparatively unpolar medium of chloroform, no disturbing bimolecular complexes are formed (19). In this case the reduction is achieved by shaking with a neutral aqueous dithionite solution. The spectrum of $\cdot FH_2$ for tetra-acetyl-RF has a maximum close to 620 m$\mu$ with a shoulder at shorter wavelengths (Fig. 5$A$). Upon addition of 0.1 $N$ triethylamine about 65% of the absorption vanishes (Fig. 5B). Except for some minor deviations the decrease is proportional within the range 550–700 m$\mu$. This indicates that the main portion of the remaining absorption is caused by undissociated ·FH$_2$, and that ·FH$^-$ also in this medium may have only a rather weak

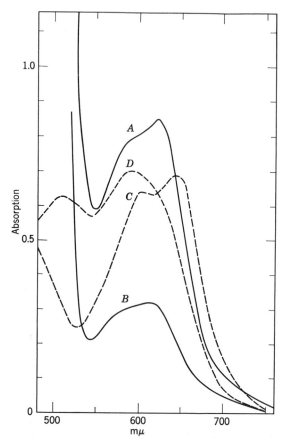

**Fig. 5.** Light absorption around 600 m$\mu$ of flavin free radicals. *A*. 10 *mM* tetraacetyl-riboflavin (or 3-ethyl acetate-lumiflavin) in CHCl$_3$, 50% reduced. *B*. The same as *A* added with 0.1 *N* triethylamine. *C*. 3-Ethyl acetate-4-(O-methyl)-lumiflavin in reduced form in chloroform, partially oxidized by I$_2$. *D*. The same compound as in *C*, dissolved in methanol, and partially reoxidized (19).

absorption at about 600 m$\mu$. After acidification with formic acid, or in aqueous HCl, the absorption maxima of the ·FH$_3^+$ are found at 486 and 358 m$\mu$, in good agreement with the results on FMN and RF by Ogura *et al.* (20).

    In order to investigate the influence of a polar medium, 3-ethyl acetate-LF in chloroform was completely reduced, O-methylated in position 4, and partially reoxidized by $O_2$ or $I_2$ (19). In chloroform the absorption of $\cdot FH_2$ is in this case similar to that of tetraacetyl-RF but has two distinct peaks and is shifted about 20 m$\mu$ toward longer wavelengths (Fig. 5C). The dried, reduced O-methylated compound was dissolved in methanol, diluted with aqueous phosphate buffer, and partially oxidized. In this milieu the radical absorption is found instead at shorter wavelengths (Fig. 5D), with the maximum at 590 m$\mu$ and an indication of a shoulder on the long-wavelength side.

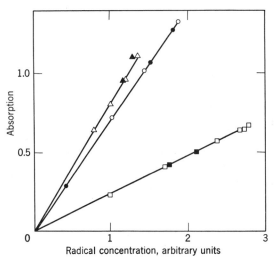

Fig. 6. Demonstration of linear relationship between light absorption and free-radical concentration, determined from the ESR absorption. Reduced 3-ethyl acetate-4-(O-methyl)-lumiflavin: in chloroform, oxidized with $I_2$ ($\square$) to maximum radical concentration and then by $O_2$ ($\blacksquare$), light absorption measured at 650 m$\mu$; in methanol-0.1 $M$ aqueous phosphate buffer (1:4), oxidized by $I_2$, with less than 1 equivalent ($\triangle$, $\bigcirc$) and more than 1 equivalent ($\blacktriangle$, $\bullet$), light absorption measured at 580 m$\mu$ (two experiments).

3-Ethyl acetate-4-(O-methyl)-LF was found to be well suited for experiments to establish the relationship between light and ESR absorption, because no radical disproportionation is taking place. Comparison of the intensity of the light absorption at 650 m$\mu$ in the chloroform solution and at 580 m$\mu$ in the aqueous solution with the amplitude of the ESR absorption upon stepwise oxidation of the reduced compound has shown that there is a strict proportionality between the two quantities (Fig. 6). This is a most convincing demonstration that just one radical species, $\cdot FH_2$, is responsible for the absorption maximum at about 600 m$\mu$ in $CHCl_3$ as well as in $H_2O$. After proper calibration the absolute radical concentrations may be estimated for the experiments in aqueous solution. As a mean for the two experiments we calculate the molar absorptivity of the radical at 580 m$\mu$ to be 4600 $M^{-1}$ cm$^{-1}$. The error in this figure may be as large as $\pm 30\%$. There is fair agreement with the values 3300 (21) and 3000 $M^{-1}$ cm$^{-1}$ (4) estimated for the absorption maximum of FMN free radicals, considering that the radicals of the two compounds may have somewhat different chemical nature.

## V. CONCLUDING REMARKS

In combination with isotopic substitution and chemical modification, ESR has proved to be a sensitive tool for studying the spin density distribution in flavin radicals. Even if the agreement with the quantum-chemical calculations is at present only fairly rough, where there is an agreement at all, this fact is nevertheless promising, considering the complexity of the flavin molecule. One of the more striking features of the ESR results is that there is no or only very little spin density in the pyrimidine moiety. This means that the molecular orbital of the unpaired electron embraces only the benzene and pyrazine rings. A functional partition within the molecule is indicated (2) with the pyrimidine ring engaged in the binding of the coenzyme to the apoprotein (22) and with the remaining portion participating in the redox reactions. In these reactions N-10 is the most likely point of attack and has the highest spin density. In the case of metal flavoproteins this fits well with the conviction that metal ions coordinate with the free radical in position N-10 (23).

It is a drawback that for enzyme-bound flavin free radicals it is not possible to resolve any ESR hyperfine structure at present (1, 2). It is now well established that the neutral flavin radical ·FH$_2$ has a light absorption band at about 600 m$\mu$. This absorption might be used for following the appearance of this radical in flavin enzymes. However, since charge-transfer complexes might *a priori* absorb in the same region, identification must in each case rely on the magnetic criterion.

The stage of protonation of transitory flavin radicals in enzyme catalysis cannot be predicted; it depends on the detailed mechanism of the reaction. Light absorption and fluorescence spectra indicate that the oxidized coenzyme is probably linked to the protein in the neutral form FH. A one-electron reduction of FH transforms it into ·FH$^-$. Consequently it is quite possible that not only ·FH$_2$ but also ·FH$^-$ has biological significance.

## ACKNOWLEDGMENT

This work was sponsored in part by Research Grant AM-5895 from the National Institute of Arthritis and Metabolic Diseases, United States Public Health Service, in part by Schweizerischen Nationalfond zur Verfügung der wissenschaftlichen Forschung, and in part by a traveling grant from Statens Naturvetenskapliga Forskningsråd, Sweden.

## REFERENCES

1. A. Ehrenberg, *Acta Chem. Scand.*, **14**, 766 (1960).
2. A. Ehrenberg, *Arkiv Kemi*, **19**, 97 (1962).
3. A. Ehrenberg, in B. Pullman, Ed., *Electronic Aspects of Biochemistry*, Academic Press, New York, 1964, p. 379.
4. A. Ehrenberg (in preparation).
5. Q. H. Gibson, V. Massey, and N. M. Atherton, *Biochem. J.*, **85**, 369 (1962).
6. K. H. Hausser, *Z. Naturforsch.*, **11a**, 20 (1956).
7. K. H. Hausser and J. N. Murrell, *J. Chem. Phys.*, **27**, 500 (1957).
8. L. E. G. Eriksson and A. Ehrenberg, *Acta Chem. Scand.*, **18**, 1437 (1964).
9. A. Ehrenberg and L. E. G. Eriksson, *Arch. Biochem. Biophys.*, **105**, 453 (1964).
10. P. Hemmerich, *Helv. Chim. Acta*, **47**, 464 (1964).
11. R. Kuhn, F. Weygand, and E. F. Möller, *Ber.*, **76B**, 1044 (1943).
12. J. P. Lambooy, R. A. Scala, and E. E. Haley, *J. Nutrition*, **74**, 466 (1961).
13. G. Karreman, *Bull. Math. Biophys.*, **23**, 135 (1961).
14. J. Baudet, G. Berthier, and B. Pullman, *Compt. rend.*, **254**, 762 (1962).
15. A. D. McLachlan, *Molecular Phys.*, **3**, 233 (1960).
16. A. V. Guzzo and G. Tollin, *Arch. Biochem. Biophys.*, **103**, 231 (1963).
17. H. Kubo, T. Shiga, M. Uozumi, and A. Isomato, *Bull. soc. chim. biol.*, **34**, 219 (1963).
18. H. Beinert, *J. Am. Chem. Soc.*, **78**, 5323 (1956).
19. K. H. Dudley, A. Ehrenberg, P. Hemmerich, and F. Müller, *Helv. Chim. Acta*, **47**, 1354 (1964).
20. Y. Ogura, S. Nakamura, and T. Nakamura, *Acta Chem. Scand.*, **17**, Suppl. 1, 184 (1963).
21. H. Beinert, *J. Biol. Chem.*, **225**, 465 (1957).
22. H. Theorell and A. P. Nygaard, *Acta Chem. Scand.*, **8**, 1649 (1954).
23. P. Hemmerich, in *Wirkungsmechanismen von Enzymen*, 14, Mosbacher Coll. Deutsch. Physiol. Gesellsch., Springer-Verlag, Heidelberg, 1963, p. 183.

*Discussion*

EHRENBERG: In our paper, we show that the position and intensity of the near-infrared absorption of dimolecular complexes vary with pH. We have already shown that with flavin free radicals the complexes are not only radical dimers, but also mixed complexes between the radical and the oxidized or reduced forms. This is further illustrated in Fig. 1.

You will note how the field of free radicals varies with pH and the degree of reduction. Under conditions where there is complex formation between the oxidized and the free-radical form, we have a maximum at low degree of reduction. Under conditions where the other form between the free radical and the reduced flavin is favored, we have a maximum at a high degree of reduction. The curve for pH 12 where we have the anion radical is completely symmetrical. This curve is not shown, but it demonstrates that we have no complications with this type of dimolecular free radical at this pH. In Fig. 2 we see that there is very little hyperfine structure at pH 9.2, where there is a complex between the oxidized and the radical forms at a low degree of reduction. At a high degree of reduction, we have more hyperfine structure, because there is no complicating extra free radical. In fact, if

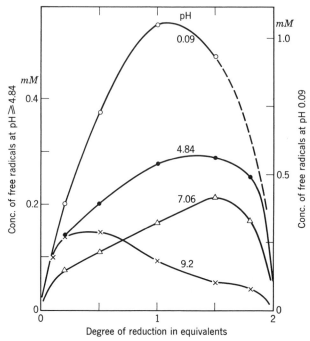

**Fig. 1.**  The yield of FMN free radicals at various pH values as a function of the degree of reduction in equivalents.  (A. Ehrenberg, in preparation.)

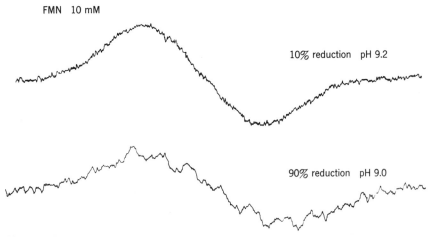

**Fig. 2.**  ESR spectra of flavin free radicals at pH 9 to 9.2 at low and high degree of reduction.

we control the pH carefully, we can show that the former type of spectrum is just an addition of the broad spectrum without any hyperfine structure and the spectrum at a high degree of reduction. It should also be noted that the light absorption in the near infrared is not constant. The maximum shifts with the degree of reduction. At pH 9.2 the extrapolated wavelength of the maximum is 1080 m$\mu$ at zero reduction and 990 m$\mu$ at 100% reduction. The behavior is similar at other pH values where

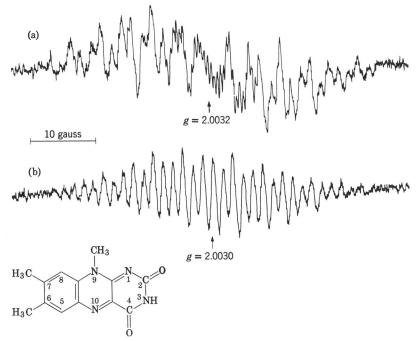

Fig. 3. ESR spectra of lumiflavin (LF) free radicals. The corresponding spectrum of the radical of LF-1,3-$^{15}$N$_2$ is identical in each case. (a) 1 $mM$ LF in 3$N$ HCl. (b) 4 $mM$ LF in a solvent mixture of 0.1 $M$ acetate buffer and cellosolve (1:1) at +65°C. Degree of reduction about 50%. [From A. Ehrenberg and G. Eriksson, *Arch. Biochem. Biophys.*, **105**, 453 (1964).]

we have this type of interaction. This clearly shows that we have more than one species under these conditions. In Tables 1 and 2 in our paper (pp. 182, 186 of this book), you will note that in positions 1 and 3 of the anion radical there is very low spin density on these two nitrogens, and this is what we found by substituting $^{15}$N into these positions. In the neutral and cation radicals, we were unable to detect any spin density for these nitrogens. This is shown in Fig. 3. These are the spectra of lumiflavin free radicals in 3$N$ hydrochloric acid, and in acetate-cellosolve mixture a wealth of hyperfine structure can be seen. The complicated spectra of normal lumiflavin and lumiflavin with $^{15}$N in positions 1 and 3 are identical in all details, really identical. So the identity of these complicated spectra rules out the possibility that there is any hyperfine interaction with N-1 and N-3 nuclei.

Since Guzzo and Tollin [*Arch. Biochem. Biophys.*, **103**, 231 (1963)] proposed a high spin density in position 1 of the cation radical, Malrieu and Pulman (*Theoret. Chim. Acta*, in press) have made calculations for this radical in a form bent along the axis through N-9 and N-10. They could show that this increased the spin density in the calculations on N-1. Since there is, in fact, no spin density in this position, we can rule out this bent form of the radical.

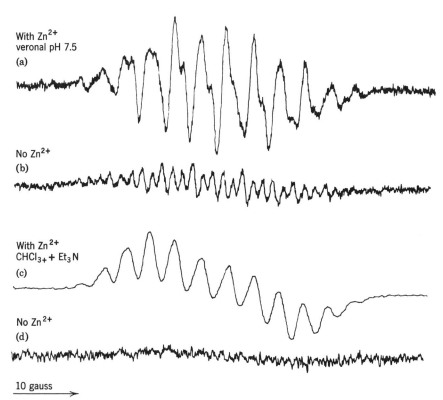

**Fig. 4.** ESR spectra of free radicals of lumiflavin-3-acetic acid in aqueous veronal buffer [(a) and (b)] and tetraacetyl riboflavin in chloroform [(c) and (d)] without and with added $Zn^{2+}$ ions.

In judging the agreement between experiment and quantum-chemical calculations, the spin density is a rougher criterion than light absorption; hence it should be easier to obtain a reasonable fit in this case. From Table 3 (p. 186) you will see that there is agreement between experiment and calculation only on certain points, whereas on other points the agreement is not good. This tells us that we have to be careful when using the quantum-chemical predictions about electron distributions in molecules of this complexity.

Dr. Hemmerich, in cooperation with people at Slater's laboratory in Amsterdam, has shown that the addition of zinc to partially reduced flavin increased the signals in the ESR. We repeated this research in Stockholm with Dr. Hemmerich and found the dramatic increase shown in Fig. 4. There is a tremendous increase that shows the great stability of these complexes. In Fig. 5, we see the correlation between the absorption at 810 m$\mu$ mentioned by Dr. Hemmerich and the radical concentration. When we vary the concentration of $Zn^{2+}$, we see that there is essentially a linear correlation. Dr. Bray and I have investigated xanthine oxidase in an attempt to find any absorption at about 800 m$\mu$ in the half-reduced state. Our preliminary experiments have so far given negative results.

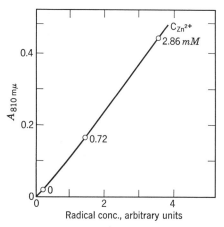

**Fig. 5.** Comparison of light absorption at 810 m$\mu$ and the integrated ESR absorption for different concentrations of added $Zn^{2+}$ ions. Half-reduced tetraacetyl riboflavin in chloroform, 14 $mM$ $(C_2H_5)_3N$, 5.5 $M$ $CH_3CN$. (From A. Ehrenberg and P. Hemmerich, *Acta Chem. Scand.*, in press.)

HANDLER: Dr. Hemmerich, is there any known flavoprotein that looks anything like the absorption spectrum in your Figs. 2 and 7?

HEMMERICH: No, I think that we have to differentiate carefully between non-redox and redox-active metal ions. In flavoproteins we find the redox-active ions, i.e., molybdenum and iron. I have shown that the spectra of the $Mo^{5+}$-flavoquinone complex and the $Fe^{2+}$-flavoquinone complex are very similar. Neither of them has this band in the near infrared. Indeed, as Dr. Handler showed in his paper, the absorption of the non-heme iron in the flavoproteins is very similar to this absorption of the charge-transfer chelate between iron and isoalloxazine. I think that we have to deal with the fact that two very similar absorptions of different components are present. Consequently, we have to face the following problem. When we start with the oxidized iron and the oxidized flavin, we have only the interaction of iron and protein, as pointed out by Dr. Handler. Upon reduction, we get the interaction of half the reduced flavin and iron giving a similar spectrum to that of the oxidized iron protein, while the oxidized iron protein spectrum is decreasing. I have compared this with the spectra Dr. Handler showed, and it seems that there is no correlation between the decrease of absorption and the redox state. This is what we would expect.

SINGER: Since the existence of zinc flavoproteins has not been brought out, I should like to mention that two zinc flavoproteins have been isolated in highly purified form, D-lactic cytochrome reductase and D-α-hydroxyacid dehydrogenase. Both of these have a constant proportion of zinc to FAD, and zinc is an essential part of a molecule involved in binding the substrate.

MASSEY: I should like to ask whether there is any evidence that iron interacts with the semiquinoid form of the flavin in metal flavoproteins.

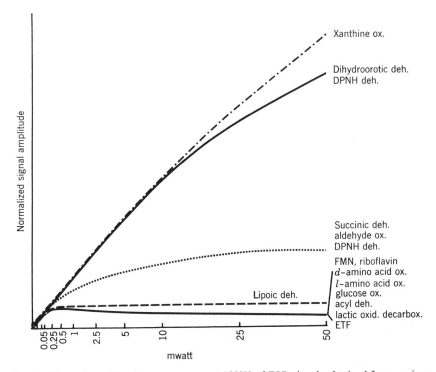

**Fig. 6.** Saturation with microwave power at 103°K of ESR signals obtained from various flavins and flavoproteins at the state of partial reduction. The data are normalized and plotted as in Fig. 1 of Beinert and Palmer, p. 570 of Volume Two.

BEINERT: We have looked at eight metal-free flavin proteins and five metallo-flavoproteins. I wonder if there are any more than five. And we find the very characteristic and easily reproducible difference in saturation with microwave power of the free radical in these enzymes. The difference is quite great. All the metal-free flavoproteins saturate almost alike, in a very similar manner to free flavin. By adding metal to the metal-free flavoproteins, we have been able to reproduce the saturation behavior of the metal flavoproteins. Figure 6 shows the saturation with microwave power of the radical signals obtained from partly reduced flavins and flavoproteins. On the ordinate, we plotted signal amplitudes normalized at low power (0.02 mwatt); as you can see, they are all superimposed. The square root of the microwave power in milliwatts is plotted on the abscissa. The values shown are those before extraction of the root. All the metal-free flavoproteins, D-amino acid oxidase, L-amino acid oxidase, glucose oxidase, acyl-Co A dehydrogenases, lactic acid decarboxylase, electron-transferring flavoprotein, and microsomal TPNH cytochrome reductase, another flavoprotein recently isolated from *Azotobacter*, show essentially the same saturation as FAD, FMN, and riboflavin.

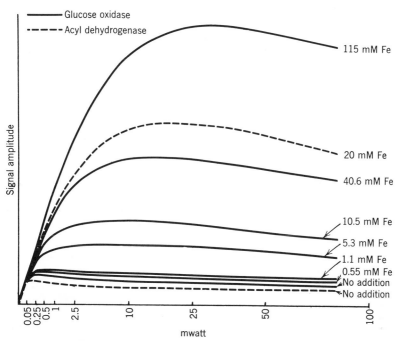

**Fig. 7.** Saturation of two flavoproteins free of endogenous metal in the absence and the presence of added $Fe^{3+}$ versenate, plotted as in Fig. 1.

Lipoic dehydrogenase is a little different, but not very much. Much less saturating are succinic dehydrogenase, aldehyde oxidase, DPNH dehydrogenase, and particularly dihydroorotic dehydrogenase and xanthine oxidase, saturating barely at the powers which are shown here. Figure 7 shows that saturation decreases for two enzymes, acyl-Co A dehydrogenase and glucose oxidase, when we produce the semiquinone in the presence of iron versenate. With an increasing amount of the iron chelate added, we get saturation behavior reminiscent of what we find in the metalloflavoproteins. Since these data are quite reproducible, we conclude that another relaxation mechanism is indeed available to the spin system in metalloflavoproteins which is not available in the metal-free flavoproteins; and it is, of course, relatively easy to guess that this relaxation mechanism is provided by the associated metal in these flavoproteins. One could think of other interpretations; but this is the most obvious one.

RACKER: Dr. Hemmerich, have you attempted to look at the changes in the spectrum of iron flavin charge-transfer complexes in the presence of phenanthroline?

HEMMERICH: We have not done that because we can be quite sure of what might happen. It would be a complete displacement of the equilibrium towards the phenanthroline chelate, because the phenanthroline has the stability of many orders of magnitude higher than the flavin radical chelate, as any very stable iron complex might have. The flavin radical chelate, however, is not tremendously stable—it has just medium stability—and that is why I think that it is important in biological oxidation.

ORGEL: I should like to ask two questions. First of all, if one looks at different metals, is it true that the saturation behavior is the same for all paramagnetic metals, or does this behavior depend on the oxidizing or reducing powers of metals?

BEINERT: We have done these experiments with nickel and iron and with zinc. With the flavoproteins, zinc has absolutely no influence, as we would have expected because it is not paramagnetic. On the other hand, nickel and iron both gave the same type of effect; I think that we would have to do this much more systematically, because what also enters here is the form in which the metals are added. Some of these metals are not soluble at the pH required for the proteins. In the case shown, we have added the iron-EDTA complex, which is very strong. I think that we have to work this through with similar complexes for each metal, and only then can we arrive at conclusions about the differences due to the properties of the metal itself.

ORGEL: I should also like to ask a second question, which in a way follows from the first. If you look at the amount of metal ion which is needed to reduce the saturation of non-metal enzymes, how does this compare with the amount of metal actually present in the metal enzymes themselves? What I am getting at is, Does there seem to be a much closer association between the metal and the flavin in the metal flavin proteins than the random association you get when you add a metal ion, say iron?

BEINERT: Yes, we have considered this question. The difference is about two orders of magnitude; therefore, when you are adding metal in the form of these chelates, you have to add roughly 100 times more in order to get the same effect as with the built-in metal of the metalloflavoproteins. I think that this makes sense.

HEMMERICH: I want to add in regard to the question of Dr. Orgel that in the metalloflavoproteins we have, let's say, approximately stoichiometric amounts of metal and iron, and with the model ligands we have also stoichiometric amounts of metal sufficient to cause the tremendous change in saturation. However, in the non-metal flavoproteins, as Dr. Beinert pointed out, we need about 100-fold higher concentration to imitate this effect.

Figure 8 might answer Dr. Orgel's question. You can see the protonated flavin radical, which is indeed isoelectronic to the radical chelates, and the dashed line shows the tremendous change in absorption obtained when you substitute position 5 by benzyl. When you do that, you get a radical which is no longer accessible to chelation. We made saturation studies with this benzylflavosemiquinonium salt. We did not get this tremendous effect of added metal, which means that the saturation effect has indeed something to do with metals being able to add specifically to nitrogen number 5. Again, this tremendous increase in absorption proves the statement of Dr. Ehrenberg that these radicals are flat in contrast to the leuco forms.

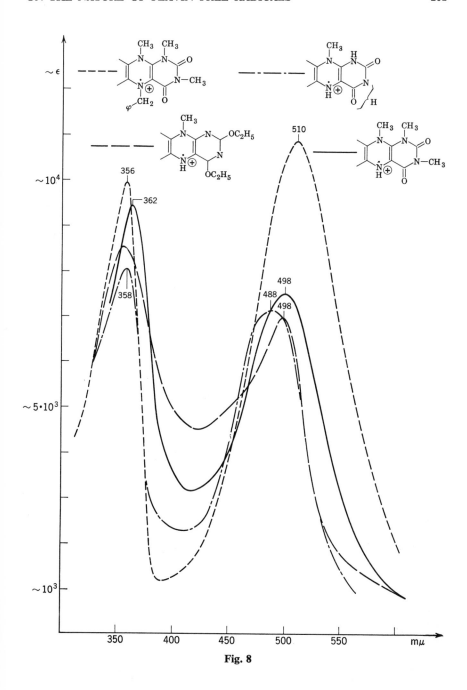

**Fig. 8**

KING: Why do all the metalloflavoproteins contain labile sulfide?

HEMMERICH: Well, I can only make a guess why they do. I think that the labile sulfide is something which has to do with the specific binding of the non-heme iron in the protein. This labile-sulfide binding is characteristic for ferroproteins and is of ternary importance in the context of flavins.

KING: Dr. Beinert, on Fig. 6 you listed succinate dehydrogenase and DPNH dehydrogenase; I wonder which succinate dehydrogenase you have used. That is my first question. Second, according to our estimates, the iron content of succinic dehydrogenase is much higher than the literature value, as shown in Table 1. This

### TABLE 1

#### Soluble Succinate Dehydrogenase

M$\mu$moles (atom)/mg

|  |  |
|---|---|
| Co Q | 0.0 |
| Heme | 0.0 |
| Flavin$^a$ |  |
|     Acid extractable | 0.0 |
|     Acid non-extractable | 3.6 |
| Non-heme iron | 30 |
| "Labile" sulfide | 28 |

$^a$ Average of six samples, flavin:Fe:sulfide = 1:8.5:1.

succinic dehydrogenase can react with the cytochrome system and contains approximately eight to nine atoms to one flavin. At the same time, the labile sulfide is in the stoichiometric ratio of almost 1:1. The six preparations contain different amounts of flavins, but the ratio is relatively constant.

BEINERT: I didn't realize that this was of importance, and I think with respect to the point that we were going to make it is not. You could use any metalloflavoprotein. We used the Singer type of preparation and the Ziegler type, and both show similar behavior. I should point out that the Ziegler enzyme has approximately the iron to flavin ratio that Dr. King finds, but these enzymes have somewhat different behavior. I think that, for the purposes we were interested in, it doesn't matter whether they are "reconstitutively active" or not.

MASSEY: Dr. Beinert, what is the effect of the added metal on the absorption spectrum of these non-metalloflavoprotein enzymes? Do you get a change, as you would predict from Dr. Hemmerich's work?

BEINERT: We have been so busy meeting deadlines and writing papers that we could not do all the relatively obvious things to be done.

MASSEY: From Dr. Beinert's work, I always thought, accepting for the moment that the $g = 1.94$ signal shown by the flavin proteins is due to iron, that in some cases, at least, there are divergent kinetics in the rate of production of the 1.94 signal and the flavin free-radical signal. Now, if this is so, how can this signal possibly be due to a complex of the iron and the flavin free radicals?

BEINERT: In regard to your "accepting for the moment" that the $g = 1.94$ is due to iron, I am afraid that you will have to accept this for a long time, not only for the moment. We have evidence from an iron protein isolated from $^{57}$Fe-grown *Azotobacter*, which I think is the strongest so far presented, that the signal really is due to iron. But I won't go into this now.

As to the divergent kinetics, actually I wanted to bring up the point that in dihydroorotic dehydrogenase and DPNH dehydrogenase the kinetics are the same, as far as we can tell, for the iron and the flavin. There is some difference in xanthine oxidase, but it is relatively small. For xanthine oxidase, I would say, we are most sure of the difference between one species of molybdenum and the iron, namely, that they are on distant ends of the electron-transport sequence. The other species of molybdenum and the flavin may well be interacting, but the xanthine oxidase is a case where you would have a good point. On the other hand, aldehyde oxidase, dihydroorotic dehydrogenase, and DPNH dehydrogenase show no difference, as far as we can tell.

HEMMERICH: May I answer these two questions of Dr. Massey's? First, I do not think that the flavin spectra of metalloflavin proteins to which metals were added would show this behavior of the chelates. We do not claim that chelates can be made just by adding metals to enzymes that contain no metal naturally. But there is a direct binding; this can be a single contact between a coordination position of the metal and a coordination position of the flavin radicals. This binding is sufficient to obtain the saturation. As for the divergent kinetics, I think that, at first, when the substrate is reducing the flavin in metalloflavoproteins, we get a free flavin radical which gives the ESR absorption with a $g$-value of 2.00. This causes the rearrangement of the active side of the enzyme, with the non-heme iron.

HANDLER: I hope we can return later to Dr. Massey's question about the alleged divergent kinetics. My statement is addressed to Dr. King. I think that it is misleading to focus attention on the idea that there is labile sulfide in these iron flavoproteins with emphasis on the flavin component. The emphasis belongs on the iron aspect; sulfides have been found in virtually every non-heme iron protein examined where the iron is functional in the sense of undergoing valence change. I suspect that, in the long run, this will explain why it seems that in every one of these instances one pumps only one electron into the total package of irons which are so connected. Emphasis belongs not on the flavin, but on the acid-labile sulfide remaining in the iron proteins which we make by stripping the flavin away from the iron flavoproteins.

KING: My question was prompted by Dr. Hemmerich's comment on the interaction of metal with flavin. I agree completely with Dr. Handler; indeed, I think of the interaction of metal and sulfide, as we have emphasized in a recent publication [*Biochem. Biophys. Research Communs.*, **16**, 511 (1964)].

HEMMERICH: We have to face the fact that the electron has to come into the iron or what I may call the iron chain (namely, all the irons that are present in succinate dehydrogenase), at the beginning of this chain. There is the interaction of one iron and the flavin in the half-reduced state. The remainder of the iron is bound to the inorganic sulfur and makes some quite specific coordinations in a polynuclear complex, but this has nothing to do with flavin in itself, as Dr. Handler pointed out.

# PART II

# Copper-Containing Oxidases

# Two Forms of Copper
# in Copper-Containing Oxidases

... B. G. MALMSTRÖM

## I. INTRODUCTION

A number of chemical experiments (1, 2) carried out about seven years ago indicated that all eight copper atoms found in a molecule of ceruloplasmin are not bound in identical manner but exist in at least two different states. In 1960 my collaborators and I (3), on the basis of electron spin resonance (ESR) experiments, suggested that half the copper exists as $Cu^{2+}$ and the other half as $Cu^{1+}$ in the oxidized form of the protein. Studies of this type caused a renewed interest in the question of the valence state of the metal in copper-containing oxidases, a problem which was first approached in the classical work of Kubowitz (4). In the past few years, most copper-containing oxidases have been reinvestigated in this regard [see (5)], particularly by physical methods, such as ESR and magnetic susceptibility. It is now evident that this group of enzymes contains two distinct forms of copper, one which exists as $Cu^{2+}$ in the oxidized form but can be reduced to $Cu^{1+}$ by substrates and reoxidized by $O_2$, and another which is present as $Cu^{1+}$ even in the absence of substrates and in the presence of $O_2$.

In this paper, I will review briefly the question of the valence state of copper in copper-containing oxidases. First, a short discussion of methods used will be given. This will be followed by an attempt to arrive at the best answer to the problem for a number of individual proteins [cf. (5)]. The main portion of the discussion will then be devoted to the bonding and function of the two forms of copper.

## II. THE VALENCE STATE OF COPPER IN PROTEINS

### A. Methods Used in Experiments

Quite a variety of methods has been employed in attempts to arrive at an answer to the valence problem with copper-containing oxidases. Unfortunately two non-experimental approaches are still cited in some discussions. A teleological one argues that, in view of the function of the enzymes, it is almost self-evident that they must contain $Cu^{2+}$ in the resting form, and that this oxidizes the substrates while being reduced to $Cu^{1+}$. Reasoning by analogy, i.e., assuming that once the problem has been solved experimentally for one enzyme the answer is at hand for the whole group, is equally dangerous, as will be evident from the discussion of individual proteins.

Regrettably, some of the experimental methods used are almost equally unreliable. Kubowitz (4) removed the metal from tyrosinase by treatment with $CN^-$; and, as the enzyme could be reactivated with $Cu^{2+}$, he suggested that this is the valence state in the native protein. Obviously, reduction of the metal by groups previously reduced on removal of the metal cannot be excluded. In fact, with tyrosinase the inhibition by CO (4) would suggest the presence of $Cu^{1+}$. This effect of CO was often used in early studies of copper-containing oxidases. However, it is now known that some enzymes whose activity is not affected by CO, e.g., laccase (6), contain $Cu^{1+}$ as well as $Cu^{2+}$ (7). In recent years, the use of valence-specific reagents, e.g., biquinoline for $Cu^{1+}$ (8), has been quite common. On the basis of this technique, Kertész (9) suggested that tyrosinase contains $Cu^{1+}$ instead of $Cu^{2+}$. However, it was soon pointed out [e.g., (10)] that reducing groups in the protein may give false positive results for $Cu^{1+}$. Although inclusion of a chelating agent in the reaction mixture appears to prevent this in some cases (8), it is not obvious that this precaution will always be sufficient. In addition, some copper present as $Cu^{1+}$ *in situ* may be oxidized to $Cu^{2+}$ before being trapped by the reagent. This danger would appear to be particularly pronounced if the $Cu^{1+}$ functions in an $O_2$ carrier, as hemocyanin. In fact, as will be discussed later, only $50\%$ of the $Cu^{1+}$ found in several proteins appears to be detected by the biquinoline method.

The rate of exchange with radioactive metal can give some information about the valence state, as $Cu^{1+}$ would be expected to exchange more rapidly than $Cu^{2+}$ (11). On the basis of such experiments (12, 13), ascorbic acid oxidase, for example, has been claimed to contain $Cu^{2+}$, which is reduced by substrates. However, the method suffers from the difficulty that $Cu^{1+}$ may not exchange if it is "buried" in the protein. Thus, in ceruloplasmin the half that does not exchange appears to be that copper which is always present as $Cu^{1+}$, whereas the $Cu^{2+}$ fraction exchanges on reduction (1).

Visible and ultraviolet spectra should also give useful information about valence. However, biochemists have often used spectra naively, and one even finds the assumption that all blue copper proteins contain $Cu^{2+}$. Most blue copper proteins, even if they contain $Cu^{2+}$, as do laccase and ceruloplasmin, are not typical $Cu^{2+}$ complexes, since the visible extinction is at least 10 times higher than usual. Thus, charge-transfer bands are probably involved, as discussed, among others, by Williams (14, 15). Strong charge-transfer absorptions can be found also with $Cu^{1+}$ complexes, such as oxyhemocyanin (16). Mixed $Cu^{2+}$-$Cu^{1+}$ complexes often have high extinction coefficients also [e.g., (17)].

In view of the difficulties associated with the methods discussed so far, it is fortunate that two methods are available which allow a more rigorous answer to the valence problem, namely, ESR and magnetic susceptibility measurements. While $Cu^{1+}$ is diamagnetic and thus gives no ESR absorption, the paramagnetic $Cu^{2+}$ yields a very characteristic ESR spectrum (18), usually allowing easy identification. The first copper enzyme studied by ESR was laccase (19), which was shown to contain $Cu^{2+}$, reducible by substrate. However, this finding certainly did not solve the valence problem. First, it was not shown that the signal accounts for all the copper of the enzyme. Second, without kinetic measurements the valence change could not be related directly to the catalytic action of the enzyme. It is thus important to make quantitative estimations of the ESR signal intensity. Although measurements of intensities in ESR is a complicated problem [cf. (20)], $Cu^{2+}$ is a favorable case, as it almost invariably gives a rather narrow signal [cf. (18, 21)]. Thus, the intensity of the $Cu^{2+}$ signal should give a good estimate of the concentration of this ion. It appears very probable, therefore, that in cases where the signal does not account for all copper (22) $Cu^{1+}$ is also present. The main limitation in this reasoning·is that two paramagnetic ions in close proximity (e.g., a $Cu^{2+}$ pair) would still be expected to give a broad signal. However, this cannot apply to that half of the total copper giving an ESR signal in laccase and ceruloplasmin (22), as the signal is very narrow. If all copper were present as $Cu^{2+}$ in these two proteins, there would still have to be two classes of copper, half the copper ions being $Cu^{2+}$ not interacting with other paramagnetic species, and the other half being interacting $Cu^{2+}$ ions.

The best way of settling difficulties such as these would appear to be quantitative magnetic susceptibility measurements. It should be pointed out, however, that application of this method is difficult because of the lower sensitivity compared to ESR and of complications from diamagnetic contributions of the protein and the paramagnetism of dissolved $O_2$. On the other hand, when properly carried out, susceptibility measurements give the most rigorous answer possible to the valence question. For example, by this technique it has been shown that laccase and ceruloplasmin definitely do contain both $Cu^{2+}$ and $Cu^{1+}$ in their resting forms (7).

## B. The Valence of Copper in Ceruloplasmin, Laccase, Ascorbic Acid Oxidase, and Tyrosinase

The finding that ceruloplasmin contains both $Cu^{2+}$ and $Cu^{1+}$ (3) has been confirmed now by several groups (22–24). However, each molecule of ceruloplasmin contains 8 copper atoms, and it is somewhat problematic to state the number of these that are cupric, as the highest ratio obtained is less than 0.5, and as the content in some types of preparations (25) has been found to be quite variable (23). It deserves to be pointed out that the presence of both $Cu^{2+}$ and $Cu^{1+}$ is not due to a suitable redox potential, giving a ratio close to 0.5 at normal $O_2$ tensions. Thus, the ratio is the same if the solutions are saturated with pure $N_2$ or $O_2$ rather than air (40). If a ratio which does not correspond to an integral number of copper atoms is obtained, this must then mean that the solution is heterogeneous, containing at least two types of ceruloplasmin molecules. For example, 40% cupric copper (24) corresponds to $3.6 \, Cu^{2+}$ per molecule, and the preparation must contain some molecules with $4 \, Cu^{2+}$ and some with $3 \, Cu^{2+}$. The question arises whether this represents a real heterogeneity in the sense that the organism synthesizes different ceruloplasmins, or whether it is a result of previous treatments of the protein [cf. (23)]. Although distinct ceruloplasmins appear to exist [see (26)], they do not vary in the ratio of $Cu^{2+}:Cu^{1+}$ (22), and it would seem that the variable ratio often found is due to the previous history of the sample. One cause may be endogenous reducing groups, as ceruloplasmin solutions are bleached on storage and this bleaching is reversed by $O_2$ (41). Denaturation of the protein also changes the ratio (22).

We may then ask how many $Cu^{2+}$ are found in a native ceruloplasmin molecule. As $Cu^{2+}$ is the only chromophoric group in ceruloplasmin (22, 24), and as the activity is proportional to the blue color (27), it would appear that the most intensely colored preparations are also the most native. Blumberg et al. (23) are the investigators finding the largest variation in $Cu^{2+}$ content, but their most highly colored preparation gave a ratio of 0.43. Fresh samples, prepared by new chromatographic methods (28, 29), all gave ratios greater than 0.4 (22, 24). As has already been pointed out, such preparations must contain molecules with $4 \, Cu^{2+}$, and it appears that native ceruloplasmin contains $4 \, Cu^{2+}$ and $4 \, Cu^{1+}$.

The state of copper in a fungal laccase appears to be almost identical with that in ceruloplasmin (7, 18, 22). A molecule of fungal laccase contains 4 copper atoms, 2 of which are $Cu^{2+}$ in the resting enzyme. However, the valence of copper in the lacquer-tree enzyme is still a matter of controversy. Nakamura (30) claims that all copper is present as $Cu^{2+}$, but studies by Blumberg et al. (31) indicate a $Cu^{2+}$ content of 67% in this protein. The bonding of $Cu^{2+}$ seems different from that in the fungal enzyme, as the ESR parameters are not the same (18, 31). In view of the sensitivity of the $Cu^{2+}$ spectrum to denaturation and extraneous copper (22), the possibility may not be entirely excluded that the difference is caused by the previous treatment of the protein, particularly as the published spectrum is not well resolved (31). In any case, it appears clear that laccase from both sources contains $Cu^{1+}$ as well as $Cu^{2+}$.

Measurements (32) with $Cu^{1+}$ reagents have placed ascorbic acid oxidase also in the class of enzymes which contain both $Cu^{2+}$ and $Cu^{1+}$. The $Cu^{1+}$ content was stated, however, to be only 25%. Comparisons with results obtained with other copper proteins may indicate that this figure corresponds to a true *in situ* content of 50% $Cu^{1+}$. Thus, ceruloplasmin is found to contain 25% $Cu^{1+}$ in its "oxidized" form and 50% in its reduced state (33), while ESR (22) and susceptibility (7) measurements give a $Cu^{1+}$ content of 50 and 100%, respectively. Oxyhemocyanin probably contains only $Cu^{1+}$ (34), but the biquinoline technique indicates the presence of 50% $Cu^{1+}$. It would thus appear that this method reveals only half of the $Cu^{1+}$ present *in situ* in some proteins.

The results reviewed show that ceruloplasmin, laccase, and ascorbic acid oxidase all contain both $Cu^{2+}$ and $Cu^{1+}$. Although divergent results have been obtained for the exact content of each ion, the preceding discussion shows that most data are consistent with a $Cu^{2+}:Cu^{1+}$ ratio of 1:1. These three enzymes also have very similar spectral properties, and it is tempting to suggest that the state of copper is very similar in all of them. Possible functions of the two forms of copper will be considered in section III.

Quite a different situation is found in tyrosinase. Although this enzyme was long believed to contain $Cu^{2+}$, Kertész (9) found only $Cu^{1+}$ with the biquinoline method. The mushroom tyrosinase has been studied by ESR (35, 42). In both studies, a low (approximately 10%) but variable $Cu^{2+}$ content was found. This corresponds to less than one $Cu^{2+}$ per molecule; therefore the preparations must have been heterogeneous with respect to the state of copper, since an individual molecule cannot contain a fractional $Cu^{2+}$ ion. Thus, most molecules must have contained $Cu^{1+}$, while a small fraction contained $Cu^{2+}$. In view of the variable content, it would appear most likely that the molecules with $Cu^{2+}$ are results of denaturation and that native tyrosinase contains only $Cu^{1+}$. This assumption is strengthened by recent results with crystalline *Neurospora* tyrosinase, which contains only one copper atom per molecule and has a $Cu^{2+}$ content of less than 1% (36). Furthermore, this enzyme is colorless (36). Tyrosinase is thus in quite a different class with respect to the state of the metal than the other copper-containing oxidases, and this fact must have implications for the function of copper in the catalytic reaction.

The valence of copper in a number of non-oxidase proteins, such as hemocyanin and azurin, will not be considered here. Cytochrome oxidase will not be discussed, as I have not worked with it personally. A brief summary of results with these metalloproteins can be found in a review by Neilands and myself (5).


## III. BONDING AND FUNCTION OF
## THE TWO FORMS OF COPPER

The very narrow hyperfine structure splitting in laccase and ceruloplasmin indicates an unusual bonding of $Cu^{2+}$ in these proteins (18). Analysis of the ESR spectrum suggests a very high degree of delocalization of the $d_{x^2-y^2}$ orbital. As this is the orbital which should accept an electron on reduction of $Cu^{2+}$, the probability of overlap with the electron-donor orbital is increased. Thus, the state of $Cu^{2+}$ favors rapid electron transfer. It has been shown, in fact, that $Cu^{2+}$ is reduced by substrate and reoxidized by $O_2$ during the catalytic action of laccase and ceruloplasmin (37). With ceruloplasmin the kinetics of the valence change was studied, and it could be shown rigorously that this is the only mechanism by which $O_2$ is consumed. With laccase the reduction was too rapid to be measured, but this is what would be expected in view of the rate of the over-all reaction, which is about 1000 times greater than with ceruloplasmin (26). Presumably, ascorbic acid oxidase works by the same mechanism, whereas tyrosinase must function in a different manner, as it contains $Cu^{1+}$ only. An ESR study of ascorbic acid oxidase would be highly desirable, as it would be expected to be another example of a $Cu^{2+}$ complex with very low hyperfine splitting constants.

As $Cu^{2+}$ in laccase and ceruloplasmin are bonded in almost identical manner, it might appear difficult to explain the great difference in their catalytic activity on the basis of the mechanism discussed. However, in addition to a low activation energy, rapid reduction of $Cu^{2+}$ requires that it be accessible. Proton relaxation measurements (23) indicate that $Cu^{2+}$ is "buried" in ceruloplasmin. Together with Dr. Mildred Cohn, I have attempted to find out whether $Cu^{2+}$ in laccase is more accessible, but unfortunately complications due to the relaxing effect of $Cu^{2+}$ in denatured molecules have made it impossible to arrive at a clear answer. Apart from accessibility, the lower activity of ceruloplasmin could be due to less favorable donor properties. For example, substrate binding in laccase may result in larger delocalization of the electron-donating orbital. However, a recent hypothesis (26) for the mechanism of electron transfer, discussed at the end of this section, does not favor this explanation.

Although ESR and other spectral data allow conclusions about the electronic properties of $Cu^{2+}$ in these enzymes, unfortunately very little can be said about the chemical basis of the unusual bonding. High extinction coefficients are found in tetrahedral $Cu^{2+}$ complexes and in mixed $Cu^{2+}$-$Cu^{1+}$

complexes (15). We have studied a number of such complexes by ESR, and some illustrative results are given in Table 1. In no case are the properties closely related to those of the $Cu^{2+}$ proteins, which still remain unique. Williams (15) favors a large tetrahedral distortion, but a configuration intermediate to the usual planar and a tetrahedral one would seem more attractive. In this case, no change in configuration during reduction and reoxidation would be required, so that rapid electron transfer would be

### TABLE 1

#### ESR Parameters for Some Cupric Complexes [cf. (18)]

| Complex | $g_m$ | $g_\parallel$ | $\lvert A \rvert$, cm$^{-1}$ | Comment |
|---|---|---|---|---|
| Ceruloplasmin | 2.06 | 2.21 | 0.008 | |
| $Cu^{2+}$-formaldehyde-oxalyl dihydrazone | 2.09 | 2.19 | 0.021 | Flattened tetrahedron (15) |
| $Cu^{2+}$-bisdimethyl glyoxime | 2.07 | 2.16 | 0.022 | |
| $[Co(NH_3)_6]_2Cu_2Cl_9$ | 2.07 | 2.22 | 0.015 | Dissolved in HCl; $Cu^{2+}$-$Cu^{1+}$ complex (17) |

favored. In addition, as clearly argued by Blumberg *et al.* (23), an interaction between $Cu^{2+}$ and $Cu^{1+}$, mediated through a bridge ligand, appears very probable. The $Cu^{1+}$ would then have an electron-donating function in the charge transfer.

It has been pointed out repeatedly that the bonding of $Cu^{2+}$ in these proteins is unique (18, 22) among $Cu^{2+}$ complexes, similar properties not being found with any low-molecular-weight complexes studied so far. It would appear natural, therefore, to attribute the uniqueness to the protein. Small ligands, even in the case of a chelate, always have a relatively large degree of flexibility. Thus, the configuration of a complex is a compromise between the steric demands of the ligand and of the metal ion. The co-operative effect of the large number of weak forces stabilizing the tertiary structure of a protein could, however, create a preformed chelating site with very little flexibility. If the spatial arrangement of the ligand atoms in this site were in conflict with the demands of the cupric ion (for example, nitrogen atoms pushed in closer than the normal covalent $Cu^{2+}$—N distance), this could be thought to lead to electron delocalization by electrostatic inter-actions. The energy for the distortion would then be derived from the tertiary folding of the protein, and these enzymes would be examples of the "rack" mechanism of Lumry (38). It might be possible to treat this situation theoretically to see whether it has the observed effect on the ESR spectra.

Furthermore, the strength of binding of $Cu^{2+}$ should be weakened as compared to non-distorted chelates with the same ligand atoms. Thus, identification of the ligand atoms and a determination of stability constants would be highly desirable.

The previous discussion has concerned mainly the electron-accepting cupric ion, and the unchanging cuprous ion has been considered only as a

TABLE 2

**The Inhibition of Laccase with 1,10-Phenanthroline**

Substrate: $10^{-3}$ $M$ N,N-dimethyl-$p$-phenylene-diamine in 0.1 $M$ sodium acetate buffer, pH 5.9. Varying concentrations of inhibitor were added. Laccase concentration: approximately 0.1 $\mu$g/ml; temperature: 25°. The activity is expressed as the absorbancy change per minute in a 1-cm cell at 552 m$\mu$.

| Inhibitor Concentration, $M$ | Activity |
|---|---|
| ... | 0.335 |
| $10^{-4}$ | 0.315 |
| $10^{-3}$ | 0.260 |
| $10^{-2}$ | 0.196 |

possible electron donor in a charge transfer. In addition to this function, it probably partakes also in substrate binding by interaction with the $\pi$-electron system of the aromatic ring, as suggested earlier (37). Some preliminary inhibition data give added support to this hypothesis. Thus, substances known to form $\pi$-complexes with $Cu^{1+}$, such as 1,10-phenanthroline, function as inhibitors of laccase and ceruloplasmin, as shown for laccase in Table 2. The substrate concentration used ($10^{-3}$ $M$ with laccase) was twice $K_m$ for the respective enzymes. No inhibition was found at high substrate concentrations, indicating competition. However, a proper study of the kinetics has not yet been carried out. That the inhibitor does not cause any appreciable loss of copper under the conditions of the activity measurements was shown by experiments in which dialysis was continued until all inhibitor was removed, so that the duration of contact was much greater than in the kinetic experiments. Still, in one such experiment the copper content decreased only to 98 $\mu$g/ml, compared to 104 $\mu$g/ml in the control. Electron spin resonance measurements showed that the interaction with the inhibitor does not involve $Cu^{2+}$. On the other hand, there is an increase in ultraviolet absorption, with a maximum about 340 m$\mu$, on binding of the inhibitor. The extinction change is similar to that for the formation of a $Cu^{1+}$-phenanthroline complex.

It would appear that not only does $Cu^{1+}$ bind the substrate but also electron transfer from substrate to $Cu^{2+}$ is mediated by the $Cu^{1+}$ via the $\pi$-bonding of the aromatic ring. This would explain why addition of two methyl groups to the amino groups of $p$-phenylenediamine does not alter the reaction rate very greatly (39). This mechanism of electron transfer also requires an interaction between $Cu^{2+}$ and $Cu^{1+}$, as discussed earlier. A further treatment of the detailed structure and events at the active site, including the reduction of $O_2$, has been given by Broman (26).

## ACKNOWLEDGMENTS

The original investigations of my co-workers and myself have been supported by grants from the Swedish Natural Science Research Council and from the Division of General Medical Sciences, United States Public Health Service (GM-06542-05).

## REFERENCES

1. I. H. Scheinberg and A. C. Morell, *J. Clin. Invest.*, **36**, 1193 (1957).
2. G. Curzon, *Nature*, **181**, 115 (1958).
3. B. G. Malmström, *Federation Proc.*, **20**, Suppl. 1, 60 (1961).
4. F. Kubowitz, *Biochem. Z.*, **299**, 32 (1938).
5. B. G. Malmström and J. B. Neilands, *Ann. Rev. Biochem.*, **33**, 331 (1964).
6. D. Keilin and T. Mann, *Nature*, **145**, 304 (1940).
7. A. Ehrenberg, B. G. Malmström, R. Aasa, and T. Vänngård, *J. Molecular Biol.*, **5**, 450 (1962).
8. G. Felsenfeld, *Arch. Biochem. Biophys.*, **87**, 247 (1960).
9. D. Kertész, *Nature*, **180**, 506 (1957).
10. S. Takemori, I. Sekuzu, and K. Okunuku, *Biochim. et Biophys. Acta*, **38**, 158 (1960).
11. L. Pauling, *The Nature of the Chemical Bond*, 2nd Ed., Cornell University Press, Ithaca, 1940, p. 104.
12. M. Joselow and C. R. Dawson, *J. Biol. Chem.*, **191**, 11 (1951).
13. R. J. Magee and C. R. Dawson, *Arch. Biochem. Biophys.*, **99**, 338 (1962).
14. R. J. P. Williams, *Proceedings of the 5th International Congress of Biochemistry*, 1963, Vol. 4, p. 133.
15. R. J. P. Williams, *J. Polymer Research*, Symp. 1, 515 (1964).
16. I. M. Klotz and T. A. Klotz, *Science*, **121**, 477 (1955).
17. M. Mori, *Bull. Chem. Soc. Japan*, **33**, 985 (1960).
18. B. G. Malmström and T. Vänngård, *J. Molecular Biol.*, **2**, 118 (1960).
19. B. G. Malmström, R. Mosbach, and T. Vänngård, *Nature*, **183**, 321 (1959).
20. R. Aasa and T. Vänngård, *Proceedings of the 7th International Conference of Coordination Chemistry*, Almqvist & Wiksell, Stockholm, 1962, p. 137.
21. T. Vänngård and R. Aasa, *Proceedings of the 1st International Congress of Paramagnetic Resonance*, Academic Press, New York, 1963, p. 509.
22. L. Broman, B. G. Malmström, R. Aasa, and T. Vänngård, *J. Molecular Biol.*, **5**, 301 (1962).

23. W. E. Blumberg, J. Eisinger, P. Aisen, A. G. Morell, and I. H. Scheinberg, *J. Biol. Chem.*, **238**, 1675 (1963).
24. C. B. Kasper, H. F. Deutsch, and H. Beinert, *J. Biol. Chem.*, **238**, 2338 (1963).
25. A. G. Morell, P. Aisen, and I. H. Scheinberg, *J. Biol. Chem.*, **237**, 3455 (1962).
26. L. Broman, "Chromatographic and Magnetic Studies on Human Ceruloplasmin," *Acta Soc. Med. Upsaliensis*, **69**, Suppl. 7, (1964).
27. C. B. Laurell, in F. W. Putman, Ed., *The Plasma Proteins*, Vol. 1, Academic Press, New York, 1960, p. 349.
28. H. F. Deutsch, C. B. Kasper, and D. Walsh, *Arch. Biochem. Biophys.*, **99**, 132 (1962).
29. L. Broman and K. Kjellin, *Biochim. et Biophys. Acta*, **82**, 101 (1964).
30. T. Nakamura, *Biochim. et Biophys. Acta*, **30**, 640 (1958).
31. W. E. Blumberg, W. G. Levine, S. Margolis, and J. Peisach, *Biochem. Biophys. Research Communs.*, **15**, 277 (1964).
32. W. N. Poillon and C. R. Dawson, *Biochim. et Biophys. Acta*, **77**, 27 (1963).
33. G. Felsenfeld, in *Symposium on the Function of Metal Ions in Biological Processes*, American Chemical Society Meeting, New York, 1960.
34. T. Nakamura and H. S. Mason, *Biochem. Biophys. Research Communs.*, **3**, 297 (1960).
35. S. Bouchilloux, P. McMahill, and H. S. Mason, *J. Biol. Chem.*, **238**, 1699 (1963).
36. M. Fling, N. H. Horowitz, and S. F. Heinemann, *J. Biol. Chem.*, **238**, 2045 (1963).
37. L. Broman, B. G. Malmström, R. Aasa, and T. Vänngård, *Biochim. et Biophys. Acta*, **75**, 365 (1963).
38. R. Lumry, *J. Biophys. (Japan)*, **1**, 1 (1961).
39. W. G. Levine and J. Peisach, *Biochim. et Biophys. Acta*, **63**, 528 (1962).
40. R. Aasa, B. G. Malmström, and T. Vänngård, unpublished studies.
41. L. Broman, unpublished studies.
42. R. Aasa, D. Kertész, T. Vänngård, and R. Zito, unpublished studies.

*Discussion*

HEMMERICH: I should like to make some general comments on the inorganic chemistry of the problem. I am in perfect agreement with what Dr. Malmström has pointed out, and I want to draw your attention to three points. The first is the strong configurational changes that may be involved in electron transfer between cuprous copper and cupric copper. We have found a new method for going into the coordination chemistry of cuprous copper in aqueous solution, $Cu[CH_3CN]_2^+$ [P. Hemmerich and C. Sigwart, *Experientia*, **19**, 488 (1963)]. For example, if you titrate glycine cation with cuprous copper,

$$Cu^+ + 2\overset{\oplus}{NH_3}-CH_2-COOH \rightleftharpoons [(HOOCCH_2NH_2)_2Cu]^+$$

you get at first a complex having the structure of a cuprous copper diammine, which is perfectly stable and colorless if oxygen is excluded. Now, if you go on neutralizing the carboxyl protons, you cannot obtain a tetradentate cuprous copper complex of glycine in solution. It will disproportionate into $Cu^{2+}$ glycinate and metallic copper. Thus, you have to take into consideration that cupric copper chelated to amino acids is not a one-electron acceptor at all under physiological conditions. So you have to consider other ligands that might stabilize the cuprous copper, and the only protein functional groups which might, under physiological conditions, stabilize cuprous copper are mercaptide ions, disulfide, and imidazole. The two first stabilize cuprous copper because they can accept from it $d$-electrons, and thus complexes are stabilized by $(d, d)\pi$-backbonding. The imidazole, on the other hand, is a unique base: it has a very suitable $pK_a$ to bind cuprous copper under physiological conditions, whereas aliphatic amino groups have not.

Now, as my second point, if you titrate cysteine in the presence of $Cu^+$ you obtain a complex in which the amino group and the carboxyl group are not involved

$$Cu^+ + HSCH_2CR \!\!\begin{array}{c} NH_3^+ \\ \diagup \\ \diagdown \\ COOH \end{array} \rightarrow 1/n(CuS)_n \begin{array}{c} \\ \ulcorner\!\!-CH_2CH \begin{array}{c} NH_3^+ \\ \diagup \\ \diagdown \\ COOH \end{array} \end{array}$$

at all, and the complex is in a somewhat polymerized state depending on ligand excess. It is neutral in the dipolar state, but if you dissociate $NH_3^+$ at higher pH, this will form a stable solution which is perfectly colorless and becomes deep violet upon admission of air, indicating a stable mixed-valence state.

Third, if you titrate cysteine, you see that again the amino group and the carboxyl group do not react at all, as long as excess ligand is present:

$$Cu^+ + \begin{array}{c} SR \\ | \\ SR \end{array} \rightleftharpoons Cu \rightarrow \begin{array}{c} SR \\ | \\ SR \end{array}$$

Indeed you can make the analogous complex with any disulfide.

Now, if we have such complexes, as shown in Fig. 1, there is an equilibrium between (cuprous copper/disulfide) and (cupric copper/mercaptide). Now you add, let's say, a mercaptide-specific reagent: $p$-CMS. Then you will get AsHgSR plus cupric copper. On the other hand, if you add a cuprous copper-specific reagent (let's say thiourea, which is specific for cuprous copper and does not react at all with cupric copper), you obtain cuprous copper thiourea complex and you liberate disulfide. This shows that any chemical determination of actual valence in such complexes is unreliable, as it will not reveal anything about the actual valence state of the metal.

In Dr. Beinert's laboratory we have made some studies on the ESR absorption of Cu-SR complexes in the "mixed-valence" state (Fig. 1). We have to ask ourselves what intermediate complexes might be stable under physiological conditions, because to make one disulfide, you need two electrons, and if you get the electron from copper only you need two atoms to be reduced. This can happen only in an enzyme if two copper atoms are able to transmit electrons to each other. The preferable structures would be those which would not undergo any big configurational change along with the change in metal valence. Actually, we allowed $Cu^{2+}$ to react with $2RSH$ to get $1/n(Cu^+SR)_n + \frac{1}{2}(RS)_2$, colorless. This, as expected, gave no ESR signal. Now, upon adding $I_2$, the violet color of the mixed-valence state appeared but the ESR signal that we obtained was not of the same intensity. In fact we get only a very small cupric copper signal, which indicates that the mixed-valence state complex gives no signal.

We have added $p$-CMS to this system and then found that cupric copper came out in the expected amount. In order to explain why Dr. Malmström found cupric copper signal in his $Cu_2Cl_9^{6-}$ complex, we have to postulate that this complex is at least a little bit dissociated into $Cu_2Cl_6^{4-} + CuCl_3^{-2}$. This might give the signal, whereas the biggest part of it might give no signal. That's why I should like to ask him if he has made any integration upon that.

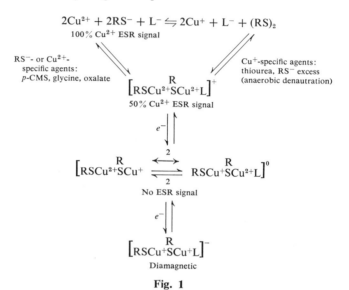

$$2Cu^{2+} + 2RS^- + L^- \leftrightharpoons 2Cu^+ + L^- + (RS)_2$$
100% $Cu^{2+}$ ESR signal

$RS^-$- or $Cu^{2+}$-
specific agents:
$p$-CMS, glycine, oxalate

$Cu^+$-specific agents:
thiourea, $RS^-$ excess
(anaerobic denautration)

$$\left[RSCu^{2+}SCu^{2+}L\right]^+$$
$R$
50% $Cu^{2+}$ ESR signal

$e^-$

$$\left[RSCu^{2+}SCu^+ \underset{2}{\overset{2}{\rightleftharpoons}} RSCu^+SCu^{2+}L\right]^0$$
$R$                                $R$
No ESR signal

$e^-$

$$\left[RSCu^+SCu^+L\right]^-$$
$R$
Diamagnetic

Fig. 1

MALMSTRÖM: I appreciate very much all the aid we get from Dr. Hemmerich in trying to understand what might the be bonding situation in this protein. As far as I can see, the only point where he might possibly be in disagreement with me is his final one, but I must admit that I think this point is well taken. The compound that we studied, i.e., a mixed-valence compound, can be shown only in the solid, crystallized compound. However, this of course we could not study in ESR, and we had to dissolve it in $H_2O$ and rapidly freeze it. It is crystallized all the way clear through, and we haven't really done careful integrations to know that it is a cupric-cuprous interaction, that the signal we see is due to that part of the complex. However, I should like to add that this doesn't really change too much, I think, my whole picture of the protein because, as I said before, I am not in favor of trying to explain the ESR properties of these proteins on the basis of a cuprous-cupric interaction. I do want to have a rather Lewis type of interaction just to be able to transmit the electrons to the cupric ion.

MASON: I'm surprised that neither Dr. Malmström nor Dr. Hemmerich has mentioned that the *Pseudomonas* Cu protein has the same high extinction coefficient as ceruloplasmin and laccase, and similar narrow, hyperfine structure of the ESR spectra, but contains only one copper per molecule. The question I'd like to ask is directed toward what I consider to be a crucial calculation of molar susceptibility from $g$ values [A. Ehrenberg, B. G. Malmström, L. Broman, and R. Mosbach, *J. Molecular Biol.*, **5**, 450 (1962)]. We know that the $g$-value determinations of paramagnetic compounds in solution are imprecise because the anisotropic absorptions overlap, and it is difficult to resolve the $g_x$, $g_y$, and $g_z$ absorptions. How exact can your calculations of molar susceptibility from imprecise $g$ values be?

MALMSTRÖM: In regard to the *Pseudomonas* protein, as you know, we have also studied azurin, which is a similar protein. This is mentioned in my paper, but I didn't have time to discuss it here. I don't really believe that our $g$-value calculations are so inaccurate. Part of that hasn't been published, but we have used the same method. First, we studied single crystals and then polycrystalline samples. We determined $g$ values on a single crystal and saw what we got on the polycrystalline sample. The agreement was quite good. Second, Vänngård has developed a means of theoretically reconstructing the spectra, and calculating the $g$ values from the theoretical reconstruction. This gives, I think, better estimates of the $g$ values.

Maybe I should also go back to the bacteria protein. I think it is incorrect to say that it is really similar to laccase and ceruloplasmin. It has an even narrower hyperfine splitting and is rather dissimilar. In fact, it is the only one of the proteins whose spectrum Vänngård cannot reproduce in his theoretical calculations. This protein seems to be in quite another category with respect to copper binding.

MASON: It seems to me, then, that the assumptions Vänngård uses are not comprehensive enough to explain the case of a protein containing a single copper atom which has actually very similar properties to proteins with several copper atoms. I mean that this question of similarity is one of fine detail rather than of general characteristics.

MALMSTRÖM: I really can't agree with that, but even so it wouldn't be in any conflict with our interpretation because I do think of the cupric copper as being rather a separate entity, the ESR properties not being explained by cupric-cuprous interaction but rather the presence of cupric copper in a given environment.

KING: Can the protein be in polymerized form so that how much copper per protein does not matter? What I mean is that Dr. Mason said that there is one copper per protein. If that protein is in polymerized form, then we have two proteins and two copper atoms.

MALMSTRÖM: No, it is not quite that because azurin has one copper and also one cupric copper. These other ones have some cupric copper which Dr. Mason likes to think of as similar to Cu protein, but which I really don't think it is. However, they also have cuprous copper or other copper which is not seen. Polymerization would not produce that case of ceruloplasmin where there are two distinct forms of copper.

FRIEDEN: I want to make a comment about the fact that some years ago Dr. Walter and I also observed the inhibition of ceruloplasmin by 1,10-phenanthroline, confirming its laccase properties), as Dr. Malmström reported. Neocuproine does not inhibit ceruloplasmin actions. I want to make a couple of comments also about the copper interactions mentioned earlier. I assume that the intensity of the absorptions or the molar extinction coefficients of a compound like copper-formaldehyde oxalyldihydrizide are larger in general than the molar extinction of copper in ceruloplasmin. I wonder whether you were dealing here with the red complex in Table 1 of your text. These have tremendous intensity as reported.

MALMSTRÖM: All I want to show was that this was an example and that we had looked at several different compounds that had high extinction coefficients, not necessarily in the same range. The point is that neither spectral properties nor ESR properties are similar.

FRIEDEN: Well, this particular complex definitely has an ESR signal. One other comment that I want to make is about the specificity of so-called $Cu^{1+}$ and $Cu^{2+}$ reagents. Now I gather that the parents of all these reagents are probably the J. F. Smith compounds, biquinoline and 2,9-dimethyl-1,10-phenanthroline, but 2,9-dimethyl-1,10-phenanthroline is preferential for $Cu^{1+}$, certainly not specific for $Cu^{1+}$. It does chelate with $Cu^{2+}$ but at about 100 times the concentration. I wonder whether this might be true for reagents like thiourea; we ought to be very careful about terming these things specific $Cu^{1+}$ reagents.

MALMSTRÖM: Our data show that they are not specific.

FRIEDEN: Also, I have a comment about the level of interactions of $Cu^{2+}$ with amino acids. Most people seem to be overly impressed, I think, with these interactions. They occur at relatively high concentrations unless they are histidines, but nowhere near in the range of such chelators as phenanthrolines, thyroxine, and histidine. The simple interaction of even polyglycine or at least multiple-glycine peptides is relatively ineffective by most criteria.

EHRENBERG: I just had a question about this interpretation of the small hyperfine splitting in the ESR spectra. You say that it indicates a great delocalization of the unpaired electron. As I understand it, it is a change in the hybridization of the orbital containing the unpaired electron that makes a change of the Fermi contact term and thus alters the hyperfine splitting. Does that necessarily mean a big delocalization of this unpaired electron, or could this change occur without delocalization?

MALMSTRÖM: Yes, I think that it could, but it is by no means proved that we have this high degree of delocalization. It is just the interpretation which seems most attractive, since it would favor rapid electron transfer. There are a good many other objections that could be raised to our interpretation.

EHRENBERG: Do you need to have a hyperfine structure from the other atoms where it is delocalized for a proof?

MALMSTRÖM: Yes.

GREEN: I was very much interested in your speculations about the relationship of copper to the $a$ heme in cytochrome oxidase. Perhaps this might be the proper occasion to make a comment about our own studies in our laboratory. Dr. Tzagoloff and Dr. McLennan have succeeded in isolating from cytochrome oxidase a copper protein with a molecular weight of 25,000, with apparently two coppers per protein molecule. The idea that the copper is bonded with the heme exclusively may have to be abandoned. One would have to think in terms of a copper protein as well as a hemoprotein which are very closely bonded together, but with the copper associated with its own specific protein rather than being an adjunct of the hemes.

DAWSON: Do you have any views as to how one can explain the remarkable stability of these natural copper-protein complexes, particularly their stability to exchange with radioactive cupric ions, which, in the case of laccase, of ascorbic acid oxidase, and of ceruloplasmin, occurs only when the enzyme is functioning? How do you fit all this in with your picture of the cuprous-cupric relationship?

MALMSTRÖM: One can always, of course, invoke some protein conformation; in regard to the cupric part, I am not certain that it really is remarkably stable compared to other compounds.

# On the Apoenzyme
# of Ascorbate Oxidase

... ZELDA G. PENTON* and CHARLES R. DAWSON

## I. INTRODUCTION

Ascorbate oxidase, isolated from the yellow squash, *Cucurbita pepo condensa*, is a copper-containing protein that is highly active as a catalyst in the aerobic oxidation of L-ascorbic acid (1, 2). The oxidation of the vitamin to dehydroascorbic acid by molecular oxygen in the presence of the enzyme results in the consumption of $\frac{1}{2}$ mole of oxygen per mole of ascorbic acid oxidized. When purified ascorbate oxidase is used as the catalyst, only trace amounts of hydrogen peroxide can be detected as a terminal product of the reaction (3), but when the aerobic oxidation reaction is catalyzed by cupric ion, a mole of oxygen is consumed and essentially stoichiometric quantities of hydrogen peroxide are produced (4).

Ascorbic acid      Dehydroascorbic acid

The enzyme-catalyzed reaction differs from the cupric ion-catalyzed oxidation in other important respects. Most noteworthy is the fact that the

* Taken from the dissertation submitted to the Faculty of Pure Science of Columbia University by Zelda G. Penton in partial fulfillment of the requirements for the Ph.D. degree.

catalytic activity of the enzyme copper is more than one thousand times as great as that of an equivalent amount of ionic copper. Furthermore, the enzyme exhibits a high order of specificity toward L-ascorbic acid and is much less active on closely related compounds (5). Cupric ion catalyzes the aerobic oxidation of many substances.

During the oxidase-catalyzed reaction the enzyme becomes inactivated, and the loss in activity has been attributed to the effect of very small amounts of hydrogen peroxide produced by a slow and secondary reaction involving copper bonded to the enzyme protein at sites not involved in the enzymatic function (3, 6).

Concentrated aqueous solutions of the purified oxidase are intensely blue, and this color is very rapidly bleached to a pale yellow or lack of color when an excess of substrate is added. The original blue color, characterized by an absorption peak at 606 m$\mu$, is rapidly restored by molecular oxygen (7), and the reversible color change has been related to a reversible reduction and oxidation of the valence state of the enzyme's prosthetic copper during the catalytic process (8).

$$\text{P-Cu}^{2+} \xrightarrow{\text{substrate}} \text{P-Cu}^{1+}$$

$$\text{Blue} \xleftarrow{\quad O_2 \quad} \text{Colorless}$$

The prosthetic copper of the oxidase is very tightly bonded to the protein. Under physiological conditions the copper is not removed by exhaustive dialysis or by treatment with cationic exchange resins. The catalytic function of the enzyme is not inhibited by strong copper chelating agents such as EDTA* (9), bathocuproin, cuproine, and cuprizone (10). When exposed to radioactive cupric ions, the enzyme does not exchange its copper with the radioactive ions except when it is actively catalyzing the aerobic oxidation of L-ascorbic acid (9, 11, 12).

Recent studies in these laboratories (13) have shown that the homogeneous enzyme, purified by DEAE-cellulose chromatography and by zone electrophoresis, contains 0.34% copper and has a molecular weight of about 140,000 (ultracentrifuge). These values correspond to eight copper atoms per oxidase molecule. The valence state of the copper in the resting (nonfunctional) enzyme appears to be mixed; 75% of the copper (6 atoms) are in the $Cu^{2+}$ state and 25% (2 atoms) in the $Cu^{1+}$ state (10).

In 1941, Meiklejohn (14) described the removal of copper from crude preparations of cucumber ascorbate oxidase by dialysis against 0.1 $N$ HCl or 0.1 $M$ NaCN. The inactive copper-free protein (apoenzyme) was then treated with cupric ion to restore the catalytic activity. In the case of the acid-dialyzed enzyme no activity could be recovered, presumably because the

---

* The following abbreviations are used in this paper: EDTA, ethylenediaminetetraacetate; DEAE-cellulose, diethylaminoethyl cellulose; SH, sulfhydryl; p-CMB, p-chloromercuribenzoate; ESR, electron spin resonance.

protein had been denatured. However, the cyanide-dialyzed preparation (apoenzyme) was partially restored to activity by the addition of cupric ion. Numerous attempts to confirm this observation in these laboratories, utilizing highly purified samples of the oxidase, have been unsuccessful. The addition of cupric ion to apoenzyme prepared by cyanide dialysis resulted in no restoration of activity (15).

It is the purpose of this paper to report that the apoenzyme of highly purified ascorbate oxidase, prepared by cyanide dialysis, can be largely restored to the activity of the native enzyme by treatment with cuprous ion rather than cupric ion. This observation has made possible a further investigation of the SH groups in the enzyme. It is known from work in these laboratories (16) that the native enzyme contains no detectable SH groups and is not inhibited by $p$-CMB. However, the urea- or detergent-treated enzyme contains 10–12 sulfhydryl groups. In the present study it has been found that the apoenzyme likewise contains about 10 sulfhydryl groups, and the effect of $p$-CMB on the restoration of activity and blue color by treatment with cuprous ion has been investigated.

## II. EXPERIMENTAL DETAILS

All the chemicals used in this study were of reagent grade and were used as obtained from various manufacturers without further purification.

Copper-free water, obtained by the distillation of tap water in a Loughborough all-glass still with chromium-plated element from Bellco Glass, Inc., was used throughout this study. This water contained less than 0.01 ppm copper.

All the glassware used was copper-freed by soaking in chromic acid cleaning solution, rinsing with tap water, and finally rinsing several times with copper-free water.

The buffer used throughout this investigation was 0.2 $M$, pH 5.6, McIlvaine's buffer, prepared by dissolving the appropriate amounts of citric acid and dibasic sodium phosphate in copper-free water.

All dialyses were carried out with slow magnetic stirring in a refrigerator that maintained a temperature of about 5°C.

Solutions were made anaerobic by placing them in Thunberg tubes, freezing the contents in ice-salt mixtures, evacuating, and thawing. This procedure was repeated twice.

### A. Enzyme Preparations

Ascorbate oxidase was prepared from the yellow crookneck squash, *C. pepo condensa*, and the green zucchini, *C. pepo medullosa*, by the method of

Dawson and Magee (17). The enzyme was dialyzed against several changes of buffer to remove traces of ionic copper. Protein content was determined on the earlier preparations by the dry-weight method described elsewhere (17). The protein contents of the latter preparations were found by measuring the absorption at 280 m$\mu$ on a Beckman DU spectrophotometer. The molar extinction coefficient, obtained by comparing the absorption at 280 m$\mu$ with dry-weight value, was found to be 285,000. Copper was determined by the

### TABLE 1

#### Assay of Preparations of Ascorbate Oxidase

| Enzyme Preparation No. | Units[a] of Activity | | Copper, % |
|---|---|---|---|
| | Per $\mu$g Copper | Per mg Protein | |
| 37A | 820 | 2300 | 0.28 |
| 37C | 740 | 2000 | 0.27 |
| 38Y | 780 | 1800 | 0.23 |
| 38E | 730 | 2130 | 0.29 |
| 38E′ | 730 | 2030 | 0.28 |
| 38E″ | 730 | 1980 | 0.27 |
| 38EF | 700 | 2180 | 0.31 |
| 38EF′ | 600 | 2340 | 0.39 |
| 39C | 670 | 2470 | 0.37 |

[a] One unit is defined as that amount of ascorbate oxidase required to effect the manometric uptake of 10 $\mu$l of $O_2$ per minute during the enzymatic oxidation of L-ascorbic acid at 25°C.

method of Stark and Dawson (18). The activity was measured by manometrically following the uptake of oxygen during the oxidation of L-ascorbic acid as described elsewhere (17). Table 1 lists the characteristics of the enzymes used in this study.

### B. Preparation of the Apoenzyme

Stock solutions of ascorbate oxidase were diluted to approximately 1 mg/ml with buffer. A 0.1 M cyanide solution was prepared in the McIlvaine buffer, and the pH was raised from 5.6 to about 7.0 by the cyanide. To another sample of buffer was added 1 M NaOH, until the pH was within 0.1 pH unit of the buffer and cyanide mixture. About half of the enzyme solution (4–8 ml) was dialyzed against the buffered cyanide (approximately 100 ml). The other half of the enzyme mixture was dialyzed against the buffer at pH 7.0. After a period of 18–20 hr, the clear, colorless apoenzyme was removed from the buffered cyanide, and the control was removed from the pH 7.0 buffer. Both apoenzyme and control were dialyzed against buffer (in different beakers) to remove cyanide and to restore the pH to 5.6. The buffer volume was large (about 500 ml), and the buffer was changed every 20 min for from 2 to 3 hr.

## C. Treatment of the Apoenzyme with Ionic Copper

**Preliminary Experiments.** A 0.1 $M$ cupric ion solution (635 $\mu$g Cu$^{2+}$/ml) was prepared by dissolving reagent grade CuSO$_4$·5H$_2$O in buffer and adjusting the pH to 5.6. The solution was made 2% in sodium chloride. To prepare cuprous ion, aliquots of the cupric ion solution were chemically reduced under anaerobic conditions in Thunberg tubes.

EXPERIMENT 1. Cupric ion was added aerobically to the apoenzyme. In the preliminary experiments, the molar ratio of added copper to enzyme was 50:1. After incubating for 2 hr, the treated apoenzyme was dialyzed against buffer to remove excess copper and assayed. A control (native enzyme) was treated identically.

EXPERIMENT 2. The cupric ion solution described above was reduced with 5 equivalents of ascorbic acid or with a 22 molar excess of hydroxylamine hydrochloride. Two portions of the same apoenzyme sample were made anaerobic. One sample was treated with cuprous ion in the presence of excess L-ascorbic acid, and the other was treated with cuprous ion in the presence of hydroxylamine hydrochloride. Anaerobic incubation with cuprous ion took place for 2 hr. Controls of native enzyme were treated identically. As in experiment 1, the enzymes were dialyzed to remove excess copper and then assayed.

EXPERIMENT 3. The procedure was identical to that of experiment 2, with the exception that one portion of cupric ion solution was reduced by 5 equivalents of L-ascorbic acid, and the other was only partially reduced by 0.8 equivalent of L-ascorbic acid. The results of the preliminary experiments are shown in Table 2.

**Simplified Experiments.** The cupric ion solution was diluted 1:5 and reduced anaerobically by 5 equivalents of L-ascorbic acid. To 1.8 ml of apoenzyme solution was added aerobically 0.2 ml of cuprous ion solution. After $\frac{1}{2}$ hr of aerobic incubation, the samples were dialyzed against buffer to remove excess copper and were assayed. Native enzyme controls were treated identically. The results are shown in Tables 3 and 4.

## D. Treatment of Apoenzyme with Small Quantities of Cuprous Ion

A standard cupric ion solution was prepared according to the procedure of Stark and Dawson (18). This solution contained 24.86 $\mu$g copper/ml.

Apoenzyme solutions (1.8 ml) were placed in Thunberg tubes. Cupric ion was added, so that the molar ratio of copper to enzyme varied from 0 to 9.5. The total volumes were adjusted to 2.0 ml. The side-arms of the Thunberg tubes contained 1–2 mg of L-ascorbic acid. Each Thunberg tube was evac-

TABLE 2

**Preliminary Experiments on Apoascorbate Oxidase, Showing the Restoration of Activity[a] and Copper[a]**

| Exp't Description | Enzyme Prep. No. | Before Treatment with Ionic Copper | | After Treatment with Ionic Copper | |
|---|---|---|---|---|---|
| | | Activity, %[a] | Copper, %[a] | Activity, %[a] | Copper, %[a] |
| 1 Treatment of apo- | 37A | 0.0 | 5.1 | 0.0 | 32.3 |
| enzyme with cupric | 37A | 1.1 | 0.0 | 1.3 | 88.7 |
| ion | 38EF | 0.9 | 11.8 | 2.1 | 18.6 |
| 2 Treatment of apo- enzyme with cuprous ion | | | | | |
| A. Reduced with 5 equivalents L-ascorbic acid | 37A | 1.1 | 0.0 | 49.1 | 52.0 |
| B. Reduced with 22 moles NH₂OH·HCl | | | | 49.5 | 52.0 |
| 3 Treatment of apo- enzyme with cuprous ion | | | | | |
| A. Reduced with 5 equivalents L-ascorbic acid | | | | 74.8 | 84.2 |
| B. Partially reduced with 0.8 equivalent L-ascorbic acid | 37C | 0.6 | 6.0 | 79.4 | 97.2 |

[a] In every experiment, a control of native enzyme was treated identically to the apoenzyme. The % activity and % copper are based on the assignment of 100% activity and 100% copper to the control.

uated, and the contents were mixed. After standing for 18–20 hr, the tubes were opened to the air, the absorption at 606 m$\mu$ was measured on a Beckman DU spectrophotometer, and the activity was determined. Figure 1 describes the results.

## TABLE 3

Percentage Activity[a] and Copper[a] in Samples of Apoascorbate Oxidase before and after Treatment with Cuprous Ion

| Enzyme Prep. No. | Before Treatment with Cuprous Ion | | After Treatment with Cuprous Ion | |
|---|---|---|---|---|
| | Activity, %[a] | Copper, %[a] | Activity, %[a] | Copper, %[a] |
| 38Y | 0.0 | 4.3 | 81.5 | 83.8 |
| 38Y | 0.0 | 18.1 | 97.7 | 82.5 |
| 38E | 0.0 | 27.6 | 84.1 | 114.0 |
| 38E′ | 0.9 | 3.6 | 81.2 | 97.2 |
| 38EF | 2.2 | 15.4 | 91.4 | 92.9 |
| 38EF | 0.0 | 11.4 | 55.2 | 51.4 |
| 38EF | 0.9 | 11.8 | 67.1 | 72.2 |
| 38EF | 0.0 | 0.0 | 82.1 | 70.2 |
| 38E″ | 0.0 | 8.1 | 86.7 | 84.6 |
| 39C | 1.7 | 0.0 | 73.4 | 85.7 |

[a] The % activity and % copper are based on the assignment of 100% activity and 100% copper to the identically treated control.

## TABLE 4

Average Characteristics[a] of Restored Apoascorbate Oxidase Preparations and Controls

| | Units of Activity | | |
|---|---|---|---|
| | Per $\mu$g Copper | Per mg Protein | Copper, % |
| Restored apoenzyme | 482 | $1540 \pm 160^{b}$ | $0.32 \pm 0.04^{b}$ |
| Control | 508 | $1930 \pm 150^{b}$ | $0.38 \pm 0.04^{b}$ |

[a] This table shows the average assay of the apoenzymes and controls in Table 3.
[b] Average deviations.

## E. Determination of SH Groups in the Apoenzyme

The freshly prepared apoenzymes were titrated for SH with silver ion, according to the amperometric titration method, devised by Benesch, Lardy, and Benesch (19). The procedure used was identical to that of Stark (16).

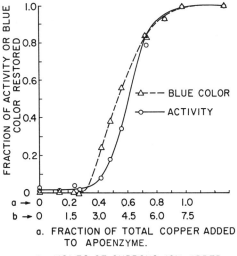

a. FRACTION OF TOTAL COPPER ADDED
   TO APOENZYME.

b. MOLES OF CUPROUS ION ADDED
   PER MOLE OF ENZYME.

**Fig. 1.** The dependence of the recovered activity and the blue color (absorption at 606 m$\mu$) upon the amount of cuprous ion added anaerobically to the apoenzymes of preparations 38EF and 38EF′. Both apoenzyme samples showed a slight activity but contained no measurable copper. Maximum activity (1470 units/mg protein for 38EF, and 1880 units/mg protein for 38EF′) was attained upon the addition of 7.5 moles of cuprous ion per mole of enzyme. Each experimental point is the average value obtained with the two different apoenzymes.

## F. Treatment of the Apoenzyme with *p*-CMB

Solutions of *p*-CMB were prepared by dissolving 10 mg in 2 ml of 1 *M* NaOH and then diluting to 50 ml with buffer. Several 2-ml samples of apoenzyme were treated with from 0 to 0.2 ml of *p*-CMB solution, so that the molar ratio of *p*-CMB to apoenzyme varied from 0 to 16. The total volume of each solution was adjusted to 2.2 ml. After incubation for 18 hr, 0.2 ml of cuprous ion solution (125 $\mu$g copper/ml), reduced by 5 equivalents of L-ascorbic acid, was added aerobically to each sample. After incubation for 1 hr with copper, the samples were dialyzed and assayed (see Fig. 2).

## III. RESULTS

### A. Treatment of the Apoenzyme with Ionic Copper

The data in Table 2 (experiment 1) show that treatment of the apoenzyme with cupric ion did not result in restoration of activity, even though appreciable copper was rebonded to the protein. These results confirm earlier

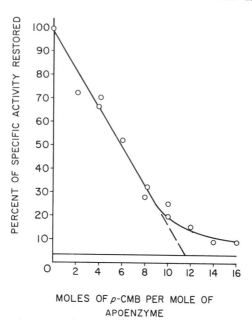

MOLES OF $p$-CMB PER MOLE OF
APOENZYME

**Fig. 2.** The ability of $p$-CMB to prevent restoration of activity to apoascorbate oxidase. The apoenzyme of preparation 39C was treated with $p$-CMB before the addition of cuprous ion. The untreated apoenzyme had about 3% of the activity of the fully restored apoenzyme. This was used as the base line in the graph.

findings in these laboratories. However, as shown by the data in Tables 2, 3, and 4, apoenzyme treated either anaerobically (Table 2) or aerobically (Tables 3 and 4), with cuprous ion recovered a great deal of enzymatic activity. The fact that L-ascorbic acid (used as the reducing agent to convert cupric to cuprous ion) is the substrate for the enzyme did not have any unique influence on the results. Thus, as can be seen in Table 2 (experiment 2), the activity-restoration results were not significantly different when hydroxylamine [not a substrate (15) for the enzyme] was used to reduce the cupric ion to cuprous ion. Furthermore, as can be seen from the results of experiment 3 in Table 2, a large excess of the reducing agent was not necessary for effective recovery of the enzyme's activity. Of particular interest is the fact that anaerobic conditions were not necessary for the activity restoration. As can be seen from the data in Table 3, ten different apoenzymes treated with cuprous ion under aerobic conditions (5 equivalents of L-ascorbic acid) showed an average activity restoration of 80.0 ± 8.9% (average deviation, a.d.) when compared to identically treated controls, and an average copper-content restoration of 83.5 ± 11.5% (a.d.) of that of the controls. Figure 1 also reveals that an excess of copper is not required to restore the activity to apoascorbate oxidase.

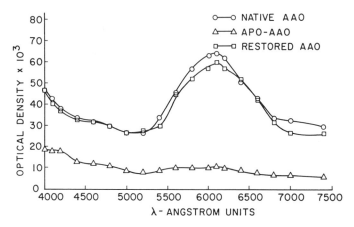

**Fig. 3.** The visible spectra of native, apo, and restored ascorbate oxidase as determined point by point on a Beckman DU spectrophotometer. Enzyme preparation 39C was used; protein concentration was $5 \times 10^{-6}$ $M$ or 0.75 mg/ml. The solvent was 0.2 $M$, pH 5.6, McIlvaine's buffer.

As expected, the colorless apoenzyme did not absorb in the visible region. However, the rebinding of the copper resulted in a blue protein that showed a visible spectrum almost identical to that of the original native enzyme (see Fig. 3).

## B. Investigation of SH Groups in the Apoenzyme

The amperometric titration of apoenzyme with silver ion revealed the presence of SH groups (see Table 5). Apoenzyme that was titrated within 2 hr after dialysis to remove cyanide* was found to contain about 10 SH groups. The number of SH groups found in the apoenzyme decreased with time as shown in the table. These data are similar to those obtained in a study of the urea-treated enzyme (16).

It was previously demonstrated that the native enzyme functions with virtually no inhibition in the presence of a very large molar excess of *p*-CMB, a finding that is in agreement with the observation that the native enzyme contains no detectable SH groups (16). However, as pointed out above, the apoenzyme contains about 10 measurable SH groups; and as can be seen from Fig. 2, treatment of the apoenzyme with *p*-CMB, before the addition of cuprous ion, prevented the restoration of activity. The extrapolated value of 12 moles of *p*-CMB required to prevent completely the restoration of activity is in good agreement with the value of 10 SH groups per mole, obtained by the amperometric titration of the apoenzyme. It is interesting

---

* Cyanide interferes with the silver titration and must be removed by dialysis.

TABLE 5

Amperometric Titrations of Apoascorbate Oxidase Preparations

| Enzyme Prep. No. | Age,[a] days | SH/Mole | Number of Determinations |
|---|---|---|---|
| 38E | 0 | 10.6 ± 0.3[b] | 4 |
| | 1 | 5.6 ± 0.2 | 2 |
| | 7 | 3.2 ± 0.6 | 2 |
| 38EF | 0 | 9.7 ± 0.2 | 4 |
| | 2 | 4.4 ± 0.0 | 2 |

[a] The apoenzymes were considered to be zero days old on the day after cyanide dialysis was begun. They were tested within 2 hr after dialyzing to remove cyanide.
[b] Average deviations (a.d.).

to note that $p$-CMB did not prevent copper from becoming bonded to the apoenzyme as effectively as it prevented the recovery of activity.* The restoration of the blue color to the $p$-CMB-treated apoenzyme was roughly proportional to the activity, rather than to the copper content.


## IV. DISCUSSION

The results just presented reveal that only cuprous ion is capable of restoring activity to the apoenzyme of ascorbate oxidase. However, evidence exists which supports the contention that much of the copper in the native enzyme is in the $Cu^{2+}$ state. Using specific complexing agents for cuprous ion, Poillon and Dawson (10) have obtained data indicating that the copper in the native enzyme is 75% $Cu^{2+}$. An ESR study has not yet been conducted on ascorbate oxidase. Since much of the copper in ascorbate oxidase is believed to exist in the cupric state, the fact that only cuprous ion will restore the activity to the apoenzyme might appear unexpected. However, much of the copper in native ceruloplasmin and laccase exists in the cupric state, as shown by ESR studies (20). The apoproteins of these substances are also restored only by cuprous ion (21, 22). Omura (22) has suggested the possibility that the removal of copper from laccase may result in reversible oxidation of the functional groups that bind copper. The excess L-ascorbic acid present with the cuprous ion may reduce these groups back to the states in which they are capable of forming the specific copper-protein linkages. In the present

* For example, apoenzyme treated with 10 moles of $p$-CMB and then with cuprous ion attained an activity of only 25% of that of the control and a copper content of 75% of that of the control.

study, an excess of reducing agent was always present during the reconstitution of the apoenzyme, either L-ascorbic acid, hydroxylamine, or cuprous ion. The question of whether cuprous ion *per se* is necessary to restore the activity has not yet been resolved.

The curve in Fig. 1 reveals that there is not a simple linear relationship between recovered activity or blue color and added copper. Workers on ceruloplasmin (23) have reported that, when apoceruloplasmin is mixed with less than the amount of cuprous ion required for complete recovery of the activity, only two species are present: fully reconstituted and apoceruloplasmin. If this were true of ascorbate oxidase, a linear curve would have been expected in Fig. 1. The curve in Fig. 1 suggests that in ascorbate oxidase the apoenzyme can bind fewer than the eight coppers required for complete restoration, and the copper atoms interact in some way, so that most of the copper must be bonded before the enzyme can become catalytically active.

Spectrophotometric studies on ascorbate oxidase indicate that the copper is probably bonded to nitrogen rather than to sulfur (7). Removal of the copper from the enzyme by cyanide dialysis or by urea reveals SH groups. In the case of the cyanide-dialyzed enzyme, blocking of these groups with *p*-CMB prevents recovery of most of the activity and blue color, but much of the copper is rebonded. A possible explanation of these observations is that SH groups are located near the active site, and the presence of copper prevents their detection. Perhaps *p*-CMB may disrupt the structure of the protein near the potentially active site in the apoenzyme, so that some of the copper can be rebonded, but the specific conformation required for the activity and the characteristic absorption at 606 m$\mu$ cannot be attained. There is no evidence to suggest that SH groups play a role in the activity.

The apoenzyme solutions were quite free of precipitate. After being stored for several weeks in the refrigerator, they retained much of their ability to be restored to active enzyme.* It does not appear, therefore, that copper is important in maintaining the gross structure of ascorbate oxidase.

## V. SUMMARY

1. The apoenzyme of the blue copper protein, ascorbate oxidase, has been prepared by dialysis against aqueous buffered cyanide. Treatment of the colorless, inactive apoprotein with cupric ion results in a partial rebonding of the copper but no recovery of activity.

2. Almost all the catalytic activity and blue color are regained upon treatment of the apoenzyme with cuprous ion. An excess of cuprous ion is not required.

* Additional experimental details are available in the dissertation of Zelda Penton, a microfilm copy of which may be obtained from the Columbia University Library.

3. The freshly prepared apoenzyme is found, on titration with silver ion, to contain about 10 SH groups per mole. These sulfhydryl groups cannot be detected in the native enzyme.

4. Blocking the SH groups in the apoenzyme with 12 moles of $p$-CMB, before treatment with cuprous ion, prevents the restoration of activity and blue color. However, the $p$-CMB-treated apoenzyme retains much of its capacity to bind copper. Consequently, it is concluded that the primary copper-binding group in ascorbate oxidase is probably not sulfur.

### ACKNOWLEDGMENTS

We wish to thank Mr. Stanley Lewis for his assistance in purifying the enzyme preparations used in this investigation. We are indebted also to the National Institutes of Health, United States Public Health Service, for the financial aid received from Grant A-3200.

### REFERENCES

1. C. R. Dawson, in *Copper Metabolism*, The Johns Hopkins Press, Baltimore, 1950, p. 18.
2. F. Dunn and C. R. Dawson, *J. Biol. Chem.*, **189**, 485 (1951).
3. K. Tokuyama and C. R. Dawson, *Biochem. et Biophys. Acta*, **56**, 427 (1962).
4. A. F. Hess and L. J. Unger, *Proc. Soc. Exptl. Biol. Med.*, **19**, 119 (1921).
5. J. Dayan, Ph.D. thesis, Columbia University, New York, 1960.
6. W. N. Poillon and C. R. Dawson, *Biochim. et Biophys. Acta*, **77**, 37 (1963).
7. D. M. Kirschenbaum, Ph.D. thesis, Columbia University, New York, 1956.
8. C. R. Dawson, *Ann. N.Y. Acad. Sci.*, **88**, 353 (1960).
9. R. Magee and C. R. Dawson, *Arch. Biochem. Biophys.*, **99**, 338 (1962).
10. W. N. Poillon and C. R. Dawson, *Biochem. et Biophys. Acta*, **77**, 27 (1963).
11. M. Joselow and C. R. Dawson, *J. Biol. Chem.*, **191**, 1 (1951).
12. M. Joselow and C. R. Dawson, *J. Biol. Chem.*, **191**, 11 (1951).
13. K. Tokuyama, E. E. Clark, and C. R. Dawson (to be published).
14. G. T. Meiklejohn, *Biochem. J.*, **35**, 755 (1941).
15. B. W. Greenwald and C. R. Dawson (to be published).
16. G. Stark and C. R. Dawson, *J. Biol. Chem.*, **237**, 712 (1962).
17. C. R. Dawson and R. Magee, in S. P. Colowick and N. O. Kaplan, Eds., *Methods of Enzymology*, Vol. II, Academic Press, New York, 1955, p. 831.
18. G. Stark and C. R. Dawson, *Anal. Chem.*, **30**, 191 (1958).
19. R. E. Benesch, H. A. Lardy, and R. Benesch, *J. Biol. Chem.*, **216**, 663 (1955).
20. L. Broman, B. G. Malmström, R. Aasa, and T. Vängård, *J. Molecular Biol.*, **5**, 301 (1962).
21. A. G. Morrell and I. H. Scheinberg, *Science*, **127**, 588 (1958).
22. T. Omura, *J. Biochem. (Tokyo)*, **50**, 389 (1961).
23. P. Aisen and A. G. Morrell, *Federation Proc.*, **23**, 362 (1964).

*Discussion*

RACKER: I have two questions to ask Dr. Dawson. First, I don't quite understand how in your very early experiment many years ago, when you tried the effect of cupric ion, you could have missed the reactivation by cuprous ions, since you always used ascorbic acid as substrate.

DAWSON: No, no.

RACKER: You must have had cuprous ions in the test under these conditions.

DAWSON: The early experiments were done quite differently. The cupric copper was added to the apoenzyme, and the system after incubation was dialyzed or treated with a cation spin before carrying out the activity assay in the presence of ascorbate. Dilute systems, suitable for activity assay directly, were not feasible because the blue color and copper content could not be measured on such systems. High concentrations are required.

RACKER: High concentrations of enzyme?

DAWSON: Yes.

RACKER: The dilute condition of the test just doesn't work! My second question is in regard to your observations concerning sulfhydryls. I am worried about attributing the effect of *p*-CMB to sulfhydryl groups because this is very treacherous ground. The question I specifically want to ask is whether the combining activity of the apoenzyme which had been exposed and apparently oxidized in the course of aging can be restored by reducing agents such as SH compounds.

DAWSON: That experiment is on the agenda but has not been tried. I'm sorry.

RACKER: You have no comments regarding the treacherousness of *p*-CMB?

DAWSON: Well, all I can say is that I am well aware of the treacherousness of *p*-CMB experiments. In fact, we were brought into this type of experimental work because it was reported that *p*-CMB has an inhibiting effect on ascorbate oxidase. We found that large amounts of *p*-CMB do affect the native enzyme to some degree, but *p*-CMB has no inhibitory effect on the native holoenzyme when used in what you might call reasonable concentrations. All I can say here is that the apoenzyme has been treated with relatively small amounts of *p*-CMB, amounts that are reasonable in terms of the hypothesis we have made.

RACKER: Reasonable for us or for the enzyme?

DAWSON: For the enzyme. It causes the apoenzyme to lose the ability to be restored by cuprous ion. I can't say any more at the moment.

CAUGHEY: One is struck by the fact there could well be units which contain *four* copper atoms in those enzymes characterized by reactions where oxygen is reduced to water, a process which of course requires *four* electrons per oxygen molecule. Thus, there are four copper atoms in laccase, and eight in both ceruloplasmin and ascorbate oxidase. A possible structure which I have not heard mentioned here is an arrangement of four copper atoms in a linear array bridged or bonded in such a manner as to minimize the inner-sphere rearrangement and spin-multiplicity problems for electron transfer. Such a model also appears fully compatible with Dr. Malmström's recently mentioned finding that complete enzyme reduction occurs before oxidation by molecular oxygen. I should appreciate hearing comments on the feasibility of such a model.

DAWSON: I can tell you that we have no experimental data for such models, but many models of this kind have been conceived, put on blackboards, and discussed in seminars. However, I'm not ready to publish, as we have insufficient experimental evidence. It's an attractive idea, however.

FRIEDEN: Do you imagine any intermediate forms of the enzyme with maybe one or two or more intermediate numbers of sulfhydryl exposed? Have you ever encountered evidence for such forms, and do you picture them as being a possible part of the denaturation process that you observe?

DAWSON: As you denature the enzyme or whatever you do to it when you treat it with urea, there is a parallel loss in copper, activity, blue color, and the exposure of sulfhydryl groups. We have work going on at the present time, which I will publish subsequently, that reveals a very great likelihood that under certain conditions this enzyme has a subunit structure. It is possible that the sulfhydryl picture will prove very interesting.

FRIEDEN: Are the sulfhydryls exposed in this subunit structure?

DAWSON: I can't say at the moment.

HEMMERICH: First, I should like to emphasize once more that the dissociation of copper as $Cu^{1+}$ or $Cu^{2+}$ by the action of so-called valence-specific reagents might in certain enzymes be a question of kinetics rather than thermodynamics.

Second, why do you give so much weight to the binding of copper by the inactivated enzyme? Any protein exhibiting *no* copper affinity at all would appear rather unsound to me. Thus, I would not believe that such a copper binding of the inactive apoprotein is very significant. Consequently, I feel that everything in your data points to the fact that sulfur *is* involved in the primary metal binding in your enzyme.

DAWSON: Well, you have a right to your own opinion. I am surprised that you think the sulfur is the primary binding site in the face of the evidence presented in our paper.

HEMMERICH: That's it—I wouldn't give much significance to the fact that when you treat the apoenzyme with *p*-CMB its activity is lost and the blue color recovery is lost, and yet you can still bind copper to this inactive protein. This wouldn't be of any significance to me.

DAWSON: Well, that's very interesting.

MALMSTRÖM: I should just like to add a few more words to what Dr. Hemmerich mentioned about the unreliability of the valence-specific reagents. The same type of ratios that Dr. Dawson finds, namely, 25% cuprous and 75% cupric, is what Dr. Felsenfeld (G. Felsenfeld, in *Symposium on the Function of Metal Ions in Biological Processes*, American Chemical Society Meeting, New York, 1960) found in native ceruloplasmin, where we now definitely know that there is a 50:50 situation. At the same time, when one has completely reduced ceruloplasmin, where there is only cuprous copper, he finds 50:50. You have a similar situation with oxyhemocyanin, for which most evidence is in favor of cuprous copper. There the Klotzes [I. M. Klotz and T. A. Klotz, *Science*, **121**, 477 (1955)] many years ago found a 50:50 ratio. It does seem that cuprous copper as bound in some of these proteins comes out partly as cupric ion. As for the point that Dr. Caughey mentioned, in a recent thesis Dr. Broman [L. Broman, *Acta Soc. Med. Upsaliensis*, **69**, suppl. 7 (1964)] does suggest such a picture for ceruloplasmin, but we have abandoned it because we feel fairly convinced of the permanent cuprous copper having another function; and if this were so, then we don't have four coppers to deal with—we have only two coppers. However, this really isn't a very good objection because certainly our evidence for the other function of the permanent cuprous copper is still rather shaky—more in the realm of what we like to think.

DAWSON: I should like to reply to your comment about the valence-specific agents, first making my position clear that I am not challenging your contention or necessarily defending mine. What I am anxious to point out, however, is that if you will read the original papers you will see that all our experiments were done with numerous controls. We were most aware of, and most concerned about, the problem that we might not be trapping the right things or that something might be happening to the liberated cupric ion before we could trap it. All our data, as judged against the controls, led us to conclude that the controls were giving us the right order of magnitude for the different copper values. For example, when we liberated the ionic copper with acid in the presence of bathocuproine without EDTA, our $Cu^{1+}$ values were high and time dependent. When the experiment was repeated with EDTA, we got a $Cu^{1+}$ value that was constant with time. I will be the first to admit, however, that we need confirmation in this case by ESR work, and I am hopeful that such studies will be done in the very near future.

SINGER: I wonder if Dr. Dawson has examined whether the regenerated holo-enzyme made from cuprous ions and apoenzyme with hydrazine or without hydrazine, but not with ascorbic acid present in the resting state, has two different valence states of copper, as did the original holoenzymes.

DAWSON: I'm sorry, I cannot give you an answer. That experiment has not been done.

JACOBS: I was just going to ask whether there was any evidence of an association in subunits after the removal of copper, but apparently you've deferred that for later publication.

DAWSON: The work on the subunit situation is an outgrowth of experiments we have been doing for some time, equilibrating this enzyme at different temperatures against increasing hydrogen-ion concentrations. Incidentally, you do not get a smooth liberation of copper from this protein as you treat it with acid. There is a very definite break in the copper-liberation curve; a break that appears to correspond again to two different copper-binding situations, one being approximately a third of the other. We have found it possible to examine some of these resulting systems in the ultracentrifuge, and it looks as though we have subunits in some cases and aggregated units in others. These results will be published in the near future.

KING: Some years ago you said that the exchange of labeled copper takes place only during reaction. Did you also explain this phenomenon as the unfolding of the peptide chain? A sort of conformation change in the reduced state?

DAWSON: No, not at that time. We suggested an explanation based primarily on the difference in binding strength of $Cu^{1+}$ and $Cu^{2+}$ atoms.

KING: I should think this could be explained in terms of the unfolding of the peptide chain so that the copper becomes more exposed, as in the case of cytochrome $c$, where conformational changes take place and the conformations are different in the oxidized and the reduced state.

DAWSON: This could very well be. More recently we have suggested such conformational changes, particularly in reference to the inactivation of the enzyme, but we have no direct experimental evidence which I can cite at this time.

KNOX: The reconstitution of the apoenzyme with cuprous ion is an exciting thing. It reminds me of the point that Dr. King mentioned about the exchange of the copper only during reaction, that is, under conditions in which the added cupric would only exist as cuprous. Do you know, or do you think it is possible, that cupric added with hydroxylamine, which would then be cuprous with no reaction going on, would also exchange?

DAWSON: That's on the agenda too. I don't know the answer at the present time. I have the feeling that the answer is going to be no, and I will tell you why. If we treat the enzyme with ascorbic acid under anaerobic conditions, the enzyme is completely bleached. Presumably the enzyme copper is entirely in the cuprous form. It will not exchange with radioactive cupric ion. But if we put the same system together in air so that the cycle is moving, then we get very rapid exchange of radioactive cupric ion.

RACKER: Did you reconstitute the holoenzyme anaerobically?

DAWSON: Yes.

MASON: The fact that copper enzymes do undergo conformational changes was indicated by an experiment of Kubowitz [*Biochem. Z.*, **292**, 221 (1937); **296**, 443 (1938); **299**, 32 (1938)] some years ago with tyrosinase, in which he found that carbon monoxide was bound by the reduced enzyme only in the presence of substrate.

SLATER: I am not quite sure whether this point is being discussed by the proper experts. I may not have understood it properly. How do you interpret the 75% of the copper which you find in the cupric form? Do you believe that this is six atoms of cupric copper and two atoms of cuprous copper, or is this a statistical average? Is this sort of equilibrium possible?

$$Cu^{2+}\!\!-\!\!\rule{0pt}{12pt}\qquad Cu^{1+}\!\!-\!\!\rule{0pt}{12pt}$$
$$\rightleftharpoons$$
$$:S\!\!-\!\!\rule{0pt}{12pt}\qquad \cdot S\!\!-\!\!\rule{0pt}{12pt}$$

DAWSON: I think that it is very definitely a possibility. I am sure that the six atom-two atom picture within the same molecule is an oversimplification. It is just a working idea at the present time; and, as I am quite prepared to suspect, it may very well be that the ESR picture will change it to four-four. In our opinion, however, there are definitely two different types of copper in this enzyme. Part of the copper is non-functional catalytically. Part of the copper is responsible for hydrogen peroxide, which produces the marked reaction inactivation. Here is another interesting and important point. The resting, non-functioning copper protein reacts not at all with bathocuproine, which is a cuprous-specific chelating agent. But in the presence of functioning ascorbic acid oxidase, a bathocuproine complex is formed which can be measured spectrophotometrically. The formation of the complex has no effect on the activity, and the amount that is measured spectrophotometrically is in correspondence with about two copper atoms.

JACOBS: Following the lead of Dr. Morrison [*J. Biol. Chem.*, **238**, 2220 (1963)], have you tried removing the chelate once formed by passing your preparation through Sephadex gel?

DAWSON: It has not been tried with Sephadex. We have tried it with anionic exchange resins and dialysis. No, the chelate is not removable. The bathocuproine is firmly complexed with the protein.

MALMSTRÖM: There was one thing I want to make clear: that in a sense we have three forms of copper here. We have, in my view, quite a variable content of cupric ion. It is very easy, when these enzymes are denatured, to get false values in both directions and also to get too much cuprous copper. My point is that, in at least two enzymes that we have studied, when we have the most native preparations there are still two types of copper—cupric and cuprous, but if you do not take care to avoid denaturation, you get more cuprous copper. However, the more native the enzyme is, the more active it is, and such preparations tend towards a ratio of 1:1 in the enzymes which I have been working with.

MASON: With respect to cupric and cuprous copper in the case of tyrosinase, as Dr. Malmström mentions, the purified enzyme contains up to 10 or 15% cupric copper, and he correctly discusses this in his paper in terms of some sort of extraneous copper. We have found (P. McMahill and H. S. Mason, unpublished data) that if the enzyme is passed through Chelex, the cupric copper can be removed entirely without affecting the activity. Dr. Malmström's conclusion that in this case the activity depends entirely upon cuprous copper, a point originally established by Kertesz, is correct.

DAWSON: I'd like to refer again to the question that Dr. Malmström asked in regard to this point. You state that there is one copper atom per molecule in tyrosinase?

MALMSTRÖM: This is just in the *Neurospora* enzyme. In the other there is more. I have corrected that in the final version of my paper. However, it is less than one cupric ion; even the high-molecular-weight enzyme has less than one cupric copper per molecule.

MASON: I think that Horowitz's data [M. Fling, N. F. Horowitz, and S. F. Heinemann, *J. Biol. Chem.*, **238**, 2045 (1963)] with respect to the *Neurospora* enzyme, which indicate a tyrosinase with a single copper atom, show that the subunit containing a single copper atom can associate throughout the range of association up to 120,000 molecular weight. Therefore, it is impossible to say from the data presented in that paper that the subunit containing a single copper atom is a catalytic unit. I would be inclined to believe that the subunit is in equilibrium with at least dimers, but more probably tetramers, in a functional system and that these polymers carry the activity.

# The Catalytic Activity
# of Ceruloplasmin and Its Inhibition

. . . E. FRIEDEN, J. A. MCDERMOTT,
and S. OSAKI

## I. INTRODUCTION

Over twenty well-defined copper proteins have now been recognized, even if we count the many different tyrosinases and hemocyanins as only one each. As shown in Table 1, their distribution is ubiquitous—from a specific copper protein in plants, plastocyanin, to the widely distributed terminal respiratory enzyme, cytochrome oxidase. They range in size from 14,600 for azurin to almost 7,000,000 for hemocyanin. They may be absolutely essential in their biological function, like hemocyanin and cytochrome oxidase, or play a limited catalytic role, like uricase. Catalytic activity has not been associated with all these proteins, but in our opinion the versatility of copper ion as a catalyst makes every copper protein a prime suspect for enzymic activity. So far the catalytic role of these copper proteins emphasizes oxidation, but participation in hydrolytic or transfer reactions should not be excluded, since we doubt that the identity and function of all the copper proteins have been recognized (1).

Among the copper proteins there is a group for which no obvious physiological function other than transfer or storage can be ascribed. Probably the most prominent of these mysterious copper proteins is ceruloplasmin (CP), the widely distributed blue copper protein of animal serum. Although hundreds of papers have been published about CP since Holmberg and Laurell (2) first reported its isolation in 1948, its function is still in doubt. Serum CP levels have proved to be a remarkable weathervane for a variety of endocrinological and pathological states, including pregnancy, Wilson's disease, carcinoma, hyperthyroidism, and many others (3, 4). Since CP is relatively plentiful, comprising 0.5% of the serum proteins and over 90% of the copper in normal human sera, it is most convenient to assume that this protein is also involved in copper storage and transfer. But the limited facts

## TABLE 1

### Copper Enzymes and Proteins[a]

| Name | Major Source | Cu, % | Mol. Wt., $10^3$ g | Cu/mole | Enzymic Activity |
|---|---|---|---|---|---|
| Tyrosinase | | | | | |
| Mold (47)[b] | Neurospora | 0.21 | 33 | 1 | L-Dopa |
| Plant (48) | Mushrooms | 0.21 | 119 | 4 | Phenol and polyphenol oxidation |
| Insect phenol oxidase (49) | Blowfly | ... | 500 | ... | Oxidation of dopamine |
| Mammalian (50) | Melanoma, skin | 0.09 | ... | 1 | Tyrosine, dopa oxidation, melanin formation |
| Cytochrome oxidase (51) | Virtually all cells | 0.25 | 70 | 1 | Reduced cytochrome c oxidation |
| Ascorbic acid oxidase (52) | Plants: squash | 0.22 | 146 | 6 | Ascorbate to dehydroascorbate |
| Laccase (53) | Plants: lacquer tree | 0.06 | 120 | 4 | Oxidation of aromatic amines, phenols |
| Uricase (54) | Liver | 0.17 | 120 | 1 | Uric acid to allantoin |
| β-Mercaptopyruvate transsulfurase (55) | Liver | | 35 | 1 | β-Mercaptopyruvate to pyruvate |
| Galactose oxidase (56) | Mold | 0.085 | 75 | 1 | Galactose oxidation to D-galactohexodialdose |
| Rhus vernicifera blue protein (31) | Japanese lac tree | 0.33 | 25 | 1 | Electron transport |
| Pseudomonas blue protein | Pseudomonas | 0.35 | 17 | 1 | Electron transport |
| Plastocyanin (58) | Chloroplasts | 0.58 | 21 | 2 | Photosynthesis (photoreduction) |
| Azurin (29) | Bacteria; Bordetella (pertussis) | 0.45 | 14.6 | 1 | Oxidation of reducing agents, cys. GSH; reoxidation by $O_2$, cytochrome c, cytochrome oxidase |
| Monoamine oxidase (59) | Animal serum | 0.088 | 225 | 4 | Oxidation of substituted aliphatic amines to corresponding aldehydes |
| Ceruloplasmin (2) | Animal serum | 0.34 | 160 | 8 | Ascorbate, epinephrine, p-phenylenediamine, arylamine oxidation |
| Hemocyanin (60) | Lobster plasma | 0.16 | 780 | 20 | Oxygen carrier |
| | Snail plasma | 0.19 | 6700 | 200 | Oxygen carrier |

a Non-enzymic Cu proteins include cerebrocuprein, erythrocuprein, hemocuprein, hepatocuprein, and additional Cu proteins from liver, milk, yeast, and vaccinia virus.

b Numbers in parentheses refers to an appropriate reference.

available do not support a simple picture of the role of CP in copper transport (1, 3, 4). When Bush *et al.* (5) fed [64]Cu to a normal adult human male, it first appeared in the plasma as [64]Cu, probably associated with serum albumin. In about 2 hr, the plasma [64]Cu began to fall, while the liver continued to increase its uptake. Only after the uptake of [64]Cu by the liver did CP begin to show appreciable radioactivity, which gradually increased to comprise over 90% of the serum [64]Cu. Thus it is presumed that liver synthesis of CP must precede the incorporation of [64]Cu. Before this point no transport function of CP can be discerned. Later, Sternlieb *et al.* (6) failed to demonstrate the exchange of CP copper *in vivo*, making it less likely that CP has a transferrin-like function. Thus, although decisive experiments to confirm the role of CP in copper transport remains to be done, its catalytic properties have assumed increasing importance in efforts to rationalize its physiological function.* Therefore, in this brief review, we shall concentrate on the catalytic properties of CP.

## II. MOLECULAR PROPERTIES OF CERULOPLASMIN

First, let us explore what is known about CP as a protein. An extensive study of the physicochemistry of human CP has been published by Kasper and Deutsch (9). Certain key molecular-kinetic parameters are summarized in Table 2. Ceruloplasmin is a sky-blue $\alpha$-2 globulin which has been prepared in the crystalline state from human blood by Deutsch (11) and from porcine blood by Osaki *et al.* (10), but efforts to dissociate it have resulted either in subunits with a molecular weight near 50,000 (9) or heterogeneous fragments (12). Reports of the heterogeneity of CP (13–16) may be accounted for by

### TABLE 2
#### Molecular Parameters of Ceruloplasmin (9)

| | Ceruloplasmin | Apoceruloplasmin |
|---|---|---|
| Molecular weight | 160,000 | 167,000–186,000 |
| $S_{20}$ | 7.1 | 6.1 |
| Cu, % | 0.32 | 0.01 |
| Per mole | 8.0 | 0.3 |
| Carbohydrate, % | 7–7.7 | … |
| $D$, cm$^2$ sec$^{-1}$ × 10$^7$ | 3.8 | 3.1 |
| Axial ratio | 11 | 17 |
| $E_{1\,cm}^{1\%}$ at 280 m$\mu$ | 14.9 | … |
| $E_{1\,cm}^{1\%}$ at 610 m$\mu$ | 0.68 | 0 |

* The reports (7, 8) that CP is a controlling factor in the hematopoetic system and that apo-CP is erythropoietin remain to be confirmed. Early efforts to correlate serum oxidase levels with schizophrenia have not been substantiated (3, 4).

its lability and conversion into derivatives of higher electrophoretic mobility by agents that effect reduction, loss of copper, or both. However, immuno-chemical studies of crystalline human CP indicate that it is antigenically complex (17), suggesting the possibility of subtle microheterogeneity.

Other than its 0.32% copper content, the most unusual feature of CP is its 7–7.7% carbohydrate content. Kaya *et al.* (18) found that the sugars in porcine CP include glucose, mannose, and xylose. Fifteen sialic acid residues per molecule of human CP were reported by Schultze and Schwick (19). In addition, CP contains 3.4% tryptophan or 27 residues, a value con-siderably higher than that found in most proteins, and numerous tryosine, aspartic, and glutamic acid residues (9). Comparison of pH and spectro-photometric titrations of CP and its apoprotein suggest that histidyl, lysyl, or, less likely, tyrosyl residues in the protein are concerned with the binding of the copper. Of course, neither of these methods is likely to reveal the interaction between the carbohydrate moiety and the copper ion. The sugar moiety may be involved in the inhibition of CP by borate ion (20). A more certain identification of the copper-binding site of CP obviously must await the isolation and analysis of appropriate copper-containing CP peptide fragments.

## III. COPPER AND THE CATALYTIC ACTIVITY OF CERULOPLASMIN

The early experiments of Holmberg and Laurell (21) established the total dependency of the oxidase activity and the intense blue color on the copper content of CP. But the preparation of apo-CP has not proved as easy as first anticipated. As with most copper proteins, the copper ion must be in the reduced state before removal or recombination. For CP, ascorbate or sulfhydryl compounds constitute effective reducing agents, and diethyl-dithiocarbamate, in a proper ionic environment, has been used to remove the $Cu^{1+}$ with a minimum of molecular distortion. As indicated in Table 2, the apo-CPs prepared by Kasper and Deutsch (9) with cyanide or diethyl-dithiocarbamate show a marked increase in axial ratio as well as reduction in sedimentation and diffusion constants. Although it appears that modified CPs can be produced by degradation (9, 22), the report of Aisen and Morell (23) that no intermediate copper-containing proteins could be obtained from the careful addition of $Cu^{1+}$ to apo-CP is of great interest.

A wealth of valuable information is emerging from electron spin resonance (ESR) studies of CP, which because of its low molecular activity is especially convenient for a combined ESR-kinetic approach. Thus several papers (24, 25) have reported that the eight coppers of CP exist as four $Cu^{1+}$ and four $Cu^{2+}$ on the basis of quantitative ESR and magnetic susceptibility measurements. Broman *et al.* (24) reported that the intense absorption at 610 m$\mu$ and the oxidase activity are directly related to the intensity of the ESR signal. It has long been appreciated that the blue color of CP is due to $Cu^{2+}$. Blumberg *et al.* (26) and Beinert *et al.* (27) initially postulated that the color is due to a charge-transfer complex involving a $Cu^{1+}$-$Cu^{2+}$ pair in which one electron is promoted from $Cu^{1+}$ to the empty $3d$ orbital of $Cu^{2+}$. However, Broman *et al.* (24, 28) suggest that a different ESR signal would be expected for such a $Cu_2^{3+}$ complex. Although the idea of a $Cu^{1+}$-$Cu^{2+}$ pair is attractive and simple, there are several intensely blue proteins with only one $Cu^{2+}$ per molecule, e.g., azurin (29), *Pseudomonas* (30), and *Rhus vernicifera* blue proteins (31).

What part do the two valence states of copper play in the catalytic activity of CP? It seems certain that the $Cu^{2+}$ is responsible for at least the first step in the oxidation of the substrate. The ability of the resulting $Cu^{1+}$ to be oxidized by oxygen is a requirement for catalytic activity. A function of the $Cu^{1+}$ in substrate binding has been proposed by Broman *et al.* (28). The best CP substrates are disubstituted aromatic compounds with a high density of $\pi$-electrons in the ring (32). These $\pi$-electron systems are predicted to complex preferentially with $Cu^{1+}$ (33). Obviously, more information is required to describe fully the nature of the interaction between CP's copper and its substrates.

## IV. SUBSTRATES OF CERULOPLASMIN

The compounds which serve as substrates for CP can be grouped into three different classes:
1. Aromatic polyamines and polyphenols.
2. Certain other reducing agents.
3. Enediols-ascorbic acid.

The first group constitutes by far the most numerous and well-studied substrates, including *p*-phenylenediamine (*p*-PD), and serves as the basis for the early comparison of CP to laccase (21). Levine and Peisach (34) have showed that the rates of oxidation of a large number of the arylamines and polyphenol substrates of CP are directly related to Hammett sigma values. Compounds having substituents with high positive sigma values (electron withdrawing) show little or no activity, whereas compounds with negative sigma values (electron releasing) are reactive. Therefore they concluded that the ease of oxidation of the substrate increases with increasing electron density in the ring. The compounds tested can be placed in the following order with respect to ease of oxidation:

*p*-PD > N,N-dimethyl *p*-PD > N-methyl *p*-PD > *p*-aminophenol

> hydroquinone > N,N-dimethyl *m*-PD > *m*-PD

For the oxidation of $p$-PD, Peisach and Levine (32) proposed the following reaction sequence, which proceeds through four steps:

1. The formation of a charge-transfer complex between substrate and CP—$Cu^{2+}$.

$$AH_2 + CP—Cu^{2+} \rightarrow AH_2—CP—Cu^{2+}$$

2. Transfer of a single electron from substrate to CP—$Cu^{2+}$ to form a free radical.

$$AH_2—CP—Cu^{2+} \rightarrow AH\cdot + H^+ + CP—Cu^{1+}$$

3. The loss of another electron from the free radical either through disproportionation or by reaction with the enzyme.

$$2\,AH\cdot \rightarrow A: + AH_2$$
$$AH\cdot + CP—Cu^{2+} \rightarrow A: + H^+ + CP—Cu^{1+}$$

4. The reaction of the diradical species with more $p$-PD to form a product usually measured in colorometric CP tests, and the oxidation of CP—$Cu^{1+}$ by molecular oxygen.

$$A: + AH_2 \rightarrow Product$$

A similar mechanism was proposed for durenediamine oxidation, in which the diradical product rearranges and is hydrolyzed. Broman et al. (28) suggested that the radical intermediate formed in the oxidation of $p$-PD is the $AH_2^+$ and not $AH\cdot$; however, the principle involved is the same.

Peisach and Levine (32) confirmed the earlier discovery of Holmberg and Laurell (21) that monoamines (aniline) and monophenols (pentamethylphenol) are not oxidized by CP. The factors common to all aryl substrates tested are that each possesses a minimum of two electron-supplying groups, and each has no strong electron-withdrawing groups, suggesting definite electronic requirements in addition to the steric requirements.

Walaas et al. (35) have studied the oxidation of catecholamines by CP. The mechanism of the reaction is as follows:

$$CP—Cu^{2+} + Catecholamine \xrightarrow{k_1} CP—Cu^{1+} + Catecholamine\ (oxid.)$$

$$CP—Cu_n^{1+} + \frac{n}{4}O_2 + nH^+ \longrightarrow CP—Cu_n^{2+} + \frac{n}{2}H_2O$$

The catecholamine oxidation product may be a free radical which reacts further as in the mechanism outlined previously.

The relative rates of oxidation of typical catecholamine substrates expressed as $k_1$ in $M^{-1}$ sec$^{-1}$ are as follows: dopamine, 143; noradrenaline, 120; adrenaline, 99; isopropylnoradrenaline, 85; dopa, 7. The larger rate constants for compounds with unsubstituted amine side chains suggest that this group is involved in the interaction with CP. If the $\pi$-electrons are primarily involved in the binding of the $p$-PD series referred to earlier, the interaction of the catecholamines may occur at a different site on CP (35).

The oxidation of NADH and NADPH has been observed in a system containing CP and appropriate substrates. Walaas and Walaas (36) have shown that the reaction proceeds thus:

$$\text{NAD}^+ \diagdown \quad \diagup 2\,\text{AH}_2 \diagdown \quad \diagup \text{CP--Cu}_2^{2+} \diagdown \quad \diagup \text{H}_2\text{O}$$
$$\text{NADH} \diagup \quad \diagdown 2\,\text{AH}_2^{+} \quad \diagdown \text{CP--Cu}_2^{1+} \quad \diagdown \tfrac{1}{2}\text{O}_2$$

Thus a free radical is probably an intermediate of the CP-catalyzed reaction. These free radicals in turn oxidize the NADH or NADPH by acting as one-electron acceptors. There is no evidence for a direct reaction between NADH and CP. By measuring the micromoles of $\text{NAD}^+$ or $\text{NADP}^+$ formed in 5 min Walaas and Walaas determined the relative rates as follows:

|            | Dimethyl $p$-PD | Noradrenaline | $p$-PD | Adrenaline | Serotonin |
|------------|-----------------|---------------|--------|------------|-----------|
| With NADH  | 0.195           | 0.175         | 0.14   | 0.04       | 0.03      |
| With NADPH | 0.20            | 0.20          | 0.17   | 0.06       | 0.08      |

Holmberg and Laurell (2) have demonstrated that sodium hydrosulphite ($\text{Na}_2\text{S}_2\text{O}_4$), hydroxylamine ($\text{H}_2\text{N--OH}$), thioglycolic acid ($\text{HS--CH}_2\text{CO}_2\text{H}$), and potassium hexacyanoferrate(II) ($\text{K}_4[\text{Fe(CN)}_6]$) are CP substrates. They represent a class of strong reducing reagents about which information is lacking concerning their mode of action or relative rates of oxidation. However, there is some specificity, probably a steric limitation, in the ability of reducing agents to react with CP, since cysteine and gluathione do not react. This group of substrates is now being studied in our laboratory.

Another function for CP has been proposed by Brown and White (37), who have shown that it can act as an electron acceptor for the respiratory chain. In the presence of cytochrome $C$ and substrate, heart-muscle particles have been shown to reduce CP. The reaction occurs under anaerobic conditions with succinate, NADPH, or reduced cytochrome $C$ as substrate, and is reversed by molecular oxygen. However, under aerobic conditions the oxidized form of CP inhibits the electron-transport system.

The ascorbate oxidase activity of CP will be discussed later in this paper.

## V. INHIBITORS AND MODIFIERS

The numerous compounds which affect CP activity, principally as inhibitors, may be classified as follows:

1. Anions.

2. Certain polyacids.
3. Metal ions.
4. Copper ion chelators.
5. Substrate isosteres.

In 1951 Holmberg and Laurell (38) observed complex effects by anions on the oxidase activity of CP, the activity being increased by low concentrations and inhibited by high concentrations. They observed that both the inhibitory and accelerating effects of the monovalent anions, $Cl^-$, $Br^-$, $NO_3^-$, $CH_3CO_2^-$, $HCO_3^-$, and $SCN^-$, were dependent on pH. However, the polyvalent anions, phosphate, sulfate, and oxalate, displayed a different type of inhibition in that they caused an induction period in the rate which could be eliminated by adding monovalent anions. To explain their results Holmberg and Laurell postulated two types of binding sites on the enzyme. Later Broman (13) showed that $Cl^-$ concentration affected the rate of color development with $p$-PD, resulting in apparently different rate constants for the oxidation of $p$-PD by CP. It was suggested that $Cl^-$ was modifying the rate of decay of a radical intermediate ($AH_2^+$) formed by CP and was not directly affecting CP (28). When Curzon (39) saturated the "activation" sites with acetate and oxalate, he observed only inhibition by other anions.

Broman (13) and Curzon (39) extended the list of polyvalent inhibitors by demonstrating inhibition at moderate concentrations with numerous dicarboxylic acids, e.g., malate, fumarate, phthalate, and oxalate. The stronger inhibitory power of these polyvalent organic acids may represent an exaggerated anionic effect, but the especially powerful inhibition by citrate, presented in detail later, does not appear to fit into this category. Citrate is the strongest reversible inhibitor of CP oxidase activity by several orders of magnitude (40).

Borate is another polyvalent anion which may have a unique mechanism of inhibition. On the basis of earlier observations that CP contained an appreciable carbohydrate moiety, Osaki (20) found borate inhibition to be reversible and non-competitive. He concluded that the effect of borate did not involve direct combination with CP—Cu.

Stimulation of CP oxidase activity by low concentrations of certain metal ions has also been observed. Curzon (39) reported that $Fe^{2+}$ and $Fe^{3+}$ at concentrations as low as $4 \times 10^{-7}$ $M$ enhanced the CP-catalyzed oxidation of $p$-PD. Other metal ions ($Ni^{2+}$, $Zn^{2+}$, $Co^{2+}$) also showed some stimulation, but $Cu^{2+}$ was inactive. He proposed a coupled CP-iron system in which $p$-PD would be rapidly oxidized, and explained EDTA inhibition, noted earlier by Broman on crude CP (13), in terms of iron chelation. However, Curzon detected no iron in his system, and all attempts to remove metal ions from the reagents did not alter the inhibition shown by EDTA. Levine and Peisach (41) reinvestigated the effects of heavy metals on CP-catalyzed oxidations and presented evidence which suggested that EDTA and other chelating agents may inhibit by at least two different mechanisms: first, by removal of contaminating metal ions, suspected as an impurity in commercial p-PD samples, and second, by virtue of a non-specific ionic effect.

Earlier, Holmberg and Laurell (21) found that a wide range of general metal complexers inhibited CP. More recently, Walter (42) studied the effects of a series of somewhat more specific copper ion chelators on the oxidase activity of CP. He found competitive inhibition by 8-hydroxyquinoline and stoichiometric inhibition by EDTA, cyanide, and 1,10-phenanthroline, but no inhibition by thyroxine and 2,9-dimethyl-1,10-phenanthroline (neocuproine).

Since it is known that the CP concentration varies in certain disease states and that CP catalyzes the oxidation of serotonin, Aprison et al. (43) tested tryptophan metabolites as isosteric CP inhibitors. Of thirteen tryptophan metabolites, serotonin, 5-hydroxytryptophan, 5-hydroxyindole-3-acetic acid, bufotenine, and 3-hydroxyanthranilic acid inhibited the dimethyl p-PD oxidase activity of CP.

## VI. THE ASCORBATE OXIDASE ACTIVITY
## OF CERULOPLASMIN

We have postponed any discussion of the ascorbate oxidase activity of CP because of confusion in the literature regarding this subject (44, 45). Because of the low molecular activity of this copper enzyme toward ascorbate and the high rates of $Cu^{2+}$ catalysis at high non-physiological ascorbate concentration, it was concluded that CP has no ascorbate oxidase activity (44). We believe that there is conclusive proof for the existence of this activity and that this property of CP may be significant in its biological role. It is agreed that all CP preparations have some ascorbate oxidase activity. The question is whether it is due to the enzyme or $Cu^{2+}$ contamination in the enzyme or reagents. Using Chelex-100-treated CP and reagents, we have made every effort to eliminate contamination by $Cu^{2+}$. As will be shown, however, all the evidence does not depend upon the absence of contaminating $Cu^{2+}$. The reaction is clearly not stoichiometric. Many hundred times the number of ascorbate molecules of CP—Cu can be oxidized by this copper protein. This can be shown by using either a spectrophotometric method to measure the disappearance of ascorbate or a manometric technique to observe oxygen uptake.

The strongest independent evidence for the ascorbate oxidase activity of CP is derived from the difference in the susceptibilities of CP and $Cu^{2+}$ catalysis toward various inhibitors. As shown in Fig. 2 and Table 3, $Cu^{2+}$ catalysis of ascorbate oxidation is strongly inhibited by serum albumin and

## TABLE 3

Summary of Differences between the Ceruloplasmin- and $Cu^{2+}$-Catalyzed Oxidation of Ascorbate[a,b]

| Parameter or Property | Ascorbate Oxidation Catalyzed by: | |
| --- | --- | --- |
| | Ceruloplasmin | $Cu^{2+}$ |
| $K_m$, $\mu$moles | 13[c] | 7000[d] |
| Zero-order constant, | | |
| $\mu$moles ascorbate/min/$\mu$mole | 14.4[e] | 150[d] |
| As measured at 265 m$\mu$ | 11.9 | ... |
| As measured by $O_2$ uptake | 11.4 | ... |
| First-order rate constant, | 0.053 | 0.023 |
| min/$\mu$mole copper | | 0.033[f] |
| Reaction order at 100 $\mu$moles | Zero | First |
| ascorbate | | |
| Activation energy, kcal/mole | 12.5 | 16.5 |
| Optimum pH | 6.0 | > 7.5 |
| $H_2O_2$ formation | None | Stoichiometric: |
| | | $\dfrac{(H_2O_2)}{Ascorbate} = 1$ |
| Inhibition, % | | |
| By 10 $\mu$moles citrate | 94 | 3 |
| By 16 $\mu$moles neocuproine | 0 | 100 |
| By 0.2% albumin | 0 | 99 |

[a] Full experimental details can be found in the *J. Biol. Chem.*, **239**, 3570 (1964), from which this table is taken by permission.

[b] Kinetic parameters were obtained at pH 5.2 and 30° unless otherwise stated.

[c] Osaki *et al.* (45).

[d] Walter (42).

[e] Estimated from the data at pH 5.5 and 37° by Morell *et al.* (44).

[f] At pH 5.5 and 37° [Morell *et al.* (44)].

neocuproine, but the CP reaction is not affected by these reagents. Conversely, citrate strongly inhibits the CP reaction in concentrations ($10^{-4}$ *M* to $10^{-5}$ *M*) which do not alter the $Cu^{2+}$-catalyzed process (Fig. 5).

The two reactions differ in numerous other ways summarized in Table 3. As shown in Figs. 1a and 1b, no $H_2O_2$ is formed during the CP reaction, whereas a stoichiometric amount is formed during $Cu^{2+}$ catalysis of ascorbate. A marked difference is observed in the pH dependencies of the two reactions depicted in Fig. 3. The CP reaction shows maximum activity around pH 6.0 with the activity gradually declining on both sides of this optimum pH—a typical enzyme pH-dependency curve. The $Cu^{2+}$ reaction increases consistently from pH 5 through 7.5. The activation energies for the two reactions when tested between 5° and 35° differ by 3.8 kcal/mole with CP yielding the lower figure, 12.5 kcal/mole. The dependency of activity on ascorbate concentration varies for the two catalysts as shown in Fig. 2. At equal copper concentration, the CP reaction quickly reaches saturation and zero-order kinetics with a $K_m$ of 13 $\mu$moles. The $Cu^{2+}$ reaction remains first order

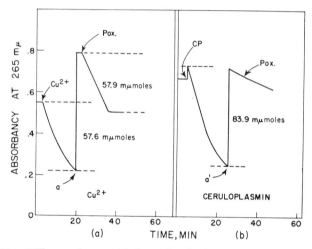

**Fig. 1a, 1b.** Difference in peroxide formation in the $Cu^{2+}$-(1a) and CP-(1b) catalyzed oxidation of ascorbate. The time course of the absorbancy change at 265 m$\mu$ is reproduced from the recording chart. At zero time, the reaction mixture contained $4 \times 10^{-5} M$ ascorbic acid in 0.2 $M$ acetate buffer of pH 5.2 at 30°. In the case of CP used as catalyst, 5 $\mu M$ neocuproine was added to the reaction mixture from the beginning to block any effect due to contamination by $Cu^{2+}$. Then ascorbate was oxidized either by $Cu^{2+}$ (1.6 × $10^{-6} M$) or by CP (2.7 × $10^{-7} M$). At a point indicated by $a$ and $a'$ in the figures, a mixture of neocuproine and citirc acid, or citric acid by itself, together with 20 $\mu$l of 5.7 $mM$ ascorbic acid solution was added to each reaction mixture. The final concentration of neocuproine and citrate in the reaction mixture was 6 $\mu M$ and 80 $\mu M$, respectively. The oxidation by $Cu^{2+}$ was stopped completely by neocuproine, and the CP oxidation was inhibited up to 90% citrate. Then 4 $\mu g$ of peroxidase was added to each reaction mixture to detect hydrogen peroxide, using ascorbic acid as the hydrogen donor at the point where indicated by $P_{ox}$. with arrow. [From S. Osaki, J. McDermott, and E. Frieden, *J. Biol. Chem.*, **239**, 3570 (1964), by permission.]

until a much higher concentration with an estimated $K_m$ of 7 mmoles. The data in Table 3 account for some of the earlier confusion about these two reactions. At low concentrations of ascorbate, in the region of serum ascorbate levels, the CP reaction proceeds more rapidly, but at much higher ascorbate concentrations the $Cu^{2+}$ reaction is faster for an equivalent amount of metal ion. This explains why Morell *et al.* (44) contended that the ascorbate reaction as catalyzed by CP was insignificant compared to the $Cu^{2+}$ reaction at 0.0057 $M$ ascorbate.

## VII. POSSIBLE SIGNIFICANCE OF THE OXIDASE ACTIVITY OF CERULOPLASMIN

Does the ascorbate oxidase activity of CP have any *in vivo* significance? To answer this question, we estimated the half-life of ascorbate, assuming that serum is a closed system with respect to it (i.e., ascorbate is moving neither in nor out) and that zero-order kinetics apply at $5 \times 10^{-5}$ $M$ ascorbate

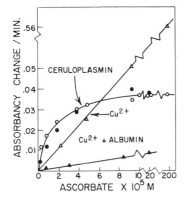

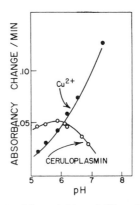

**Fig. 2.** Kinetic differences between CP and $Cu^{2+}$ catalysis of ascorbate oxidation. The rate of ascorbate oxidation as the absorbancy change at 265 m$\mu$/min is plotted against substrate concentration. $1.95 \times 10^{-7}$ $M$ CP or $1.6 \times 10^{-6}$ $M$ $Cu^{2+}$ was used with or without 0.15% bovine serum albumin as indicated. [From S. Osaki, J. McDermott, and E. Frieden, *J. Biol. Chem.*, **239**, 3570 (1964), by permission.]

**Fig. 3.** The activities of CP and $Cu^{2+}$ are plotted against various pH's between 5 and 7.5. Acetate was used as a buffer throughout this experiment, and no pH change was observed at the higher pH's due to insufficient buffering. The concentrations of the substrate, CP, and $Cu^{2+}$ were $4 \times 10^{-5}$ $M$, $2.7 \times 10^{-7}$ $M$, and $1.5 \times 10^{-6}$ $M$, respectively. [From S. Osaki, J. McDermott, and E. Frieden, *J. Biol. Chem.*, **239**, 3570 (1964), by permission.]

(50 $\mu M$). As shown in Table 3, the zero-order rate for ascorbate oxidation is 11.9 $\mu$moles ascorbate/min/$\mu$mole CP at pH 5.2. From Fig. 3 we can correct this rate downward at pH 7.4 to about 6 $\mu$mole ascorbate/min/$\mu$mole CP, since the rate at serum pH is about one-half the rate at pH 5.2. The average concentration of CP in normal human serum is $2 \times 10^{-6}$ $M$ or 2 $\mu M$. Thus every minute we can expect the oxidation of 12 $\mu$moles ascorbate. In slightly over 2 min approximately 25 $\mu$moles ascorbate will be oxidized. Therefore, on this basis, the half-life of serum ascorbate in serum is conservatively estimated to be slightly over 2 min.

This unbelievably short half-life of serum ascorbate appeared to be inconsistent with the expected stability of ascorbate in normal human sera. Therefore, we sought an alternative explanation for the stability of serum ascorbate.

We found evidence for a dialyzable serum inhibitor which proved to be citrate (40). The high serum concentration of citrate and its powerful inhibition of CP suggest that the ascorbate oxidase activity of CP in serum is held in check by the common metabolite, citrate. The activity of CP in promoting the oxidation of members of the catecholamine group is not as high as the $p$-PD series, but it is comparable to ascorbate. The activity toward the serotonin series is considerably less. Furthermore, adrenochrome has been shown to be a product of the action of CP on adrenaline (36). If

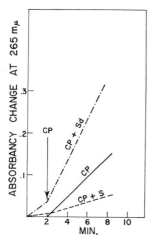

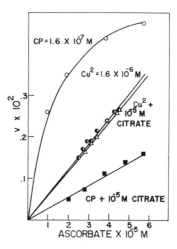

**Fig. 4.** Effect of dialysis on CP activity in serum. At zero time, fresh serum ($S$) and dialyzed serum ($Sd$)were added to $3.5 \times 10^{-5}$ $M$ ascorbic acid in 0.2 $M$ acetate buffer, pH 5.2. No addition was made to a third sample containing the same reaction mixture. At 2 min, $1.93 \times 10^{-7}$ $M$ CP was added to all three reaction mixtures. [From S. Osaki, J. McDermott and E. Frieden, *J. Biol. Chem.*, **239**, PC 364 (1964), by permission.]

**Fig. 5.** Comparison of the effects of citrate on both the Chelexes-CP- and cupric ion-catalyzed oxidation of ascorbate measured spectrophotometrically at 30°. The velocity ($v$) in terms of absorbancy change per minute at 265 m$\mu$ was measured at various concentrations of ascorbate. The reaction mixture of 3.0 ml total volume was buffered in 0.2 $M$ acetate buffer, pH 5.2.

the hypothesis of Hoffer (61) and Osmond relating adrenochrome levels to schizophrenia is correct, the control of the catalytic activity of CP assumes added prominence. Therefore, it is conceivable that, because of its high concentration and despite its relatively low molecular activity, CP might be expected to oxidize appreciable fractions of serum epinephrine, serotonin, and their analogs if the enzyme's activity was not effectively blocked by citrate. Thus the citrate control of the stability in serum of epinephrine, serotonin, and their analogs, as well as ascorbate, may be of considerable importance in maintaining normal serum levels of these important compounds with their far-reaching pharmacological activities.

## VIII. CITRIC ACID AS THE PRINCIPAL SERUM INHIBITOR OF CERULOPLASMIN

The presence of a dialyzable serum inhibitor of CP can be easily seen in a simple experiment as shown in Fig. 4. Undialyzed serum $(S)$ inhibits the rate of oxidation of added CP. After dialysis the CP of the serum $(Sd)$ or CP when added becomes fully active. The inhibitor was identified by concentrating the serum ultrafiltrate from freshly clotted normal blood, passing the concentrate through a CG-120 column and adsorbing it on a CG-4B column. The eluate was further purified by paper chromatography, and the eluted inhibitor gave a single spot on paper chromatograms. Four different solvent mixtures with $R_f$'s identical with that of citrate were used. The inhibitor was also identified as citrate by pentabromoacetone and $SOCl_2$ tests. The amount of citrate that will restore the inhibitory effect to dialyzed serum was shown to correspond to the original concentration of citrate in serum (40). It should be noted that an unidentified dialyzable serum inhibitor of CP was reported by Walshe (46), who also found evidence for a non-dialyzable inhibitor in serum from patients with Wilson's disease.

## IX. SPECIFICITY AND KINETICS OF CITRATE INHIBITION

Among the common naturally occurring organic acids, citrate is the only acid which is sufficiently inhibitory and sufficiently concentrated to account for the inhibition of CP by serum. As revealed in Table 4, only isocitrate approaches citrate in inhibitory activity, but it is barely detectable ($10^{-8}$ $M$) in serum. Certain earlier studies on the inhibition of CP by other organic acids did not reveal any inhibitors as effective as these tribasic acids (13, 39). Further studies with additional structurally related compounds are in progress.

Kinetic studies on the citrate inhibition of the oxidase activity have been reported, with representative data shown in Figs. 6 and 7. It was eventually established that citrate was a competitive inhibitor of the CP-catalyzed oxidation of at least three substrates, ascorbate, $p$-PD, and N,N-dimethyl $p$-PD. However, the simple competitive inhibition equation did not give common intercepts in $v$ vs. $v/(s)$ plots at different inhibitor concentrations. This discrepancy was explained by the fact that the equivalence of inhibitor and enzyme concentration did not permit the assumption that the free inhibitor concentration was not being depleted by enzyme-inhibitor interaction, since the $K_i$ is below $10^{-6}$ $M$. A more complex equation was derived:

$$v = V_m - K_m \left[ 1 + \frac{(I_0) - (E_0)}{K_i} \right] \frac{v}{(S_0)} - \frac{K_m}{K_i k_2} [K_m + (S_0)] \left[ \frac{v}{(S_0)} \right]^2$$

### TABLE 4
### Inhibition of Ceruloplasmin by Organic Acids[a]

| Acid | Concentration, $\mu M$ | Inhibition,[b] % |
|---|---|---|
| Citric | 1 | 64 |
| | 100[c] | 95 |
| Citric, pH 7.0 | 0.33 | 40 |
| | 16.7 | 87 |
| DL-Isocitric | 60 | 30 |
| | 330 | 80 |
| Oxalic | 660 | 25 |
| Oxaloacetic | 660 | 25 |
| cis-Aconitic | 660 | 0 |
| Lactic | >1000 | 0 |

[a] No inhibition was observed by the following related acids at the indicated micromolarity: oxalosuccinic, 33; glyceric, 660; malonic, 660; pyruvic, 660; α-ketoglutaric, 660; dihydroxymaleic, 330; malic, 660; fumaric, 330; succinic, 330.

[b] Ascorbate was $3.8 \times 10^{-5} M$ in a 3.0 ml volume containing 0.2 M acetate buffer at pH 5.2, unless otherwise stated; temperature was 30°. Ceruloplasmin (homogeneous and treated with Chelex-100) concentration was $2.0 \times 10^{-7} M$.

[c] This concentration corresponds to that of citrate in human blood.

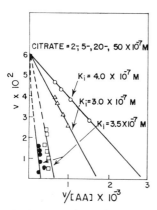

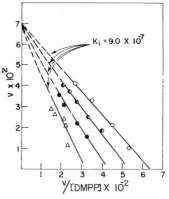

**Fig. 6.** A comparison of the experimental values with the calculated values obtained for the effect of citrate on the CP-catalyzed oxidation of ascorbate. The calculated values are indicated by solid lines, and the experimental values by the points. Respective $K_i$ values are indicated by arrows.

**Fig. 7.** A comparison of the experimental values with the calculated values obtained for the effect of citrate on the CP-catalyzed oxidation of N,N-dimethyl p-PD. The calculated values are indicated by the solid lines, and the experimental values by the points. $K_i$ values are indicated by the arrows. Citrate concentrations, corresponding to lines right to left, are 0, $2.0 \times 10^{-7} M$, $5.0 \times 10^{-7} M$, and $10 \times 10^{-7} M$.

All the symbols have the usual meaning recommended by the Committee on Enzymes of the International Union of Biochemists. $E_0$, $I_0$, and $S_0$ refer to initial concentrations of enzyme, inhibitor, and substrate, respectively. By the use of experimentally determined $K_m$ and $V_m$ values and an estimated $K_i$, calculated $v$ and $v/(S_0)$ values were obtained from the complex equation by means of an IBM-709 computer program. This equation predicts curved lines from a $v$ vs. $v/(S_0)$ plot which eventually intersect at $V_m$ on the vertical axis. As shown in Figs. 6 and 7, the data fit the predicted lines, with good agreement for $K_i$ values at several different citrate concentrations. Average $K_i$'s for citrate against the various substrates were as follows: ascorbate, $4 \times 10^{-7} M$; $p$-PD, $8 \times 10^{-7} M$; and N,N-dimethyl $p$-PD, $7 \times 10^{-7} M$. Since the average citrate concentration in normal human serum is $5$–$10 \times 10^{-5} M$ the oxidation of any of these substrates will be blocked in serum. Greater concentrations of citrate are required to inhibit CP activity when this is determined by oxygen uptake, because the ascorbate concentration used is 100 times greater than in the spectrophotometric method. However, no inhibition by citrate of the NADH-noradrenaline reaction catalyzed by CP has been detected. Thus citrate may be affecting the CP reaction at a step which is by-passed in the NADH system.

## X. SUMMARY

The catalytic activity of CP and its modification have been reviewed. Current knowledge of its molecular properties and of the equal occurrence of cuprous and cupric ions has been related to its mechanism of action. The substrate specificity, activation, and inhibition of CP have been surveyed, and proof has been presented for its ascorbate oxidase activity. The possible importance of the oxidase activity of this enzyme in serum has led to the isolation and identification of citric acid as the principal serum inhibitor of CP. Comparitive kinetic studies reveal that citrate is by far the most effective reversible inhibitor of CP and may constitute a significant factor in the control of the activity of this serum enzyme.

## ACKNOWLEDGMENTS

These studies have been supported in part by Grant HE-08344, United States Public Health Service, and by Contract AT-(40-1)-2690, Division of Biology and Medicine, United States Atomic Energy Commision.

We are grateful to the Blood Program of the American National Red Cross for various blood fractions and for some purified ceruloplasmin.

# REFERENCES

1. E. Frieden, in M. Kasha and B. Pullman, Eds., *Horizons in Biochemistry*, Academic Press, New York, 1962, p. 461.
2. C. G. Holmberg and C. B. Laurell, *Acta Chem. Scand.*, **2**, 550 (1948).
3. I. H. Scheinberg and I. Sternlieb, *Pharmacol. Revs.*, **12**, 355 (1960).
4. S. J. Adelstein and B. L. Vallee, *New Engl. J. Med.*, **265**, 892 941 (1961).
5. J. A. Bush, J. P. Mahoney, H. Markowitz, C. J. Gubler, C. E. Cartwright, and M. M. Wintrobe, *J. Clin. Invest.*, **34**, 1766 (1955).
6. I. Sternlieb, A. G. Morell, W. D. Tucker, M. W. Greene, and I. H. Scheinberg, *J. Clin. Invest.*, **40**, 1837 (1961).
7. M. Shimizu, Y. Maruyama, M. Kukita, Y. Yanagisawa, T. Sato, and S. Osaki, *J. Biochem. (Tokyo)*, **49**, 673 (1961).
8. Y. Hatta, Y. Maruyama, N. Tsuruoka, A. Yamaguchi, M. Kukita, C. T. Sho, F. Sugata, and M. Shimizu, *Acta Haem. (Japan)*, **25**, 8 (1962).
9. C. B. Kasper and H. F. Deutsch, *J. Biol. Chem.*, **238**, 2325 (1963).
10. S. Osaki, T. Kaya, T. Kanayawa, S. Ogiwara, T. Sato, and M. Shimizu, *Proc. Japan Acad.*, **37**, 54 (1961).
11. H. F. Deutsch, *Arch. Biochem. Biophys.*, **89**, 225 (1960).
12. M. D. Poulik, *Nature*, **194**, 842 (1962).
13. L. Broman, *Nature*, **182**, 1655 (1958).
14. R. Richterich, A. Temperli, and H. Aebi, *Biochim. et Biophys. Acta*, **56**, 240 (1962).
15. S. Hirschman, A. G. Morell, and I. H. Scheinberg, *Ann. N.Y. Acad. Sci.*, **94**, 960 (1961).
16. M. D. Poulik, in H. Peters, Eds., *Protides of the Biological Fluids*, Vol. 10, Elsevier Publishing Co., Amsterdam, 1963, p. 182.
17. C. B. Kasper and H. F. Deutsch, *J. Biol. Chem.*, **238**, 2343 (1963).
18. T. Kaya, S. Osaki and T. Sato, *J. Biochem. (Tokyo)*, **50**, 27 (1961).
19. H. E. Schultze and G. Schwick, *Clin. Chim. Acta*, **4**, 15 (1959).
20. S. Osaki, *J. Biochem. (Tokyo)*, **50**, 29 (1961).
21. C. G. Holmberg and C. B. Laurell, *Acta. Chem. Scand.*, **5**, 476 (1951).
22. F. L. Humoller, M. P. Mockler, J. M. Holthaus, and D. J. Mahler, *J. Lab. Clin. Med.*, **56**, 222 (1960).
23. P. Aisen and A. G. Morell, *Federation Proc.*, **23**, 161 (1964).
24. L. Broman, B. G. Malmström, R. Aasa, and T. Vänngård, *J. Molecular Biol.*, **5**, 301 (1962).
25. A. Ehrenberg, B. G. Malmström, L. Broman, and R. Mosbach, *J. Molecular Biol.*, **5**, 480 (1962).
26. W. E. Blumberg, J. Eisinger, P. Aisen, A. G. Morell, and I. H. Scheinberg, *J. Biol. Chem.*, **238**, 1675 (1963).
27. H. Beinert, D. E. Griffiths, D. C. Wharton, and R. H. Sands, *J. Biol. Chem.*, **237**, 2337 (1962).
28. L. Broman, B. G. Malmström, R. Aasa, and T. Vänngård, *Biochim. et Biophys. Acta*, **75**, 365 (1963).
29. I. W. Sutherland and J. F. Wilkinson, *J. Gen. Microbiol.*, **30**, 105 (1963).
30. H. S. Mason, *Biochem. Biophys. Research Communs.*, **10**, 11 (1963).
31. T. Omura, *J. Biochem.*, **50**, 394 (1961).
32. J. Peisach and W. G. Levine, *Biochim. et Biophys. Acta*, **77**, 615 (1963).
33. L. E. Orgel, in *Introduction to Transition-Metal Chemistry—Liquid Field Theory*, Methuen, London, 1960, p. 132.
34. W. G. Levine and J. Peisach, *Biochim. et Biophys. Acta*, **63**, 528 (1962).

35. O. Walaas, E. Walaas, F. Henriksen, and R. Lovstad, *Acta Chem. Scand.*, **17**, 85263 (1963).
36. E. Walaas and O. Walaas, *Arch. Biochem. Biophys.*, **95**, 151 (1961).
37. F. C. Brown and J. B. White, *J. Biol. Chem.*, **236**, 911 (1961).
38. C. G. Holmberg and C. B. Laurell, *Acta Chem. Scand.*, **5**, 921 (1951).
39. G. Curzon, *Biochem. J.*, **77**, 66 (1960).
40. S. Osaki, J. A. McDermott, and E. Frieden, *J. Biol. Chem.*, **237**, PC364 (1964).
41. W. G. Levine and J. Peisach, *Biochim. et Biophys. Acta*, **77**, 602 (1963).
42. C. Walter, M. S. and Ph.D. dissertations, Florida State University, Tallahassee, 1959.
43. M. H. Aprison, K. M. Hanson, and D. C. Austin, *J. Nervous Mental Disease*, **128**, 249 (1959).
44. A. G. Morell, P. Aisen, and I. H. Scheinberg, *J. Biol. Chem.*, **237**, 3455 (1962).
45. S. Osaki, C. Walter, and E. Frieden, *Biochem. Biophys. Research Communs.*, **12**, 1 (1963).
46. J. M. Walshe, *J. Clin. Invest.*, **42**, 1048 (1963).
47. N. H. Horowitz and M. Fling, *Genetics*, **38**, 360 (1953).
48. D. Keilen and T. Mann, *Proc. Roy. Soc.*, **125**, 187 (1938).
49. P. Karlson and H. Schmidt, *J. Physiol. Chem.*, **300**, 35 (1955).
50. F. C. Brown and D. N. Ward, *Proc. Soc. Exptl. Biol.*, **100**, 701 (1959).
51. K. S. Ambe and A. Venkataraman, *Biochem. Biophys. Research Communs.*, **1**, 133 (1959).
52. F. T. Dunn and C. R. Dawson, *J. Biol. Chem.*, **189**, 485 (1951).
53. T. Nakamura, *Biochim. et Biophys. Acta*, **30**, 49 (1958).
54. H. R. Mahler, G. Hubschler, and H. Baum. *J. Biol. Chem.*, **216**, 625 (1955).
55. E. Kun and D. W. Fanshier, *Biochim. et Biophys. Acta*, **32**, 338 (1959).
56. D. Amaral, L. Bernstein, D. Morse, and B. L. Horecker, *J. Biol. Chem.*, **238**, 2281 (1963).
57. T. Horio, *J. Biochem. (Tokyo)*, **45**, 267 (1958).
58. S. Katoh, *Nature*, **186**, 533 (1960).
59. H. Yamada and K. T. Yasunobu, *J. Biol. Chem.*, **237**, 1511 (1962).
60. F. Ghiretti, in O. Hayaishi, Ed., *Oxygenases*, Academic Press, New York, 1962, p. 517.
61. A. Hoffer, *Diseases Nervous System*, **25**, 173 (1964).

*Discussion*

FRIEDEN: I want to discuss an interesting copper complex which may be the first synthetic oxygen-carrying copper-ion complex. In collaboration with Drs. S. Osaki and H. Kobayashi we have isolated an interesting copper-containing compound (Fig. 1) which emulates many of the properties of ceruloplasmin and hemo-

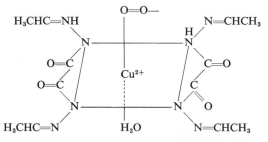

**Fig. 1.** Proposed structure of oxygenated $Cu^{2+}$ (oxalyl dihydrazide)$_2$ $(CH_3CHO)_4$.

TABLE 1

**Stoichiometry of Chromogenic Copper Compounds**

| Color | (molar) | $Cu^{2+}$ | $O{=}C{-}NH{-}NH_2$ / $O{=}C{-}NH{-}NH_2$ | $CH_3CHO$ | Interaction with $O_2$ |
|---|---|---|---|---|---|
| None | 0 | 1 | 2 | 4 | 0 |
| Blue (605) | $14.0 \times 10^3$ | 1 | 2 | 4 | + |
| Red (565) | $29.5 \times 10^3$ | 1 | 2 | >100 | + |

cyanin. As indicated in Table 1, the second compound is blue. It may have been overlooked, although I think that Nilsson [*Acta Chem. Scand.*, **4,** 205 (1950)] mentions it in passing in some of his early work. But in any case, this blue compound shows up only after oxygenation, and the intensification of the blue color and its very high molar extinction coefficient actually led to its discovery. Before oxygenation, the mixture is colorless; once you increase the proportion of acetaldehyde, you get the violet color, similar, I guess, to that of the compound that Dr. Malmström mentioned, which has an even higher extinction coefficient. And this is a compound that is frequently used, probably as the most sensitive colorimetric means for the microdetermination of copper. Now, as you'll see later on, these oxygen-carrying properties are quite different, I think, but they are reminiscent of the cobalt bissalicylaldehydeamine oxygen carriers studied extensively by Calvin and associates, and the cobalt-histidine complexes described by Hearon and Burk some years ago. Hearon and Burk did not find that they could form copper chelates which bound oxygen.

In Table 2, we have made a qualitative comparison of certain properties of the blue compound with those of ceruloplasmin and hemocyanin. The blue compound absorbs more intensely than either copper protein per atom of copper. It loses its

TABLE 2

**Comparison of Hemocyanin, Ceruloplasmin, and the Blue Copper Compound**

| Property | HC | CP | Blue Cu Compound |
|---|---|---|---|
| Absorption max., mμ | 590 | 605 | 605 |
| Extinction coefficient max. (per mole of Cu) | 750 | 1200 | $14.0 \times 10^3$ |
| Loss of color (acid or base) | + | + | + |
| Evidence of $O_2$ interaction (polarography) | + | + | + |
| Loss of color by removal of $O_2$ | + | 0 | + |
| ESR signal with $O_2$ | 0 | + | 0 |
| Reducibility with ascorbate (decolorization) | 0 | + | + |
| *p*-Phenylenediamine oxidation | 0 | + | + |
| Catalysis of $H_2O_2$ decomposition | + | 0 | 0 |

blue color after acid or base treatment, perhaps because of a change of the ligand groups around the copper iron; all three substances show evidence of oxygen interaction by a shift in the $O_2/O_2^-$ half-way potential on polarography. Then the properties begin to diverge. Like hemocyanin, but unlike ceruloplasmin, the blue compound loses its color on removal of oxygen and shows no ESR signal for $Cu^{2+}$. But in its potential catalytic activity, the blue compound imitates ceruloplasmin in decolorization by ascorbate, catalysis of $p$-phenylenediamine oxidation, and lack of any comparable effect on $H_2O_2$ decomposition. Now these things are very qualitative. I have no idea of their relative intensity. We are just at the beginning of this work, but it may have some bearing on the question of the blue color exhibited by the copper protein, at least in a qualitative way. I was reminded of some efforts by Dr. Dawson, for example, in trying to make copper complexes with intense absorption. As I recall, he used naturally occurring types of materials like serum albumin and glycine peptides; the highest molar extinction coefficient obtained·was about 95 at 580 m$\mu$ with $Cu^{2+}$ bistetraglycine; the new chelate has a much higher extinction. I think Dr. Dawson concluded, as we all would under these circumstances, that the type of bonding must be quite different.

I want to make one final point: that the blue color is composed of a highly chelatable amine, an aldehyde, copper ion, and oxygen. Now we have the corresponding groups comparable to this highly chelatable amine, in the amino groups of histamines, lysine, terminal groups, and so forth. But the early model systems which included $Cu^{2+}$, amine ligands, and oxygen did not account for the properties of copper enzyme. The one difference is the aldehyde in the complex—I haven't even tried to write a structure for this; we're certainly still working on it, but there are many possibilities. It may be that the aldehyde derivatives lay an important role in these color formations. It is well known that many of the copper proteins contain carbohydrate moities. It has been suggested, I believe, that the copper would be involved not only with protein combination but with carbohydrate combination as well.

ORGEL: How many times can you go through the cycle?

FRIEDEN: Freely, just by reducing the oxygen tension, you can decolorize and you can re-form at will.

ORGEL: Can you tell how much of the ligand is present compared to the copper in this?

FRIEDEN: The molar ratios are exactly the same.

HEMMERICH: I think the demonstration of reversibility should include liberation of oxygen by nitrogen and complete recovery of the ligand without reducing agent; otherwise there are alterations in the ligands that are reversed by reducing agents. I don't think that many reducing agents are present other than the components of the complex that I mentioned. But this is a hydrazine ligand, and we know that hydrazines undergo oxidation-reduction changes under these conditions, with copper.

FRIEDEN: The point is that it can be cycled around many times.

INGRAHAM: As I understood you, you added cupric ion to this mixture, so that clearly there must have been some oxidation and reduction going on. As Dr. Hemmerich pointed out, hydrazides are powerful reducing agents, so this is a real danger. I would think that there could be successive oxidation-reduction as you sweep out the oxygen.

FRIEDEN: Well, I haven't specified that I believe this in the $Cu^{2+}$ or $Cu^{1+}$ state. The ESR signal was absent.

DAWSON: I'd like to return to your work on ceruloplasmin activity, which I think you demonstrated very effectively. However, you refer to it as ascorbate oxidase activity of ceruloplasmin. I should like to point out that our ascorbate oxidase, at least, is not inhibited by citrate, so there must be something rather different here. Would you care to comment on this point?

FRIEDEN: Well, I will certainly concede that it is different in many respects. Certainly the activity levels, the molecular activities, are nowhere near the levels of the plant enzyme. Other than the many other differences in structure, and so forth, I can't make any reasonable explanation as to why one should be susceptible to citrate and one not.

DAWSON: You're not implying that ceruloplasmin has ascorbate oxidase activity! What is the implication?

FRIEDEN: Well, yes, I certainly would say that it has ascorbate oxidase activity, but not necessarily in the same way that the plant enzyme does. I think we have shown this in Warburg experiments, as well as with the disappearance of the 265 m$\mu$ peak. These studies are done with chelated crystalline ceruloplasmin, so I have to conclude that we don't have any intermediate carrier.

STAUDINGER: I would ask in this connection if you have ever determined the $K_m$ for oxygen for ceruloplasmin.

FRIEDEN: No, we have not. We've certainly talked about it, and we are actually studying it a number of ways, but we don't have any results.

MALMSTRÖM: I should just like to add a few words to the discussion between Dr. Dawson and Dr. Frieden. In a recent study, as I think I mentioned in my paper, we showed by direct kinetic measurements that ceruloplasmin does function entirely by substrate reducing the cupric copper and this cuprous copper is then reoxidized by oxygen. Ascorbic acid does reduce cupric copper in ceruloplasmin. As a consequence, unless somehow the reoxidization is inhibited, which it is not, it must by definition have ascorbic acid oxidase activity in the sense that it catalyzes the oxidation of ascorbic acid, though it does so slowly because the reduction is rather slow compared with other substrates.

HANDLER: Do you agree with that, Dr. Frieden?

FRIEDEN: Yes.

# PART III

# Iron-Containing Oxidases

# Molecular Oxygenation by Iron-Activated Enzymes in Mammalian Metabolism

. . . DANA I. CRANDALL

## I. INTRODUCTION

The enzymes included in this discussion are as follows:
1. Homogentisate oxygenase.
2. 3-Hydroxyanthranilate oxygenase.
3. Tryptophan oxygenase.
4. Heme α-methenyl oxygenase.
5. Inositol oxygenase.
6. p-Hydroxyphenylpyruvate oxygenase.

Of these, numbers 1, 2, and 4 are activated by ferrous ions but their iron content has not been established; number 3 is activated by hematin; number 5 contains one atom of iron per mole; and number 6 gives no evidence of either requiring iron or containing it. Nevertheless it appears to belong in this group because of the nature of the substrate reaction.

The substrate reaction in all cases utilizes 1 mole of $O_2$ and does not involve an external reducing agent in its stoichiometry. Except in the case of number 4, $^{18}O$ experiments have been conducted to demonstrate the incorporation of oxygen atoms derived from $O_2$ in the product.

All the enzymes are present in the cell sap of liver and/or kidney.

It is obvious from these statements that any attempt to arrive at a final classification for these oxidases is premature in view of certain gaps in our knowledge of their properties and actions. In terms of previously proposed classifications, numbers 1, 2, 3, 4, and possibly 5 are "true" oxygenases and number 6 and possibly number 5 are internal mixed-function oxygenases in the terminology of Hayaishi (1) or oxygen transferases and mixed-function oxidases in the terminology of Mason (2).

It is the plan of this paper to discuss these enzymes individually first with regard to the nature of the substrate reaction and then with regard to the nature of the enzyme and its iron prosthetic group. Finally an attempt to deal with general considerations will be made; this will turn out to consist of a few unanswered and provoking questions.

## II. HOMOGENTISATE OXYGENASE

Homogentisate oxygenase, present in the soluble phase in mammalian and avian liver and kidney (3), has all the qualifications of a "true" oxygenase except that only one atom of oxygen in the product, maleylacetoacetate (4), can be shown to arise from $^{18}O_2$ (5).

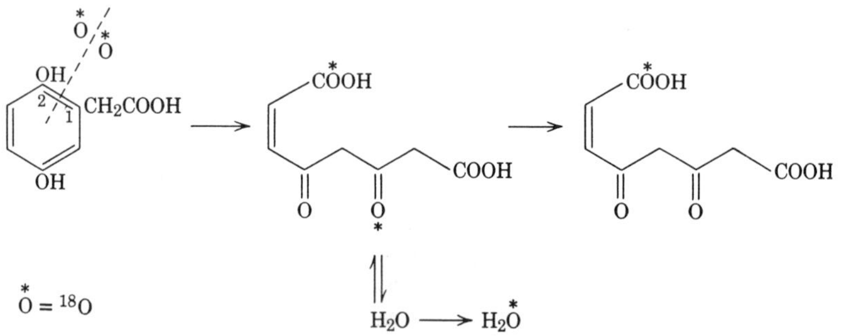

**Fig. 1.**　Conversion of homogentisate to maleylacetoacetate.

As shown in Fig. 1, the carbonyl oxygen at $C_3$ undergoes a sufficiently rapid exchange with water to be consistent with the hypothesis that this oxygen atom was initially derived from the gas phase (5). The presumptive incorporation of two atoms of oxygen into the product does not rule out an oxidase-peroxidase mechanism involving initial dehydrogenation to form $H_2O_2$ and benzoquinone acetic acid followed by the addition of $H_2O_2$ across the $C_1$-$C_2$ bond. The failure of catalase to affect the reaction or of $H_2O_2$ and benzoquinone acetic acid to form maleylacetoacetate in the presence of the enzyme, however, eliminates this possibility (6).

The ferrous iron requirement of the enzyme, originally discovered by Suda and Takeda (7), has been studied extensively by Tokuyama (8, 9, 10) and by Flamm and Crandall (11), who fail to confirm certain of Tokuyama's findings, namely, (a) that mercurial inhibition is prevented by preincubation of the iron-free enzyme with homogentisate, suggesting that the essential sulfhydryl groups combine with substrate (9), and (b) that an imidazole rather than an SH residue appears to serve as an iron-binding group (10). The latter conclusion was based upon the apparent $K_{Fe}$ evaluated by means of a rate equation relating enzymatic activity to $H^+$, $Fe_2^+$, and homogentisate concentrations. These studies were conducted with a fifty-fold purified enzyme prepared from an acetone powder of beef liver. Most of the experiments were carried out in phosphate buffer, and the assumption was made that the ferrous ion concentration could be calculated from the amount added. Tokuyama also reported that $Fe^{2+}$ protected the apoenzyme against inactivation by tyrosinase, suggesting the participation of a phenolic residue in iron binding (9), and observed increased exchange in enzyme-bound iron with the medium during oxidative activity.

Flamm and Crandall (11) reinvestigated the $Fe^{2+}$ requirement of this oxygenase with a 130-fold purified enzyme prepared from a 10,000 × $g$-supernatant of calf liver. Early in this study it was found that in phosphate buffer the purified enzyme (highly unstable) was dependent not only on $Fe^{2+}$ but on GSH and ascorbate as well. The ascorbate was shown to enhance activity by maintaining high ($10^{-3}$ $M$) soluble ferrous iron levels in phosphate buffers, and GSH was required at pH 7.0 in all buffer systems regardless of the level of soluble $Fe^{2+}$. Both GSH and ascorbate requirements were eliminated by using acetate buffer at pH 5.4. This made it possible to study the action of sulfhydryl inhibitors in the absence of GSH and also permitted high soluble ferrous-ion levels to be maintained in the absence of complexing agents such as ascorbate. With this simplified system highly reproducible results were obtained in a variety of experiments in which $H^+$, $Fe^{2+}$, homogentisate, and $O_2$ levels were varied and the action of sulfhydryl inhibitors was studied. Under these conditions $p$-chloromercuribenzoate ($p$-CMB) (Fig. 2), methyl mercuribromide, and Lewisite were shown to act as competitive inhibitors with respect to $Fe^{2+}$ but not to homogentisate. At the low concentrations of mercurial ion employed, these results suggest competition with $Fe^{2+}$ for a sulfhydryl anion.

A rate equation relating $O_2$, $H^+$, and $Fe^{2+}$ (but not homogentisate) concentrations was developed on the assumption that activation of the iron-free enzyme proceeded by the following sequence:

(1) $EH + Fe^{2+} \rightleftharpoons EFe + H^+$

(2) $EFe + O_2 \rightleftharpoons EFeO_2$

(3) $EFeO_2 \rightarrow EFe + \text{Oxygenated product}$

and was found to be in agreement with the data. Evidence for the role of $Fe^{2+}$ as a coupling activator between oxygen and the active center is shown in Fig. 3.

Further evidence for the existence of essential ferrous mercaptans was obtained by protecting the apoenzyme against irreversible aerobic inactivation not only with reducing agents but also with $Fe^{2+}$ and with mercurials, indicating that a common binding site for $Hg^{2+}$ and $Fe^{2+}$ is oxylabile. Finally, the apparent $K_{Fe}(K_{Fe^{2+}}/K_{H^+})$ was determined for a variety of thiols at pH 5.3 and compared with that of the enzyme. Only thiols containing a carboxylate

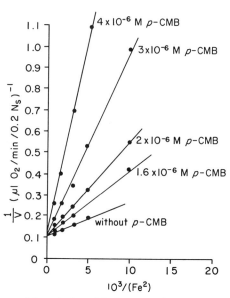

**Fig. 2.** Dependence of the velocity of the homogentisate oxygenase reaction on the ferrous ion concentration at different $p$-chloromercuribenzoate levels. Acetate buffer at pH 5.4 was used.

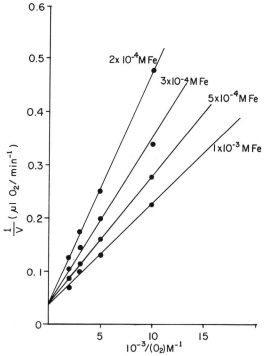

**Fig. 3.** Dependence of the velocity of the homogentisate oxygenase reaction on the oxygen concentration at different $Fe^{2+}$ levels. Acetate buffer at pH 5.4 was used.

anion in close proximity to the SH group bound ferrous ions appreciably and comparably to the enzyme, suggesting that a COO⁻ in addition to the SH was responsible for iron binding. These observations are readily correlated with an abrupt increase in the iron requirement of the enzyme upon lowering the pH from 5.2 to 4.9, which could reflect protonation of the carboxyl anion of glutamic acid residue.

Flamm and Crandall propose that oxygen is activated by ferrous mercaptans at the active center. Further progress in the study of this oxygenase will require preparation of the purified holoenzyme and a comparison of the iron and sulfhydryl contents with molecular weight.

## III. 3-HYDROXYANTHRANILATE OXYGENASE

3-Hydroxyanthranilate oxygenase is similar in its properties and action to homogentisate oxygenase and is also present in the soluble phase of liver

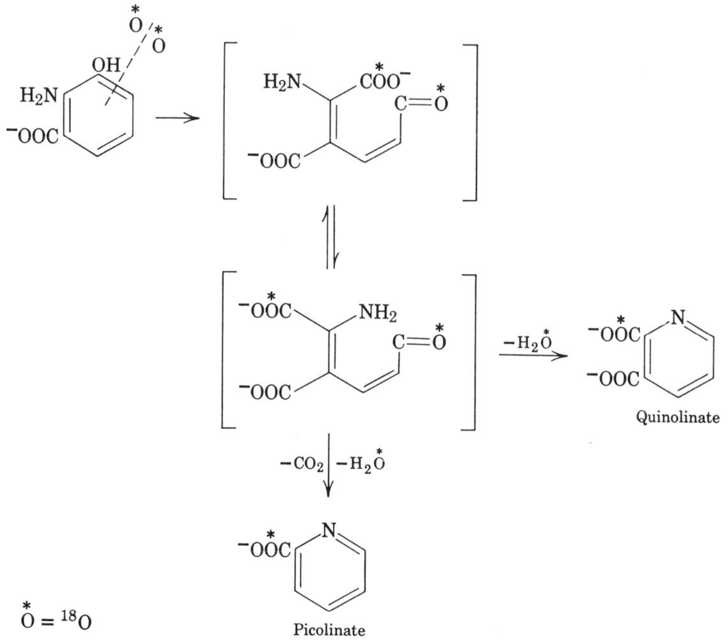

Fig. 4.  3-Hydroxyanthranilate oxygenation.

and kidney. The immediate product of the oxidation, a hypothetical transient intermediate (2-amino-3-carboxymuconic semialdehyde), has not been isolated because of ring closure to form either picolinic acid (enzymatically) or quinolinic acid (spontaneously) as shown in Fig. 4. Evidence for its existence, reviewed by Mehler (12) and by Mason (2), is extensive and completely consistent with this structure. Wiss and Bettendorf have isolated the 2,4-dinitrophenyl hydrazone from enzymatic incubations (13).

In enzymatic experiments conducted in $^{18}O_2$ by Hayaishi, Rothberg, and Mehler (12, 14) 1 mole of oxygen was consumed and one atom of $^{18}O$ was found in the picolinic or quinolinic acid isolated from the reaction mixture. Since the carbonyl oxygen of the intermediate is lost to the medium by ring closure, the results are consistent with the interpretation that the enzyme is a "true" oxygenase. It should be noted that no $^{18}O$ was found in the products when the enzyme was incubated in $H_2^{18}O$.

3-Hydroxyanthranilate oxygenase has been shown to require a combination of ferrous ion and GSH for maximal reactivation of dialyzed crude preparations and to be inhibited by low concentrations of mercurials (15). Earlier studies of ferrous iron activation included demonstrations of inhibition by $\alpha,\alpha$-dipyridyl and other chelating agents (16). These preliminary results in crude enzyme experiments suggested the emergence of properties parallel to those of homogentisate oxygenase. Later work with highly purified 3-hydroxyanthranilate oxygenase enzyme preparations, however, seems to indicate a dissimilarity in the characteristics of ferrous iron activation of the two enzymes.

Substantial purification of 3-hydroxyanthranilate oxygenase from beef liver has been reported by Decker et al. (17), who obtained an 1850-fold increase in specific activity with an 830% yield by means of activation by acid, by heat, by base, and by ammonium sulfate during the purification sequence. The purified enzyme, however, was not homogeneous and was partially protected against p-chloromercuribenzoate inhibition by substrate. The authors postulate that acid, heat, and ammonium sulfate facilitate reactivation of the enzyme with ferrous iron by causing a prerequisite change in protein conformation.

A 3500-fold purification of the liver enzyme in 800% yield has been reported by Vescia, di Prisco, and Boeri (18, 19) who conducted the entire operation in the presence of substrate, $FeSO_4$, and cysteine with anaerobic conditions maintained during heat treatment. The purified enzyme was highly unstable and particularly sensitive to inhibition by ferric ions. Their method of purification was derived from earlier observations by Iaccarino, Boeri, and Scardi (20) that the enzyme was inactivated by oxygen during the course of substrate oxidation.

Finally, Mitchell et al. (21) have concluded, from a study of reaction inactivation of the purified enzyme freed from exogenous ferrous ions and desalted by Sephadex filtration, that the role of added ferrous ion in retarding this inactivation was a non-specific one involving the reduction of protein-bound ferric ion, which could be accomplished also by other reducing agents.

These authors point out that purified Sephadex-filtered enzyme, in contrast to earlier preparations, is not inhibited by α,α-dipyridyl and suggest that the previously reported dipyridyl inhibition is due to chelation of exogenous iron, thus reducing the level of protective reducing agent. They also imply that a ferrous iron requirement therefore does not necessarily mean that enzymatic iron is loosely bound (and therefore vulnerable to the action of chelating agents) but merely oxidized *in situ*. According to this view, homogentisate and 3-hydroxyanthranilate oxygenases would be similar to the pyrocatechases in retaining tightly bound iron atoms throughout purification but would differ in their sensitivity to the oxidation of bound iron. It is also postulated that this tightly bound iron is unreactive toward dipyridyl because of complete chelation by enzymatic ligands and is therefore able to react with oxygen, as in the case of hemoglobin, but not with the organic substrate.

Proof of the validity of these interesting suggestions will depend upon a demonstration that purified iron-dependent enzyme contains the full quota of bound $Fe^{3+}$. It is difficult to see how these postulates apply when the requirement for ferrous iron is specific, as in the case of homogentisate oxygenase (11) and in most of the studies of 3-hydroxyanthranilate oxygenase (17, 18).

## IV. TRYPTOPHAN OXYGENASE

Tryptophan oxygenase, which initiates the catabolism of tryptophan in liver (and microorganisms), was shown by Knox and Mehler (22) to require 1 mole of oxygen per mole of substrate, to require $H_2O_2$, and to be inhibited by catalase. It was therefore thought to catalyze a two-step "peroxidase-oxidase" reaction in which the initial addition of $H_2O_2$ to tryptophan was followed by dehydrogenation with $O_2$, resulting in the regeneration of $H_2O_2$ and a net gain of two oxygen atoms by the tryptophan molecule in its conversion to formylkynurenine.

However, in *Pseudomonas* extracts the enzyme was shown by Hayaishi *et al.* (23) to be an oxygenase. In experiments conducted with $^{18}O_2$ in the presence of kynurenine formylase, one atom of $^{18}O$ was recovered in the isolated kynurenine and one atom was found in the formate as shown in Fig. 5. When the reaction was conducted in $H_2{}^{18}O$, a small amount of $^{18}O$ was found in the kynurenine presumably because of $C=O/H_2{}^{18}O$ exchange, and one atom of $^{18}O$ was found in the formate as a result of its formation by hydrolysis.

The peroxidase-oxidase mechanism is not eliminated by these $^{18}O$ experiments, since it would have resulted in the incorporation of gaseous oxygen into the regenerated $H_2O_2$ and thence into the formylkynurenine, but by an additional experiment showing the inactivity of 2,3-dihydroxytrytophan in this system (23). The enzyme therefore appears to be a true oxygenase catalyzing the direct addition of molecular oxygen to the 2,3 double bond.

The *Pseudomonas* enzyme was found to exhibit the spectra of an iron porphyrin after 35-fold purification by Tanaka and Knox (24) and to require catalytic amounts of peroxide for the reduction of the inactive (presumably autoxidized) enzyme to the active ferrous form. The enzyme after reduction could be inhibited by combination with CO in the absence of light and by cyanide before reduction. The authors concluded from these and other observations that the enzyme was a heme protein and suggested revival of the name originally proposed for the enzyme by Itagaki and Nakayama, namely, tryptophan pyrrolase (25).

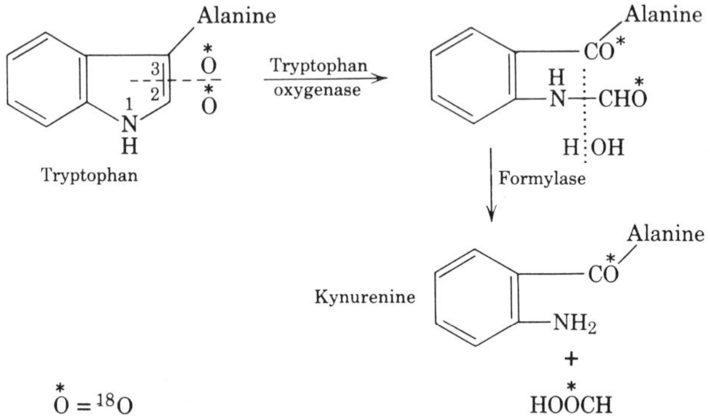

**Fig. 5.**   Conversion of tryptophan to kynurenine.

Further work on the crude mammalian enzyme was stimulated by the report of Knox and Mehler (26) that a 10–20-fold increase in oxygenase level occurred in the livers of animals after administration of L-tryptophan. Feigelson and Greengard (27) observed that, although the microsomal fraction of homogenized rat liver had no tryptophan oxygenase activity, it increased the activity of the cell sap severalfold. Further investigation of this activation revealed that microsomes release a ferriprotoporphyrin into the cell sap for which hematin can be substituted. The tryptophan-induced increase in activity was shown to involve initially a saturation of existing enzyme protein with microsomal cofactor followed by an increase in the amount of total enzyme protein (28).

These authors have purified the rat-liver enzyme 300- to 1000-fold in 10% yield by a series of three steps ending with DEAE-cellulose chromatography which converted the holo- to the apoenzyme (29). The purified protein was homogeneous in the ultracentrifuge and combined with hematin to form an active hemoprotein with an apparent $K_m$ (for hematin) of approximately $1 \times 10^{-8}\ M$.

The apparent $K_m$ for tryptophan was approximately $1 \times 10^{-4}\ M$. Both these apparent Michaelis constants were inversely dependent on the concentration of the other substance, suggesting that hematin cofactor and substrate interact reciprocally to facilitate their binding to the active center, thus providing a kinetic explanation for the effect of tryptophan in increasing the saturation of the apoenzyme by microsomal cofactor (28). It should be noted that in these studies the activation of the purified apoenzyme by hematin did not require the addition of a reducing agent.

Tokuyama and Knox (30) have reinvestigated the purification procedure of Feigelson and Greengard and have reported a 116-fold purification of the hematin-free enzyme from rat-liver supernatant in 20% yield. Reactivation with hematin required the addition of a reducing agent (ascorbate, borohydride, or dithionite); otherwise an appreciable lag period preceded the onset of full activity. Although removal of the iron-porphyrin prosthetic group during purification occurred at the DEAE-cellulose step, hematin could not be removed from the reconstituted holoenzyme by gel filtration or dialysis without prior reduction to heme by added ascorbate. This dissociation of the heme was repressed by tryptophan. For maximal reactivation of the apoenzyme, it was necessary for the addition of hematin to precede the addition of reducing agent and substrate. All these observations support the conclusion that the activated heme enzyme dissociates more readily than the hematin enzyme except in the presence of substrate.

The presence of inhibitory heme-binding proteins in liver-cell sap has been reported by Feigelson and Greengard (31), who noted counteraction by hematin and microsomes. The presence of L-tryptophan was shown to favor the transfer of heme from the other heme-binding proteins to tryptophan pyrrolase.

The reader is referred to a more detailed review on tryptophan oxygenase by Mehler (32).

## V. HEME α-METHENYL OXYGENASE

Heme α-methenyl oxygenase, described by Nakajima $et$ $al.$ (33), is present in the soluble phase of mammalian liver (and to a lesser extent in kidney). It catalyzes the conversion of pyridine hemichromogen or hemoglobin-haptoglobin complex into a verdochrome with an open tetrapyrrolic structure containing one atom of iron and a formyl group at the site of ring cleavage, as evidenced by its stoichiometric conversion to biliverdin, formaldehyde, and $Fe^{2+}$ by acid hydrolysis (34). The porphyrin-cleavage reaction therefore appears to involve oxygenation of the methenyl bridge as shown in Fig. 6.

To date, no $^{18}O$ experiments have been reported for this enzymatic reaction, and the stoichiometry has not been proven but inferred from the apparent structure of the cleavage product. The requirement for molecular oxygen is obligatory. It is highly probable that the interpretation of $^{18}O$ experiments conducted with this enzyme could be complicated $CO/H_2O$ oxygen exchange.

Anan and Mason (35) found 1.5 atoms of oxygen derived from $H_2^{18}O$ incorporated into biliverdin precursors by non-enzymatic exchange in a study of the autoxidation of hemoglobin. Nevertheless, the incorporation of one atom of oxygen into biliverdin was demonstrated (35).

In the enzymatic system of Nakajima (34) the substrate reaction with pyridine hemichromogen is thought to involve the following stages: (a) reduction of ferriporphyrin to ferroporphyrin, followed by the replacement of one pyridine residue by $O_2$, (b) oxygenation of the α-methenyl double bond, and (c) cleavage by rearrangement to form the verdochrome. The occurrence of a transient "hyperchromic" precursor of the verdochrome was shown

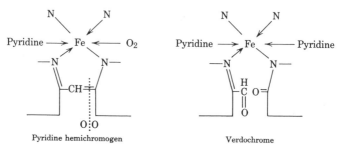

Pyridine hemichromogen                    Verdochrome

**Fig. 6.**   Heme α-methenyl oxygenation.

spectrophotometrically (33) and by paper chromatographic analysis of the reaction mixture at successive time intervals (34).

A central iron atom is required, as indicated by the inactivity of protoporphyrin IX in the system. Nakajima considers the valence change of this iron atom (ferric to ferrous) to be essential to the reaction, since pyridine hemochromogen is inactive. However, it should be noted that oxyhemoglobin-haptoglobin is almost as reactive as methemeglobin-haptoglobin.

Hemoglobin-haptoglobin complex is probably the natural substrate for this liver enzyme. These experiments are of great physiological interest in assigning a probable role to haptoglobin *in vivo*.

The 14-fold purified enzyme was prepared from an extract of beef-liver acetone powder by ammonium sulfate fractionation, hydroxyapatite, and DEAE-cellulose chromatography (33). It exhibited many of the properties associated with the other mammalian oxygenases, namely, location of the supernatant fraction of homogenized liver, an $Fe^{2+}$ requirement, instability toward oxygen, and inhibition by α,α-dipyridyl and p-chloromercuribenzoate. Catalase was not inhibitory. In addition, the enzyme has other properties which appear to be atypical or special: a requirement for TPNH in catalytic amounts ($10^{-4}$ M) and for a heat-stable, dialyzable activator present in liver nuclei and shown not to be TPNH or $Fe^{2+}$.

The role of TPNH as an external reducing agent in the substrate reaction appears improbable, since only catalytic amounts are required to activate partially purified enzyme. Its role as a component of the active center involved in intramolecular hydrogen transfer is not inconceivable in view of the complexity of the substrate reaction. Nakajima *et al.* suggest that this reaction is analogous to the action of tryptophan oxygenase. Perhaps TPNH is required merely to reactivate the enzyme as a consequence of autoxidation.

## VI. INOSITOL OXYGENASE

Inositol oxygenase, which catalyzes the conversion of *myo*inositol to D-glucuronate, has been purified 450-fold from the supernatant fraction of rat kidney and characterized by Charalampous (36), who, in addition, studied

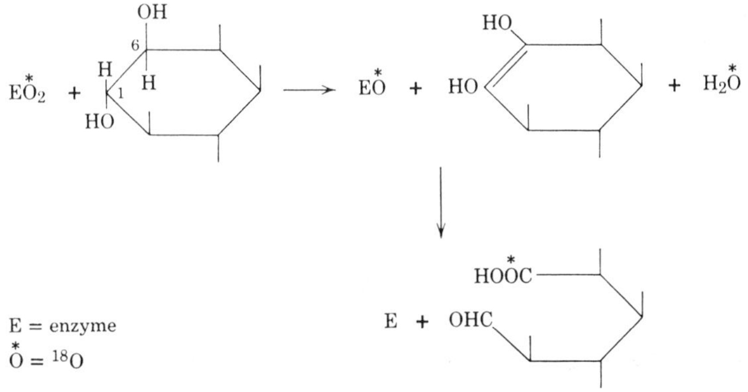

Fig. 7. Conversion of inositol to glucuronate by dehydrogenation-oxygenation.

the mechanism of the substrate reaction with $^{18}O$ (37), The D-glucuronate isolated from the reaction mixture was shown to contain one atom of oxygen derived from $^{18}O_2$, and no oxygen was derived from $H_2^{18}O$. The stoichiometry of the reaction was also determined; 1 mole of $O_2$ is consumed per mole of inositol converted to glucuronate. These results are summarized in Fig. 7, in which the enzyme is shown to function as an intramolecular mixed-function oxygenase in accord with Charalampous' interpretation.

An alternative possibility, equally in accord with the experimental findings, is shown in Fig. 8, in which enzymatic dehydration precedes molecular oxygenation of the resulting double bond. The labeled carbonyl oxygen of the newly formed glucuronic acid then is lost to the medium by $CO/H_2O$ oxygen exchange.* According to this interpretation, the enzyme would be a

---

* Although the carbonyl oxygen of glucose is relatively stable to $C{=}O/H_2O$ exchange, it is possible that complete exchange of carbonyl oxygen of glucuronate occurred during the isolation procedure employed in these experiments.

dehydrase-oxygenase. The dehydration-hydration equilibrium is reversible (38), but the equilibrium would be shifted far to the right by immediate oxygenation of the double bond. Oxygen from $H_2O$ would not be incorporated into glucuronate by this mechanism. An argument in favor of dehydrogenation (Fig. 7) rather than dehydration (Fig. 8) as a means of generating the double bond between carbons 1 and 6 is that here dehydration would require *cis* elimination of the elements of water. Conversely, dehydrogenation would involve *trans* elimination, which has been shown to occur much more readily than *cis* elimination when HCl is split out of benzene hexachloride (39).

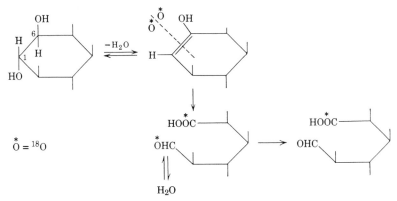

**Fig. 8.** Conversion of inositol to glucuronate by dehydration-oxygenation.

The purified enzyme was homogeneous in the ultracentrifuge and in moving-boundary electrophoresis. The pure protein had a molecular weight of 68,000 and contained one iron atom per mole. No pyridine nucleotide, flavine, or hemin residue could be detected. The enzyme was inhibited by cyanide, azide, and 8-hydroxyquinoline but not by α,α-dipyridyl. It was inhibited by sulfhydryl-binding reagents (*p*-chloromercuribenzoate, $PhHgNO_3$, arsenite, and iodoacetate). The pH optimum lay between 6.8 and 7.1. Substitution of oxygen for air resulted in a three-fold increase in activity, and the instability of the enzyme was reduced by the exclusion of oxygen.

These properties of the enzyme are similar to those of the true oxygenases and, in particular, the pyrocatechases, which have also been purified and found to contain firmly bound iron (40, 41) but with two atoms per molecule (mol. wt. 80–95,000).

If, however, inositol oxygenase is an intramolecular mixed-function oxygenase, it provides an important indication that the iron-prosthetic group is also involved in this type of enzyme. Iron has been shown to be involved in the enzymatic oxidation of 2,5-diketocamphane, but here FMN and DPN are also required for the mixed-function oxygenation (42) and the enzyme has been separated into two components.*

## VII. p-HYDROXYPHENYLPYRUVATE (p-HPP) OXYGENASE

The conversion of p-hydroxyphenylpyruvate to homogentisate is probably the most complicated reaction which has been attributed to the action of a single enzyme. One mole of oxygen is consumed per mole of p-HPP converted by hydroxylation, oxidative decarboxylation, and rearrangement to homogentisate and $CO_2$ (43, 44). The migration of the side chain to the *ortho* position originally proposed by Neubauer and Falta (45) has been conclusively proved to occur by Schepartz and Gurin (46) employing 1,3,5-[14]C-ring-labeled phenylalanine *in vivo* and in incubations with liver slices. The reaction has been investigated with [18]O and the purified enzyme by Yasunobu, Tanaka, Knox, and Mason (47), who reported that one atom of oxygen was derived from $O_2$ and two atoms from $H_2O$. They concluded that the enzyme is an intramolecular mixed-function oxidase presumably acting as shown in Fig. 9.

The two atoms of oxygen derived from water are incorporated into homogentisate by a sequence involving solvation of the carbonyl group of p-HPP, and dehydrogenation of this ketol by one atom of molecular $O_2$, resulting in their fixation in the newly formed carboxyl group. Simultaneously the other oxygen atom displaces the decarboxylated side chain (dehydro-acetate radical) from carbon 1 to form a phenoxide, which then directs o-substitution of the "dehydroacetate radical" on the ring. The formation of the new hydroxyl group (on position 1 of homogentisate) involves the displacement of the side chain instead of a hydrogen atom as in the case of steroid hydroxylation (48). It is of interest that in the oxidative decarboxylation of lactate to acetate by the lactate oxygenase obtained from *M. phlei* Hayaishi and Sutton (49) found that the new carboxyl oxygen was derived from $O_2$ rather than $H_2O$.

This reaction has been represented in Fig. 9 as a concerted rather than a three-step process as originally proposed by Neubauer (45) and shown in

* A strong indication that inositol cleavage is not initiated by dehydrogenation is provided by the absence of appreciable amounts of flavin in the purified enzyme. In a mixed-function oxygenase of the same stoichiometry, FMN functions as a hydrogen carrier between the organic substrate and molecular oxygen. This is the lactic oxygenase of *M. phlei* shown by Hayaishi and Sutton (49) to catalyze the following reaction:

$$\overset{**}{CH_3CHOHCOO^-} + O_2 \rightarrow \overset{*}{CH_3COO^-} + CO_2 + \overset{*}{H_2O}$$

The presence of FMN in the crystalline enzyme [W. B. Sutton, *J. Biol. Chem.*, **226**, 395 (1957)] and its absence in purified inositol oxygenase (36) favors the dehydration-oxygenation mechanism proposed in this review.

Fig. 10. Neubauer's proposal followed logically from the facts that 2,5-dihydroxyphenylpyruvate formed homogentisate in the alcaptonuric (45) and that the hypothetical quinol intermediate is homologous with an intermediate in the conversion of *p*-cresol to methylhydroquinone (50). 2,5-Dihydroxyphenylpyruvate is ketogenic in liver homogenates and forms homogentisate

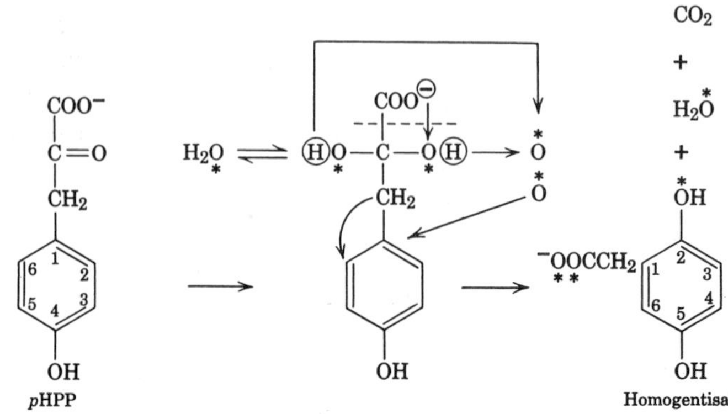

$\overset{*}{O}$ = oxygen derived from $O_2$

$\underset{*}{O}$ = oxygen derived from $H_2O$

**Fig. 9.** Conversion of *p*-hydroxyphenylpyruvate to homogentisate.

in crude enzyme preparations (44, 51). It is, however, totally inactive when incubated with the partially purified enzyme prepared from beef and pig liver (43) and from dog liver (44). To date, it has been impossible to demonstrate separate single steps of the total enzymatic process, as indicated by the

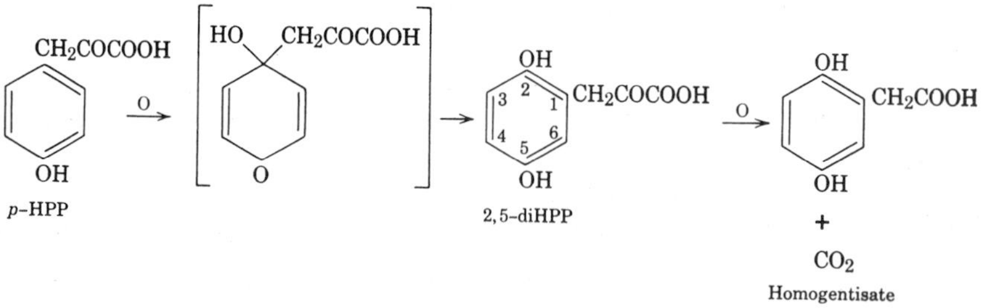

**Fig. 10.** Neubauer's hypothesis.

inactivity of the compounds listed in Table 1 when incubated with the enzyme.

The inactivity of these compounds plus the inability of Hager, Gregerman, and Knox to detect a separation of the "enzyme" into components during fifty-fold purification (43) strongly favors the concerted reaction hypothesis.

On the other hand, the inactivity of p-methoxyphenylpyruvate and phenyl-pyruvate and, in particular, the highly inhibitory action of the latter (43) suggest that the p-hydroxyl group of p-HPP plays a role in the reaction and that the quinol of p-hydroxyphenylpyruvate may be attacked by the enzyme.*

Separation of the purified enzyme into two protein fractions, one of which could be replaced by catalase, has been reported by La Du and Zannoni (53). This finding was not confirmed by Knox et al. (43) with the fifty-fold purified enzyme; they found that a requirement for catalase and also for reducing agents (DCPP, ascorbate, and GSH) could be eliminated by replacing

### TABLE 1
#### Inactivity of p-HPP Analogs with the Purified Oxidase

| Ref. | Substrate Analogs | Process Which Might Have Occurred upon Incubation with Enzyme |
| --- | --- | --- |
| (44, 43) | 2,5-Dihydroxyphenylpyruvate | Oxidative decarboxylation |
| (44) | p-OH phenylacetone | Hydroxylation + rearrangement |
| (43) | p-OH phenylacetate | Hydroxylation + rearrangement |
| (52) | p-OH phenylacetate "quinol" | Rearrangement |

manometric enzyme assay with a spectrophotometric procedure in which "milder" conditions (lower oxygen tension) were maintained.

The fifty-fold purified enzyme was inhibited by high concentrations of $\alpha,\alpha$-dipyridyl and much lower concentrations of diethyldithiocarbamate, azide, and mercurials. These authors concluded that because of lack of peroxide formation it was not a flavoprotein oxidase, and because of its insensitivity to $CN^-$ and CO not a hemoprotein, but that it was a single enzyme protein resembling the copper oxidases (43). (Copper was found to be the principal metal present.) Uchida et al. (54) report that a combination of vitamin $B_{12}$, DPN, and diphosphothiamine is required by a partially purified rabbit-liver enzyme. To date there has been no indication that the enzyme is activated by ferrous ions or that it contains iron.

If both the aromatic ring and the side chain of p-HPP are bound to the enzyme, extensive conformational changes in the active center and pre-sumably of the entire protein must accompany this complex reaction.

* The recent demonstration by Taniguchi, Kappe, and Armstrong [J. Biol. Chem., **239**, 3389 (1964)] that the conversion of phenylpyruvate to o-hydroxyphenylacetate, and of 4-fluorophenylpyruvate to 5-fluoro-2-hydroxyphenylacetate, is catalyzed by a protein which may be identical with p-HPP oxidase strongly suggests that the hydroxyl group of p-HPP does not participate in the reaction but probably aids in the attachment of substrate to enzyme.

## VIII. GENERAL CONSIDERATIONS

The diversity in apparent iron-prosthetic groups (ranging from loosely bound non-heme iron to iron-porphyrin) manifested by these ring-cleavage enzymes is perplexing in view of the obvious assumption that the iron is primarily involved in the binding and activation of molecular oxygen for essentially the same reaction in each case. It is reasonable to assume that the different cleavage reactions, all of which involve the addition of oxygen to a C-C double bond, are closely equivalent energetically. Therefore, it would appear as though differences in the "secondary structure" of the substrate are in some obscure way related to the differences in the mode of iron attachment.

Differences in the affinity of enzyme for oxygen might be expected, and apparent $K_{O_2}$ values, estimated from the available data, are shown in Table 2.

TABLE 2

$K_m$ Values for Oxygen for Mammalian Oxygenases

| Substrate | Approx. $K_{O_2}$ | Reference |
|---|---|---|
| Homogentisate | $1 \times 10^{-3}$ | (11) |
| 3-Hydroxyanthranilate | $1 \times 10^{-4}$ | (20) |
| Tryptophan | $1.3 \times 10^{-4}$ | (24) |

If anything, the differences are unimpressive. For a more complete tabulation see Hayaishi (55). In view of the uncertainty involving the binding and activation of both $O_2$ and organic substrate, it does not appear fruitful to speculate upon a generalized molecular model involving the catalytic function of the iron atom at the active center. Suffice it to say that the iron, if present, must bind and activate $O_2$ and that the primary need is for more definitive information concerning the presence or absence of iron and the number of iron atoms per mole of pure holoenzyme in each case.

It seems appropriate to question the *raison d'etre* for oxygenases when highly active hydration-dehydrogenation systems are present and account for most of the incorporation of oxygen into organic substrates (acetyl-CoA and succinate production) in the cell. Is the apparently consistent requirement for molecular oxygenation in ring-cleavage reactions to be explained on purely chemical grounds, or is it due to the location of these enzymes in the cell sap, where access to the DPNH oxidase system may be limited?

Certainly, the one-enzyme oxygenase unit is more compact than the four- or five-stage system which would probably be required to achieve the same result by hydration-dehydrogenation. It appears, however, that the possibility of the explanation lying in the nature of the oxidative ring-cleavage reaction itself should be explored. In this reaction, there is a net replacement of a C-C double bond with two carbonyl oxygens which, in contrast to the fatty acid cleavage step, is oxidative rather than thiolytic. In attempting to visualize this net oxidative cleavage in terms of hydration-dehydrogenation, it becomes apparent that, in three of the five reactions discussed here, the first step would involve hydration of an aromatic double bond, which is without enzymatic (38) or chemical precedent. Further discussion therefore is restricted to an alternative method of cleavage for the aliphatic double bond, as in the case of inositol and heme α-methenyl oxygenases.

Two dehydrogenations followed by hydrolytic cleavage of the resulting α-diketone would provide a plausible enzymatic sequence for the conversion of inositol to glucuronic acid:

$$
\begin{array}{ccccccc}
\diagdown & & \diagdown & & \diagdown & & \diagdown \\
\text{HCOH} & \xrightarrow{-2\text{H}} & \text{C}=\text{O} & \xrightarrow{-2\text{H}} & \text{C}=\text{O} & \xrightarrow{\text{HOH}} & \text{COOH} \\
| & & | & & | & & \\
\text{HOCH} & & \text{HOCH} & & \text{C}=\text{O} & & \text{CH}=\text{O} \\
\diagup & & \diagup & & \diagup & & \diagup
\end{array}
$$

Inositol $C_1-C_6$

In the case of the α-methenyl bond of heme two hydration-dehydrogenations would yield an α-hydroxyketone capable of tautomeric cleavage into ketone and aldehyde:

$$
\begin{array}{ccccccc}
\diagdown\diagup & & \diagdown\diagup & & \diagdown\diagup & & \diagdown\diagup \\
\text{C} & \xrightarrow{\text{H}_2\text{O}} & \text{CH} & \xrightarrow{-2\text{H}} & \text{CH} & \rightleftharpoons & \text{C} \\
\| & & | & & | & & \| \\
\text{CH} & & \text{HCOH} & & \text{C}=\text{O} & & \text{COH} \\
| & & | & & | & & | \\
\end{array} \xrightarrow{\text{H}_2\text{O}}
$$

Heme α-methenyl

$$
\begin{array}{ccccc}
\diagdown\diagup & & \diagdown\diagup & & \diagdown\diagup \\
\text{COH} & \xrightarrow{-2\text{H}} & \text{COH} & \rightarrow & \text{C}=\text{O} \\
| & & | & & + \\
\text{HCOH} & & \text{C}=\text{O} & & \text{HC}=\text{O} \\
| & & | & & |
\end{array}
$$

Although quite plausible in terms of single steps which could occur by enzymatic dehydrogenation via pyridine nucleotides, substitution of these pathways for the oxygenative single step would seem to be an unnecessary complication unless the economy of the cell required storage of this cleavage energy (∼80 kcal) by stepwise release to the DPNH oxidase system. The possible evolutionary significance of the oxygenases has been discussed by Bloch (56).

With regard to stability the oxygenases are well suited to their environment in the cell sap, in which the oxygen tension is relatively low (∼30 mm Hg) and oxygen inactivation probably minimal. On the other hand, at these concentrations tryptophan pyrrolase would be 50% saturated, but homogentisate oxygenase only 5% saturated, with oxygen.

Although much remains to be learned at the atomic and subatomic levels about the details of the catalytic process at the active centers of the oxygenases, the same can be said for most enzymes whose prosthetic groups are often known structures and whose function and operation are clearly related to the economy and architecture of the cell. Perhaps the greatest deficiency in our knowledge of the oxygenases is the lack of a basic explanation for the occurrence of this seemingly aberrant process in certain restricted segments of cellular metabolism.

## REFERENCES

1. O. Hayaishi, in O. Hayaishi, Ed., *Oxygenases*, Academic Press, New York, 1962, p. 3.
2. H. S. Mason, in F. F. Nord, Ed., *Advances in Enzymol.*, **XIX**, 79 (1957).
3. D. I. Crandall and D. N. Halikis, *J. Biol. Chem.*, **208**, 629 (1954).
4. W. E. Knox and S. W. Edwards, *J. Biol. Chem.*, **216**, 479 (1955).
5. D. I. Crandall, R. C. Krueger, F. Anan, K. Yasunobu, and H. S. Mason, *J. Biol. Chem.*, **235**, 3011 (1960).
6. D. I. Crandall, *J. Biol. Chem.*, **212**, 565 (1955).
7. M. Suda and Y. Takeda, *J. Biochem. (Tokyo)*, **37**, 381 (1950).
8. K. Tokuyama, *J. Biochem. (Tokyo)*, **46**, 1379 (1959).
9. K. Tokuyama, *J. Biochem. (Tokyo)*, **46**, 1453 (1959).
10. K. Tokuyama, *J. Biochem. (Tokyo)*, **46**, 1559 (1959).
11. W. G. Flamm and D. I. Crandall, *J. Biol. Chem.*, **238**, 389 (1963).
12. A. H. Mehler, in O. Hayaishi, Ed., *Oxygenases*, Academic Press, New York, 1962, p. 100.
13. O. Wiss and G. Bettendorf, *Z. physiol. Chem.*, **306**, 145 (1957).
14. O. Hayaishi, S. Rothberg, and A. H. Mehler, *Abstract of the American Chemical Society, 130th Meeting, Atlantic City, 53C, 1956*.
15. C. O. Stevens and L. M. Henderson, *J. Biol. Chem.*, **234**, 1188 (1959).
16. A. Miyake, A. H. Bokman, and B. S. Schweigert, *J. Biol. Chem.*, **211**, 391 (1954).
17. R. H. Decker, H. H. Kang, F. R. Leach, and L. M. Henderson, *J. Biol. Chem.*, **236**, 3076 (1961).
18. A. Vescia and G. di Prisco, *J. Biol. Chem.*, **237**, 2318 (1962).
19. G. di Prisco, A. Vescia, and E. Boeri, *Arch. Biochem. Biophys.*, **95**, 400 (1961).
20. M. Iaccarino, E. Boeri, and V. Scardi, *Boll. soc. ital. biol. sper.*, **36**, 1716 (1960).
21. R. A. Mitchell, H. H. Kang, and L. M. Henderson, *J. Biol. Chem.*, **238**, 1151 (1963).
22. W. E. Knox and A. H. Mehler, *J. Biol. Chem.*, **187**, 419 (1950).
23. O. Hayaishi, S. Rothberg, A. H. Mehler, and Y. Saito, *J. Biol. Chem.*, **229**, 889 (1957).
24. T. Tanaka and W. E. Knox, *J. Biol. Chem.*, **234**, 1162 (1959).
25. C. Itagaki and Y. Nakayama, *Z. physiol. Chem.*, **270**, 83 (1941).
26. W. E. Knox and A. H. Mehler, *Science*, **113**, 237 (1951).
27. P. Feigelson and O. Greengard, *J. Biol. Chem.*, **236**, 153 (1961).
28. O. Greengard and P. Feigelson, *J. Biol. Chem.*, **236**, 158 (1961).
29. O. Greengard and P. Feigelson, *J. Biol. Chem.*, **237**, 1903 (1962).
30. K. Tokuyama and W. E. Knox, *Biochim. et Biophys. Acta*, **81**, 201 (1964).

31. P. Feigelson and O. Greengard, *J. Biol. Chem.*, **237**, 1908 (1962).
32. A. H. Mehler, in O. Hayaishi, Ed., *Oxygenases*, Academic Press, New York, 1962, p. 110.
33. H. Nakajima, T. Takemura, O. Nakajima, and K. Yamaoka, *J. Biol. Chem.*, **238**, 3784 (1963).
34. H. Nakajima, *J. Biol. Chem.*, **238**, 3797 (1963).
35. F. K. Anan and H. S. Mason, *J. Biochem. (Tokyo)*, **49**, 765 (1961).
36. F. C. Charalampous, *J. Biol. Chem.*, **234**, 220 (1959).
37. F. C. Charalampous, *J. Biol. Chem.*, **235**, 1286 (1960).
38. Bo G. Malström, in P. D. Boyer, H. Lardy, and K. Myrbäck, Ed., *The Enzymes*, Vol. 5, Academic Press, New York, 1961, p. 455.
39. P. Sykes, *A Guidebook to Mechanism in Organic Chemistry*, John Wiley, New York, 1961, p. 175.
40. O. Hayaishi, M. Katagiri, and S. Rothberg, *J. Biol. Chem.*, **229**, 905 (1957).
41. H. Taniuchi, Y. Kojima, A. Nakazawa, and O. Hayaishi, *Federation Proc.*, **23**, 429 (1964).
42. H. E. Conrad, K. Lieb, and I. C. Gunsalus, *Federation Proc.*, **23**, 429 (1964).
43. S. E. Hager, R. I. Gregerman, and W. E. Knox, *J. Biol. Chem.*, **225**, 935 (1957).
44. B. N. La Du and V. G. Zannoni, *J. Biol. Chem.*, **217**, 777 (1955).
45. O. Neubauer and W. Falta, *Z. physiol. Chem.*, **42**, 81, (1904).
46. B. Schepartz and S. Gurin, *J. Biol. Chem.*, **180**, 663 (1949).
47. K. Yasunobu, T. Tanaka, W. E. Knox, and H. S. Mason, *Federation Proc.*, **17**, 340 (1958).
48. M. Hayano, in O. Hayaishi, Ed., *Oxygenases*, Academic Press, New York, 1962, p. 197.
49. O. Hayaishi and W. B. Sutton, *J. Am. Chem. Soc.*, **79**, 4809 (1957).
50. E. Bamberger, *Chem. Ber.*, **28**, 245 (1895); **36**, 2028 (1903).
51. W. E. Knox and M. LeMay Knox, *Biochem. J.*, **49**, 686 (1951).
52. B. Witkop and S. Goodwin, *Experientia*, **8**, 377 (1952).
53. B. N. La Du and V. G. Zannoni, *J. Biol. Chem.*, **219**, 273 (1956).
54. M. Uchida, S. Suzuki, and K. Ichihara, *J. Biochem. (Tokyo)*, **41**, 41 (1954).
55. O. Hayaishi, in J. M. Luck, Ed., *Ann. Rev. Biochem.*, **31**, 28 (1962).
56. K. Bloch, *Federation Proc.*, **21**, 1058 (1962).

## Discussion

CRANDALL: An indication that inositol cleavage is not initiated by dehydrogenation is provided by the absence of appreciable amounts of flavin in the purified enzyme. In a mixed-function oxygenase of the same stochiometry, FMN functions as a hydrogen carrier between the organic substrate and molecular oxygen. This is the lactic oxygenase of *M. phlei* shown by Hayaishi and Sutton [*J. Am. Chem. Soc.*, **79**, 4809 (1957)] to catalyze the following reaction:

$$\overset{**}{CH_3CHOHCOO^-} + O_2 \rightarrow CH_3\overset{*}{COO^-} + CO_2 + \overset{*}{H_2O}$$

The presence of FMN in the crystalline enzyme [W. B. Sutton, *J. Biol. Chem.*, **226**, 395 (1957)] and its absence in purified inositol oxygenase [F. C. Charalampous, *J. Biol. Chem.*, **234**, 220 (1959)] favor the dehydration-oxygenation mechanism proposed in this review.

KNOX: I was pleased to read in Dr. Crandall's paper that, of the six enzymes he lists, *p*-hydroxyphenylpyruvate oxidase "gives no evidence of either requiring iron or containing it. Nevertheless it appears to belong in this group because of the nature of the substrate reaction." For the past couple of years, Dr. H. M. D. Goswami and I have been investigating this enzyme to understand something about its biological role. We have only this week published its iron requirement. This enzyme catalyzes the reaction in tyrosine metabolism which is blocked in scorbutic guinea pigs. That fact gave rise to the idea that perhaps ascorbic acid functioned as a coenzyme in this particular reaction. The cell-free enzyme did in fact require ascorbic acid, but this was true whether the enzyme was obtained from scorbutic or normal guinea pigs. Instead of the expected cofactor-like effect, ascorbic acid allowed the reaction to continue longer rather than to go faster. And by using somewhat milder conditions of assay we were able to get the reaction to continue long enough so that we could measure it before it became inactivated by its own reaction. We then showed that all that was wrong with tyrosine metabolism in scorbutic guinea pigs fed tyrosine was that this enzyme was inactivated *in vivo*. We could also inactivate the enzyme *in vitro* equally well. It is a type of reaction inactivation *in vivo* or *in vitro* by aging or by prolonged dialysis which can be reversed by incubation of the enzyme with a mixture of a dye and glutathione. The inactivation could also be produced by mild or strong oxidizing agents, such as peroxide, ferricyanide, and dichromate, and then reversed by the dye plus gluta-thione or by treatment with other reducing agents such as aldehydes or stannous ions.

RACKER: Reversed or protected?

KNOX: Reversed. The oxidation to inactivate it and the reduction to reactivate it take place equally well in the presence of reagents which react with sulfhydryl groups, so that the oxidizable-reducible group of the enzyme is not a thiol group. This corrects an error in the conclusion that we drew years ago about the sulfhydryl nature of this enzyme. We were at that time probably removing the traces of thiol in the medium that were necessary to reduce the dye we had there to keep the enzyme active. The enzyme itself doesn't require thiol groups. The next possibility was a metal. Various chelators inhibited the enzyme, the most important ones being *o*-phenanthroline and some of its derivatives. One derivative which is rather more specific for iron than for copper inhibited, and the one relatively specific for copper did not. Evidence that it is specifically iron in the enzyme rests on two points. The *o*-phenanthroline-treated and dialyzed enzyme lost about half its activity, which was restored by ferrous iron and no other metal ions. This Dr. Goswami has published (*Biochim. et Biophys. Acta*, July, 1964). In addition to this point, Dr. K. Tokuyama (K. Tokuyama and W. E. Knox, unpublished) has shown that, at the stage of about a hundredfold purifications, the enzyme loses about half of its activity, which is restored only by addition of ferrous iron.

RACKER: I have two questions. The first one is to Dr. Crandall, asking an elaboration of the evidence that iron does react with sulfhydryl groups. What is the evidence for this interaction with sulfhydryl groups? The *p*-CMB reaction I would not consider evidence.

The second question is whether Dr. Knox could elaborate on the restoration of this activity, whether this can go on indefinitely or whether he finds that the enzyme becomes unstable under these conditions.

CRANDALL: The very low concentrations of functional mercurial we used in these experiments have been reported to be specific for sulfhydryl groups.

RACKER: The evidence rests on the interaction with mercurials then.

CRANDALL: Mercurials and lewisite, and comparison of the apparent $K_{Fe}$ of the enzyme with that of known thiol compounds.

GUNSALUS: I think that Dr. Racker's point is that, if the mercurials reacting with sulfhydryl groups result in the release of the iron, it does not necessarily mean that the iron was on those sulfhydryl groups.

KNOX: Dr. Racker asked if this inactivation and reactivation by the change in the valence state of the iron was reversible. This is a very important question because the enzyme has been studied over a series of years by Drs. LaDu and Zannoni, who have attempted to explain the inactivation phenomenon by loss of some cofactor. They have successfully considered the possibilities of ascorbic acid, folic acid, coenzyme Q, etc., as being lost. Of course we have repeatedly tried this inactivation and then reactivation by things which didn't contain these biological agents, in order to see whether there was a loss of something. We have not done this indefinitely, but five or six times. The possibility that a cofactor in the preparation was exhausted and then restored was explored adequately. We are certain that we were simply changing the valence of something on the enzyme.

RACKER: I was specifically concerned with the possibility that the inactive enzyme may be less stable than the active one.

KNOX: The inactive enzyme can be kept for several weeks and still restored to its activity.

GUNSALUS: What do you know about the release of sulfur from these enzymes on acidification? Is there any non-heme iron with labile $H_2S$ as found in ferrodoxin?

CRANDALL: This has not been reported for the enzymes I have discussed.

STAUDINGER: I should like to put a question to Dr. Knox. What can you say about the stoichiometry of ascorbic acid in relation to the other reductants, such as dyes? Is there any information concerning the need of electrons to reduce the metal?

KNOX: No, there is no stoichiometric relationship between the ascorbic acid or other reductants and the substrate oxidized. This was shown many years ago: trace amounts or catalytic amounts of these reducers were effective. Now there may be a stoichiometric relationship between these reductants and the iron in the enzyme. In fact, I would think there might well be. These are measurements that we simply haven't made.

RACKER: I take it now that you don't feel that this is the physiological function of the ascorbic acid, since the reactivation seems to be unspecific. Am I correct on that point?

KNOX: Well, perhaps not the physiological function of ascorbic acid. There is a physiological phenomenon in the scorbutic guinea pig fed tyrosine in which the enzyme is inactivated by its reaction *in vivo*. There appears to be no mechanism in the scorbutic guinea pig by which the iron in this enzyme can become reduced into its active state again. We take it out of the guinea pig and incubate it with a reducing agent; then it works. Or we give ascorbic acid *in vivo* to the scorbutic guinea pig, and then it works. I don't want to elevate reduced dichlorophenolindophenol to the status of an antiscorbutic agent, but it certainly does work. This appears to me to be a physiological function, but not the antiscorbutic physiological function of ascorbic acid.

GUNSALUS: Dr. Knox, I have a vague memory that there is a similar block in the premature human infant, who presumably is not scorbutic. How does that come about?

KNOX: That is correct. It is related to the maturation of these enzymes. We don't have enough samples of human fetal livers as yet to prove it there, but in the rat I can tell you exactly what happens. The enzyme which precedes this one in the metabolic path develops sooner, so tyrosine given to the baby rat accumulates at this stage. Later, the ratio of the two enzymes approaches unity, so that the block no longer occurs.

CRANDALL: I should like to say one additional thing to Dr. Racker about our conclusion that we were dealing with ferrous mercaptans. We can show that the group which combines with the mercurial is oxygen-labile. We can protect the apoenzyme against oxygen inactivation by combining it with mercurial and then displace the mercurial with iron and restore activity.

GUNSALUS: Could we go back to the Sutton enzyme? Is there, in fact, any metal in the FMN enzyme which carries out oxidative decarboxylation of lactate?

CRANDALL: I don't believe that this has been determined.

HAYAISHI: I think that Dr. Sutton ran a metal analysis of his crystalized enzyme and found a considerable amount of copper, but not in stoichiometric quantity. So it has not been well established that copper is actually participating.

GREEN: I believe that Dr. Sutton has recently described the presence of a completely new cofactor for that enzyme, which he originally thought was FMN. Now he has considerable doubts as to whether it is an FMN-containing enzyme. The nature of the new cofactor is yet unknown.

BEINERT: We have some indirect evidence from ESR saturation data of the free radical of this flavoprotein, the lactic oxidative decarboxylase, that it is not a metal flavoprotein.

MASON: Some question on nomenclature about this enzyme has arisen. Dr. Sutton himself has called the enzyme "lactic oxidative decarboxylase," which seems to be clear enough.

GUNSALUS: I am wondering whether anyone has really considered the mechanism of this oxygenation reaction. We've worked with ketone oxygenations, and the lactate reaction could be written as the addition of a bound oxygen on the reduced enzyme to the 2-carbon of pyruvate, followed by a cleavage by bond migration, as you would write a Baeyer-Villiger reaction in a "peroxidative" attack by peracids, thus:

$$EF_{ox} + \overset{H \quad OH}{\underset{CH_3 \quad COO^-}{C}} \rightleftharpoons EF_r + \overset{}{\underset{CH_3 \quad COO^-}{C}}=O \qquad (1)$$

$$EF_r + O_2 \rightleftharpoons EF_rO_2 \rightleftharpoons EF_{\frac{1}{2}r}O_2^- \qquad (2)$$

$$EF_{\frac{1}{2}r}O_2^- + CH_3-\overset{\displaystyle |}{\underset{\displaystyle \underset{O^-}{|}}{C}}{=}O \;\rightleftharpoons\; EF_{ox}O^{2-} + CH_3-\underset{\displaystyle \underset{O}{\diagdown}}{C}{=}O \qquad (3)$$

$$\underset{\diagup}{\overset{\diagup}{C}}{=}O$$

$$O^-$$

$$EF_{ox}O^{2-} + 2H^+ \rightleftharpoons EF_{ox} + H_2O \qquad (4)$$

where $EF_{ox}$ = flavin enzyme (FAD) oxidized, and $EF_r$ = flavin enzyme reduced. Reaction 1 would certainly be reversible, e.g., $EF_{ox}$-$EF_r$ and lactate-pyruvate; and if reaction 2 were reversible, an oxygen-release reaction would be indicated, but pertinent data are not available. Reversibility of reactions 3 and 4 is less likely, but not clearly ruled out, especially if coupled to energy-generating mechanisms.

MASON: On that point, Dr. Sutton and I did some ESR studies. We examined the possibility that a free radical was formed from lactate. Our studies were directed primarily to the question of free-radical formation from substrate, and we were unable at high concentrations of reagents to detect substrate free radical. We have reductively titrated this enzyme for determination of the free-radical formation constant, which we have obtained. I regret that I don't recall the figure.

GUNSALUS: What sort of titration would this be?

MASON: This was done with anaerobic dithionite—dithionite standardized in the manner of Bray and Ehrenberg, using FMN as an indicator. There is an equilibrium formation of flavin free radical during titration.

GUNSALUS: Right. And the oxygen said nothing about free-radical formation.

MASON: We didn't detect anything.

KING: Have you actually found valence change for iron in homogentisate oxidase?

CRANDALL: No, we have not. I think that Dr. Knox has previously shown inhibition of this enzyme with different chelating agents, which would suggest that both ferric and ferrous iron can exist during the reaction. I must refer that question to him if he'd care to comment on it.

KNOX: My experiments on the inhibition of homogentisate oxidase by reagents for ferric or ferrous iron should only be interpreted as moving whatever iron was there in or out of the enzyme. I don't think that they specify the valence state of the iron in the enzyme.

# Comparative Studies
# on Pyrocatechase and Metapyrocatechase

. . . OSAMU HAYAISHI

## I. INTRODUCTION

During the course of investigation on the metabolism of various aromatic compounds, especially aromatic amino acids, a number of enzymes have been described which catalyze oxidative cleavage of the aromatic rings of these compounds. A novel characteristic of such enzymic reactions was discovered in 1955, when enzymic incorporation of molecular oxygen into organic substrates was established through the use of a heavy oxygen isotope, $^{18}O$ (1). Since then our efforts have been devoted to the elucidation of the properties of this new group of enzymes, for which we proposed the name oxygenases (2). Pyrocatechase and metapyrocatechase are examples of such oxygenases, both of which act upon the most simple substrate, catechol, and which have been obtained as homogeneous proteins in our laboratory. It is the purpose of this paper to compare various properties of these two highly purified oxygenases and to discuss possible mechanisms of action of such phenolytic oxygenases in general.

The experiments in this paper have been carried out in collaboration with a number of investigators. Most experiments with pyrocatechase were performed by Hiroshi Taniuchi, Yutaka Kojima, Atsushi Nakazawa, Fuminori Kanetsuna, Hitoshi Fujisawa, and Junko Takei. Those on metapyrocatechase were carried out by Mitsuhiro Nozaki, Hiroyuki Kagamiyama, Teruko Nakazawa, and Katsuhiko Ono. We are indebted to Dr. H. Hatano and Dr. S. Sano of Kyoto University and Dr. B. Witkop and Dr. E. Gross of the National Institutes of Health, Bethesda, Maryland, for the analyses of amino acid composition.

## II. EXPERIMENT AND DISCUSSION

### A. Purification and Properties

Pyrocatechase was first isolated from *Pseudomonas* in 1950 and was shown to produce *cis,cis*-muconic acid from catechol (3) (Fig. 1). According to recent nomenclature (4), this enzyme is called catechol:oxygen 1,2-oxido-reductase (1.13.1.1). Metapyrocatechase was first described by Dagley and Stopher (5). It was partially purified (6), and the product was shown

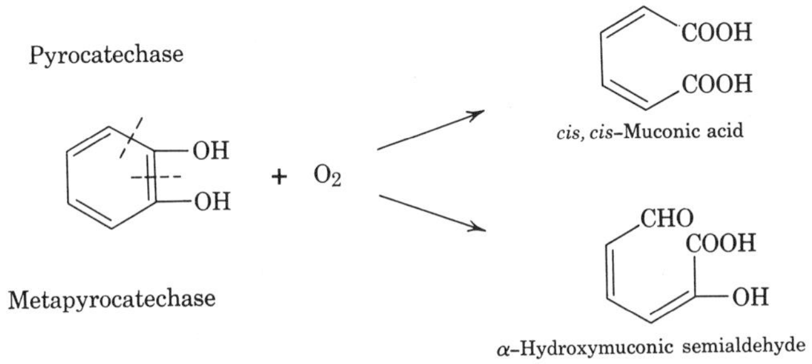

Fig. 1. Two catechol-cleaving oxygenases: pyrocatechase (catechol:oxygen 1,2-oxido-reductase) and metapyrocatechase (catechol:oxygen 2,3-oxidoreductase).

to be α-hydroxymuconic semialdehyde (Fig. 1). The systematic name is catechol:oxygen 2,3-oxidoreductase (1.13.1.2). Recommended trivial names for the two enzymes are catechol 1,2-oxygenase and catechol 2,3-oxygenase, respectively.

The methods of purification are summarized in Table 1. Pyrocatechase was purified from cells of *Pseudomonas* sp. which had been grown with benzoic acid as a major carbon source and inducer. The over-all purification was about forty-fold, with the yield about 8%.

Metapyrocatechase was purified from the cells of *Pseudomonas arvilla* grown in the presence of benzoic acid (8). As will be discussed in section IIC, the crude enzyme is very unstable, and all the purification procedures were carried out in the presence of 10% acetone, which is a potent stabilizing agent. Crystalline preparations are much more stable than the crude enzyme.

Figure 2 shows the pattern obtained when the purified enzymes were examined in the analytical ultracentrifuge. These results, together with those of free boundary electrophoresis (Fig. 3), establish the homogeneity of these enzyme preparations.

Analytical results are summarized in Table 2. Molecular weight was calculated from sedimentation and diffusion constants. The values obtained by Archibald's method were in essential agreement. It is noteworthy that

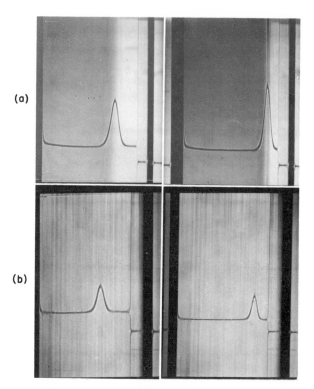

Fig. 2. Ultracentrifuge patterns of pyrocatechase (a) and metapyrocatechase (b). (a) The protein concentration was $1\%$ in $0.04\ M\ K_2HPO_4$ solution. The pictures were taken at 8 min (right) and 40 min (left) after reaching 59,780 rpm at $14.6°C$. (b) The protein concentration was approximately $1.0\%$ in $0.05\ M$ phosphate buffer, pH 7.5, containing $10\%$ acetone. The photographs were taken at 24 min (right) and 48 min (left) after reaching 60,000 rpm at $20.7°C$.

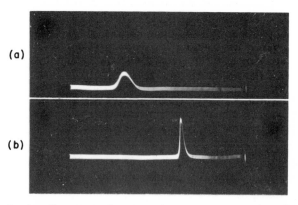

Fig. 3. Electrophoretic pattern of pyrocatechase at a concentration of $1.1\%$ in $0.05\ M$ Tris buffer, pH 7.96, 0.1 ionic strength with NaCl at $5°C$. (a) Descending pattern after 60 min of migration. The direction of migration is toward the right. (b) Ascending pattern after 60 min of migration. The direction is toward the left.

## TABLE 1
### Purification of Enzymes[a]

| Pyrocatechase | | | Metapyrocatechase | | |
|---|---|---|---|---|---|
| Fraction | Specific Activity, $\mu$moles/ min/mg | Yield, % | Fraction | Specific Activity, $\mu$moles/ min/mg | Yield, % |
| Sonic extract | 0.68 | 100 | Sonic extract | 4.0 | 100 |
| Streptomycin treatment | 0.74 | 87.0 | Acetone fraction | 20.9 | 81.0 |
| Ammonium sulfate | 2.16 | 67.5 | DEAE-cellulose | 105.0 | 51.7 |
| DEAE-cellulose | 11.4 | 41.2 | First crystallization | 110.0 | 22.4 |
| Hydroxyl apatite eluate | 28.0 | 8.1 | Third crystallization | 116.0 | 15.0 |

[a] Assays were carried out spectrophotometrically as described previously (7, 8).

pyrocatechase contains approximately two atoms of inorganic iron per mole of enzyme protein, whereas metapyrocatechase contains one atom of inorganic iron per mole of enzyme protein. No other heavy metals were detectable in a significant amount in either preparation. As judged by the color reaction (9) and experiments with the ESR spectra, the iron is present as ferrous iron.

Table 3 summarizes the catalytic properties of the two enzymes. The $K_m$ for oxygen was calculated from the data of polarographic experiments. The amino acid composition of the two enzymes is shown in Table 4. Although metapyrocatechase contains considerably greater numbers of residues of

## TABLE 2
### Analytical Results

| Property | Pyrocatechase | Metapyrocatechase |
|---|---|---|
| Molecular weight | 85,000 | 140,000 |
| $S_{20,w}$, Svedbergs | 4.31 | 5.54 |
| $D_{20,w}$, $10^{-7}$ cm²/sec | 4.5 | 3.92 |
| Partial specific volume, cc/g | 0.725 | (0.75) |
| Absorbancy, $A_{1cm}^{1\%}$, at 280 m$\mu$ | 8.93 | 13.5 |
| Iron content, atoms/mole | 2 | 1 |

TABLE 3

Catalytic Properties of Enzymes

| Property | Pyrocatechase | Metapyrocatechase |
|---|---|---|
| Specific activity, $\mu$moles/min/mg | 28.0 | 116.0 |
| Molecular activity, moles/min/mole | 2400 | 16,000 |
| $K_m$ for catechol | $0.5 \times 10^{-6}\ M$ | $3 \times 10^{-6}\ M$ |
| $K_m$ for oxygen | $2 \times 10^{-5}\ M$ | $0.7 \times 10^{-5}\ M$ |

TABLE 4

**Amino Acid Composition**

| Amino Acid Residue | Pyrocatechase | Metapyrocatechase |
|---|---|---|
|  | Number of Residues per Molecule | |
| Asp | 116 | 142 |
| Thr | 50 | 66 |
| Ser | 35 | 39 |
| Glu | 109 | 111 |
| Pro | 33 | 49 |
| Gly | 76 | 99 |
| Ala | 82 | 97 |
| Val | 54 | 92 |
| Met | 7 | 40 |
| Ileu | 33 | 40 |
| Leu | 75 | 140 |
| Tyr | 23 | 26 |
| Phe | 35 | 60 |
| $\frac{1}{2}$ Cys[a] | 3 | 12 |
| Lys | 13 | 60 |
| His | 26 | 59 |
| NH$_3$ | 95 | 99 |
| Arg | 55 | 75 |
| Try[b] | 5 | 15 |

[a] Half-cystine was determined after performic acid oxidation, according to the method of Moore (10).

[b] Tryptophan was determined by a spectrophotometric method (11).

methionine, cysteine, and tryptophan, both enzymes are similar in amino acid composition and both are acidic proteins.

Substrate specificity is shown in Table 5. Among various catechol derivatives tested, only catechol and α- and β-methyl catechol were metabolized at a significant rate. A pyrocatechase with somewhat broader substrate specificity has been reported (12).

### TABLE 5
#### Substrate Specificity[a]

| Substrate | Pyrocatechase | Metapyrocatechase |
|---|---|---|
|  | Relative Activity, % | |
| (benzene ring)—OH, —OH | 100 | 100 |
| $H_3C$—(benzene ring)—OH, —OH | 100 | 100 |
| (benzene ring)—OH, —OH; $CH_3$ | 5.5 | 100 |
| $Cl$—(benzene ring)—OH, —OH | 0.5 | ... |
| (benzene ring)—OH, —OH; $Cl$ | ... | 10 |

[a] The following compounds were tested but were inactive as substrate for both enzymes: pyrogallol, 2,3-dihydroxybenzoic acid, protocatechuic acid, 4,5-dihydroxyphenylacetic acid, and DOPA.

## B. Pyrocatechase; Spectral Properties

Whereas metapyrocatechase is completely colorless, pyrocatechase is distinctly red. There is no indication of a heme or flavin coenzyme as judged by the absorption spectra (Fig. 4). No significant change was observed upon addition of $10^{-3} M$ dithionite or substrate, or under anaerobic or degassed conditions. Pyrocatechase shows a shoulder at about 320 m$\mu$ and a broad peak at about 400–600 m$\mu$.

When the enzyme lost its activity during storage at 4°C, the spectra underwent a marked change. The red color was completely bleached, and the shoulder at 320 m$\mu$ and the broad peak at 400–600 m$\mu$ disappeared simultaneously (Fig. 5). The addition of urea (6 $M$) or guanidine (5 $M$) to

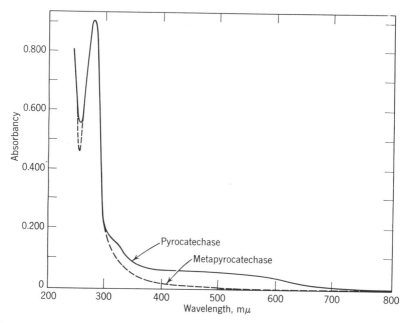

**Fig. 4.** Absorption spectra of pyrocatechase and metapyrocatechase. Absorption spectra were recorded with a Cary spectrophotometer. Pyrocatechase: 3.0 mg of protein in 3.0 ml of 0.05 $M$ Tris buffer, pH 8.0. Metapyrocatechase: 2.0 mg of protein in 3.0 ml of 0.05 $M$ phosphate buffer, pH 7.5.

solutions of active enzyme caused similar changes in the spectrum accompanied by the loss of activity. The color and the spectrum of active pyrocatechase preparation are similar to those of ferrous cysteine complex (Fig. 5), although the instability of the latter makes accurate comparison difficult.

The spectra were dependent upon the acidity of the solution, as shown in Fig. 6. The enzyme is fairly stable at pH 8–9. Below pH 5 and over pH 12 irreversible spectral change took place, and at the same time the enzyme was completely inactivated.

The correlation between heat inactivation of the enzyme and the absorbancy change at 500 m$\mu$ is shown in Fig. 7. When the absorbancy at 500 m$\mu$ was determined after various periods of time at 43° and 45°C, the decrease of absorbancy was exactly in parallel with the decrease of enzymic activity.

Excitation and fluorescence spectra of pyrocatechase and metapyro-catechase are shown in Fig. 8. The fluorescence at about 350 m$\mu$ was observed with both preparations, but the fluorescence at about 480 m$\mu$ was seen only with the pyrocatechase. The fluorescence spectra remained essentially

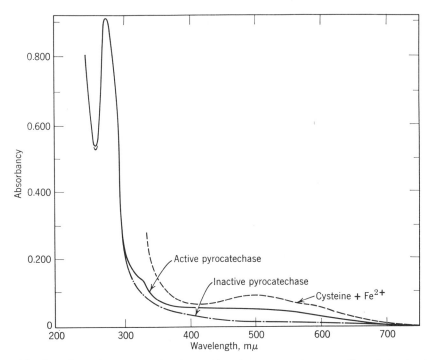

**Fig. 5.** Absorption spectra of active and inactive pyrocatechase as well as of cysteine-iron complex. Protein concentration was 0.1 % in 0.05 $M$ Tris buffer, pH 9.0. As the inactive pyrocatechase, the homogeneous preparation which had been stored at $-10°$C about 6 months and had a specific activity of 0.7 $\mu$mole/min/mg was used. The dotted line shows the spectrum which was recorded immediately after mixing 0.15 $\mu$mole of FeSO$_4$ and 0.15 $\mu$mole of cysteine in 3.0 ml of 0.1 $M$ Tris buffer, pH 7.0.

unchanged under anaerobic conditions even in the presence of substrate. Although the spectral characteristics of pyrocatechase may not be of general significance, they may provide some clue as to the nature of iron, its linkage with protein, and the mechanism of action of pyrocatechase.

### C. Metapyrocatechase; Active Center

Many oxygenases have been thought to be too unstable to be extensively purified. Metapyrocatechase is extremely unstable and is easily inactivated in the presence of air. The purification of this enzyme appeared to be almost

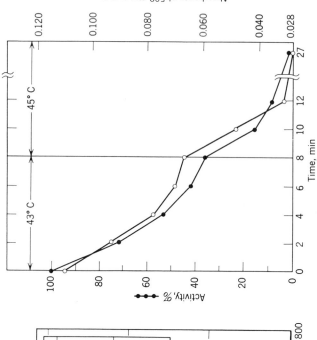

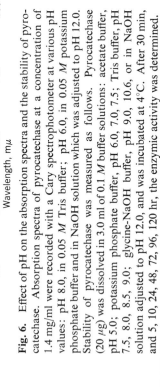

**Fig. 7.** Heat inactivation of pyrocatechase and absorbancy change at 500 m$\mu$. Incubation mixture contained 0.05 $M$ Tris buffer, pH 8.0, and 12 mg pyrocatechase in a final volume of 5.0 ml. Incubation was carried out at 43° and 45°C as shown, and both enzymatic activity and absorbancy at 500 m$\mu$ were measured simultaneously at 2 min intervals.

**Fig. 6.** Effect of pH on the absorption spectra and the stability of pyrocatechase. Absorption spectra of pyrocatechase at a concentration of 1.4 mg/ml were recorded with a Cary spectrophotometer at various pH values: pH 8.0, in 0.05 $M$ Tris buffer; pH 6.0, in 0.05 $M$ potassium phosphate buffer and in NaOH solution which was adjusted to pH 12.0. Stability of pyrocatechase was measured as follows. Pyrocatechase (20 $\mu$g) was dissolved in 3.0 ml of 0.1 $M$ buffer solutions: acetate buffer, pH 5.0; potassium phosphate buffer, pH 6.0, 7.0, 7.5; Tris buffer, pH 7.5, 8.0, 8.5, 9.0; glycine-NaOH buffer, pH 9.0, 10.6, or in NaOH solution adjusted to pH 12.0, and was incubated at 4°C. After 30 min, and 5, 10, 24, 48, 72, 96, 120 hr, the enzymic activity was determined.

294

impossible (6). Since the inactivation can be partly prevented if the air is replaced by nitrogen gas, and the activity of the air-inactivated enzyme is temporarily restored by the addition of a reducing agent, borohydride ($NaBH_4$), we have proposed that this inactivation is due mainly to the oxidation of ferrous iron in the molecule (13). Various other conditions and reagents which would prevent inactivation were tested. No significant

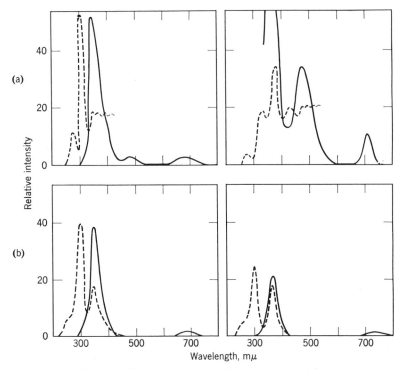

**Fig. 8.** Excitation and fluorescence spectra of pyrocatechase (a) and metapyrocatechase (b). The spectra of protein solutions (0.5 mg/ml) were taken at pH 8.0 in 0.05 $M$ Tris buffer with an Aminco-Bowman spectrophotofluorometer. Dotted lines indicate excitation spectra, and solid lines fluorescence spectra.

protection was observed to result from the addition of reducing agents or metals (8). Catalase was found to protect the enzyme from inactivation to some extent, suggesting that hydrogen peroxide produced from endogenous reductants in crude extracts would inactivate the enzyme. In fact, the enzyme became more stable as its purity increased. Furthermore, as shown in Fig. 9, the presence of a low concentration of organic solvent, such as acetone or ethanol, was found to protect the enzyme almost completely from inactivation by air even at 30°. Therefore, all the purification procedures were carried out in the presence of 10% acetone in a buffer, and the crystallization of

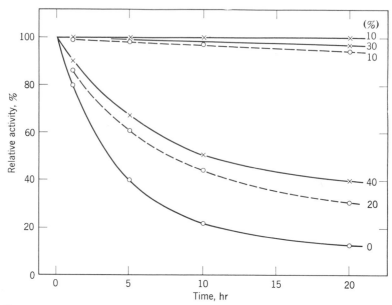

**Fig. 9.** Stability of metapyrocatechase in organic solvents. The acetone fraction was stored at 30° in 0.05 $M$ phosphate buffer, pH 7.5, containing different concentrations (as indicated in the figure in per cent) of an organic solvent. After 1, 5, 10, and 20 hr, activity was measured spectrophotometrically by the standard method (8). —○—, without organic solvent; —×—, in acetone; – –○– –, in ethanol.

**Fig. 10.** Photograph of thrice-crystallized metapyrocatechase (×1000).

metapyrocatechase has been achieved with about thirty-fold purification, as shown in Table 1. Figure 10 shows the photograph of thrice-crystallized metapyrocatechase.

Participation of ferrous iron and SH groups in the action of oxygenases has been suggested by a number of investigators, but the precise mechanism is still obscure. Although metapyrocatechase contains iron as pyrocatechase does, the absorption spectrum of thrice-crystallized metapyrocatechase

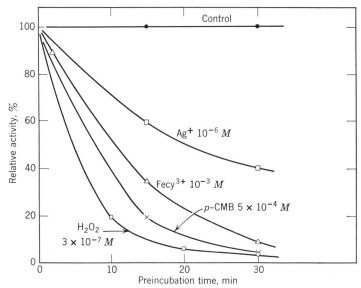

**Fig. 11.** Inactivation of metapyrocatechase. Incubation mixtures contained 0.05 $M$ phosphate buffer, pH 7.5, inhibitors (concentrations as indicated), and about 10 $\mu$g of dialyzed crystalline enzyme in a final volume of 1 ml. Each time an aliquot was pipetted out, and the activity was measured by the standard method. Incubations were carried out at 20°, and the control was without inhibitor. Fecy³⁺ is the abbreviation for ferricyanide.

showed no significant peak in the visible range, while the purified pyrocatechase has a red color (Fig. 4). The results of inhibition experiments are shown in Fig. 11. When the enzyme was incubated at 20° in the presence of various oxidizing agents (ferricyanide, $H_2O_2$) or SH inhibitors [$p$-chloromercuribenzoate ($p$-CMB), $Ag^+$], it was gradually inactivated. No significant inhibition was observed to occur from the simultaneous addition of these inhibitors in the reaction mixture.

As shown in Fig. 12, after the enzyme was treated with $3 \times 10^{-7}$ $M$ $H_2O_2$ at 20° for 30 min and all activity had almost disappeared, the preparation was subjected to dialysis. The subsequent addition of either cysteine or ferrous iron alone brought about only a partial reactivation, whereas after addition of both cysteine and ferrous iron the activity was almost completely

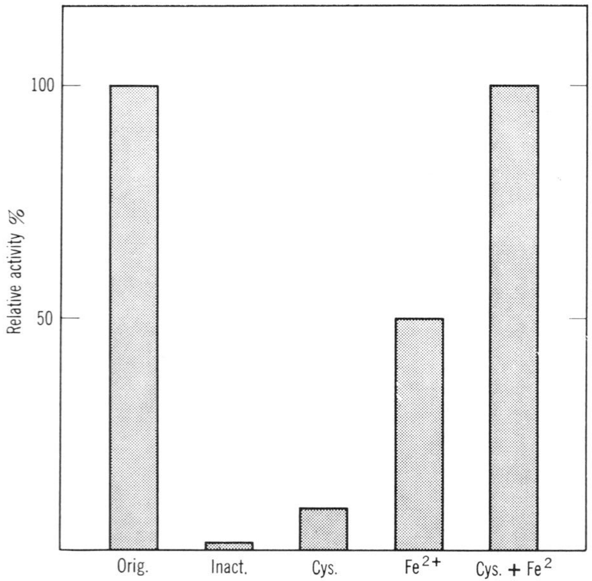

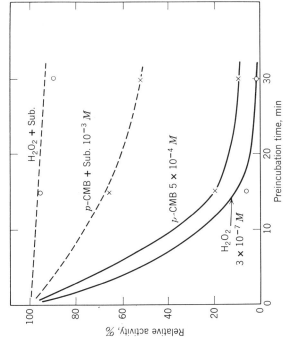

**Fig. 13.** Protection by the substrate catechol. Incubation conditions were the same as in Fig. 11, except that $10^{-3}$ $M$ of catechol was present in the incubation mixture as indicated (dotted line), and all the incubations were carried out under anaerobic conditions.

**Fig. 12.** Reactivation of metapyrocatechase inactivated by $H_2O_2$. Inactivated enzyme was prepared by treatment with $3 \times 10^{-7}$ $M$ $H_2O_2$ at $20°$ for 30 min, followed by dialysis against $0.05$ $M$ phosphate buffer, pH 7.5, for several hours. The inactive enzyme thus prepared was incubated with either $10^{-3}$ $M$ cysteine or $10^{-3}$ $M$ ferrous iron, or both cysteine and ferrous iron at $20°$ for 30 min under anaerobic condition; then the activities were measured as previously described. The first column is the activity of the original preparation before $H_2O_2$ treatment, and the second column is that of inactivated enzyme without further treatment.

restored. These results indicate that both ferrous iron and SH groups are involved in the catalytic activity.

The inactivation by oxidizing agents and SH inhibitors can be prevented by the presence of substrate (Fig. 13), indicating that the substrate binding site may be closely associated with ferrous iron and SH groups.

As stated above, crystalline enzyme contains approximately 12 cysteine residues, among which four can be titrated readily by $p$-CMB (14). However, even after all the four free SH groups were titrated by $p$-CMB,

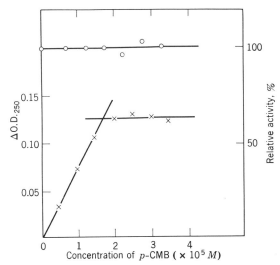

**Fig. 14.** Titration of free SH groups in metapyrocatechase by $p$-CMB. Increments in absorbancy at 250 m$\mu$ as a result of the formation of SH–$p$-CMB complex were measured approximately 15 min after addition of $p$-CMB to 4.6 × 10$^{-6}$ $M$ metapyrocatechase in 0.05 $M$ phosphate buffer, pH 7.5, at 20°. Enzyme activities were also measured by the standard method after each addition of $p$-CMB. —×—, Δ O.D. at 250 m$\mu$; —○—, relative activity.

almost 100% activity remained (Fig. 14), suggesting that masked SH groups rather than free ones are intimately involved in the catalytic activity. These observations made it difficult to carry out kinetic analysis with SH inhibitors.

The mechanism of the protection by acetone is not completely understood. However, inactivations due to oxidizing agents or SH inhibitors could also be prevented almost completely by the presence of 10% acetone during the preincubation of the enzyme and inhibitors (Fig. 15). Nevertheless, acetone inhibited the enzyme activity nearly competitively when it was present in the reaction mixture (Fig. 16). This inhibition is presumably associated with the protection in some way.

Various chelating agents, including $o$-phenanthroline and α,α′-dipyridyl,

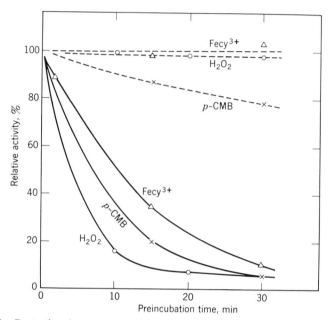

**Fig. 15.** Protection by acetone. 10% acetone was present in the incubation mixture (dotted line). Other conditions and concentrations of inhibitors were the same as in Fig. 11.

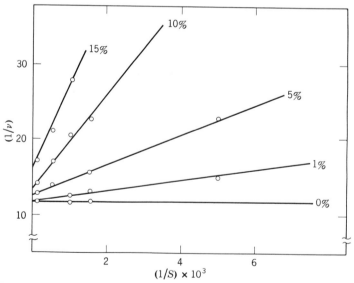

**Fig. 16.** Inhibition by acetone. Concentrations of acetone and substrate were as shown. Enzyme activities were measured spectrophotometrically.

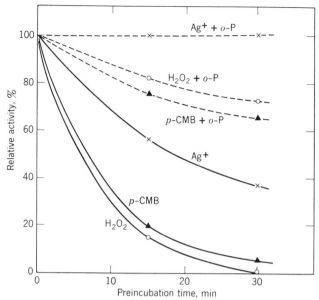

**Fig. 17.** Protection by *o*-phenanthroline. $10^{-3}$ *M* *o*-phenanthroline was present in the incubation mixture (dotted line). Other conditions and concentrations of inhibitors were the same as in Fig. 11. *o*-P is the abbreviation for *o*-phenanthroline.

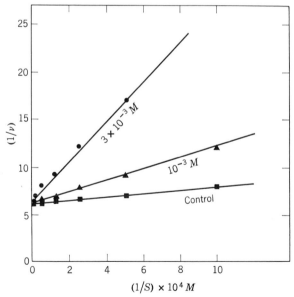

**Fig. 18.** Competitive-type inhibition of metapyrocatechase activity by *o*-phenanthroline. Concentrations of *o*-phenanthroline and substrate were as indicated. Enzyme activity was measured spectrophotometrically.

unexpectedly exerted protective effects not only against oxidizing agents but also against SH inhibitors, as ahown in Fig. 17. On the other hand, when such chelating agents were present in the reaction mixture, competitive-type inhibition for substrate was observed (Fig. 18).

These observations make it possible to suggest a scheme, shown in Fig. 19, as a tentative hypothetical model of the active center of metapyrocatechase. Essential SH groups are not free SH groups and are somehow associated

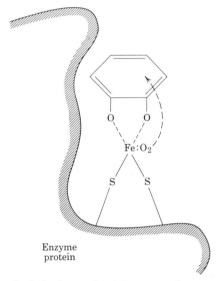

**Fig. 19.**   Hypothetical scheme of activity center of metapyrocatechase.

with ferrous iron and substrate. Experiments with $o$-phenanthroline or $\alpha,\alpha'$-dipyridyl indicate that these chelating agents do not remove the iron from the enzyme but merely combine with the iron which remains on the enzyme surface. To judge from the competitive inhibition by chelating agents, the site of inhibition is probably identical with the site of attachment of the substrate, catechol. Although the inhibition by chelating agents or acetone is not competitive with respect to oxygen, it is plausible to assume that the same ferrous iron is oxygenated to produce the active form of oxygen, since there is only one atom of ferrous iron in 1 mole of enzyme.

## ACKNOWLEDGMENTS

The experiments presented in this paper are supported in part by research grants from the United States Public Health Service (CA-04222), the Rockefeller Foundation, the Jane Coffin Childs Memorial Fund for Medical Research, the Squibb Institute for Medical Research, and a Scientific Research Fund of the Ministry of Education of Japan.

## REFERENCES

1. O. Hayaishi, M. Katagiri, and S. Rothberg, *J. Am. Chem. Soc.*, **77**, 5450 (1955).
2. O. Hayaishi, S. Rothberg, and A. H. Mehler, *Abstracts of the* 130*th Meeting of the American Chemical Society, Atlantic City, New Jersey, 1956*, p. 53C.
3. O. Hayaishi and Z. Hashimoto, *J. Biochem.*, **37**, 371 (1950).
4. *Enzyme Nomenclature: Recommendations of the International Union of Biochemistry*, Brisbane, 1964, p. 88.
5. S. Dagley and D. A. Stopher, *Biochem. J.*, **73**, 16P (1959).
6. Y. Kojima, N. Itada, and O. Hayaishi, *J. Biol. Chem.*, **236**, 2223 (1961).
7. O. Hayaishi, M. Katagiri, and S. Rothberg, *J. Biol. Chem.*, **229**, 905 (1957).
8. M. Nozaki, H. Kagamiyama, and O. Hayaishi, *Biochem. Z.*, **338**, 582 (1963).
9. A. E. Harvey, Jr., J. A. Smart, and E. S. Amis, *Anal. Chem.*, **27**, 26 (1955).
10. S. Moore, *J. Biol. Chem.*, **238**, 235 (1963).
11. G. H. Beaven and E. R. Holiday, in M. L. Anson, K. Bailey, and J. T. Edsall, Eds., *Advances in Protein Chemistry*, Vol. VII, Academic Press, New York, 1952, p. 373.
12. H. Nakagawa, H. Inoue, and Y. Takeda, *J. Biochem.*, **54**, 65 (1963).
13. H. Taniuchi, Y. Kojima, F. Kanetsuna, H. Ochiai, and O. Hayaishi, *Biochem. Biophys. Research. Communs.*, **8**, 97 (1962).
14. P. D. Boyer, *J. Am. Chem. Soc.*, **76**, 4331 (1954).

## Discussion

HAYAISHI: I will add two points concerning our latest experiments on the mechanism of pyrocatechase and metapyrocatechase. They both contain ferrous iron as a cofactor, but no other metals, electron carriers, or coenzymes were detected. The properties of these two enzymes are very similar except that pyrocatechase is deep red and metapyrocatechase is colorless. Recently two more oxygenases were reported to be obtained in crystalline form, 3,4-dihydroxyphenyl acetate oxygenase by Dr. Seno and his co-workers [*Seikagaku*, **36**, 40 (1964)] and homogentisate oxygenase by Dr. Takeda and his colleagues [*Seikagaku*, **36**, 40 (1964)]. These are colorless.

As stated in my paper, the kinetic experiments with crystalline metapyrocatechase indicate the formation of a tertiary complex of ferrous iron, substrate catechol, and oxygen. The main body of evidence is as follows. When *o*-phenanthroline or α,α-bisdipyridyl was added to the incubation mixture, a typical competitive type of inhibition was observed with respect to substrate concentrations. The substrate, catechol, as well as these chelating agents, when added to the enzyme solution, exerts a protective effect against inactivation of the enzyme by air oxidation or hydrogen peroxide, presumably by binding the ferrous ion and preventing its oxidation.

An ESR signal of iron in the ferric state at a $g$ value of about 4.2 appeared on the addition of substrate in the presence of oxygen (work done in collaboration with Professor T. Yamano of Osaka University) (Fig. 1). Such an increase of signal could not be seen if metapyrocatechase was omitted from the reaction mixture even in the presence of inorganic ferric iron. Tiron (catechol-3,5-disulfonic acid) is a non-metabolizable substrate analog and a well-known chelating agent for trivalent iron. When tiron was added instead of catechol, a similar signal was observed and the enzyme was gradually inactivated (Fig. 2).

In consistency with this observation, when the metapyrocatechase was pre-incubated with tiron under aerobic conditions, the enzyme was gradually inactivated. Under anaerobic conditions, this inactivation was much slower. This evidence further supports the existence of a complex of a transient ferric form of iron, oxygen, and substrate. Further studies are necessary to rule out a possibility that

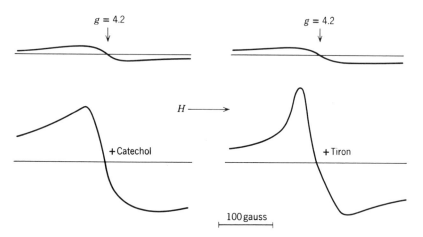

**Fig. 1.** ESR spectra of metapyrocatechase. Incubation mixtures contained 0.3 $mM$ of metapyrocatechase, in 0.05 $M$ potassium phosphate buffer, pH 7.5, containing 10% acetone and 0.01 $M$ of catechol or 0.01 $M$ of tiron in a final volume of 0.11 ml. The incubation was carried out at 25° for 5 min with catechol or 30 min with tiron. ESR spectra were measured before (above) and after (below) addition of catechol or tiron with a Varian ESR spectrometer, model 4500, with 100 kc modulation unit. Modulation amplitude, 32 gauss; temperature, 123°K.

the observed signal may be due to the inactive form of enzymes. On the basis of this experimental evidence, we are proposing tentatively a reaction of metapyro-catechase shown in Fig. 3.

MASON: Readers of Dr. Hayaishi's paper will have noticed that three sets of nomenclature are used for the same enzymes. The trivial names of the enzymes are pyrocatechase and metapyrocatechase. The systematic names of the enzymes are catechol:$O_2$-2,3-oxidoreductase and catechol:$O_2$-1,2-oxidoreductase. The other new, trivial names are catechol:1,2-oxygenase and catechol:2,3-oxygenase, respectively. This multiplicity of names raises a serious question with respect to not only Dr. Hayaishi's nomenclature but also the nomenclature proposed by the International Commission on Enzymes. The guiding principle which I believe all of us use in enzyme nomenclature is that the reaction which is catalyzed should be the basis of the name of the enzyme. Unfortunately, the names for these enzymes proposed by the International Commission on Enzymes are ambiguous. For example, the name catechol:$O_2$-1,2-oxidoreductase can mean enzymic catalysis of

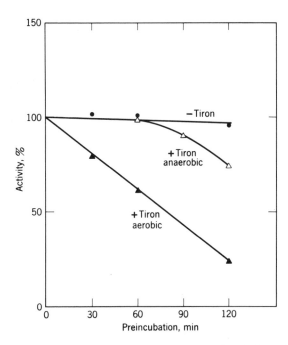

Fig. 2. Inactivation of metapyrocatechase by tiron. Preincubation mixture contained 94 μg of metapyrocatechase in 0.05 $M$ potassium phosphate buffer, pH 7.5, containing 10% acetone, in a final volume of 1.1 ml. 10 $mM$ of tiron was added as indicated. The incubations were carried out at 25° under aerobic or anaerobic conditions in a Thunberg tube. Activities were measured spectrophotometrically by the standard assay method [M. Nozaki, H. Kagamiyama, and O. Hayaishi, *Biochem. Z.*, **338**, 582 (1963)].

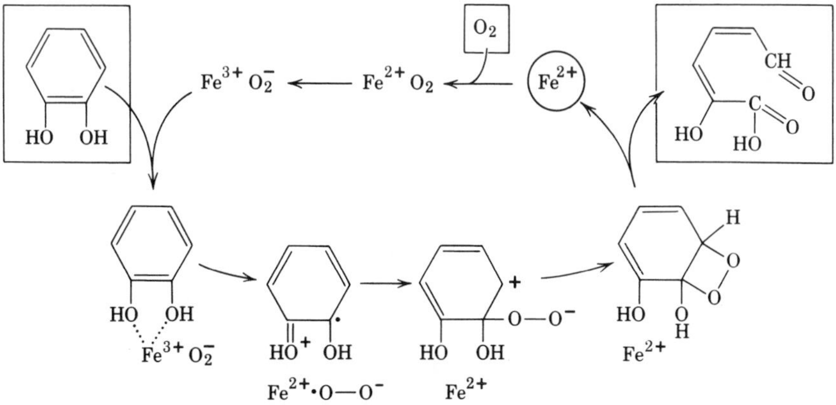

Fig. 3. A proposed mechanism of metapyrocatechase reaction.

the dehydrogenation of catechol in the 1,2-position, the addition of oxygen across the 1,2-double bond to form a peroxide, the formation of hydroperoxides in the 1,2-positions, or the cleavage of the benzene ring in the 1,2-position. Therefore, the recommended oxidase nomenclature contains ambiguity and is unsatisfactory. The trivial nomenclature recommended by Dr. Hayaishi is unsatisfactory for the same reason. "Oxygenase," the enzymic addition of molecular oxygen, can produce either hydroperoxides, the peroxide group by addition across the double bond, or ring splitting; the term does not clearly communicate the nature of the reaction being catalyzed.

CRANDALL: Dr. Hayaishi asked for comment and discussion about the color of the pyrocatechase and the lack of color of the metapyrocatechase. It seems to me that the crucial question is whether in pyrocatechase, which has two atoms of iron per molecule, there is one active center or two. If you have one center which has two atoms of iron, possibly with sulfur binding, there is a very good chance of developing a colored complex. Furthermore, it would change the mechanism of the reaction. I think that you would then have to speculate on another mechanism in which the number of iron atoms is related to the number of phenolic groups substituent on the double bond being cleaved by the oxygenation.

HAYAISHI: I think that it is a very interesting question. We are now trying to remove iron quantitatively and to see whether the activity disappears, and if so to what extent, but we have not been able to succeed in these experiments. As to the number of iron in various crystalline oxygenases, I was told by Drs. Takeda and Feno that their crystalline enzymes contain four to five irons per mole, although this figure is preliminary.

HANDLER: The red iron proteins in which the ligand seems to be established with some security are not enzymes. They are proteins like conalbumin, in which the ligand is clearly tyrosyl.

MASSEY: Dr. Hayaishi, does the $g = 4$ signal that you see in metapyrocatechase disappear when oxygen is removed in the presence of the substrate?

HAYAISHI: Yes, when oxygen is used up.

MASSEY: I take it that the signal does not appear with your inactivated metapyrocatechase.

HAYAISHI: That is right.

INGRAHAM: You would certainly expect $FeO_2^{2+}$ to be diamagnetic. However, there are quite low-lying empty orbitals in $FeO_2^{2+}$ antiorbitals, and it may be that these become degenerate in conditions where there are certain types of ligands around the iron. It may be possible that we are dealing here with an entirely different electronic structure, where it is paramagnetic now because of degeneracy, and we do approach a situation of ferric and $O_2^-$.

SINGER: It has been found (possibly others are aware of this) that one easy way to remove iron with only very minor injury, sometimes not detectable, to the protein, from quite a large group of enzymes of this type is to pass them through Sephadex G-200, sometimes even G-100. If the ferrous iron is weakly bonded, Sephadex picks it up and has an extremely high affinity for it. This is a very much more convenient way to remove iron than prolonged dialysis.

KING: I would just like to direct a question to Dr. Hayaishi. Some time ago you published an ingenious paper about the reactivation of pyrocatechase or whatever the name of the enzyme is—I'm confused now. You used borohydride, and I think that no one can appreciate Dr. Hayaishi's work on the borohydride reactivation on pyrocatechase unless one has worked on an unstable enzyme. My question is, Do you have some idea what borohydride does on SH or iron or other groups?

HAYAISHI: We haven't done any further analysis to determine whether the borohydride is reducing only ferric iron or also reducing SH groups, so at this moment I really cannot say whether it is reducing both or only ferric iron.

WINFIELD: It would be very helpful to have knowledge of the extinction coefficients in the visible and the near ultraviolet. Dr. Hayaishi, have you considered the possibility that in the iron sulfide enzymes in general, in one or the other oxidation states, one electron is missing from the assembly of iron atoms and sulfur atoms? No one particular iron atom is in a different oxidation state from the others. The color is due to a particular state resembling that which we have described in those cobalt peroxo complexes in which there is an electron deficiency. Even in states where there is no electron deficiency we think that a strong color change could occur on protonation of one or more of the bridging atoms, in this case, sulfur.

HAYAISHI: We have not done very careful analysis. All we did was to see whether the color would change visibly by the addition of various reducing agents, and we did not detect a significant change of the color.

DAWSON: In your paper you describe the fact that the red pyrocatechase changes on storage. It loses its color and also activity. A similar phenomenon occurs in the presence of urea and guanidine. Is there simultaneous loss in iron content of your preparation during this change, or simply a modification of structure without loss in iron? Do you know?

HAYAISHI: We have not determined whether the iron is lost or not, or whether the iron is oxidized or not, so that I cannot answer your question.

HANDLER: Dr. Dawson, I can comment on that point in connection with the kind of iron proteins we play with. When they are treated with low concentrations of urea or guanidine, the red spectrum disappears. The red color goes while the iron is still held rather firmly. You still can pass the protein over Sephadex, for example, and keep the iron on, so that there is an intermediate stage here. If you raise the urea quantity sufficiently, the iron then comes off.

DAWSON: This is very interesting, because in the case of the copper oxidases the reverse is true. A loss in copper accompanied by the unfolding by urea or guanidine, and loss in activity on long storage is accompanied by copper loss. I wonder whether the same thing is true in the iron case.

MASON: The ESR spectra are very interesting; the signal in the neighborhood of $g = 4$ suggests that the iron is in a unique intermediate spin state. Experience has been that signals around $g = 4$ are often associated with ferric compounds with a spin of $\frac{3}{2}$.

ORGEL: I should like to hear what people have to say about the $g = 4.2$ signal. It seems to me this is very mysterious and interesting, and it was a new thing for me to hear, concerned with ferric iron with spin of $\frac{3}{2}$.

MASON: In the paper which Dr. Morita and I [*Proc. 6th Intern. Congr. Biochem.*, **4**, 323 (1964)] presented at the 6th International Congress of Biochemistry, we reported a spin resonance survey of heme proteins. In the case of cytochrome $c$ we found a low-level signal at $g = 4.3$, which seems to be consistent with a suggestion which was made, I believe by Dr. George, that an intermediate spin state of iron in cytochrome $c$ is in equilibrium with the remainder of the cytochrome $c$.

MALMSTRÖM: I want to mention that we have studied some ferric complexes which definitely do give $g = 4$ signals and are not of any mixed spin state. I'll just mention one example—transferrin and conalbumin that Dr. Handler mentioned. Dr. Ehrenberg's previous susceptibility measurements show that this complex has the high spin ferric state and does give a $g = 4$ signal, so I don't think that it is restricted to mixed spin states.

GEORGE: I should like to make one or two comments on the question of these magnetic properties that has been raised. First, some years ago I did some work with Ingraham and Bennett [*Nature*, **176**, 394 (1955)] in England on the $g$-values of the ferrimyoglobin complexes. For the azide complex we definitely got a $g$-value in the region of 4. Now, subsequently with Beetlestone and Mullins [*Revs. Modern Phys.*, **36**, 441–458 (1964)], we have been following up this question of the somewhat anomalous magnetic susceptibilities of ferrihemoprotein complexes, and it seems that a fairly satisfactory explanation of intermediate paramagnetic susceptibilities is that there is a thermoequilibrium between the high and the low spin states of the molecule. As far as ferric compounds containing three unpaired electrons are concerned, John Griffith showed [*J. Inorg. & Nuclear Chem.*, **2**, 1, 229 (1956)] on theoretical ground some years ago that, provided with a symmetrical octahedral complex, that state would be unstable with respect to the states containing five unpaired electrons or one unpaired electron. But of course what could conceivably happen when one has an unsymmetrical octahedral field? I certainly would not like to guess, and I wonder whether any theoreticians would.

EHRENBERG: I just want to make a small comment in relation to what Dr. George has said. I had a discussion some years ago with Dr. Masao Kotani, Department of Physics, University of Tokyo, and we came to the conclusion that iron with three unpaired electrons should give an absorption of $g = 4$. This was a very rough calculation. We have looked at a great number of these heme proteins with intermediate susceptibilities, and we have never seen a $g = 4$ signal which could be ascribed to the heme. We see signals with $g = 6$ and around $g = 2$, and the intensities vary with temperature just as if they were mixtures of proteins.

MASON: We have observed exactly the same thing with cytochrome $c$ monomer furnished by Dr. Margoliash, but in addition, characteristic of the monomeric form, is a signal at $g = 4$ comprising about 1% of the total integrated area.

SLATER: Dr. Mason, have you considered the possibility that the signal which you find in cytochrome $c$ is due to the approximately 15% of non-heme iron present in purified cytochrome $c$ preparations?

MASON: No, I haven't.

KING: I remember a couple of reports from Hebrew University on ESR of iron in solid-state solution with respect to theory and some experimental results. $Fe^{2+}$ in MgO has been observed at $g = 3.428$ and 6.86. Results indicate considerable covalent binding. For $Fe^{2+}$ in tetrahedral ZnS, one $g$-value is found at 2.25, and optical absorption at 3 $\mu$ and 0.3 $\mu$ [W. Low and M. Weger, *Phys. Rev.*, **118**, 1119, 1130 (1960)].

# PART IV

# Flavin-Containing Oxidases

# The Action Mechanism of Flavin Enzymes

. . . TAKAO NAKAMURA, JUNKO YOSHIMURA,
SATOSHI NAKAMURA, and YASUYUKI OGURA

In 1936 Michaelis *et al.* (1) proposed on the basis of their finding of a semiquinone type of redox dyes, including flavin, the so-called univalent oxidation theory, according to which the oxidation and reduction of flavin proceed by successive one-electron transfer steps through a semiquinoid radical as an intermediate compound. Haas (2) observed later that a red complex could be formed by mixing TPN+ with the old yellow enzyme that had been reduced by dithionite under anaerobic conditions. For a long time, this red complex was thought by many investigators to be a free radical in the flavin moiety of the old yellow enzyme, although Haas assumed it to be a compound between the enzyme and TPN+ or TPNH. In the past decade, intermediary compounds of different flavin enzymes have been reported by many authors. However, it is still a matter of uncertainty as to whether all flavin enzymes undergo in their catalytic actions the univalent oxidation process according to Michaelis *et al.* Our studies are concerned with the modes of action of three kinds of flavin enzymes: glucose oxidase, D-amino acid oxidase, and the old yellow enzyme, whose kinetics and titration with reducing agents were investigated mainly by the spectrophotometric method.

## I. GLUCOSE OXIDASE

Glucose oxidase, which was studied first by Müller (3), is known to be a flavin enzyme containing two molecules of flavin adenine dinucleotide (FAD) per molecule (4, 5, 6); it catalyzes the oxidation of $\beta$-D-glucose to D-glucono-$\delta$-lactone in the presence of a suitable electron acceptor such as molecular oxygen (7, 8, 9, 10). The enzyme sample used in this study was prepared from culture media of *Penicillium amagasakiense* which were kindly supplied by Dr. Kusai.

### A. Spectrophotometric Titration and Change of Absorption Spectrum in the Course of the Reaction

With diothionite as a reducing agent, titration of glucose oxidase was carried out spectrophotometrically at pH 5.6 under anaerobic conditions. As seen in Fig. 1, the absorption spectrum of the oxidized form changed stepwise into that of the reduced form with increasing amount of dithionite added. No evidence was obtained to suggest the intermediate formation of a semiquinone or charge-transfer type. Massey *et al.* (11) performed the anaerobic titration of glucose oxidase of *Aspergillus niger* with D-glucose and

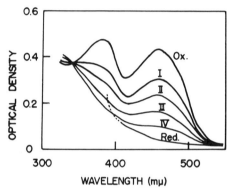

**Fig. 1.** Spectrophotometric titration of glucose oxidase with dithionite. Experiments were carried out at pH 5.6. Enzyme concentration was 37.6 $\mu M$ in terms of the quantity of FAD. Ox: absorption spectrum of oxidized form; Red: absorption spectrum of reduced form which resulted on addition of a small amount of solid dithionite. I: With 4.5 $\mu M$ dithionite; II: with 7.5 $\mu M$ dithionite; III: with 15 $\mu M$ dithionite; IV: with 33 $\mu M$ dithionite.

dithionite. They found that in contrast with our data a semiquinone showing an absorption maximum at 570 m$\mu$ was formed in the titration with dithionite, but not in the titration with D-glucose. They assumed that the semiquinone obtained by reduction with dithionite may not be a form appearing in the normal enzyme reaction.

We investigated the absorption spectrum of the enzyme at the steady state by using the stopped-flow method (12). When the enzyme, which had been reduced by addition of substrate, was mixed with a solution containing molecular oxygen, a change of optical density at a given wavelength, which was caused by the oxidation of FAD moiety of the enzyme, was traced on a recording paper (Fig. 2). The absorption spectrum of the enzyme at the steady state was obtained by plotting the values of the maximum change of optical density thus obtained against the wavelength as shown in Fig. 3. The

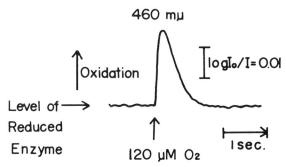

**Fig. 2.** Change of optical density of glucose oxidase at 460 m$\mu$. Experiment was performed by the stopped-flow method. Glucose concentration, 10 $mM$; enzyme concentration, 4.0 $\mu M$.

steady-state spectrum obtained was almost the same as the difference spectrum of the oxidized minus the reduced form of the enzyme and did not show any absorption peak around 540–550 m$\mu$. These findings indicate either that the formation of a semiquinone or a charge-transfer complex did not take place during the course of the reaction, or that the lifetime of semiquinone produced, if any, is so short as to be undetectable experimentally. The spectrophotometric results we obtained are in good harmony with those reported by Beinert and Sands (13) and Mason *et al.* (14), who found, using the ESR technique, no evidence for the formation of semiquinone in the reaction mixture of glucose oxidase system.

### B. Kinetic Analysis of Glucose Oxidase Reaction

By assuming that no semiquinone is formed in the course of the reaction, the rates of reduction and oxidation of the enzyme were obtained by Chance's

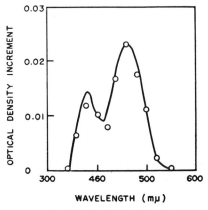

**Fig. 3.** Difference spectrum (oxidized minus reduced) of glucose oxidase at steady state.

method (15, 16) from the kinetic curve shown in Fig. 2. Since the rate of reduction of flavin moiety, $k_{red}$, depends on the concentration of the substrate, [S], the reciprocal values of $k_{red}$ were plotted against those of [S]. Figure 4 shows a linear relationship between $1/k_{red}$ and $1/[S]$. The reciprocal of the

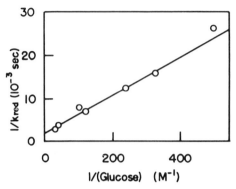

**Fig. 4.** Plot of $1/k_{red}$ against $1/[glucose]$ in the reaction of glucose oxidase. Experiments were carried out at pH 5.65 and 25°C. Enzyme concentration, 4.0 $\mu M$.

intercept on the ordinate represents the maximum velocity $(k_{red}^{max})$ of the reduction of the oxidized enzyme. By assuming that the quantity of the enzyme is represented by moles of FAD attached to the enzyme protein, the $k_{red}^{max}$ value was calculated to be $5.5 \times 10^2$ sec$^{-1}$ at pH 5.65 and 25°C. The rate of oxidation, $k_{ox}$, of the flavin moiety caused by molecular oxygen was measured

**TABLE 1**

**The Values of $k_{ox}$ of Glucose Oxidase at Different Oxygen Concentrations**

| $[O_2]$, $\mu M$ | $k_{ox}$, $10^6$ $M^{-1}$ sec$^{-1}$ |
|---|---|
| 6 | 1.7 |
| 34 | 1.4 |
| 48 | 1.6 |
| 60 | 1.3 |
| 120 | 1.0 |
| 360 | 1.5 |

by the rapid-flow and stopped-flow methods. The data obtained at various oxygen pressures are summarized in Table 1. Within the range of the oxygen pressure applied, the value of $k_{ox}$ was found to be constant independently of the oxygen pressure. Thus the reaction between the reduced enzyme and molecular oxygen can be expressed as a simple second-order reaction which proceeds without any formation of an intermediary complex.

Assuming that the oxidation and reduction of flavin moiety proceed with the mechanism of two-electron transfer and that the enzyme-substrate complex is formed in the course of the reaction, the following set of reactions may be proposed as the mechanism of the glucose oxidase action:

$$P\text{-}FADH_2 + O_2 \xrightarrow{k_{ox}} P\text{-}FAD + H_2O_2$$

$$P\text{-}FAD + S \underset{k_{-1}}{\overset{k_1}{\rightleftharpoons}} S\text{-}P\text{-}FAD$$

$$S\text{-}P\text{-}FAD \xrightarrow{k_2} P\text{-}FADH_2 + Lactone$$

where $P\text{-}FADH_2$ stands for the reduced form of the enzyme unit, $P\text{-}FAD$ the oxidized form, $S\text{-}P\text{-}FAD$ the enzyme substrate complex, and S the D-glucose; the $k$'s are the rate constants of the respective reactions.

From the scheme mentioned above, the rate of the over-all reaction ($v$) at the steady state is derived as follows;

$$v = \frac{k_2 e_0}{1 + K_m/[S] + k_2/k_{ox}[O_2]}$$

where $e_0$ stands for the total concentration of the enzyme unit added, and $K_m$ the Michaelis constant. The rate of the over-all reaction can be determined experimentally from the amount of oxygen uptake measured with the aid of an oxygen electrode. From Lineweaver and Burk's plot of the data obtained in the over-all reaction kinetics, the values of $K_m$ and $V/e_0$ were found to be $1.2 \times 10^{-2}$ $M$ and $6.4 \times 10^2$ sec$^{-1}$ at pH 5.6 and 25°C. The observed value of $v$ was $1.9 \times 10^{-6}$ $M$ sec$^{-2}$ at $[O_2] = 210$ $\mu M$, $[S] = 0.05$ $M$, and $e_0 = 5.8 \times 10^{-9}$ $M$. By assuming that $k_2 = k_{red}^{max}$ and by applying the values of $k_{red}^{max}$ and $k_{ox}$ to the rate equation described above, the value of $v$ was calculated to be $1.4 \times 10^{-6}$ $M$ sec$^{-1}$. The fact that the observed and calculated values were in fairly good agreement may be taken as supporting the validity of the reaction mechanism we have proposed.

## II. D-AMINO ACID OXIDASE

It is well known that D-amino acid oxidase, discovered by Krebs (17), contains FAD as prosthetic group (18, 19) and has a capacity to catalyze, in the presence of molecular oxygen, the oxidation of D-amino acid into a keto acid, ammonia, and hydrogen peroxide. Our sample was prepared from hog kidneys and purified by the method of Kubo et al. (20).

### A. Absorption Spectra of Semiquinone and Intermediary Complex

The oxidized form of D-amino acid oxidase was titrated spectrophotometrically with a dithionite solution at pH 8.3 under anaerobic conditions.

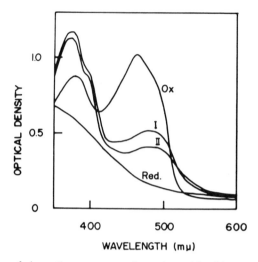

**Fig. 5.** Change of absorption spectrum of D-amino acid oxidase caused by titration with dithionite. Ox: oxidized form; Red: reduced form. I, II: partially reduced forms.

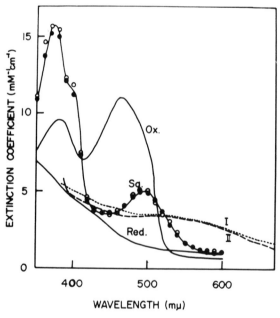

**Fig. 6.** Absorption spectra of oxidized, reduced, semiquinone, and intermediary complex forms of D-amino acid oxidase. Ox: oxidized form; Red: reduced form; Sq: semiquinone type; I: intermediary complex observed at the steady state in the stopped-flow method (dotted line); II: trapped intermediary complex (broken line).

The partially reduced solution contained, besides the reduced and oxidized forms, an intermediate, which is evinced by the absence of an isosbestic point, as may be seen from the data presented in Fig. 5. The ESR measurement to be discussed in section IIB further confirmed that the solution just described was an equilibrium mixture of oxidized, reduced, and semiquinone forms of the enzyme. Massey *et al.* (21) also confirmed the formation of semiquinone, in agreement with our results, when the enzyme was titrated anaerobically with dithionite. We obtained the absorption spectrum of semiquinone of flavin moiety by the graphical method described previously (22, 23, 24). As may be seen in Fig. 6, the semiquinone form of the enzyme has absorption maxima at 370 and 495 m$\mu$.

Massey *et al.* (25) observed a red intermediate which was formed rapidly on the addition of substrate under anaerobic conditions and changed further to the fully reduced form after several minutes. Kubo *et al.* (20, 26) found independently that, when the reaction was started by adding D-alanine to the enzyme solution (oxidized form), the absorbancy at 460 m$\mu$ remained unchanged until the exhaustion of molecular oxygen dissolved in the test solution, and that a new broad absorption at 550 m$\mu$ appeared with simultaneous decrease of the absorbancy at 460 m$\mu$ and then disappeared slowly after passing through a maximum absorbancy. They also reported that the enzyme could be trapped at an intermediary state by the addition of both D-alanine and reaction products. As seen in Fig. 6, however, the absorption spectrum of the trapped intermediary complex, which was supposed by Kubo *et al.* to be a semiquinone form of the enzyme, was markedly different from that of the semiquinone obtained by anaerobic titration with dithionite.

## B. ESR Measurements

As expected, no significant free-radical signal was recorded with the solutions of oxidized and reduced forms of the enzyme. In contrast, a distinct ESR absorption was detected when the test was performed on an enzyme solution reduced partially by dithionite. The data shown in Fig. 7 indicate that D-amino acid oxidase in 50% reduced state contained free spin concentration of 75% of the total enzyme, which is in good accord with the value of 66% determined by the spectrophotometric titration. Hence, it is reasonable to conclude that the complex having absorption maxima at 370 and 495 m$\mu$ is a semiquinone form of the enzyme.

In contrast with the semiquinone form, another intermediary complex having a broad absorption maximum at 550 m$\mu$ showed a hardly perceptible ESR signal. Massey *et al.* (21) also found that the intermediary red complex had no ESR signal, in agreement with our data. On the other hand, Yagi and Ozawa (27) reported that they observed an ESR signal on crystals of the trapped intermediary complex having an absorption maximum at 550 m$\mu$.

Although no quantitative data concerning the signal strength was given in their report, the amount of free spin contained in the intermediary complex seemed to be much smaller than that of the semiquinone having absorption maxima at 370 and 495 m$\mu$. From the results obtained, it may be concluded that the intermediary complex having an absorption maximum at 550 m$\mu$ is not a semiquinone of the enzyme, as has been believed hitherto by other

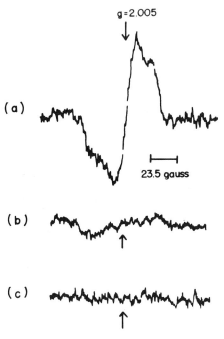

**Fig. 7.** ESR signals of D-amino acid oxidase at pH 8.3. (a) Signal of 0.12 $mM$ enzyme reduced 50% with dithionite. (b) Signal of 0.081 $mM$ enzyme obtained at the steady state using flow apparatus. (c) Signal of 0.24 $mM$ enzyme obtained at the trapped intermediate state.

authors. Although little is known at present about the detailed nature of the intermediary complex in question, it is presumed to be a diamagnetic (or weakly paramagnetic) change-transfer complex between the enzyme-bound flavin semiquinone and alanine free radical, or between reduced enzyme and reaction products.

### C. Kinetic Analysis

By using a flow apparatus, a solution of the trapped intermediate was mixed with oxygen, and the changes of optical density at 460 and 526 m$\mu$ were recorded (Fig. 8). A typcial record showed that the intermediary complex having an absorption maximum at 550 m$\mu$ was rapidly oxidized on mixing with molecular oxygen, and the oxidized enzyme thus formed was reduced back to the intermediate state on exhaustion of the added oxygen. The rate of the reduction ($k_{red}$) of the oxidized enzyme into the intermediary complex and that of the oxidation ($k_{ox}$) of the intermediary complex into the

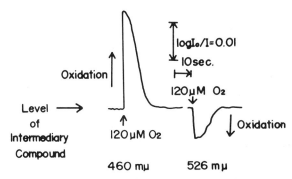

**Fig. 8.** Stopped-flow experiments of D-amino acid oxidase reaction at pH 8.3. Concentrations of enzyme, D-alanine, pyruvate, and $NH_4^+$ were 4.0 $\mu M$, 35 $mM$, 250 $mM$, and 250 $mM$, respectively.

oxidized form can be computed from the spectrophotometric trace according to Chance's formula (15, 16). In Table 2 are summarized the $k_{ox}$ values obtained at varied oxygen pressures. As was the case with glucose oxidase, the reaction between the intermediary complex and molecular oxygen was of a simple second order within the range of the oxygen pressure tested.

**TABLE 2**

**The Values of $k_{ox}$ of D-Amino Acid Oxidase at Different Oxygen Concentrations**

| $[O_2]$, $\mu M$ | $k_{ox}$, $10^5\ M^{-1}\ sec^{-1}$ |
|---|---|
| 7.1 | 1.5 |
| 13 | 1.1 |
| 20 | 1.1 |
| 120 | 1.2 |

Figure 9 shows the relationship between the reciprocals of $k_{red}$ and those of D-alanine concentration, and also Lineweaver and Burk's plot of the data obtained by over-all reaction kinetics. From this plot, the maximum rate of over-all reaction per unit concentration of enzyme, $V/e_0$, was found to be 4.6 sec$^{-1}$ at pH 8.3 and 25°C, in good agreement with the value of $k_{red}^{max}$ obtained according to Chance's formula. The value of the Michaelis constant obtained from the over-all reaction kinetics was 10 $mM$ under the said conditions.

To account for the kinetic data obtained, the following scheme may be proposed for the action of D-amino acid oxidase, in which the sequence of reactions is assumed to proceed through the intermediary compound having an absorption maximum at 550 m$\mu$:

$$\text{P-FAD} + \text{S} \underset{k_{-1}}{\overset{k_1}{\longleftrightarrow}} \text{S-P-FAD}$$

$$\text{S-P-FAD} \xrightarrow{k_2} \text{X}$$

$$\text{X} + \text{O}_2 \xrightarrow{k_{\text{ox}}} \text{P-FAD} + \text{Pyruvate} + \text{NH}_3 + \text{H}_2\text{O}_2$$

$$\text{X} \overset{\text{very slow}}{\dashrightarrow} \text{P-FADH}_2 + \text{Pyruvate} + \text{NH}_3$$

where P-FAD stands for the oxidized form of the enzyme unit, S-P-FAD the enzyme-substrate complex, X the intermediary compound having a broad

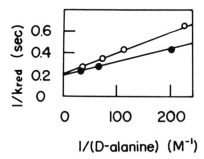

I/(D-alanine)  (M⁻¹)

**Fig. 9.**   Plot of $1/k_{\text{red}}$ against $1/$[D-alanine] in the reaction of D-amino acid oxidase.   ●: Values obtained by the stopped-flow method; ○: values obtained from data of over-all reaction kinetics according to Lineweaver and Burk. Experiments were performed at pH 8.3 and 20°C.

absorption peak at 550 m$\mu$, P-FADH$_2$ the reduced form of the enzyme unit, and S the substrate, D-alanine; the $k$'s are the rate constants of the reactions indicated.

Although the details of the data were not reported, the scheme proposed by Massey *et al.* (21) was almost the same as that given above. At the steady state,

$$v = \frac{k_2 e_0}{1 + K_m/[\text{S}] + k_2/k_{\text{ox}}[\text{O}_2]}$$

where $v$ represents the rate of over-all reaction and $e_0$ the total concentration of the enzyme unit, which is expressed by the molar concentration of FAD attached to the enzyme protein. The rate equation obtained was apparently the same as that of glucose oxidase reaction. Since $k_2$ may be assumed to be equal to $k_{\text{red}}^{\max}$, the rate of over-all reaction can be computed by using the values of $k_2$, $k_{\text{ox}}$, and $K_m$ obtained. When [S] = 30.5 $mM$, [O$_2$] = 240 $\mu M$, and $e_0 = 0.74 \ \mu M$, the rate calculated was 2.4 $\mu M$ sec$^{-1}$, and the observed value, which was determined by the measurement of oxygen uptake, was 3.5 $\mu M$ sec$^{-1}$, which is in good agreement with the calculated value.

## III. THE OLD YELLOW ENZYME

The old yellow enzyme, which was discovered by Warburg and Christian (28) and crystallized by Theorell and Åkeson (29), is a flavoprotein containing two molecules of flavin mononucleotide (FMN) per enzyme molecule (29, 30). It has a capacity for catalyzing the oxidation of DPNH or TPNH in the presence of a suitable electron acceptor such as molecular oxygen or methylene blue.

### A. Spectrophotometric Titration

The titration of the oxidized form was carried out spectrophotometrically at pH 7.0 by successive additions of dithionite solution under anaerobic conditions. As was observed in the case of D-amino acid oxidase, the absorbancy at 540 m$\mu$ first increased with increasing amounts of dithionite added, and then decreased after passing through a maximum absorbancy. The absorption spectrum of the reddish intermediary complex of the enzyme could be obtained by using a graphic method described previously (22, 23, 24). As may be seen in Fig. 10, this compound has absorption maxima at 380 and 490 m$\mu$ within the range from 320 to 600 m$\mu$. The data obtained by ESR measurements seem to suggest that the compound is a semiquinone of FMN attached to the enzyme molecule.

When the anaerobic titration was performed at pH 7.0 by using DPNH or TPNH as reductant, the oxidized form turned simply to the reduced form without passing through an intermediary compound. The results obtained accord with those reported by Beinert (31). When the reduced form of the enzyme which was previously treated with dithionite was titrated with DPN$^+$ or TPN$^+$ solution at pH 7.0 and 25°C under anaerobic conditions, the absorption at 470–475 m$\mu$ increased with added amount of DPN$^+$ or TPN$^+$; however, the oxidized form of the enzyme was not observed even on addition of an adequate amount of DPN$^+$ or TPN$^+$. These results suggest that the following equilibrium is established:

$$\text{Reduced form} + \text{PN}^+ \xleftarrow{\quad K \quad} \text{Complex}$$

and that the equilibrium constant of the reaction

$$\text{Complex} \leftrightarrow \text{Oxidized form} + \text{PNH}$$

is very small, so that the concentration of oxidized enzyme is negligible under the experimental conditions. Since the total flavin concentration is appreciably smaller than that of $PN^+$ added, the following relationship between $\Delta$ O.D. at a given wavelength and $PN^+$ concentration will be obtained:

$$\frac{1}{\Delta \text{ O.D.}} = \frac{1}{\epsilon e_0}\left(\frac{1}{K}\frac{1}{[PN^+]} + 1\right)$$

where $\Delta$ O.D. stands for the optical density of the complex formed minus that of the reduced enzyme, $\epsilon$ is the molecular extinction coefficient of the

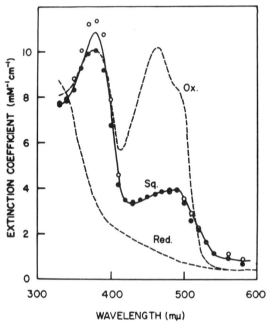

**Fig. 10.** Absorption spectra of oxidized, reduced, and semiquinone forms of the old yellow enzyme at pH 7.0.

complex minus that of the reduced enzyme, and $e_0$ is the total concentration of FMN bound to the enzyme. By plotting the values of $1/\Delta$ O.D. against those of $1/[PN^+]$, a linear relationship was obtained at each wavelength, as shown in Fig. 11. The values of $\epsilon$ and $K$ were determined from the intercepts on the ordinate and abscissa, respectively. The absorption spectrum of the complex described above could be obtained by plotting the calculated $\epsilon$ value at each wavelength against the wavelength. As seen in Figs. 12 and 13, the absorption spectrum of the complex between the reduced enzyme and $DPN^+$ has a maximum at 475 m$\mu$, and the spectrum obtained on the addition of $TPN^+$ to the reduced enzyme has a maximum at 470 m$\mu$. The absorption spectra of the reduced enzyme-$PN^+$ complexes, however, seem to be different

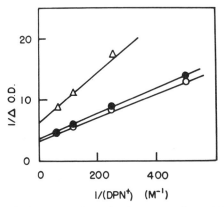

**Fig. 11.** Relationship between reciprocals of concentrations of DPN⁺ and of the changes of optical density shown by the old yellow enzyme. Changes of optical density were measured at 420 m$\mu$ ( $\triangle$ ), 460 m$\mu$ ( $\bullet$ ), and 480 m$\mu$ ( $\circ$ ).

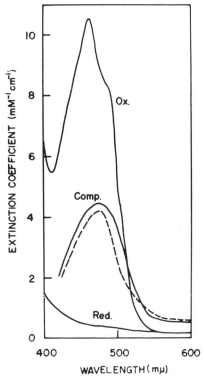

**Fig. 12.** Absorption spectra of oxidized, reduced, and intermediary complex types of the old yellow enzyme. Enzyme was treated with DPNH or DPN⁺. Ox: oxidized form; Red: reduced form. Comp: trapped intermediary complex (solid line) and the red complex observed at the steady state (broken line).

from those of the semiquinone type which was formed on addition of dithionite under anaerobic conditions. The reduced enzyme-TPN$^+$ complex having an absorption maximum at 470 m$\mu$ which we obtained seems to be the same as that studied by Haas (2), which had an absorption maximum at 475 m$\mu$. Ehrenberg and Ludwig (32) reported also on the red complex formed on

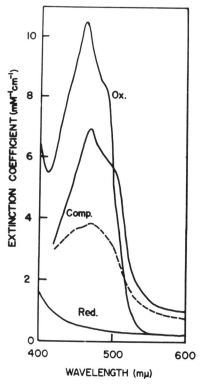

**Fig. 13.** Absorption spectra of oxidized, reduced, and intermediary complex types of the old yellow enzyme. Enzyme was treated with TPNH or TPN$^+$. Ox: oxidized form; Red: reduced form. Comp: trapped intermediary complex (solid line) and the red complex observed at the steady state (broken line).

addition of an excess amount of TPNH to the enzyme and claimed that this complex was the same as that obtained by Haas. On the basis of their data obtained by the ESR technique, Ehrenberg and Ludwig (32) suggested that the red complex might be not a semiquinone but a complex containing TPN$^+$ in addition to FMN, as assumed by Haas (2). Since Ehrenberg's red complex was very stable in this form and the extinction at 475 m$\mu$ was higher than that of the complex observed by Haas and also by us, it seems doubtful that Ehrenberg's complex was identical with ours.

By using the stopped-flow method, a solution of the oxidized enzyme was mixed with DPNH or TPNH solution at pH 7.0 and 25°C under aerobic conditions, and the change of optical density at a given wavelength due to the reduction of FMN moiety was traced on a recording paper as shown in Fig. 14. By plotting the value of $\Delta$ O.D. between the steady state and the oxidized level against each wavelength, the absorption spectrum of the complex formed at the steady state of the reaction was obtained. When DPNH was used as a substrate, the absorption spectrum at the steady state appeared to be the same as that of the complex formed on addition of DPN$^+$ to the reduced form of the enzyme. In contrast, the absorption spectrum at the steady state obtained on addition of TPNH showed lower absorbancy

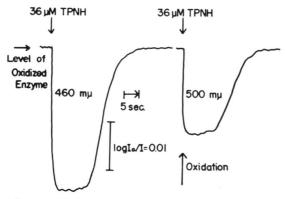

**Fig. 14.** Stopped-flow experiments of the old yellow enzyme reaction at pH 7.0. Experiments were carried out at 25°C under aerobic conditions. Enzyme concentration, 5 $\mu M$.

than that of the reduced enzyme-TPN$^+$ complex observed at the equilibrium state, although both spectra had the same absorption maximum at 470 m$\mu$. The relevant data are shown in Figs. 12 and 13.

## B. Kinetic Analysis

Figure 15 shows the trace of optical density change obtained under anaerobic conditions by using the stopped-flow method. As may be seen, the intermediary complex, which was rapidly formed on mixing the oxidized form of the enzyme with DPNH (or TPNH), decayed with time and changed to the fully reduced form. Since the decay reaction of the complex proceeded according to the first-order kinetics, we can compute the rate constant ($k_d$) of the forward reaction described below, and from the values of $k_d$ and $K$ we can calculate also the rate constant of the reverse reaction ($k_{-d}$),

$$\text{Complex} \underset{k_{-d}}{\overset{k_d}{\longleftrightarrow}} \text{Reduced form} + \text{PN}^+$$

From the data presented in Fig. 14, the rate constants ($k_{\text{red}}$ and $k_{\text{ox}}$) of the two reactions described below can be computed by using Chance's formula (15, 16),

$$\text{Oxidized form} + \text{PNH} \xrightarrow{k_{\text{red}}} \text{Intermediary complex at steady state}$$

and

$$\text{Intermediary complex at steady state} + O_2 \xrightarrow{k_{\text{ox}}} \text{Oxidized form}$$

The values of the rate constants found are summarized in Table 3. From the kinetic data obtained, the following scheme may be proposed as representing the mechanism of the action of the old yellow enzyme:

$$\text{P-FMN} + \text{PNH} \xrightarrow{k_{\text{red}}} \text{X}$$

$$\text{X} \underset{k_{-d}}{\overset{k_d}{\longleftrightarrow}} \text{P-FMNH}_2 + \text{PN}^+$$

$$\text{X} + O_2 \xrightarrow{k_{\text{ox}}} \text{P-FMN} + H_2O_2$$

$$\text{P-FMNH}_2 + O_2 \xrightarrow{k_{\text{ox}}} \text{P-FMN} + H_2O_2$$

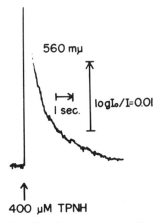

**560 mμ**

$\log I_0/I = 0.01$

I sec.

↑
**400 μM TPNH**

**Fig. 15.** Decay reaction of intermediary complex of the old yellow enzyme at pH 7.0 and 25°C. Experiments were performed by measuring the change of optical density at 560 mμ under anaerobic conditions. Enzyme concentration, 40 μM.

where P-FMN stands for the oxidized form of the enzyme unit, the concentration of which is expressed by that of FMN attached to the enzyme protein, P-FMNH$_2$ the reduced form, and X the intermediary complex having an absorption maximum at 475 mμ for DPN$^+$ (or at 470 mμ for TPN$^+$); the $k$'s are the rate constants of the reactions indicated. In the case of the old yellow enzyme, since the straight line representing the relationship between $1/k_{\text{red}}$ and $1/[\text{PNH}]$ passed almost through the origin, the value of $k_{\text{red}}^{\max}$ could not be obtained experimentally. For this reason, the Michaelis-Menten complex was tentatively omitted in the scheme described above.

When DPNH was used as substrate, the relationship of $k_{\text{red}}[\text{DPNH}] > k_{\text{ox}}[O_2] > k_d$ could be satisfied at the steady state of reaction under the conditions of $[O_2] = 0.2\ mM$ and $[\text{DPNH}] = 0.1\ mM$, as a result of which the amount of the intermediary complex formed during the reaction was almost equal to the total concentration of the enzyme added. This may also account for the fact that the complex obtained at the steady state was the same as that observed at the equilibrium state between the reduced enzyme and DPN$^+$ under anaerobic conditions.

The situation was different when TPNH was used as substrate. Then the value of $k_d$ was of the same order of magnitude as that of $k_{\text{ox}}[O_2]$, and the value of $k_{\text{red}}[\text{TPNH}]$ was far larger than that of $k_d$ or $k_{\text{ox}}[O_2]$. Consequently, a part of the intermediary complex formed was oxidized directly by molecular oxygen to the oxidized form, but the other part was transferred to the fully reduced form and then oxidized to the oxidized form during the course of the reaction. It is also explicable why in this case the absorption spectrum of the intermediary complex observed at the steady state was that of a mixture of the reduced form and the intermediary complex obtained at the equilibrium state under anaerobic conditions.

Since in either case (DPNH or TPNH as substrate), $k_{ox}[O_2] < k_{red}[PNH]$, that is, the oxidation of X or P-FMNH$_2$ by molecular oxygen is the rate-limiting step in the over-all reaction, the rate of over-all reaction determined

TABLE 3

Equilibrium and Rate Constants of the Old Yellow Enzyme

| | Substrate | |
|---|---|---|
| Constant | DPNH | TPNH |
| $K$, $M^{-1}$ | 200 | 3300 |
| $k_d$, sec$^{-1}$ | 0.046 | 0.5 |
| $k_{-d}$, $M^{-1}$ sec$^{-1}$ | 9.2 | 1650 |
| $k_{red}$, $M^{-1}$ sec$^{-1}$ | $2.0 \times 10^4$ | $1.6 \times 10^5$ |
| $k_{ox}$, $M^{-1}$ sec$^{-1}$ | $2.0 \times 10^3$ | $2.0 \times 10^3$ |

by the measurement of oxygen uptake may be expected to be of the same order of magnitude as the value of $k_{ox}[O_2]$. Such a deduction seems to be supported by the fact that the observed value of the rate of over-all reaction was 0.20 sec$^{-1}$ for DPNH and 0.24 sec$^{-1}$ for TPNH under the conditions of $[O_2] = 0.2$ $mM$ and $[PNH] = 0.6$ $mM$, and the value of $k_{ox}[O_2]$ was computed to be 0.4 sec$^{-1}$.

## IV. DISCUSSION

The experimental results which we have described showed that the modes of action of the three flavin enzymes investigated are different from each other. In the case of glucose oxidase there was no indication for the formation of semiquinone on titrating the enzyme with dithionite. Nor could be detected spectrophotometrically the formation of an intermediary complex of a charge-transfer type on mixing the reduced enzyme with an excess amount of D-glucono-δ-lactone. Absence of these intermediates in the case of glucose oxidase was also evinced by the fact that the absorption spectrum obtained at the steady state of the enzyme reaction was simply a difference spectrum of the oxidized minus the reduced form of the enzyme. In contrast, the formation of a semiquinone and a charge-transfer complex was clearly demonstrated in the experiments with D-amino acid oxidase and the old yellow enzyme. Taking these differences into consideration, and assuming that in the case of glucose oxidase the intermediary complex between the reduced enzyme and D-glucono-δ-lactone is very unstable and that the complex formed during the course of the reaction dissociates very rapidly into the reduced enzyme and the product, we were able to propose a uniformly applicable picture for the action mechanisms of the three kinds of flavin enzymes—glucose oxidase, D-amino acid oxidase, and the old yellow enzyme.

## ACKNOWLEDGMENTS

The authors wish to express their gratitude to Professor Hiroshi Tamiya for his valuable criticism of this work.

## REFERENCES

1. L. Michaelis, M. P. Schubert, and C. V. Smythe, *J. Biol. Chem.*, **116**, 587 (1936).
2. E. Haas, *Biochem. Z.*, **290**, 291 (1937).
3. D. Müller, *Biochem. Z.*, **119**, 136 (1928); **205**, 111 (1929); **213**, 211 (1929); **232**, 423 (1931).
4. D. Keilin and E. F. Hartree, *Nature*, **157**, 801 (1946).
5. R. Cecil and A. G. Ogston, *Biochem. J.*, **42**, 229 (1948).
6. K. Kusai, I. Sekuzu, B. Hagihara, K. Okunuki, S. Yamaguchi, and M. Nakai, *Biochim. et Biophys. Acta*, **40**, 555 (1960).
7. K. Kusai, *Ann. Rept. Sci. Works, Fac. Sci. Osaka Univ.*, **8**, 43 (1960).
8. D. Keilin and E. F. Hartree, *Biochem. J.*, **42**, 221 (1948).
9. W. Franke and M. Deffner, *Ann.*, **541**, 117 (1939).
10. D. Keilin and E. F. Hartree, *Biochem. J.*, **50**, 331, 341 (1952).
11. B. E. P. Swoboda, V. Massey, Q. H. Gibson, and N. M. Atherton, *Proc. Biochem. Soc.*, *430th Meeting* (see *Biochem. J.*, **84**, No. 1, 37P).
12. B. Chance, *Acta Chem. Scand.*, **1**, 236 (1947).
13. H. Beinert and R. H. Sands, in M. S. Blois, Jr. *et al.*, Eds., *Free Radicals in Biological Systems*, Academic Press, New York, 1961, p. 17.
14. H. S. Mason, T. Nakamura, I. Yamazaki, E. Spencer, and D. Nebert, *5th International Congress of Biochemistry, Moscow, 1961.*
15. B. Chance, *J. Biol. Chem.*, **151**, 553 (1943).
16. B. Chance, *Arch. Biochem. Biophys.*, **71**, 130 (1957).
17. H. A. Krebs, *Biochem. J.*, **29**, 1620 (1935).
18. O. Warburg and W. Christian, *Biochem. Z.*, **296**, 294 (1938).
19. O. Warburg and W. Christian, *Biochem. Z.*, **298**, 150 (1938).
20. H. Kubo, G. Iwatsubo, H. Watari, H. Shiga, A. Isomoto, and N. Okamoto, *Symposia on Enzyme Chem.* (in Japanese), **14**, 80 (1960).
21. V. Massey, W. H. Gibson, B. Curti, and N. M. Atherton, *Proc. Biochem. Soc.*, *430th Meeting* (see *Biochem. J.*, **84**, No. 1, 54P).
22. S. Nakamura, T. Nakamura, and Y. Ogura, *J. Biochem.*, **53**, 143 (1963).
23. Y. Ogura, S. Nakamura, and T. Nakamura, *Acta Chem. Scand.*, **17**, 184 (1963).
24. T. Nakamura, S. Nakamura, and Y. Ogura, *J. Biochem.*, **54**, 512 (1963).

25. V. Massey, G. Palmer, and R. Bennett, *Biochim. et Biophys. Acta*, **48**, 1 (1961).
26. H. Kubo, H. Watari, and T. Shiga, *Bull. Soc. chim. biol.*, **41**, 981 (1959).
27. K. Yagi and T. Ozawa, *Biochim. et Biophys. Acta*, **67**, 685 (1963).
28. O. Warburg and W. Christian, *Naturwiss.*, **20**, 688 (1957).
29. H. Theorell and Å. Åkeson, *Arch. Biochem. Biophys.*, **65**, 439 (1956).
30. A. Ehrenberg, *Acta Chem. Scand.*, **11**, 1257 (1957).
31. H. Beinert, *J. Biol. Chem.*, **225**, 465 (1957).
32. A. Ehrenberg and G. D. Ludwig, *Science*, **127**, 1177 (1958).

*Discussion*

OGURA: When the old yellow enzyme was titrated with dithionite under anaerobic conditions, an ESR signal was obtained with a $g$ value of 2.003. The concentration of the compound which gave the ESR signal at 50% reduction was in accord

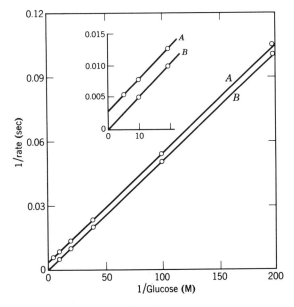

Fig. 1.

with that of the intermediate determined by the spectrophotometric method. This compound may be a semiquinone of the old yellow enzyme. When the enzyme was reduced by TPN or DPN, ESR measurements showed an unpaired electron. The $g$ values of these complexes were the same as that of semiquinone of this enzyme. The concentrations of these complexes were in accord with those estimated by the spectrophotometric method.

GIBSON: I have a number of small points in which I would like to extend some of Dr. Ogura's observations. Figure 1 is an analog of Fig. 4 in Dr. Ogura's paper. The line $A$ is the exact analog of the line which he gave, where he analyzes the

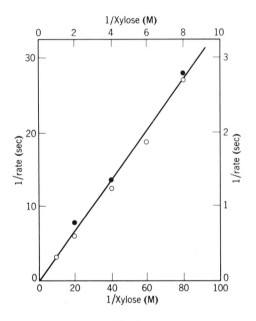

Fig. 2.

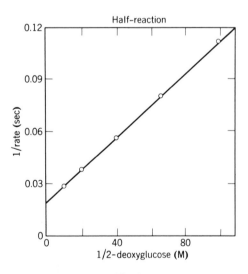

Fig. 3.

action of the enzyme into two halves, the reaction of reduced enzyme with oxygen and of oxidized enzyme with glucose. This deals with the oxidized enzyme reacting with glucose. My line A is in very good agreement with Dr. Ogura's and would appear to give a Michaelis constant and a limiting rate, since the line A has a definite intercept in terms of turnover number. Now line A represents the behavior of oxidized enzyme in the presence of glucose as deduced from turnover experiments, but line B is what we actually obtained when oxidized enzyme and glucose were mixed. The rate of reaction with glucose appeared to increase without limit as the glucose concentration was raised; in fact, the line goes through the origin. This would seem to suggest that no Michaelis complex is formed in the case of glucose, or alternatively, if it is formed the concentration for half-formation must be at least several molar.

This behavior is not confined to glucose. Figure 2 contains two sets of scales indicating that over a wide range of xylose concentrations (and the highest concentrations, as you can see, are very high) just the same behavior is shown by xylose. There appears to be no upper limit to the rate in terms of xylose concentration, and there is no sign of the formation of an enzyme-substrate complex. We got just the same sort of behavior with mannose and galactose. Figure 3 shows the very different behavior of 2-deoxyglucose, where we have a perfectly straightforward case with the half-reaction of the oxidized enzyme with 2-deoxyglucose, giving a well-marked limiting rate and a perfectly obvious Michaelis constant.

MASSEY: When the enzyme glucose oxidase from *Aspergillus niger* is titrated with dithionite anaerobically, a semiquinoid form of the enzyme is produced, as shown on Fig. 4. Here curve 1 is a spectrum of the oxidized enzyme, and curves 2, 3, 4, and 5 represent successive additions of small amounts of dithionite. There is a very broad band out in the 500–600 m$\mu$ region, and this passes through a peak, in fact, at a little over one-half mole dithionite per mole of enzyme-bound flavin. There is a good correlation between the extent of that 570 m$\mu$ band formation and the appearance of ESR signal. This is an interesting example of how the same enzyme isolated from two different sources can have very different properties.

Figure 5 deals with D-amino acid oxidase. Yagi [*Biochim. et Biophys. Acta*, **67**, 685 (1963)] has claimed that the substrate-produced form of D-amino acid oxidase has an ESR signal. I don't think from my reading of Dr. Ogura's paper that he really believes this either, but just to demonstrate, when you make the substrate form of D-amino acid oxidase (the stabilized Kubo intermediate form), with its spectrum 3, there is no ESR signal, even when the solution is kept for long periods in the dark. However, if you keep a solution of this enzyme anaerobically even in room light, you get the slow development of an ESR signal. In this particular experiment we held the enzyme in an anaerobic cuvette about 5 in. away from a 60-watt light bulb and found fairly rapid production of ESR signal. At the same time as that ESR signal develops, there are very pronounced changes in the absorption spectrum of the enzyme, ending with the spectrum of the free semiquinoid form of the enzyme which is obtained on titration with dithionite. In other words, there is low absorption in this region, a peak at 490, a shoulder at 400, and increased absorption at 370 m$\mu$.

CHANCE: There are remarkable parallels in the different oxidation rates of flavins and those of hemoproteins. What controls the oxidation rate of flavins? Is there any parallel with hemoproteins? I think that it has much to do with the configuration of the active site and with ligands which might influence oxidation rates.

BEINERT: There is a variety of very peculiar examples of flavoproteins which, when no substrate or product is present, react very rapidly with oxygen, whereas they do not do so in the presence of substrate or product. This would pose a very serious limitation on what proteins will do to the autoxidizability of flavin. I think that this makes the solution of the problem which Dr. Chance has posed very

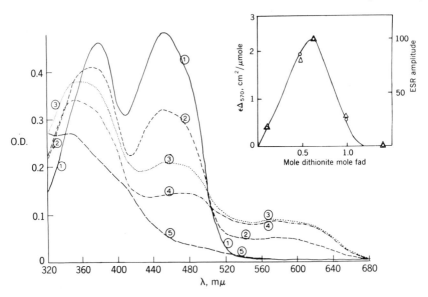

Fig. 4. Anaerobic titration of glucose oxidase with $Na_2S_2O_4$ at $20°$ in 0.1 $M$ phosphate, pH 6.3. Curve 1, oxidized enzyme; curve 2, with 0.32 mole $Na_2S_2O_4$ per mole enzyme-bound FAD; curve 3, with 0.50 mole; curve 4, with 0.60 mole; curve 5, with 1.30 mole. The insert shows the correlation between ESR signal and the absorbancy at 570 m$\mu$ obtained in this titration; ($\triangle$), amplitude of ESR signal; ($\circ$), increase in absorbancy at 570 m$\mu$. [From V. Massey and Q. H. Gibson, *Federation Proc.*, **23**, 18 (1964).]

difficult. An example is the Martius-Ernster DT-diaphorase, which barely reacts with oxygen when substrate is present, or the acyl-CoA dehydrogenases, which are very strongly protected from oxygen by substrates or the products formed.

SINGER: To return to Dr. Chance's question, if one looks over the list of known flavoproteins one finds very little correlation between the presence of metal or of any special type of metal and the repression of autoxidation. But there appears to be an excellent correlation between whether or not a flavoprotein is linked to the respiratory chain in its normal habitat and the repression of autoxidation. It is of obvious physiological importance that the enzymes which are linked to the cytochrome chain are in each case non-autoxidizable, within the limits of measurement, with the only conceivable exception being cytochrome $b_2$, whose status in the respiratory chain is debatable. The repression of autoxidation is just one of many reactions of free flavins which are hindered in the native structure of these enzymes.

Thus, the reactivity of free flavins with DPNH and TPNH, among other reactions, is similarly inhibited in the respiratory-chain-linked dehydrogenases.

GIBSON: I should just like to put in a word regarding Dr. Chance's problem. I feel that perhaps we ought to phrase the question the other way around. The point is that free flavin is autoxidized comparatively slowly, but flavoproteins are oxidized

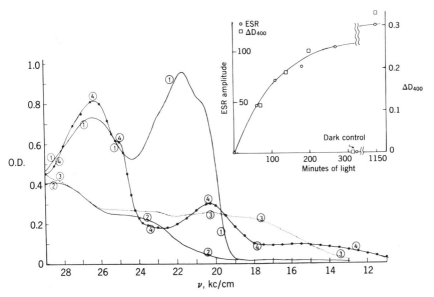

**Fig. 5.** The production of the free-radical form of D-amino acid oxidase by light irradiation of the purple form of the enzyme produced by pyruvate and $NH_4^+$ after reduction with D-alanine. The experiments were carried out in 0.1 $M$ pyrophosphate, pH 8.5, at 10°. Curve 1, oxidized enzyme; curve 2, after reduction with 68 moles D-alanine; curve 3, after the further addition of 1020 moles pyruvate and 2800 moles $NH_4^+$; curve 4, after exposure for 1100 min to a 60-watt tungsten lamp source 3 in. from the sample. Intermediate spectra between 3 and 4 have been omitted for the sake of clarity; instead, the insert shows the progressive development of the characteristic 400 m$\mu$ (25 kc/cm) shoulder of the uncomplexed semiquinone and the appearance and development of ESR signal at intermediate light exposures. A separate dark control showed no change in spectrum from curve 3 and no development of ESR signal over 6 hr. [From V. Massey and Q. H. Gibson, *Federation Proc.*, **23**, 18 (1964).]

from hundreds of times to ten thousand times faster than free flavin. There is, as Dr. Singer has pointed out, quite a wide range of variation in the rate of autoxidation, but this variation seems to apply in general to the reduced free flavins only. Even in the case of diaphorase, which is not ordinarily thought of as autoxidizable, you can get the fully reduced form to react with oxygen with a rate constant of $10^5$ or something near that.

MASON: Dr. Chance's question can be generalized to include cuprous oxidases, ferrous oxidases, and hemoprotein oxidases. The fact that we have no theoretical answer to the question of function in terms of structure shows that this is really the key question in the oxidase field. Of the very large number of oxidases that are known, the fact of the matter is that not a single intermediate involving activated oxygen has been demonstrated, with the exception of peroxidase and catalase; it seems to me that the major problem still facing investigators in the field of oxidases is to discover exactly how oxygen is brought into reaction.

HANDLER: One thing that remains to be pointed out is that the problem is not quite so much the behavior of the flavin as the behavior of the iron. The rapidly oxidizable metalloflavoproteins transmit their electrons from the iron, as far as we can tell, to the oxygen, and the question, therefore, is why the iron of xanthine oxidase, for example, is so readily oxidizable, whereas that of succinate and DPNH dehydrogenases and/or ferredoxins generally is not. There must be a difference there of some kind which has not been recognized.

# D-Amino Acid Oxidase

. . . V. MASSEY, H. GANTHER,
P. E. BRUMBY, and B. CURTI

## I. INTRODUCTION

Pig kidney D-amino acid oxidase has been isolated as a crystalline flavo-protein (1) still possessing intact most of its bound prosthetic group, flavin adenine dinucleotide (FAD). Molecular weight analyses (2) showed that this enzyme exists in solution as a polymer. The unit molecular weight, based on flavin content after equilibrium dialysis against excess FAD, is 45,500 (1). At concentrations greater than 10 mg protein/ml, the molecular weight found was 182,000; at lower concentrations dissociation occurred, both monomers and dimers being detectable (2). This conclusion has been challenged by Yagi and co-workers (3–6) who claim that the molecular weight of the enzyme, either as the apoenzyme, holoenzyme, or benzoate complex, is 115,000. Originally, these workers maintained that the unit molecular weight, based on flavin content, was also 115,000, but this claim has now been withdrawn since it was found that the method of protein determination used was in error; the latest value quoted by Yagi and Ozawa (7) for the unit molecular weight is 55,000.

Yagi and co-workers (8–13) have also crystallized D-amino acid oxidase under a variety of conditions, including the purple form produced by the addition of D-alanine. These latter crystals have been reported to exhibit a free-radical signal when examined by electron spin resonance spectrometry (14). Previous work (15), however, has shown that, although this purple form of the enzyme is a complex of flavin semiquinone and amino acid radical, it does not exhibit an ESR signal unless exposed to light. This half-reduced intermediate has been shown by rapid reaction studies to be a catalytically important intermediate, and a reaction mechanism for D-amino acid oxidase proposed (15). In this paper we will report experiments enlarging on these points and describe some very pronounced changes in enzyme structure which occur as a function of temperature.

## II. MATERIALS AND METHODS

D-Amino acid oxidase was prepared as described previously (1). It was found, in agreement with Yagi *et al.* (5, 8), that the enzyme prepared in this manner contained some benzoate (0.2–0.5 mole benzoate/mole flavin). Following Yagi, we freed the preparation of benzoate by repeated precipitation at 0° with 0.5 saturation $(NH_4)_2SO_4$ containing 0.1 $M$ pyrophosphate, pH 8.5, and 0.10 $M$ DL-alanine. After four precipitations the benzoate-free enzyme was dissolved in 0.1 $M$ pyrophosphate, pH 8.5, and dialyzed against four changes of the same buffer. It was found that when this procedure was carried out in room light appreciable inactivation occurred. However, when care was taken to exclude light throughout the procedure, quantitative recovery of activity was obtained. Enzyme activity was assayed manometrically as described previously (1). Protein was estimated by the biuret method (16). D-Amino acids were obtained from the Nutritional Biochemicals Company, and FAD from the California Corporation for Biochemical Research. All other chemicals were reagent grade; glass-distilled water was used throughout.

## III. RESULTS

### A. Binding Constant of FAD

Many observations have led to the conclusion that, although FAD is fairly tightly bound to D-amino acid oxidase, it is nevertheless considerably more weakly bound than in most other flavoproteins. Thus, although the enzyme as isolated contains 12–16 m$\mu$moles FAD/mg protein, the content may be increased to 21–22 m$\mu$moles/mg by dialysis against $3 \times 10^{-4}$ $M$ FAD (1). Furthermore, it was noted that, whereas little FAD is lost on $(NH_4)_2SO_4$ precipitation of a concentrated solution of enzyme, proportionally greater losses were obtained as the concentration of enzyme was lowered. Quantitative evaluation of the binding constant of FAD proved to be somewhat difficult because the apoprotein formed on loss of FAD is easily denatured. Table 1 shows the results of dialysis equilibrium experiments carried out at 0–4°. As can be seen, there is a reasonable scatter of values, independent of the protein concentration. The average value of $K = \dfrac{[E][FAD]}{[E \cdot FAD]}$ is $2.2 \times 10^{-7}$ $M$. This compares reasonably with the $K_m$ value of $5.5 \times 10^{-7}$ $M$ found at 25° by manometric assay of activity when apoprotein is reacted with different concentrations of FAD. The practical consequence of such a binding constant is that in the absence of added FAD at a concentration of 10 mg/ml 3% of the FAD is free, while at a concentration of

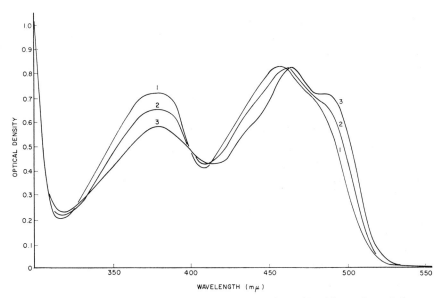

Fig. 1. The effect of benzoate on the spectrum of D-amino acid oxidase. Curve 1, benzoate-free enzyme (4.58 mg/ml) in 0.1 $M$ pyrophosphate, pH 8.3, temperature 10°. Curve 2. after the addition of 0.456 mole benzoate per mole FAD; curve 3, after 4.33 moles benzoate, Curves 2 and 3 have not been corrected for dilution, 0.8% and 6.3%, respectively.

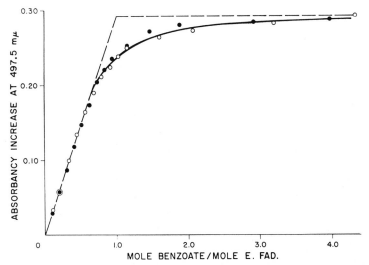

Fig. 2. Increase in absorbancy at 497.5 mμ on titration with benzoate. Conditions as in Fig. 1. The values plotted have been corrected for dilution. ○, results obtained in the absence of added FAD (FAD content of the preparation used was 15.4 mμmoles/mg). ●, results obtained on enzyme dialyzed to equilibrium against $2 \times 10^{-4} M$ FAD. The concentration of enzyme-bound FAD was $8.0 \times 10^{-5} M$.

1 mg/ml 10% would be free, and at 0.1 mg/ml 27% would be free. Thus it is clearly desirable in the isolation of the intact flavoprotein to keep the enzyme as concentrated as possible and to dialyze against several changes of small volume rather than once against a large volume of buffer.

TABLE 1

Determination of FAD-Binding Constant

Benzoate-free enzyme was dialyzed with vigorous stirring at 0–4° for 28 hr against the volumes shown of 0.1 $M$ pyrophosphate, pH 8.5. Protein concentration was measured, and molarity calculated assuming a unit molecular weight of 45,500. Free and bound FAD were estimated spectrophotometrically at 450 and 455 m$\mu$, respectively, assuming in each case an extinction coefficient of 1.13 × 10⁴ cm²/mmole.

| Protein Concentration, $M$ | Vol. of Dialysate, ml | FAD Bound (E · FAD), $M$ | Free FAD, $M$ | Free Enzyme, $M$ | $K = \dfrac{[E][FAD]}{[E \cdot FAD]}$, $M$ |
|---|---|---|---|---|---|
| 2.14 × 10⁻⁴ | 100 | 1.50 × 10⁻⁴ | 1.0 × 10⁻⁶ | 6.4 × 10⁻⁵ | 4.3 × 10⁻⁷ |
| 2.38 × 10⁻⁴ | 50 | 1.52 × 10⁻⁴ | 4.0 × 10⁻⁷ | 8.6 × 10⁻⁵ | 2.3 × 10⁻⁷ |
| 2.38 × 10⁻⁴ | 250 | 1.45 × 10⁻⁴ | 1.3 × 10⁻⁷ | 9.3 × 10⁻⁵ | 8.5 × 10⁻⁷ |
| 7.95 × 10⁻⁵ | 50 | 4.76 × 10⁻⁵ | 3.8 × 10⁻⁷ | 3.19 × 10⁻⁵ | 2.6 × 10⁻⁷ |
| 3.97 × 10⁻⁵ | 50 | 2.27 × 10⁻⁵ | 2.6 × 10⁻⁷ | 1.70 × 10⁻⁵ | 1.9 × 10⁻⁷ |
| | | | | Average | 2.2 × 10⁻⁷ |

## B. Binding of Benzoate

As described previously by Yagi *et al.* (17, 18), benzoate has a pronounced effect on the spectrum of the enzyme. Figure 1 shows the spectral shift obtained on titration of benzoate-free enzyme with benzoate. For the sake of clarity intermediate spectra have been omitted. The pronounced decreases in absorbancy in the region 350–400 m$\mu$ and 420–450 m$\mu$, as well as the increase in the region 480–520 m$\mu$, are to a large extent complete by the addition of one molecule of benzoate per molecule enzyme-bound FAD.

This is illustrated further in Fig. 2, where the increase in absorbancy at 497.5 m$\mu$ is plotted against the amount of benzoate added. No significant difference is obtained when the titration is carried out on the enzyme of higher FAD content obtained by dialysis equilibrium against excess FAD. From the results of Fig. 2 the binding constant of benzoate to the enzyme, $K = \dfrac{[E \cdot FAD][\text{free benzoate}]}{[E \cdot FAD \cdot \text{benzoate}]}$, is calculated to be 3–4 × 10⁻⁶ $M$. The fact that this constant is unaffected by added FAD and that the initial slope of the titration curve intercepts the maximum value observed at 1.0 mole benzoate per mole enzyme-bound FAD, even when significant quantities of apoprotein are present, suggests that benzoate binds weakly or not at all with the apoenzyme.

The cause of the spectral change produced by benzoate still remains obscure. Yagi and co-workers refer to this complex as an artificial Michaelis complex, suggesting that if one could experimentally observe the complex of substrate and oxidized enzyme a similar spectral shift might be noted. Although this explanation is feasible, it does not take account of the fact that many flavoproteins, such as lipoyl dehydrogenase (19), electron-transferring flavoprotein (20), old yellow enzyme (21), vitamin $K_3$ reductase (22), and yeast glutathione reductase (23), have very pronounced shoulders in the region 470–490 m$\mu$. A similar spectral change has been observed by Harbury *et al.* (24) when 3-methyl lumiflavin is dissolved in hydrophobic solvents. It thus appears possible that the flavoproteins listed with such spectral characteristics may have a structure such that the flavin prosthetic group is located in a hydrophobic environment, and that the change produced by the binding of benzoate to D-amino acid oxidase is due to a similar phenomenon, namely, the provision of a hydrophobic environment for the flavin.

## C. Effect of Temperature on Sedimentation Constant

Previous studies by Yagi and co-workers (3–6) have given values of sedimentation constants and molecular weights considerably different from those obtained by Massey *et al.* (1) and Charlwood *et al.* (2). Table 2 lists some of the discrepancies observed. Some of the earlier discrepancies between our work and that of Yagi and Ozawa may be due to the different ionic composition [0.1 $M$ phosphate, pH 7.6, in refs. (1) and (2) and 0.0167 $M$ pyrophosphate, pH 8.3, in ref. (5)]. This is indeed suggested by the differences between our earlier results and the newer ones listed in this table, which were carried out in 0.1 $M$ pyrophosphate, pH 8.5. This possibility has not yet been explored further, because of the very pronounced difference in sedimentation constant observed on the same sample of enzyme run at 3.1° and at 20°, which may provide the main explanation for the discrepancies. Table 3 lists the temperature dependence of $S_{20, H_2O}$ on a sample of holoenzyme containing approximately 0.3 mole benzoate per mole enzyme-bound FAD. At temperatures below 20° there is a very pronounced dependence of the sedimentation constant on temperature. At these lower temperatures the Schlierern pattern is quite symmetrical. At 20° and 25° there are significant quantities of a faster-moving component; the $S_{20, H_2O}$ values listed at these two temperatures are for the slower major component. This effect is perfectly reversible; a sample of enzyme incubated at 25° for 2 hr to simulate an ultracentrifuge experiment and then run at 4° gave a symmetrical Schlierern pattern and a sedimentation constant of 5.35 svedbergs. It is not yet known whether this change in sedimentation constant with temperature below 15° is due to a change in molecular weight or to protein configurational changes.

## TABLE 2
### Sedimentation Data on D-Amino Acid Oxidase

| Form of Enzyme | Protein Concentration, mg/ml | Temp., °C | $S_{20, H_2O}$, svedbergs | Molecular Weight | Ionic Medium | Ref. |
|---|---|---|---|---|---|---|
| Holoenzyme, some benzoate present, dialyzed vs. 2 × 10⁻⁴ $M$ FAD | 10 | 12 | 7.6 | | 0.1 $M$ phosphate, pH 7.6 | (1) |
| Holoenzyme, some benzoate present, dialyzed vs. 4 × 10⁻⁵ – 2 × 10⁻⁴ $M$ FAD | 19.5 | | 7.8 | | 0.1 $M$ phosphate, pH 7.6 | (2) |
|  | 16.1 | | 7.8 | | | |
|  | 11.6 | | 7.8 | | | |
|  | 8.0 | | 7.9 | 205,000 | | |
|  | 5.4 | | 7.6 | 163–197,000 | | |
|  | 4.2 | | 7.3 | 153,000 | | |
|  | 1.9 | | 7.0 | 154,000 | | |
|  | 1.1 | | 5.2 | 132,000 | | |
| Apoenzyme | Extrapolated to zero protein | | 4.5[a] | 115,000 | 0.0167 $M$ pyrophosphate, pH 8.3 | (5) |
| Holoenzyme | " | | 8.0[a] | 115,000 | | |
| Holoenzyme + excess benzoate | " | | 11.0[a] | 115,000 | | |

| | | | 0.1 $M$ pyrophosphate, pH 8.5 | This paper |
|---|---|---|---|---|
| Apoenzyme | 7.3 | 6.5 | 4.73 | |
| ,, | 2.5 | 11 | 4.43 | |
| | 1.25 | 8 | 4.50 | |
| Apoenzyme, dialyzed vs. 2 × 10⁻⁴ $M$ FAD | 7.3 | 11.5 | 6.80 | |
| ,, | 2.5 | 8.5 | 5.75 | |
| | 1.20 | 6.8 | 4.79 | |
| Holoenzyme, dialyzed vs. 2 × 10⁻⁴ $M$ FAD and 2 × 10⁻⁴ $M$ benzoate | 4.8 | 6.5 | 5.86 | |
| ,, | 2.4 | 9.8 | 5.80 | |
| | 1.2 | 4.0 | 5.46 | |
| Holoenzyme, containing ca. 0.3 mole benzoate, dialyzed vs. 3 × 10⁻⁴ $M$ FAD | 13 | 2.3 | 5.25 | |
| ,, | 10 | 3.1 | 5.18 | |
| | 10 | 20.0 | 6.65 | |

[a] In these experiments no evidence was obtained for dissociation of the enzyme on dilution; i.e., the plot of $S_{20, \text{H}_2\text{O}}$ vs. protein concentration was linear, and $S_{20, \text{H}_2\text{O}}$ decreased with increasing protein concentration.

## D. Effect of Temperature on Ultraviolet Difference Spectra

Further evidence for a temperature-dependent change in structure of D-amino acid oxidase has come from studies in the ultraviolet as a function of temperature. In such experiments benzoate-free enzyme was placed in two matched silica cells in the reference and sample beams of a Cary model 14 recording spectrophotometer. Initially both cells were thermostatted at 20°, and small variations in cell characteristics balanced at the appropriate wavelengths by adjustment of the multipotentiometers. The temperature of the sample was then lowered, and difference spectra were recorded. When the sample temperature reached 1°, the temperature of the reference cell was raised.

Figure 3 shows the results of an experiment in which enzyme in 0.1 $M$ pyrophosphate, pH 8.3, 1.18 mg/ml ($D_{280}$, 2.0), was treated in this way. The difference spectra are similar to those observed by Bigelow and Geschwind (25) with tryptophan and indole on changing the medium. It can be seen that most of the effect is elicited at low temperatures, between 1 and 15°. In Fig. 4 the optical density differences at 286.5 m$\mu$ between 30° and the observation temperature are plotted vs. the reciprocal of the absolute temperature. Two linear portions of the plot are obtained, with a sharp transition temperature of 12°. The results of a control experiment with bovine serum albumin, 3.0 mg/ml ($D_{280}$, 2.0), run under the same conditions, are also given. Over the temperature range studied, no anomalous results were obtained. The

### TABLE 3

#### Variation of Sedimentation Constant with Temperature

D-Amino acid oxidase holoenzyme as isolated, and containing *ca.* 0.3 mole benzoate per mole FAD, was dialyzed to equilibrium vs. 0.1 $M$ pyrophosphate, pH 8.5, containing $3 \times 10^{-4} M$ FAD (protein concentration, 10 mg/ml). The double-sector synthetic boundary cell of the Spinco Model E ultracentrifuge was used.

| Temperature, °C | $S_{20, H_2O}$, svedbergs |
|---|---|
| 3.0 | 5.19 |
| 4.0 | 5.35 |
| 7.0 | 5.74 |
| 10.0 | 6.02 |
| 15.0 | 6.37 |
| 20.0 | 6.65 |
| 25.0 | 6.58 |

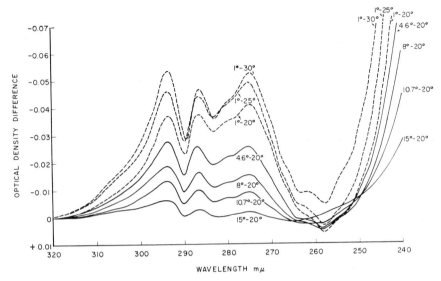

**Fig. 3.** Ultraviolet difference spectra of benzoate-free D-amino acid oxidase as a function of temperature. Conditions as in text.

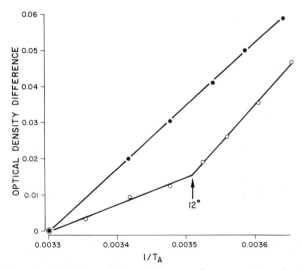

**Fig. 4.** Arrhenius plot of ultraviolet absorbancy differences. ●, results of the experiment shown in Fig. 3, using $\Delta 286.5$ m$\mu$. ○, bovine serum albumin, 3.0 mg/ml in 0.1 $M$ pyrophosphate, pH 8.3, $\Delta 292$ m$\mu$.

fact, with these and other proteins studied, that continuous changes in absorbancy in the ultraviolet are observed as a function of temperature is in itself an interesting phenomenon and presumably indicates microscopic changes in protein structure which are dependent on the temperature.

### E. Effect of Temperature on Protein Fluorescence

As the effect noted above implies some change in structure of the protein involving tryptophan residues, it was of considerable interest to observe the effect of temperature on the fluorescence of the aromatic amino acid residues

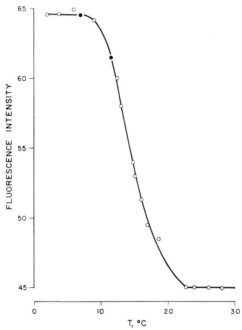

**Fig. 5.** Aromatic amino acid protein fluorescence of D-amino acid oxidase as a function of temperature. Conditions described in text. ○, values obtained on warming the solution; ●, values obtained on cooling again.

of D-amino acid oxidase. Figure 5 shows the results of such a study, carried out with Dr. G. Weber, University of Illinois. In this experiment, benzoate-free enzyme (1.48 mg/ml) in 0.1 $M$ pyrophosphate, pH 8.3, was excited with light at 295 m$\mu$ (spectral band width, 2.5 m$\mu$) and the emitted fluorescence monitored at 333 m$\mu$ (spectral band width, 3 m$\mu$). As can be seen, the fluorescence remained constant between 2 and 9° and between 23 and 28°, but at intermediate temperatures there was a dramatic decrease in fluorescence intensity with a midpoint transition of about 14.5°. As with the other physical methods, ultracentrifugation and ultraviolet difference spectra, this change was fully reversible; on lowering the temperature at the end of the experiment, the high fluorescence originally observed was regained.

## F. Effect of Temperature on Catalysis

Since such marked changes in physical properties accompany changes in temperature, it was clearly of great interest to study the effect of temperature on the catalytic properties of this enzyme. Such a study with a two-substrate enzyme involves a great amount of effort, as it has previously been shown (1, 15) that the velocity of reaction is markedly dependent on the concentration of both substrates (D-amino acid and oxygen). For meaningful results it was therefore necessary to obtain at each temperature studied the true maximum velocity by extrapolation to infinite concentrations of both D-amino acid and oxygen. As a preliminary to this study the effect of temperature was studied on the rate of the anaerobic reduction of enzyme by substrate. As documented previously (15) and illustrated in more detail in section IIIG, this reaction proceeds via an intermediate complex of enzyme flavin semiquinone and amino acid radical,

$$
\left|{-}\text{FAD} + \text{AA} \underset{k_2}{\overset{k_1}{\rightleftharpoons}} \left|\begin{array}{l}{-}\text{FAD} \\ {-}\text{AA}\end{array}\right. \underset{k_4}{\overset{k_3}{\rightleftharpoons}} \left|\begin{array}{l}{-}\text{FADH}^{\cdot} \\ {-}\text{AA}^{\cdot}\end{array}\right. \underset{k_6}{\overset{k_5}{\rightleftharpoons}} \left|\begin{array}{l}{-}\text{FADH}_2 \\ {-}\text{IA}\end{array}\right. \underset{k_8}{\overset{k_7}{\rightleftharpoons}} \left|\begin{array}{l}{-}\text{FADH}_2 \\ {+}\text{IA}\end{array}\right.
$$

where AA represents amino acid, AA$^{\cdot}$ amino acid radical, and IA imino acid. The rate of formation of the radical intermediate ($k_3$) is very much greater than the rate of full reduction ($k_5$). In keeping with the reaction scheme above, the rate of formation of the diradical is very dependent on the concentration of amino acid and can be obtained unequivocally only by extrapolation to infinite substrate concentration. However, the rate of conversion of this intermediate to the fully reduced enzyme ($k_5$) is almost completely independent of substrate concentration and so may be obtained readily. Both events can be studied conveniently at 550 m$\mu$, where only the diradical form has any absorption (15). Figure 6 shows the results obtained by using the stopped-flow technique of Gibson and Milnes (26) when $3.9 \times 10^{-5}$ $M$ enzyme was reacted with 0.002 $M$ D-alanine. The rate of diradical formation at this concentration is 1000 times greater than the rate of full reduction. This ratio is maintained constant over the whole temperature range studied. The results suggest a break in the Arrhenius plot at about 13°, i.e., in the temperature range where the physical studies show a change in protein structure.

These studies do not prove any correlation of protein structural changes and catalytic activity, since $k_5$ is too slow for this step to be concerned in catalysis, and the rate of production of the catalytically important diradical ($k_3$) can be obtained only by extrapolation to infinite concentration of substrate.

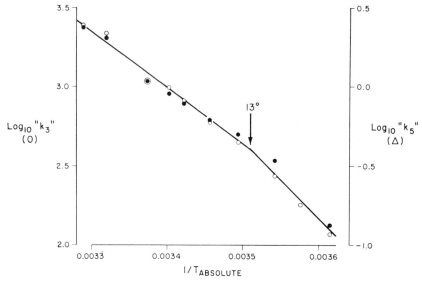

**Fig. 6.** Variation with temperature of the rates of formation of enzyme substrate intermediate, $k_3$ (○), and fully reduced enzyme, $k_5$ (●), when $3.9 \times 10^{-5}$ $M$ enzyme was reacted with 0.002 $M$ D-alanine in 0.1 $M$ pyrophosphate, pH 8.3.

Furthermore, as has been shown previously (15), the rate-determining step in catalysis is the dissociation of imino acid from the reoxidized enzyme ($k_{13}$):

$$\left|\begin{matrix}-FAD \\ +AA \\ \end{matrix}\right. \underset{k_2}{\overset{k_1}{\rightleftharpoons}} \left|\begin{matrix}-FAD \\ -AA \end{matrix}\right. \underset{k_4}{\overset{k_3}{\rightleftharpoons}} \left|\begin{matrix}-FADH^{\cdot} \\ -AA^{\cdot} \end{matrix}\right.$$

$$\left|\begin{matrix}-FADH^{\cdot} \\ -AA^{\cdot} \\ \end{matrix}\right. +O_2 \underset{k_{10}}{\overset{k_9}{\rightleftharpoons}} \left|\begin{matrix}-FADH^{\cdot} \cdots O \\ -AA^{\cdot} \ \ \cdots O \end{matrix}\right. \underset{k_{12}}{\overset{k_{11}}{\rightleftharpoons}} \left|\begin{matrix}-FAD \\ -IA \end{matrix}\right. +H_2O_2$$

$$\left|\begin{matrix}-FAD \\ -IA \\ \end{matrix}\right. \underset{k_{14}}{\overset{k_{13}}{\rightleftharpoons}} \left|\begin{matrix}-FAD \\ \end{matrix}\right. +IA$$

The effect of temperature on the over-all catalytic reaction was therefore studied. This may be done conveniently by the stopped-flow rapid-reaction technique, employing an excess of substrate over oxygen and enzyme. Figure 7 shows a typical record of optical density change at 550 m$\mu$ in such an experiment. Analog computer solutions of such experiments have shown that the

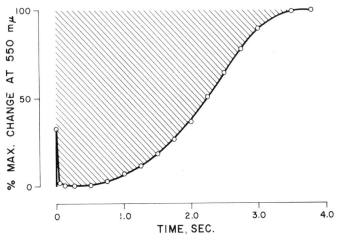

**Fig. 7.** Optical density changes at 550 m$\mu$ when 3.36 × 10⁻⁵ $M$ enzyme in the presence of 1 × 10⁻⁴ $M$ added FAD was reacted with 0.01 $M$ D-alanine and 6.35 × 10⁻⁴ $M$ O₂ (concentrations after mixing). All reactants were made up in 0.1 $M$ pyrophosphate, pH 8.5. Temperature, 27.1°.

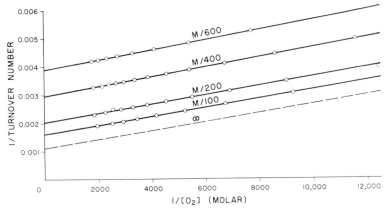

**Fig. 8.** Results of a turnover analysis of the curve shown in Fig. 7 and similar ones obtained with 0.005 $M$, 0.0025 $M$, and 0.00167 $M$ D-alanine. Temperature, 27.1°.

data fit very well the above reaction mechanism and the observed kinetic data (15).

Thus the enzyme-substrate diradical has been shown to be a mechanistically important species, and curves such as those of Fig. 7 can be used to calculate turnover numbers since the concentration of enzyme used and oxygen present are known. In such calculations it is assumed that the shaded area can be equated with the amount of oxygen originally present (27). Thus the amount of oxygen consumed in a given time can be calculated, and as the enzyme concentration is known, the turnover number may be determined at several oxygen concentrations from one experiment. Figure 8 shows the results of such calculations from four different experiments in which the concentration of D-alanine was varied. Figure 9 shows the apparent $1/V$ ($\infty$ $O_2$) plotted against the reciprocal D-alanine concentration. From such plots the

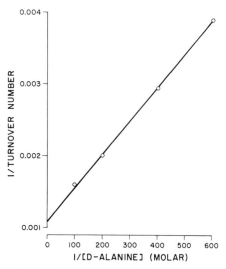

**Fig. 9.**   Estimation of maximum turnover number and $K_{\text{alanine}}$ from the results of Fig. 8.

true $V$ ($\infty$ D-alanine, $\infty$ $O_2$) can be obtained with good precision. Over the whole temperature range studied (2–35.9°), parallel plots such as those shown in Fig. 8 were obtained.

The results of this study are shown in Fig. 10, where the $\log_{10}$ maximum turnover number is plotted against the reciprocal absolute temperature. It can be seen that there is a marked break in the Arrhenius plot at a temperature of about 14°. Thus it seems apparent that the changes in physical properties detailed earlier are correlated with a change in catalytic function. Sharp discontinuities in Arrhenius plots have been observed with other enzymes, notably fumarase (28). A general discussion of such phenomena is given in Dixon and Webb (29). The present data suggest that this behavior may be due to sharp transition of the enzyme from one stable protein structure to another, both forms having similar catalytic activity but differing energies of activation.

## G. Further Support for the Proposed Reaction Mechanism

It is often the case that considerable information about enzyme reaction mechanisms may be obtained by the study of steps which clearly are not concerned in catalysis. This is true for the anaerobic full reduction of D-amino acid oxidase by substrate described in the previous section. Although with all substrates tested the rate of full reduction is far too slow for the fully reduced enzyme to be involved in catalysis (1, 15), it is nevertheless important to understand the nature of the reaction in order to define the nature of the catalytically important intermediate. This intermediate is readily distinguishable in a number of ways from the free enzyme flavin semiquinone pro-

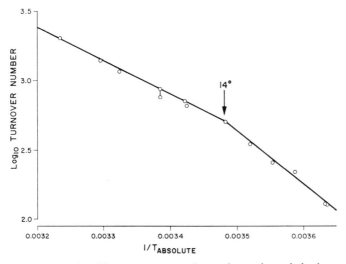

**Fig. 10.** Arrhenius plot of $\log_{10}$ turnover number against reciprocal absolute temperature.

duced by titration with sodium dithionite or catalytic reduction with platinum and $H_2$. For example, it has a very different spectrum and, unlike the free semiquinone, does not exhibit a free-radical signal when studied by ESR spectrometry. It is therefore unlikely to be a dimer of the type

$$\begin{array}{l} |\text{---FADH}^{\cdot} \\ |\text{---FADH}^{\cdot} \end{array}$$ as originally proposed (1), since this type of compound should be

formed equally well by the addition of limited quantities of dithionite.

The possibility exists that the difference between dithionite-reduced semiquinone and the substrate-produced intermediate could be due merely to the

binding of substrate or product, i.e., $\begin{array}{l} |\text{---FADH}^{\cdot} \\ |\text{---IA} \\ |\text{---FADH}^{\cdot} \end{array}$ or $\begin{array}{l} |\text{---FADH}^{\cdot} \\ |\text{---AA} \\ |\text{---FADH}^{\cdot} \end{array}$ . This would

appear unlikely since it would not provide a plausible explanation of the fact that the free semiquinone has an ESR signal, whereas the substrate intermediate does not. Futhermore, the rate of conversion of the substrate intermediate to fully reduced enzyme ($k_5$) would be expected to show some

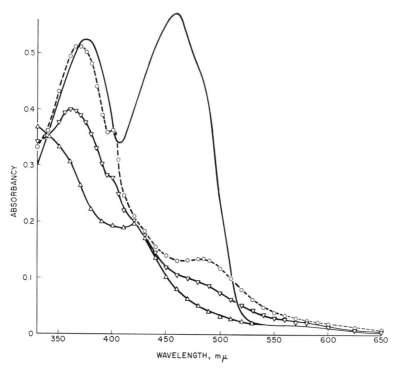

**Fig. 11.** The effect of adding D-alanine anaerobically to the free semiquinoid form of D-amino acid oxidase. Benzoate-free enzyme, $5.07 \times 10^{-5}$ M, was reacted at 10° in 0.1 M pyrophosphate, pH 8.5. Solid line without points, oxidized enzyme. $\bigcirc$, after addition of 0.6 mole $Na_2S_2O_4$, unchanged 50 min after the addition of a 15 molar excess of D-alanine. $\bigtriangledown$, 24 hr later. $\triangle$, spectrum of dithionite-reduced enzyme (separate experiment).

dependence on substrate concentration if a second molecule of substrate were to react with a diflavin radical form.

Further evidence in favor of the scheme

$$\begin{vmatrix} -FAD \\ \\ \end{vmatrix} + AA \rightleftharpoons \begin{vmatrix} -FAD \\ -AA \end{vmatrix} \rightleftharpoons \begin{vmatrix} -FADH^{\cdot} \\ -AA^{\cdot} \end{vmatrix} \rightleftharpoons \begin{vmatrix} -FADH_2 \\ -IA \end{vmatrix} \rightleftharpoons \begin{vmatrix} -FADH_2 \\ \\ \end{vmatrix} + IA$$

comes from the following experiments. When free semiquinone was prepared anaerobically by addition of 0.6 mole $Na_2S_2O_4$ per mole enzyme-bound FAD, the further anaerobic addition of a 15 molar excess of D-alanine resulted in no spectral change over the whole visible spectrum in 1 hr. Figure 11 shows that 24 hr of incubation was required to achieve approximately half-reduction of the free semiquinone. By comparison the substrate intermediate is reduced fully under these conditions in about 10 min. This experiment is explained much more readily in terms of a monomeric flavin active center such as that shown above, since any alternative formulation involving a flavin dimer radical would have a common intermediate in substrate reduction and dithionite reduction.

Another convincing test of the monomeric flavin mechanism of reduction proposed above is that it predicts that full reduction should be obtained by the

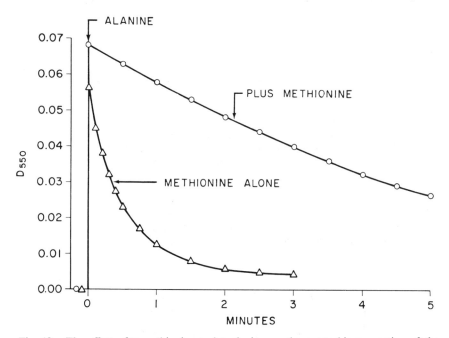

**Fig. 12.** The effect of D-methionine and D-alanine on the anaerobic conversion of the enzyme flavin semiquinone-substrate radical complex to fully reduced enzyme, followed at 550 m$\mu$ with a Gilford-Beckman DU recording spectrophotometer. Benzoate-free enzyme, $3.3 \times 10^{-5}$ $M$ with respect to FAD, in 0.1 $M$ pyrophosphate, pH 8.3, was used at a temperature of 5°. $\triangle$, reaction with $1.67 \times 10^{-3}$ $M$ D-methionine. $\bigcirc$, reaction with $1.67 \times 10^{-3}$ $M$ D-alanine. At the time marked by the arrow, $1.67 \times 10^{-3}$ $M$ D-methionine was added from the second side arm of the anaerobic cuvette.

combination and subsequent reaction of a single molecule of substrate, whereas a flavin dimer radical intermediate mechanism would require two reaction steps involving the binding of substrate. It has been observed (15) that the value of $k_5$ is much greater with methionine as substrate than it is with alanine. The proposed mechanism would predict that once reduction was started with D-alanine the time course of reduction would not be influenced by the subsequent addition of methionine. With the flavin dimer radical postulate, the subsequent addition of methionine would be expected to change the rate of full reduction. Figure 12 shows that, in fact, methionine added after alanine does not influence the rate of conversion of the inter-mediate to the fully reduced enzyme. When air was admitted to the anaerobic cuvette and mixed, the subsequent reduction was biphasic; about 50% of the total change proceeded with a rate constant similar to that with methionine alone, and the remainder at a rate similar to that with alanine. These results are readily explicable in terms of the reduction mechanism proposed and add further support to the previously postulated mechanism of catalysis.

## REFERENCES

1. V. Massey, G. Palmer, and R. Bennett, *Biochim. et Biophys. Acta*, **48**, 1 (1961).
2. P. A. Charlwood, G. Palmer, and R. Bennett, *Biochim. et Biophys. Acta*, **50**, 17 (1961).
3. K. Yagi, T. Ozawa, and T. Ooi, *Biochim. et Biophys. Acta*, **54**, 199 (1961).
4. K. Yagi and T. Ozawa, *Nature*, **193**, 483 (1962).
5. K. Yagi and T. Ozawa, *Biochim. et Biophys. Acta*, **62**, 397 (1962).
6. K. Yagi, T. Ozawa, and T. Ooi, *Biochim. et Biophys. Acta*, **77**, 20 (1963).
7. K. Yagi and T. Ozawa, *Biochim. et Biophys. Acta*, **81**, 599 (1964).
8. K. Yagi and T. Ozawa, *Nature*, **188**, 745 (1960).
9. K. Yagi, T. Ozawa, and M. Harada, *Nature*, **192**, 70 (1961).
10. K. Yagi and T. Ozawa, *Biochim. et Biophys, Acta*, **56**, 420 (1962).
11. K. Yagi and T. Ozawa, *Biochim. et Biophys. Acta*, **60**, 200 (1962).
12. K. Yagi and T. Ozawa, *J. Biochem. (Tokyo)*, **54**, 202 (1963).
13. K. Yagi and T. Ozawa, *J. Biochem. (Tokyo)*, **54**, 204 (1963).
14. K. Yagi and T. Ozawa, *Biochim. et Biophys. Acta*, **67**, 685 (1963).
15. V. Massey and Q. H. Gibson, *Federation Proc.*, **23**, 18 (1964).
16. A. G. Gornall, C. J. Bardawill, and M. M. David, *J. Biol. Chem.*, **177**, 751 (1949).
17. K. Yagi and T. Ozawa, *Biochim. et Biophys. Acta*, **56**, 413 (1962).
18. K. Yagi and T. Ozawa, *Biochim. et Biophys. Acta*, **67**, 319 (1963).
19. V. Massey, *Biochim. et Biophys. Acta*, **37**, 314 (1960).
20. F. L. Crane and H. Beinert, *J. Biol. Chem.*, **218**, 717 (1956).
21. H. Theorell and Å. Åkeson, *Arch. Biochem. Biophys.*, **65**, 439 (1956).
22. F. Märki and C. Martius, *Biochem. Z.*, **333**, 111 (1960).
23. S. Black and B. Hudson, *Biochem. Biophys. Research Communs.*, **5**, 135 (1961).
24. H. A. Harbury, K. F. LaNoue, P. A. Loach, and R. M. Amick, *Proc. Natl. Acad. Sci. U.S.*, **45**, 1708 (1959).
25. C. C. Bigelow and I. I. Geschwind, *Compt. rend. trav. lab. Carlsberg*, **31**, 283 (1960).
26. Q. H. Gibson and L. Milnes, *Biochem. J.*, **91**, 161 (1964).
27. Q. H. Gibson, B. E. P. Swoboda, and V. Massey, *J. Biol. Chem.* **239**, 3927 (1964).
28. V. Massey, *Biochem. J.*, **53**, 72 (1953).
29. M. Dixon and E. C. Webb, *Enzymes*, Academic Press, New York, 1957, pp. 155–170.

*Discussion*

MASSEY: From the results presented in the text I'd like to propose that perhaps as a general phenomenon in enzyme chemistry these temperature breaks, which have been found with many enzymes, may be explained as a configurational change of the protein as a function of temperature around the active center of the enzyme.

We have other illustrations of this; lipoic dehydrogenase, for example, shows exactly the same thing, and we are also investigating fumarase, which was one of the early marked examples of this phenomenon.

RACKER: Is the break only at 14°?

MASSEY: No, it varies from one enzyme to another. I might point out that Scheraga (H. A. Scheraga, *Protein Structure*, Academic Press, New York, 1961, p. 280) has shown that very marked melting points of ribonuclease are obtained. As a function of pH, the "melting point" varies, but clearly ribonuclease undergoes configurational changes as a function of temperature. In this case, there is as yet no correlation attempted with enzymatic activity.

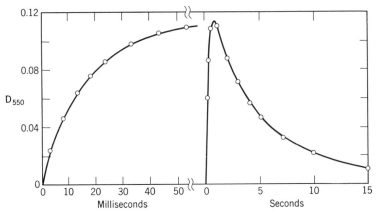

**Fig. 1.** Anaerobic reduction of $1.94 \times 10^{-5}\,M$ D-amino acid oxidase with $5 \times 10^{-4}\,M$ D-methionine in $0.1\,M$ pyrophosphate, pH 8.5 and 19°. The absorbancy changes (550 m$\mu$) are for the 2 cm path length of the stopped-flow apparatus. [From V. Massey and Q. H. Gibson, *Federation Proc.*, **23**, 18 (1964).]

Regarding more specifically the reaction mechanism of D-amino acid oxidase, we were faced with a dilemma when we were originally considering the kinetics of this enzyme. This work is partly published [V. Massey, Q. H. Gibson, and B. Curti, in V. Massey and Q. H. Gibson, *Federation Proc.*, **23**, 18 (1964)]. Figure 1 shows the changes in optical density at 550 m$\mu$ on the anaerobic addition of amino acid to the enzyme. You see the rapid formation of the new long wavelength band which Dr. Ogura has talked about, shown on a millisecond time scale. This intermediate is unstable and decays, however, at a much slower rate, as shown on a time scale of seconds. On the other hand, the rates of formation of these intermediates are extremely rapid. With the three substrates we have investigated in detail, the limiting values range from about 50,000 to 200,000 moles of enzymes converted into this form per minute at 19°. A dilemma is seen if we consider the normal type of kinetic scheme (which has become popular with flavoproteins) whereby we would convert the oxidized enzyme into a reduced form which subsequently reacts with the acceptor. If this is indeed true, one would expect that, as this rate is much faster than the overall catalytic rate of the enzyme in all cases for all amino acids, the rate-limiting step in the reaction would be the reaction with oxygen, and therefore one should observe the same maximum velocity of D-amino acid oxidase with all substrates. But this is not the case. The turnover numbers vary greatly from one amino acid ·to another, e.g., 500 with alanine and 10,000 with proline. Figure 2 shows the intermediate spectra obtained by the stop-flow technique with three amino acids, alanine, proline, and methionine, and you see that they are different. As you will remember from Dr. Ogura's paper, the spectra are also different from the intermediate free radical obtained by titrating the enzyme with dithionite.

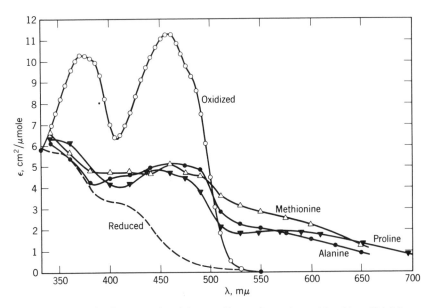

**Fig. 2.** Spectra of substrate-reduced intermediates of D-amino acid oxidase (0.1 $M$ pyrophosphate, pH 8.5, 19°). [From V. Massey and Q. H. Gibson, *Federation Proc.*, **23**, 18 (1964).]

In an attempt to overcome this dilemma, we proposed the reaction mechanism described in the text, whereby we react the flavin with amino acid to obtain a normal Michaelis complex, and from there on one electron transfer from the amino acid to the flavin to give a flavin radical and an amino acid radical. This intermediate one might expect not to have an ESR signal because of spin coupling, and we have not observed a radical signal with this substrate form. Now, as this form of the enzyme would vary depending on the nature of the amino acid, we can overcome our logical dilemma of having different reactivities with oxygen, because the reduced form of the enzyme is not the same with different substrates. We propose then the reaction of oxygen with this radical pair to give a hypothetical oxygen complex followed by the splitting off of hydrogen peroxide, the reoxidation of the flavin, and the conversion to the imino acid. The final stage of the reaction is then the dissociation of the imino acid from the oxidized enzyme.

One characteristic feature of this scheme is that you would expect during the very first turnover of the enzyme a piling up of the intermediate form because production in the first turnover is not rate limiting. The rate-limiting step in this scheme is the dissociation of the imino acid from the reoxidized enzyme. If you look at the time course of the semiquinone formation, in the early stages of the reaction, you see an overproduction of the semiquinone before going down to the steady-state level. As already shown [V. Massey and Q. H. Gibson, *Federation Proc.*, **22**, 467 (1963)], there is extremely good correlation between the observed and the calculated time course of the reaction.

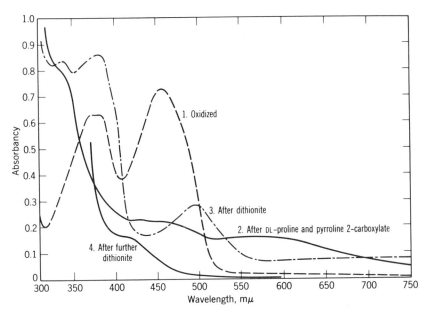

**Fig. 3.** Production of the uncomplexed semiquinone form of D-amino acid oxidase by the addition of dithionite to the substrate-product stabilized intermediate (0.1 $M$ pyrophosphate, pH 8.5, 11°). Curve 1, oxidized enzyme. Curve 2, after the addition of 16 moles D-proline and approximately 400 moles $\Delta'$-pyrroline-2-carboxylic acid. Curve 3, after 95 moles $Na_2S_2O_4$. Curve 4, 18 hr after the addition of a further 500 moles $Na_2S_2O_4$ per mole enzyme-bound flavin.

The thing which has really intrigued us is the nature of this intermediate complex. We have proposed it, of course, as a radical pair, but perhaps it could equally well be a charged transfer complex between the fully reduced flavin and the imino acid. I've examined the model systems to see whether I could demonstrate such complexes between reduced flavins and imino acids and have obtained no evidence whatsoever. This is negative and doesn't mean anything. But if you make the stabilized substrate form by the Kubo method [H. Kubo, H. Watari, and T. Shiga, *Bull. Soc. Chim. Biol.*, **41**, 981 (1959)] of reducing the enzyme and then adding an excess of imino acid, in this case the proline oxidation product, pyrroline 2-carboxolic acid, you obtain the typical substrate spectrum. If you now react this form with dithionite, you produce finally the spectrum of fully reduced enzyme, but in the process of doing so, you go through the spectrum of the uncomplexed flavin semiquinone. Therefore, we feel now reasonably confident that our original description was in fact correct, that the dithionite is reacting preferentially with the amino acid radical, reducing it to proline in this case, and leaving transitorily at least the spectrum of the uncomplexed flavoenzyme semiquinone.

CAUGHEY: This seems an appropriate time to point out something that Dr. Shellenberg and I have reported [*Federation Proc.*, **23**, 479 (1964)] in regard to this intermediate obtained on the dithionite reduction of NAD. If one reduces this N-benzonicotinamide with sodium dithionite under alkaline conditions, as you know, there is a bright yellow intermediate. This yellow intermediate was at first considered to be a free radical, which was then disproved, and more recently it has been considered to be a charge-transfer complex. We investigated the NMR spectra of the oxidized product on the one hand, and the reduced product on the other, and then compared these spectra with those of the intermediate which we could also obtain. This intermediate appeared in every respect compatible with simply the addition of $SO_2$ to the 4-position. What was clear from these NMR studies was the fact that the intermediate was indeed an addition compound and not a charge-transfer complex. I think that it is important to think in terms of Dr. Massey's experiment, the possibility of addition compounds that the amino acid might actually be adding to the flavin. Is this unreasonable?

MASSEY: It is not at all unreasonable. However, such a compound would have to have a structure such that on addition of dithionite the uncomplexed flavin semi-quinone would be formed as an intermediate.

MASON: It seems to me that a diamagnetic spin-paired complex essentially rules out a biradical. And that brings us to a crucial question: What is meant by "charge-transfer complex" in this context?

MASSEY: The term used to describe the substrate-complex of D-amino acid oxidase was "biradical." This was meant to imply some interaction between a flavin radical and an amino acid radical. Clearly we don't know exactly what sort of interaction this is; conceivably it could be a triplet state (in which the difficulty in detecting ESR signals is well established). An alternative possibility is an exchange interaction, which might be expected to result in a sufficient broadening of the ESR spectrum to make detection difficult at the concentrations used. The extreme case of the exchange interaction is of course the formation of a covalent bond: even this possibility cannot be excluded. I suspect that the difficulty between Dr. Mason and me is one of semantics. It seems clear that the intermediate formed is one involving the substrate and a half-reduced flavin. Much further work is required to define this intermediate exactly; in the meantime I hope that the term "biradical" will be acceptable.

MASON: I wonder whether Dr. Orgel might give us, from the point of view of a theoretician, those criteria which must be satisfied in order to call a substance a charge-transfer complex.

ORGEL: I have been asked to give a brief discussion of charge-transfer complexes. To do this I must say something about the history of the subject to show how the definitions arose. The first person to talk about charge-transfer complexes was Robert Mulliken, and the particular observations which led him to the name are ones familiar to all organic chemists. A certain class of molecules, including nitro compounds and quinones, when added to aromatic hydrocarbons, amines, and phenols, gives intensely colored solutions. From these solutions one can obtain well-defined crystalline complexes which are also intensely colored. Now the curious thing about these complexes is that although the spectra, that is, the colors, are completely different from those of the components, there is no evidence at all for any profound chemical interaction between the components. Infrared spectra and all the normal tests for chemical reaction suggest that no chemical reaction has occurred. The heat of formation of these complexes is rarely greater than 5 or 10 kcal, much less than the heat associated with the fomation of a chemical bond.

The contribution that Mulliken made was to point out that the color of a compound depends on the energy needed to convert the molecule from the ground state to an excited state. It is possible that, when two molecules come together, the ground state is not profoundly influenced—no strong chemical bond is formed—but completely new excited states come into existence. Mulliken suggested that if you form a complex DA between an electron donor D and an electron acceptor A, it is possible that when light is absorbed, an electron is transferred from the donor to the acceptor. We can write the reaction $DA \xrightarrow{hv} D^+A^-$.

The appearance of color is unrelated to the strength of the interaction between the donor and the acceptor; it depends on how much energy is required to take an electron away from the donor and give it to the acceptor. Mulliken, therefore, said that the energy of this transition should be related to the difference between the ionization potential of the donor and the electron affinity of the acceptor. If you have a good donor such as tetramethylphenylenediamine and a good acceptor like trinitrobenzene, you require a low energy and find an absorption well in the visible; with a poorer donor, say aniline, and a poor acceptor, say mononitrobenzene, the absorption band is in the ultraviolet.

This is the first criterion required to establish a complex as a charge-transfer complex, namely, that it has a strong absorption band, which is not present in either of the components; the spectrum of the complex is not additive in the sense that it contains, in addition to the spectra of the components, an additional band. When we are dealing with non-biological systems, we can carry out a series of further experiments to test whether we are dealing with a charge-transfer band. For example, we can keep the donor fixed and change the acceptor to increase steadily the electron affinity, by using in turn nitrobenzene, dinitrobenzene, and trinitrobenzene. If the band moves to lower energies along such a series, it is probably a charge-transfer band. In biochemistry this is not usually possible because the necessary substituted components will not enter into the biochemical reactions.

So far I have talked about spectra which provide the main operational criterion for determining whether or not we are dealing with charge-transfer complexes. It is necessary next to clear up the confusion that exists concerning the origin of the stabilization of complexes which exhibit charge-transfer spectra. The forces between molecules are of many different types: normal van der Waals forces, other types of dispersion forces, hydrogen bonding, etc. In addition, there is a charge-transfer contribution to the energy. It is recognized that in most circumstances charge-transfer interaction contributes only a part of the total interaction energy. There are many different sources of interaction energy, even between planar aromatic molecules, and it is only in specially favorable circumstances that charge-transfer energy contributes an extra 2 or 3 kcal of stabilization. Other types of force usually make equal or greater contributions, so I think that it is a mistake to try to be hard and fast in saying that a complex is held together entirely by charge-transfer forces.

To summarize, the first operational test for a charge-transfer complex is whether or not you see a new absorption band; this can be supported by further spectroscopic measurements. The energy contributed by charge-transfer forces is not easily disentangled from other intermolecular forces, although it can be important in stabilizing complexes.

ROSENBERG: I should just like to know whether Dr. Orgel intends to leave the impression that it requires light to form the charge-transfer complex.

ORGEL: No, I had no intention of suggesting that. I said that if you mix the two components together a complex results which can be detected spectroscopically. The complex forms, whether you look at it or not—this is the problem of the light in the refrigerator.

KING: How long is the distance between D and A permissible in structured systems or in any system not in solution?

ORGEL: This question can be answered precisely because a large number of charge-transfer complexes have been studied as crystalline solids. The usual intermolecular distance in the case of two planar aromatic molecules stacked on top of each other is 3.3–3.4 Å.

KING: Not any larger than that?

ORGEL: I think it might go up to 3.5 Å. This is more than twice as long as a covalent bond and is much the same distance as that between two benzene or naphthalene molecules in a crystal.

# Electron Spin Resonance and the Mechanism of Action of Xanthine Oxidase

...R. C. BRAY, G. PALMER, and H. BEINERT

## I. INTRODUCTION

Xanthine oxidase from cows' milk is one of the longest known and most continuously studied of enzymes. Its general properties [cf. (1)] are summarized in Table 1. It contains firmly bound iron, FAD, and molybdenum and has rather a low specificity with regard to both the substrate and the electron acceptor. It has interested enzymologists over the years for quite a variety of

### TABLE 1

#### Properties of Xanthine Oxidase from Milk[a]

| | |
|---|---|
| Molecular weight: | 275,000 |
| Has been obtained: | Crystalline<br>Homogeneous in ultracentrifuge<br>Homogeneous in boundary electrophoresis |
| Contains: | 8 Fe<br>2 FAD  Liberated only on denaturation<br>1–2 Mo |
| Substrates: | Purines (e.g., xanthine and<br>  hypoxanthine)<br>Pteridines<br>Many other heterocyclic  Undergo hydroxylation<br>  compounds<br>RCHO → RCOOH<br>DPNH → DPN |
| Electron acceptors: | $\{O_2$, dyes, cytochrome $c$, nitrate, ferricyanide |

[a] *References:* general: see (1); for molecular weight, see (2).

reasons, and all workers have been helped by the relative ease with which it can be obtained. Much early work was done directly with milk. Now it is a fairly easy matter to obtain xanthine oxidase, by the gram, in an almost pure state (3, 13). Early controversies centered around the question of whether one enzyme could really catalyze the oxidation of both purines and aldehydes. Ultimately, we shall have to know more about its active center before we can understand this phenomenon clearly.

## TABLE 2

### Studies on the Mechanism of Action of Xanthine Oxidase[a]

| | Method | Result | Conclusion |
|---|---|---|---|
| Chemical Methods | 1. Dissociation of cofactors | Irreversible | |
| | 2. Inhibitors | Chelators generally inhibit only weakly; some acceptor specificity (cytochrome $c$) | Metals involved? Different acceptor sites? |
| Physical Methods | 3a. Chemiluminescence (added luminol, etc.) 3b. Chemiluminescence (oxygen radicals?) | Positive | Oxygen radicals involved? |
| (Fast-reaction techniques desirable) | 4. Spectrophotometry | Spectrum complex; rapid changes followed | FAD involved; over-all kinetic constants |
| | 5. Magnetic susceptibility | Large changes (rapid) | Metals involved; radicals outside enzyme? |
| | 6. ESR | Several signals; rapid changes followed | Mo, FADH, Fe involved; probable sequence: Subs. $\rightarrow$ Mo $\rightarrow$ FADH $\rightarrow$ Fe $\rightarrow O_2$ |

[a] *References:* method 1: see (1); method 2: see (1) and (5); method 3a: see (6); method 3b: see (7); method 4: see (8); method 5: see (9) and (10); method 6: see (4), (9), (11–13).

In the late thirties, the FAD content made xanthine oxidase interesting, while in the fifties there was a fresh outburst of attention when it was found to contain molybdenum and then iron. At the present time it is perhaps most interesting from the mechanistic point of view. With one or two other enzymes, all of which are less readily available, xanthine oxidase occupies a unique position between, on the one hand, the simple oxidative enzymes, such as D-amino acid oxidase, which have a single prosthetic group, and, on the other, the complicated particulate enzyme systems of the respiratory chain. Studies on the mechanism of action of an enzyme like xanthine oxidase might therefore help to bridge the gap in our knowledge between these two types. They might show us how electron transfer can take place between three different potentially reducible groups, which are here contained within one well-defined, soluble enzyme molecule.

The aim of mechanistic work on xanthine oxidase in the last few years, then, has been to find out what the molybdenum, flavin, and iron are doing in the molecule. What we wish to know about the mechanism can be summarized as follows:

1. What are the groups in the enzyme which bind the substrate?
2. Which group is first reduced by the substrate?
3. Which groups are subsequently reduced by intramolecular electron transfer?
4. How are the electron acceptors bound and which groups of the reduced enzyme do they reoxidize?
5. When, in the catalytic cycle, do the oxidized substrate and reduced electron acceptor dissociate?
6. Which steps are rate-limiting in the cycle, and what are the velocity constants of the individual steps?

Approaches which have been used in seeking answers to some of these questions are summarized in Table 2, together with results. On the whole, ESR has given the most definitive information, and the remainder of this discussion will be devoted to this technique.

## II. ESR STUDIES OF XANTHINE OXIDASE

Over the past several years ESR spectroscopy [also called EPR; see (11) for discussion of this technique and references] has been applied increasingly to biochemical problems for studying unpaired electrons from organic free radicals and transition metals. The technique is reasonably rapid and is non-destructive of the samples, but its sensitivity is relatively low for enzyme work. Greater sensitivity is achieved, along with other effects, by making measurements near the temperature of liquid nitrogen. The use of an ultra-rapid freezing technique combined with a flow system (Figs. 1a and 1b) has enabled frozen samples for ESR to be obtained after reaction periods as short as 5–10 msec (13–15), thus making rapid kinetic studies possible.

### A. Assignment of ESR Signals

Electron spin resonance signals are characterized by "$g$ values" and also by line width, symmetry, and structure. They are normally plotted as the first derivative of the absorption curve. Figure 2 shows signals obtained from xanthine oxidase after reduction with xanthine. The resting enzyme gives no signal. Figure 2a shows the three basic signals from the enzyme: a symmetrical signal at $g = 2.00$, a somewhat asymmetric one at $g = 1.97$, and a rather broad double signal in the region of $g = 1.9$. This latter signal is very sensitive to temperature and has been detected only in the frozen state, whereas the others have been seen also at room temperature. Before considering the signals themselves in detail, we will discuss their origins.

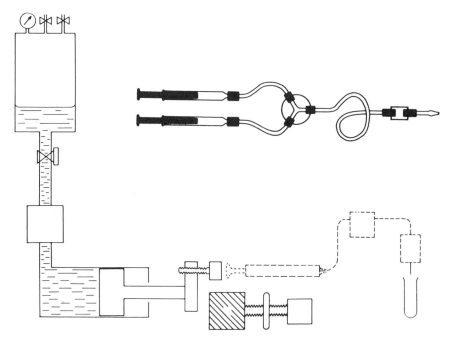

**Fig. 1a.** Diagram of the flow system for ultrarapid freezing. Two syringes containing the reagents are coupled to a fine jet via a mixing chamber and connecting tube. They are driven by a hydraulic system which enables the flow to be accelerated very rapidly, maintained constant until a suitable sample has been delivered from the jet, and then stopped, again very rapidly. (In the lower diagram, the second syringe is behind the first. Furthermore, the jet actually points vertically downward, rather than horizontally as indicated in the upper diagram.) [Reproduced from (14) with the permission of the *Biochemical Journal.*]

Semiquinones in general are known always to have $g$ values close to 2.00. Furthermore, free flavins form semiquinones on half-reduction, and the line width of their ESR signals agrees with that of the $g = 2.00$ signal of xanthine oxidase. We know of no other potential semiquinones in the enzyme, so there is every reason to believe that this signal is due to FADH.

The other two signals are probably too far from $g = 2$ to be due to organic radicals. Molybdenum compounds with valences from 2 to 6 are known, but

$Mo^{2+}$ and $Mo^{3+}$ can be excluded, from a consideration of redox potentials (16). Of the remaining valences, $Mo^{6+}$ and sometimes $Mo^{4+}$ are diamagnetic, whereas $Mo^{5+}$ is paramagnetic. What is more, simple compounds of $Mo^{5+}$ give signals with $g$ values in the range 1.95–1.99. This makes it highly probable that the xanthine oxidase signal at $g = 1.97$ is due to $Mo^{5+}$.

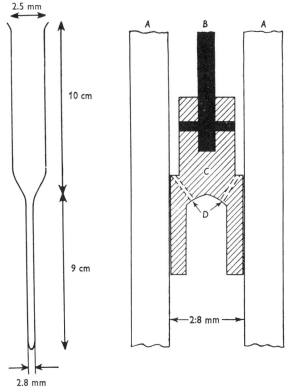

**Fig. 1b.** Diagram of a tube and packing device used for ultrarapid freezing ESR work. The reaction mixture is squirted from the jet (Fig. 1a) into isopentane at −140°C contained in the silica tube shown on the left. The ice crystals are packed into the lower part of the tube before insertion into the ESR cavity by means of the Teflon packing device, which is attached to a stainless steel rod extending to the top of the tube and which is shown on the right. *A*: lower part of silica tube; *B*: stainless steel rod; *C*: Teflon packer; *D*: small holes. [Reproduced from (15) with the permission of the *Biochemical Journal.*]

Further confirmation is provided by the hyperfine structure which we have observed (see below). The third signal is believed to be due to iron in the enzyme. Iron signals tend to be broad, and the temperature behavior of this signal could be consistent with iron. Very similar signals from other iron-containing flavoproteins have been observed by Beinert *et al.* (22).

Figures 2b–d show signals obtained from the enzyme under slightly

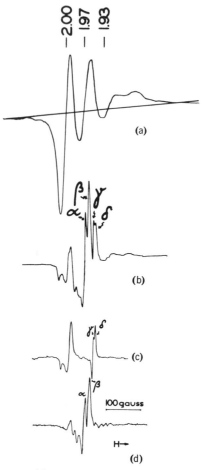

**Fig. 2.** ESR signals from xanthine oxidase reduced with xanthine, measured at about −175°C. The modulation was 12 gauss in (a) and about 4 gauss in (b)–(d). In (a) the enzyme was mixed manually with excess xanthine, whereas in (b)–(d) the rapid mixing and freezing technique (Figs. 1a and 1b) was employed. Signal (b) was obtained after a reaction time of 26 msec at pH 8.3 and 22°, (c) after 21 msec at pH 9.6, and (d) after 71 msec at pH 6.0. [(a) is reproduced from (9) with the permission of the *Biochemical Journal*; (b) and (d) from (4) with the permission of the *Journal of Biological Chemistry*.]

different conditions from those in Fig. 2a. Also, they were all run at higher resolution. It is apparent that the molybdenum signal is not a single peak but is made up of four smaller peaks, labeled α, β, γ, and δ. Most of our work (4, 13) has been carried out at pH 8.2–8.4, where under suitable conditions all four peaks can be seen (Fig. 2b). But at higher pH (Fig. 2c), only the γ and δ show up at short reaction times, while at lower pH (Fig. 2d) the α and β predominate. We have found, in a large number of kinetic experiments (4, 13), that these peaks come and go in pairs, i.e., the $\alpha$ and $\beta$ together and the $\gamma$ and $\delta$ together, and we consider that they correspond to $Mo^{5+}$ in the enzyme in two different states of bonding. The radical and iron signals are weak in Figs. 2b–d, but in other experiments we failed to find any additional structure in them beyond that shown in Fig. 2a. Figure 3 shows the $\gamma$ and $\delta$ molybdenum peaks once again, in a further experiment under alkaline conditions. The other signals are not visible here, but hyperfine structure can be seen clearly in

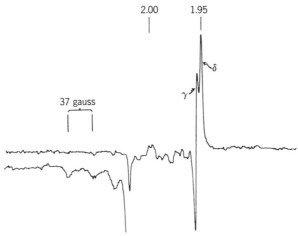

**Fig. 3.** ESR signals from xanthine oxidase reduced with xanthine, measured at about −175°C. The modulation in the main figure was 2.5 gauss. The insert on the bottom left was obtained at increased sensitivity. The xanthine oxidase concentration was 0.63 $mM$, and the reaction conditions were 8 msec at pH 9.6 and 1°C. [Reproduced from (4) with the permission of the *Journal of Biological Chemistry*.]

the form of weak lines on the low-field side of the trace, with a spacing of 37 gauss. This structure is fully in agreement with the hypothesis that the signal is due to molybdenum.

## B. Redox Systems in Xanthine Oxidase

Before we turn to the kinetics of the signals, let us consider some possible redox systems in xanthine oxidase (Fig. 4). Since a $Mo^{5+}$ signal appears on reduction, it would not be unreasonable to think that it is in the diamagnetic hexavalent state in the resting enzyme. However, disruption of the interaction between two pentavalent molybdenums [cf. (17)] within the enzyme molecule by the substrate is another possibility. Slight changes in the bonding of $Mo^{5+}$ in the enzyme during the catalytic reaction could affect the signal substantially, so two forms of $Mo^{5+}$ are shown in Fig. 4 to correspond with the $\alpha$, $\beta$ signal and the $\gamma$, $\delta$ signal.

Reduction of FAD via the semiquinone free radical to the fully reduced form involves no complications. With iron we are not entirely certain which valence is responsible for our signal. Its appearance could in principle be due to changes in bonding rather than to reduction, and it is not even certain that valances higher than three are not involved. On the whole, though, bearing in mind that the signal appears on reduction, we prefer the interpretation that it is due to $Fe^{2+}$. This premise fits in with the increase in susceptibility which

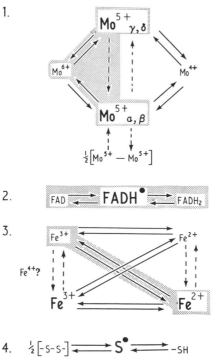

**Fig. 4.** Some possible redox systems in xanthine oxidase. Large type denotes species which might give ESR signals. The most probable reactions are denoted by shaded areas, and non-reductive reactions are indicated by dotted arrows.

takes place on reduction, if we assume that the change is from the low-spin ferric to high-spin ferrous form and that probably only two of the eight iron atoms in the molecule are involved (9). However, little is known about the ESR of iron complexes, and this is not a unique explanation of the origin of the signal.

Figure 4 also shows a sulfur radical as a possible participant [cf. (23, 24)]. However, we have no evidence in favor of this. Sulfur normally seems to give $g$ values rather above 2 [cf. (18)], and most of our signals occur at $g < 2$. Another possible source of ESR signals (not shown in Fig. 4) is oxygen radicals, but here again $g$ values are above 2 (19) and we have no evidence for them in our results.

## C. Kinetics

In regard to the kinetics, Fig. 5 shows one of the most informative experiments which we have carried out. It consisted of treating portions of xanthine oxidase with about 1 mole of xanthine in the presence of an excess of oxygen, for controlled periods of time in the range 10–700 msec, then freezing the

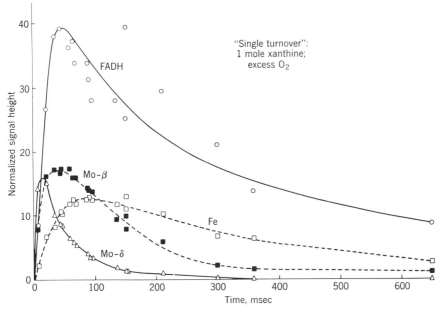

**Fig. 5.** ESR signal heights during a "single turnover" experiment. Samples were frozen, at the times indicated, by the rapid mixing and freezing technique (Figs. 1a and 1b). The pH was 8.3, and the reaction temperature 22°. The concentrations immediately after mixing were as follows: xanthine oxidase, 0.25 $mM$; xanthine, 0.37 $mM$; oxygen, 0.76 $mM$. [Reproduced from (4) with the permission of the *Journal of Biological Chemistry*.]

samples rapidly, and measuring the ESR signal heights. In this "single turnover" experiment, all the signals appeared and disappeared again in times comparable with the turnover time of the enzyme, but they all reached their peaks at different times. The Mo-$\delta$ peaked at 15 msec, the Mo-$\beta$ at 40 msec, the radical at 45 msec, and the iron at 100 msec. Thus, from this experiment, we have evidence, first, that something happens to molybdenum, to flavin, and to iron during one individual catalytic cycle of the enzyme, and, second, that changes in the molybdenum are the first thing we can detect, whereas changes in the iron appear to be the slowest to occur. The great rapidity with which the Mo-$\delta$ signal appears is shown more clearly in an

experiment under different conditions, run at 1° instead of 22°, in order to
slow the reaction down (Fig. 6).

A further experiment is shown in Fig. 7. Here there was a large excess of
xanthine but only 6.3 moles of oxygen. We calculated the time we expected
to be required for all the oxygen to be used up from the activity of the enzyme
in the standard assay system and arrived at a figure of 950 msec, after allowing
for differences of temperature and substrate concentration. The assay was

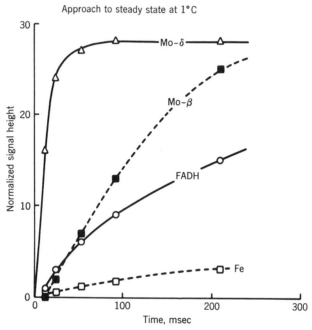

**Fig. 6.** Signal heights during the early stages of reduction of the enzyme to the steady state
at 1°C. The concentrations were as follows: xanthine oxidase, 0.105 $mM$; xanthine,
1.25 $mM$; oxygen, 1.27 $mM$; other conditions were as in Fig. 5. [Reproduced from (4)
with the permission of the *Journal of Biological Chemistry*.]

carried out with about $10^{-7}$ or $10^{-8}$ $M$ xanthine oxidase and the ESR with
about $10^{-4}$ $M$ enzyme, but it is clear that Fig. 7 is entirely consistent with the
oxygen becoming exhausted at about 950 msec. Thus, this experiment, too,
provides direct evidence that the signals are related to the catalytic reaction
and indicates, furthermore, that no inhibitors are present in the enzyme, since
activity is independent of concentration over such a wide range. We therefore
conclude that the changes in the signals correspond to reduction of the enzyme
via a steady-state period to the fully reduced form. Figure 7 shows that in the
steady state the iron signal was about half maximal, while the Mo-$\beta$ signal
was three-quarters maximal. Radicals were present in the steady state but

not at full reduction, and the Mo-$\delta$ was present in substantial amounts only during the approach to the steady-state condition.

We have also carried out (4, 13) a considerable number of other experiments on the enzyme using the same techniques. These have included runs at different pH values and with different substrates, including salicylaldehyde. We have also done anaerobic experiments, both titration type, i.e., varying

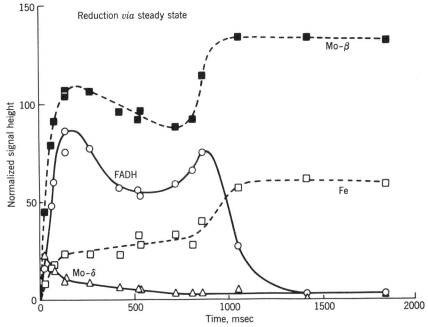

**Fig. 7.** Signal heights during reduction of the enzyme via a steady state. The concentrations were as follows: xanthine oxidase, 0.12 $mM$; xanthine, 1.25 $mM$; oxygen, 0.76 $mM$; all other conditions were as in Fig. 5. [Reproduced from (4) with the permission of the *Journal of Biological Chemistry*.]

the amount of substrate and using a fixed reaction time, and also time-course experiments. Anaerobic titrations at 102 msec and 550 msec are shown in Figs. 8 and 9. At the shorter time the radical signal was maximal with 1–2 moles xanthine and did not decrease with excess substrate, but the longer time was sufficient for full reduction of the flavin to take place, so that the radical was weak when more than 2–3 moles of xanthine was present. At present, detailed interpretation of the anaerobic experiments is not easy, however. It should be borne in mind that what occurs anaerobically is not necessarily particularly relevant to the catalytic cycle, since, in order to achieve full reduction of all the reducible groups in the molecule, extra substrate molecules have to be bound, and some of these may combine with quite low

dissociation constants. Furthermore, before the interpretation of stoichiometric aspects is taken too far, we shall have to know the reason why xanthine
oxidase has always, so far, appeared to have a non-integral molybdenum
content.

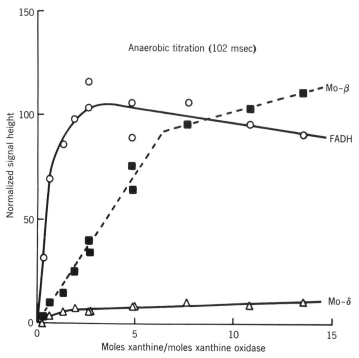

**Fig. 8.** Signal heights in an anaerobic titration of the enzyme, as a function of xanthine
concentration, measured after $102 \pm 9$ msec of reaction. The xanthine oxidase concentration was 0.093 $mM$, and the conditions were as in Fig. 5. [Reproduced from (4) with the
permission of the *Journal of Biological Chemistry*.]

## D. Conclusions Derived from ESR Studies

What, then, can be concluded from the ESR results? First, they leave little
room for doubt that molybdenum, flavin, and iron are all intimately involved
in the catalytic cycle. Second, they make it rather clear that whatever happens
to the molybdenum to produce the $Mo^{5+}$-$\gamma,\delta$ signal occurs at a very early
point in the cycle. Third, it seems equally clear that the change in the iron
takes place relatively late in the cycle. Beyond these three conclusions we are
on less certain ground, and no more direct deductions seem to be possible
from the data. To proceed further, the best we can do is to add a number of
plausible assumptions to our three conclusions and with their aid set up a
model reaction scheme for the catalytic cycle. We can then see whether

predictions made with the aid of the model are consistent with the quantitative data we have. If they are consistent, then the model still may or may not be an accurate one. But if they are not consistent, then the model is obviously wrong, and we must think again.

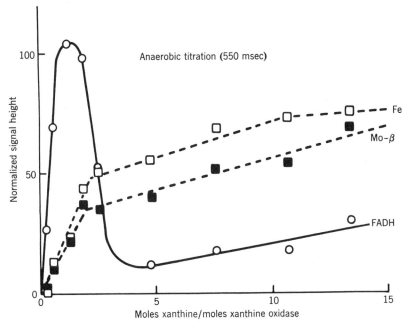

**Fig. 9.** Signal heights in an anaerobic titration of the enzyme, as a function of xanthine concentration, measured after $550 \pm 30$ msec of reaction. The xanthine oxidase concentration was 0.093 $mM$, and the conditions were as in Fig. 5. [Reproduced from (4) with the permission of the *Journal of Biological Chemistry*.]

## III. PROPOSED MODELS

Absolute quantitation of the ESR signals is difficult, and the problems are increased by ambiguity regarding the molybdenum content. Let us start, however, by assuming that we have two independent active centers in the xanthine oxidase molecule, each containing one molybdenum and one FAD atom and four iron atoms, only one of which is involved in electron transfer. Let us assume further that the ESR signals arise from the reactions shown in the shaded areas of Fig. 4. Most of the reasons for preferring these reactions have already been discussed. The little that is known about the redox potential of the $Mo^{6+}$-$Mo^{5+}$ system (16) indicates that it could well be operating in xanthine oxidase catalysis; hence, it is preferred to the alternative $Mo^{5+}$-$Mo^{5+}$ interaction scheme. It should also be noted that the (non-reductive) transformation of $Mo^{5+}$-$\gamma$,$\delta$ into $Mo^{5+}$-$\alpha$,$\beta$ is shown to be irreversible, in keeping with the transient existence of the former signals.

If we now combine our assumptions with the observation that the $Mo^{5+}$-$\gamma$,$\delta$ signal appears early and the iron signal late, the only simple conclusion we can reach is that we have electron transfer from substrate to molybdenum, to flavin, to iron, and thence to oxygen. These reactions must all be single electron transfers, and we note that each active center must be capable of accepting a maximum of four electrons, i.e., one each for the molybdenum and the iron and two for the FAD. Such a mechanism would of necessity mean that xanthine and oxygen radicals were involved. There is no evidence from the ESR work for either of these, but the possibility of their participation is not thereby excluded, since they might be so labile as to be lost in the quenching process. Furthermore, chemiluminescence has been considered evidence for the participation of oxygen radicals (6, 7), and susceptibility measurements (10) also gave indications of radicals outside the enzyme.

If we try to put this model into quantitative terms, we face two difficulties. The first is essentially mathematical. The minimum number of enzyme intermediates which we have to reckon with, in the stepwise four-electron reduction of each active center, turns out to be thirteen, even when we simplify by ignoring Michaelis complexes. The number of velocity constants for the various reactions is correspondingly large, and although it is a simple matter to write down appropriate differential equations, it is not so easy to solve them. An analog computer seems the best way, but a fairly large one is required.

Secondly, it is obvious from our model that at full reduction we would expect the iron and the Mo-$\beta$ signals to be maximally developed. Figure 7 shows that this is indeed the case. However, when we carry out the normal double integration procedure and the comparison of the signal with a standard, which is required for absolute intensity measurement, we find that the intensity of the $Mo^{5+}$-$\alpha$,$\beta$ signal is only about one-third of what it should be. Similarly, for the iron (allowing for four unpaired electrons) we have an even bigger discrepancy, and in this case the signal is only about one-eighth of what we should have expected (4, 13). What these discrepancies mean we do not know. They could simply be due to experimental errors, but this is not certain. If we ignore them, then we can simply take the ratio of observed signal height to maximum signal height as giving us the proportion of the metal in the signal-giving form, under any experimental conditions. But in ignoring the discrepancy we may, of course, be misleading ourselves. For the $Mo^{5+}$-$\gamma$,$\delta$ and FADH signals, we have no experimental conditions under which we would expect to find 100% signal development, so here quantitation is even more difficult.

It seems, then, that converting signal heights into actual proportions of the constituents of the enzyme in the signal-giving forms must at present involve a certain amount of uncertainty and guesswork. Nevertheless, we are continuing work on these lines in order to test our model reaction scheme as far as possible. Preliminary analog computer studies have indicated that the single turnover data of Fig. 5 are both qualitatively and quantitatively consistent with the model. We hope that future work will enable us either to present this model with greater confidence or else to propose a better one.

## IV. COMMENTS

Finally, even though the proposed electron-transfer pathway from substrate, to molybdenum, to flavin, to iron, to oxygen is still not absolutely established, some comments on its implications may be in order. One interesting point is the way in which organic compounds and metals alternate with one another in the pathway. Perhaps it is not surprising that molybdenum should turn out to be the first reactant. Purines seem to be tightly bound to the enzyme, possibly because of chelation with molybdenum. Consideration of the acid dissociation constants of FAD and its derivatives shows that the reaction between $Mo^{5+}$ and flavin to form the flavin semiquinone would be a simple electron-transfer reaction not involving the movement of protons, except at low pH. Such reactions would be expected to be rapid (20).

The position of iron as the constituent apparently reacting with oxygen is interesting, but how and why it fulfills this role in xanthine oxidase unfortunately remains quite obscure. Many iron-free flavoproteins do, of course, react rapidly with oxygen, and conversely preliminary results (21) on xanthine dehydrogenase from chicken liver show that this enzyme, which reacts only very slowly with oxygen, also, rather disappointingly, gave iron ESR signals, which appeared at about the same rate as they did with the oxidase. However, so far the detailed kinetics of the signals from the chicken enzyme has not been studied, so there may be differences between the two enzymes which did not show up in this preliminary work.

## REFERENCES

1. R. C. Bray, in P. D. Boyer, H. Lardy, and K. Myrbäck, Eds., *The Enzymes*, Vol. 7, Academic Press, 1963, p. 533.
2. P. Andrews, R. C. Bray, P. Edwards, and K. V. Shooter, *Biochem. J.*, **93**, 627 (1964).
3. D. A. Gilbert and F. Bergel, *Biochem. J.*, **90**, 350 (1964).
4. R. C. Bray, G. Palmer, and H. Beinert, *J. Biol. Chem.*, **239**, 2667 (1964).
5. I. Fridovich and P. Handler, *J. Biol. Chem.*, **237**, 916 (1962).
6. J. R. Trotter, E. C. De Dugros, and C. Riviero, *J. Biol. Chem.*, **235**, 1839 (1960).

7. J. Stauff, H. Schmidkunz, and G. Hartmann, *Nature*, **198**, 281 (1963).
8. H. Gutfreund and J. M. Sturtevant, *Biochem. J.*, **73**, 1 (1959).
9. R. C. Bray, R. Pettersson, and A. Ehrenberg, *Biochem. J.*, **81**, 178 (1961).
10. E. Ackermann and A. Brill, *Biochim. et Biophys. Acta*, **56**, 397 (1962).
11. R. C. Bray, B. G. Malmström, and T. Vänngård, *Biochem. J.*, **73**, 193 (1959).
12. R. C. Bray, *Biochem. J.*, **81**, 196 (1961).
13. G. Palmer, R. C. Bray, and H. Beinert, *J. Biol. Chem.*, **239**, 2657 (1964).
14. R. C. Bray, *Biochem. J.*, **81**, 189 (1961).
15. R. C. Bray and R. Pettersson, *Biochem. J.*, **81**, 194 (1961).
16. R. J. P. Williams, in S. Kirschner, Ed., *Advances in the Chemistry of Co-ordination Compounds*, Macmillan, New York, 1961, p. 65.
17. L. Sacconi and R. Cini, *J. Am. Chem. Soc.*, **76**, 4239 (1954).
18. T. Henriksen, in M. S. Blois *et al.*, Eds., *Free Radicals in Biological Systems*, Academic Press, New York, 1961, p. 279.
19. S. J. Wyard and R. C. Smith, *6th International Symposium on Free Radicals, Cambridge, 1963*, Abstract AD.
20. A. Ehrenberg, *Arkiv Kemi*, **19**, 97 (1962).
21. Unpublished experiments in collaboration with W. J. De Angelis and J. R. Totter, cited in ref. 4.
22. H. Beinert, W. Heinen, and G. Palmer, in "Enzyme Models and Enzyme Structure," *Brookhaven Symposia in Biol.*, No. **15**, 229 (1962).
23. V. Massey and Q. H. Gibson, *Federation Proc.*, **23**, 18 (1964).
24. P. Handler, K. V. Rajagopalan, and V. Aleman, *Federation Proc.*, **23**, 30 (1964).

*Discussion*

HANDLER: I have some reservations concerning the results reported by Dr. Bray, and these same reservations are applicable to our own studies on aldehyde oxidase. In these studies the time is stated to be milliseconds, that is, the time which elapsed from the instant the substrate was mixed with the enzyme to the instant it was frozen. However, the actual time elapsing between the instant it was frozen and the instant when the signal was recorded in the instrument is entirely different. It is minutes, not milliseconds. Now, the warning which is available to us comes from the photo-oxidation of cytochrome *f*, which has been accomplished in a photosynthetic system at liquid-nitrogen temperature. What bothers me is the extent to which we are being misled by events which may have happened in the enzyme in that frozen condition at liquid-nitrogen temperature so as to disturb the actual kinetic course which seems to be evidence in experiments such as this. Can we have confidence in the findings?

BRAY: I think that, if we looked at the intensities of signals from samples that had been stored for different times, from the freezing to the measuring in the ESR apparatus, we would get no evidence for changes. I think that the times varied from a few minutes up to 24 hr or more, and we have had no indications whatever of changes occurring within these periods.

EHRENBERG: It seems that all these experiments are made at low temperatures. To what extent are the low-temperature measurements relevant to the solution at 20°? Many things can happen when you freeze a protein solution. You can have conformational changes in a system with closely situated redox compounds. You could have a change in the equilibrium with the temperature. You could also have changes of ionization, as Dr. Estabrook whispered in my ear.

Figure 1 shows an example of what could happen in a system where you see nothing at room temperature, but a great difference at the low temperature. The middle curve is at pH 8, at liquid-nitrogen temperature. In the ESR we see the $g = 6$ signal and also a small $g = 4$ signal which I believe is an impurity. When we add a little ammonia at room temperature, we see little or no spectral change. But at liquid-nitrogen temperature, the upper curve shows a completely low spin

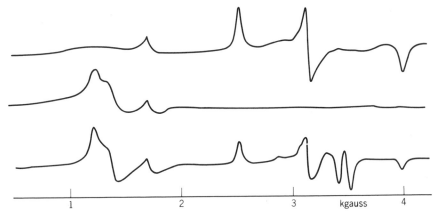

**Fig. 1.** ESR spectra of catalase from *Micrococcus lyseidikticus*, $C_{Fe} = 0.85$ $mM$, frozen and measured at 77°K. Middle curve: 80 $mM$ EDTA, pH 8.7. Upper curve: same sample as middle curve added with 100 $mM$ NH$_3$. Lower curve: unbuffered weakly ammoniacal solution before dialysis against EDTA. (A. Ehrenberg, in preparation.)

form. The lower curve shows that we can have intermediate types with both high and low spin. We should not look at all the small things just above the assignment kilogauss that come from an impurity of copper. In some experiments we did with Dr. Bray, this was found to be true in xanthine oxidase.

Figure 2 shows that there is a quite good correlation in this case with the height of the signal at $g = 1.9$ measured at low temperature on the abscissa and the susceptibility measured at 12°. There is a good correlation between these two parameters, so I think that in this case we have evidence that for the iron low-temperature measurements are also applicable to the higher temperature in the solution.

KING: How do you visualize the distance between, say, molybdenum, FAD, and iron?

BRAY: We will leave that question for theoretical people. Until more information is available, we just present these results and leave someone else to work out the answers.

KING: What is the distance between the different species for so-called "charge transfer"?

HANDLER: Nobody has the answer. I can only tell you that we have just embarked on a program of investigating both dihydroorotic dehydrogenase and

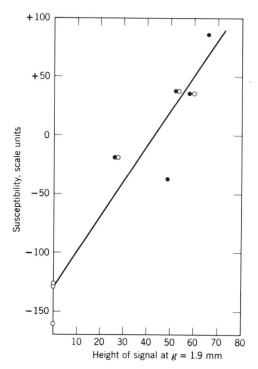

**Fig. 2.** Relationship between magnetic susceptibility increment and ESR signal in the region of $g = 1.9$, during anaerobic titration of xanthine oxidase with xanthine. The susceptibility measurements were made at 12°C after incubating enzyme and substrate for 10 min at the same temperature. ESR was measured at 77°K. ○: samples frozen after incubating for 5 min at 12°C (i.e., frozen at the time of filling the susceptometer tube). ●: samples frozen after 15 min at 12°C (i.e., samples removed from the susceptometer tube after measurement). (A. Ehrenberg and B. Bray, in preparation.)

xanthine oxidase by x-ray crystallography. It has taken a year to grow a crystal of dihydroorotic dehydrogenase big enough to give to a crystallographer, and we have used up almost 1500 gallons of culture in order to do it. Hopefully, when this work is done, we can tell you the answer.

KING: Are you willing to propose semiconductance?

HANDLER: Wait until we see what the data look like.

CHANCE: I wish to return to the question of changes in steady-state levels in freezing. So far only the respiratory chain has been found to have steady states which are relatively insensitive to temperature; we get the same ratios of oxidized-reduced states on freezing because the temperature coefficients of the intercarrier reactions are very similar.

As for Dr. King's question about the nature of the species, an independent control, such as magnetic susceptibility, is required.

Dr. Bray, you have made excellent studies that are certainly complete in themselves, yet I feel very strongly that for an evaluation of the mechanisms for enzymatic reactions, and particularly for determining reaction sequences, one must determine whether the rates of reaction of the intermediates are consistent with the rates of the over-all reaction. I hope that you determine the rate of formation of uric acid under your conditions and compare it with the rates of change of the intermediates measured in the ESR.

BRAY: No actual measurements of uric acid were made during the experiments. However, in Fig. 7 (p. 369 of this book), the steady-state-going-to-full-reduction experiment, the time calculated for exhaustion of oxygen (by extrapolating from the ordinary enzyme assay at about $10^{-7}$ $M$ enzyme, to the ESR conditions, which were about $10^{-4}$ $M$ enzyme), agreed exactly with the ESR data. We expected the oxygen to be exhausted at approximately 1 sec, and this was just about the point where the signals changed to the form we expected at full reduction.

CHANCE: In other words, the rate of oxygen reduction was no faster than the rate of reduction of any of the intermediates?

BRAY: Yes.

ESTABROOK: On Fig. 4 Dr. Bray, you indicated the formation of a sulfide radical as a possible intermediate. Yet I note that this is never included in any of the mechanisms. I wonder whether there is any evidence for or against this radical. Where do you put it, in terms of the reaction sequence?

BRAY: There is no evidence for or against. No ESR signals which we would ascribe to sulfur radicals have been detected.

MASSEY: About the question of sulfur radical, I should like to bring up the general possibility that the $g = 1.94$ signal which is being ascribed to iron here is really a form of sulfur radical associated with the iron in these proteins, as Dr. King has been pointing out from time to time during the meeting. All of these metalloflavoproteins do contain labile sulfide. Succinic dehydrogenase was the first of these to be demonstrated, a long time ago, and all these enzymes contain this labile sulfide; furthermore, it is there in stoichiometric amounts with the iron. Our work on the valence state of the iron, although admittedly subject to objections such as Dr. Beinert is going to bring up in the ceruloplasmin story, certainly indicates, when we try to do determination by chemical methods, that the iron just is not reduced fast enough to be involved in the catalysis with these enzymes. I should like to propose the possibility that what is being seen as the $g = 1.94$ signal is a form of ferric iron and sulfide radical. In other words, I suggest bringing both these observations together because, while we cannot prove the presence of sulfur radical, I believe nobody has yet given a convincing demonstration that our chemical analyses are incorrect.

The second point I should like to make concerns xanthine oxidase. Dr. Brumby in my laboratory has shown, in agreement with the results of Fridovich and Handler [*J. Biol. Chem.*, **237**, 916 (1962)], that, when you react xanthine oxidase with $p$-chloromercuribenzoate ($p$-CMB), there is no inactivation of the enzyme unless substrate is present. When $p$-CMB is added in excess and the treated enzyme passed through Sephadex to remove the excess $p$-CMB, there is no inactivation of the enzyme. If you do exactly the same experiment anaerobically with substrate added and then pass the enzyme through Sephadex, you find an almost complete loss of activity. In other words, the substrate has induced a new sulfhydryl or sulfur-reacting group with $p$-CMB, and this may possibly be some form of this labile sulfur.

BEINERT: It seems hard to decide where to start in view of all these "incrimin-ations." We are, of course, aware of the limitations of the freezing technique. We have stated this in publications and will continue to do so in the future, but in some cases you have to do the best you can. In cases where you investigate highly temperature-sensitive signals, there is not much else you can do but resort to low temperatures. I also want to point out that in some enzymes the kinetics of the iron and of the flavin go very closely parallel. This finding is open to the inter-pretation that equilibration occurs in the frozen state in such cases, a possibility which we cannot, of course, rule out. On the other hand, if equilibration between carriers does indeed occur in the frozen state, this would mean that these carriers communicate very closely and that there is an interaction between them.

In regard to the last comments of Dr. Massey, I wonder how the existence of a sulfur radical, or, let's say, the notion that a sulfur radical should be responsible for the 1.94 signal, could be reconciled with the definite effect of $^{57}$Fe substitution on the ESR signal that we find? Does Dr. Massey think the signal could be due to $Fe^{3+}$ and the sulfur radical? I would not object to this interpretation as long as the signal is due to iron.

BRAY: May I add two very small points? One is that I think all sulfur radicals which are known have $g$ values greater than 2 rather than less. The second point is that I'd like to ask Dr. Massey whether, in fact, it is true that Dr. Brumby's work with xanthine oxidase on the colorimetric determination of reduction of iron in the presence of the substrate didn't show a few per cent reduction, immediately on adding the substrate—something of the order of 3 %, I believe. I think that may be enough to be significant, since we are only suggesting reduction of two out of the eight iron atoms, and I believe Brumby and Massey's liver enzyme had only the order of a third of the specific activity of the milk enzyme, so that only a small amount of reduction of iron would in any case be expected, according to our results.

MASSEY: First, I don't see what specific activity has to do with the question. These are two different enzymes isolated from two sources. Second, the results show that one of the four irons is reduced very slowly over a period of about 24 hr. We have no difficulty in demonstrating the reduction. It just goes extremely slowly. The accuracy of the method is not great enough to know whether 3 % change is significant or not. We have on occasion observed 2 or 3 % changes. But I don't know that that's significant.

HANDLER: I want it understood that when I posed this question about freezing, I thought I was raising a straw man. The problem is real, but I do not think that it offers reasons to challenge the kinetics scheme presented by Drs. Bray and Beinert. I believe that scheme is quite correct because of the indirect evidence that one can demonstrate by other techniques that molybdenum is indeed the first thing to be reduced. In aldehyde oxidase, which does not show a flavin free radical during reduction, one can follow spectrophotometrically the reduction of the iron, and the rate of this reduction satisfies the kinetic requirements. One can show that this rate is equivalent to $V$ for that enzyme under optimal circumstances. There is indeed a sulfhydryl group which is accessible to $p$-CMB only in the presence of substrate and not in its absence or reduced form. When the enzyme is so treated, it can no longer react with substrate, suggesting that the sulfhydryl must be very close to the substrate binding site. It can't be behind the flavin where the iron is. It has to be in front of it where the flavin is.

Finally, as to whether or not the iron is reduced, you can switch the dihydroorotic dehydrogenase, which has only two irons, and when it is reduced by either substrate and allowed to equilibrate, one-half of those irons are in a reduced form.

SINGER: Returning to the question of whether the iron signal is equatable with sulfur free-radical signal, I should like to mention some recent data. Dr. Carol Lusty in our laboratory has followed the thermal degradation of DPNH dehydrogenase to DPNH cytochrome reductase, a process wherein the loss of ESR signal precisely follows the drop in the turnover number of the enzyme. She finds that iron is indeed lost from the protein at a rate commensurate with loss of ferricyanide activity and, hence, of ESR signal. Labile sulfur, however, is lost much more slowly. So the height of the ESR signal does seem to agree with the quantity of functional iron remaining, but not with the quantity of labile sulfide remaining. In the untreated enzyme the ratio of labile sulfide to iron is nearly stoichiometric.

# On the Mechanism of Action of Metalloflavoproteins*

... VICTOR ALEMAN-ALEMAN, K. V. RAJAGOPALAN,
and PHILIP HANDLER with HELMUT BEINERT
and GRAHAM PALMER

## I. INTRODUCTION

This laboratory has been engaged in a continuing study of the structure and function of a series of seemingly related metalloflavoproteins (1). This report will summarize a series of findings concerning (*a*) the operation of dihydrorotic acid dehydrogenase, perhaps the simplest of such enzymes, (*b*) information gained by study of the optical rotatory dispersion of iron proteins, (*c*) the role of molybdenum in molybdoflavoproteins, and (*d*) will describe some experiments which relate to the mechanism of action of cytochrome *c* oxidase.

## II. STUDIES OF DIHYDROOROTIC ACID DEHYDROGENASE

Dihydroorotic acid dehydrogenase, originally observed by Kornberg and his colleagues (2), was purified by Friedman and Vennesland (3), who demonstrated that the enzyme contains one molecule each of FAD and FMN and two atoms of iron. Our attention was directed to this enzyme because of the relative simplicity of its composition and the fact that, although it serves as a dehydrogenase, reversibly transferring electrons from DPNH to orotic acid, the enzyme, reduced by substrate, is rather rapidly reoxidized by atmospheric oxygen.

### A. Dihydroorotic Acid Dehydrogenase as an Iron Protein

Previous studies from this laboratory had indicated that oxygen radicals are generated during aerobic oxidation of the reduced forms of xanthine and

* This paper was not available in the preprints. Copies of the manuscript were presented to participants at the time of the meeting.

aldehyde oxidases (1). This was demonstrated by three independent techniques: initiation of the autoxidation of sulfite, obligatory dependence upon molecular oxygen in order to effect the reduction of cytochrome $c$, and the appearance of chemiluminescence when these enzymes are engaged in the aerobic oxidation of substrate in the presence of such materials as luminol. As shown in Figs. 1 and 2, dihydroorotic acid dehydrogenase (DHOD) shows

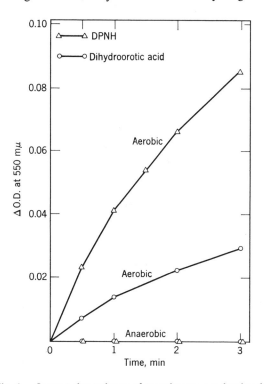

**Fig. 1.** Oxygen dependence of cytochrome $c$ reduction by DHOD.

essentially similar characteristics; it is absolutely dependent on atmospheric oxygen in order to accomplish reduction of cytochrome $c$ and can effect the initiation of sulfite oxidation. Both processes are inhibited by tiron (a catechol sulfonic acid) and myoglobin, but this enzyme is not quite as sensitive as are aldehyde and xanthine oxidases to such inhibition. This information strongly suggested that the molecular arrangement of and about the iron atoms might well be similar to that in the previously studied oxidases and that oxidation of reduced enzyme by oxygen is accomplished by electron transfer from the iron components of the enzyme to molecular oxygen. This possibility was further indicated by the fact that the absorptivity per iron atom, at both 450 and 550 m$\mu$, was identical to that observed with these other

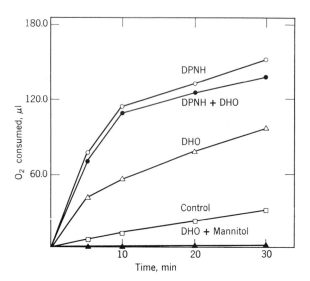

**Fig. 2.** Initiation of sulfite oxidation by DHOD in the presence of substrate.

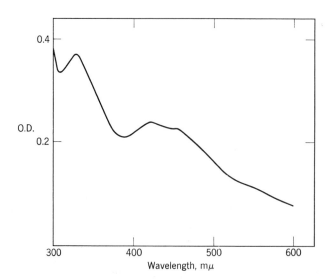

**Fig. 3.** Absorption spectrum of flavin-free DHOD. Flavin was removed by extracting with 75% of methanol at 0°C. The precipitate was dissolved in 0.2 $M$ phosphate, pH 5.8, containing 3.5 $M$ urea.

oxidases. In Fig. 3 is shown the absorption spectrum of the flavin-free, pure iron protein prepared from DHOD by precipitation with 75% methanol. This absorption spectrum is strikingly similar to those previously described for the equivalent iron proteins of xanthine and aldehyde oxidase (1).

### B. Role of Sulfhydryl Groups in Dihydroorotic Acid Dehydrogenase

Data previously presented indicated that both xanthine and aldehyde oxidases are sulfhydryl enzymes, that the sulfhydryl groups important in these enzymes are at or very close to the substrate-binding sites, and that

### TABLE 1

#### Relative Rates of Reactions Catalyzed by Dihydroorotic Acid Dehydrogenase[a]

The assay systems included, in a volume of 3.0 ml, the following: for DPNH oxidation (at pH 6.5), 0.35 $\mu$mole DPNH, 1.2 $\mu$moles orotate, and 4–20 $\mu$g enzyme; for DHOA oxidation (at pH 8.2), 1.0 $\mu$mole DPN, 4.5 $\mu$moles DHOA, and 20–70 $\mu$g enzyme. 20 $\mu$moles cysteine were used when indicated.

| Reaction | Native Enzyme | Native Enzyme + Cysteine | 1 Mole of p-CMB Enzyme | Oxidized Enzyme | Oxidized Enzyme + Cysteine |
|---|---|---|---|---|---|
| 1. DPNH → Orotate (anaerobic) | 100[b] | 200 | 42 | | |
| 2. DPNH → Orotate (aerobic) | 164 | 218 | 33 | 36 | 47.7 |
| 3. DPNH → O₂ | 105 | 61.2 | 66 | 99 | 75 |
| 1. DHOA → DPN (anaerobic) | 100[c] | 310 | 53 | 55 | 119 |
| 2. DHOA → DPN (aerobic) | 77.5 | 360 | 85 | | |
| 3. DHOA → O₂ | 16.5 | 31 | 18 | | |

[a] The anaerobic reduction of orotate by DPNH is taken as standard = 100.
[b] $\Delta$ O.D. at 340.
[c] $\Delta$ O.D. at 340 or 282 m$\mu$.

when attacked by reagents such as p-CMB, activity is completely destroyed. The sulfhydryl groups of DHOD do not appear to be at the substrate binding site but are rather remarkably significant in the function of this enzyme. Friedman and Vennesland (3) observed that the rate of catalysis of the dehydrogenase reaction in both directions was enhanced markedly by cysteine and that the rate of bleaching of the enzyme by dihydroorotate, observed at 450 m$\mu$, was rather slow in the absence of cysteine and quite rapid in its presence (3). As shown in Table 1, the addition of cysteine to the enzyme, in the state in which it is isolated, approximately doubles the rate of the dehydrogenase reaction, when followed in either direction. However, it is significant that, whereas the addition of cysteine also doubles the rate of aerobic oxidation of dihydroorotate, it reduces by half the rate of aerobic oxidation of DPNH.

Undoubtedly related to these observations is the fact that a relatively inactive form of the enzyme can be prepared by exposure of a dilute solution of the enzyme at pH 8.5 to air for some time. Such a preparation is enfeebled with respect to the dehydrogenase reaction; activity is largely restored by subsequent treatment with cysteine. Accordingly it appeared of interest to study the behavior of the enzyme with sulfhydryl reagents such as $p$-CMB

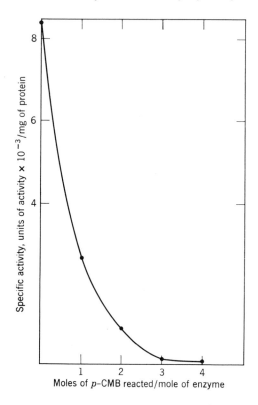

Moles of $p$-CMB reacted/mole of enzyme

**Fig. 4.** Effect of $p$-CMB on the catalytic activities of DHOD. Extent of reaction of $p$-CMB with enzyme was determined directly by increase in O.D. at 250 m$\mu$. ·———·, enzyme and $p$-CMB reacted in phosphate buffer, pH 7.0, 0.2 $M$, at 25°C. Enzyme activity was measured in terms of change in O.D. at 282 m$\mu$.

and NEM. Some of these data are summarized in Table 1 and in Fig. 4. Titration by the Boyer procedure revealed the presence of four sulfhydryl groups per mole (62,000 grams/mole). As such a titration proceeds, the enzyme remains in solution and the reaction can be followed until addition of a fifth mole of $p$-CMB per mole of enzyme, whereupon the enzyme precipitates. Similar treatment with NEM reveals only two sulfhydryl groups reactive within a few minutes, and subsequent reaction is extremely slow.

When the enzymic activities of these preparations were examined, the data strongly suggested that the attack of a single $p$-CMB molecule on an enzyme molecule results in complete abolition of the dehydrogenase reaction. This is not actually observed, presumably because of the essentially equal reactivity of the four sulfhydryl groups on each molelule, so that, after addition of a mole of reagent, some molecules of enzyme have been attacked more than once while a small fraction has not been affected, and the residual activity reflects the latter species. The course of the dihydroorotic acid → $O_2$ reaction is affected by $p$-CMB in a manner essentially identical with the dehydrogenase reaction. In contrast, $p$-CMB attack upon the enzyme has a much smaller effect on the DPNH → $O_2$ reaction. The sum of such observations suggests that all four sulfhydryl groups, or at least those most readily attacked by sulfhydryl reagents, must be in the sulfhydryl condition for the flow of electrons from DPNH to orotic acid, or the reverse reaction, to proceed. These sulfhydryl groups are equally essential to the flow of electrons from dihydroorotic acid to oxygen but are of relatively little consequence to the flow of electrons from DPNH to oxygen.

$$\begin{array}{l} \text{DPNH} \\ \qquad\qquad \text{FAD} \rightleftharpoons \text{Fe} - \text{Fe} \rightleftharpoons \text{FMN} \\ \text{DPN} \end{array} \begin{array}{l} \text{Orotate} \\ \\ \text{DHOA} \end{array}$$

$$\begin{array}{l} \text{DPNH} \\ \qquad\qquad \text{FAD} \rightleftharpoons \text{Fe} - \text{Fe} = = \rightleftharpoons \text{FMN} \\ \text{DPN} \end{array} \begin{array}{l} \text{Orotate} \\ \\ \text{DHOA} \end{array}$$

Although the sulfhydryl group(s) is clearly important to enzyme function, there is no evidence that it actually participates in electron transfer. Oxidation of these groups, or attack by sulfhydryl reagents, may instead impair enzymic function entirely by conformational changes in the protein. In the hope of observing such changes, $p$-CMB-treated enzyme was compared with native enzyme in the analytical ultracentrifuge and by study of its optical rotatory dispersion. However, no significant differences were observed.

### C. Reduction of the Enzyme by Its Substrates

Figure 5 depicts rather striking differences which were observed when comparing the reduction of reagent quantities of DHOD by each of its substrates. Whereas addition of 1 mole of dihydroorotic acid per mole of enzyme results in a diminution of absorbancy at 450 m$\mu$ approximately equivalent to that expected for the complete bleaching of a single flavin, an equivalent addition of DPNH results in a diminution in absorbancy of less than half that magnitude (35–40%). This suggests that reaction of the enzyme with 1 mole of dihydroorotic acid results in the formation of one fully reduced flavin moiety, whereas the equivalent amount of DPNH results in the

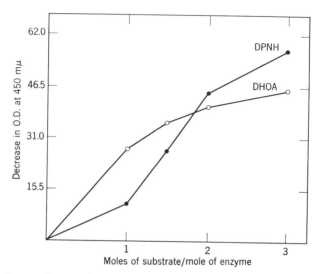

**Fig. 5.** Spectrophotometric titration of DHOD. Substrate was added under anaerobic conditions. The spectrum was recorded until maximum changes were obtained. The pH was 6.5 for DPNH reaction and 8.2 for the DHOA titration.

formation of an equimolar amount of flavin semiquinone. As shown in Fig. 6, this concept is strengthened by the appearance of absorbancy at long wavelengths after addition of 1 or 2 moles of DPNH and after 2 moles but not 1 mole of dihydroorotic acid. Addition of a second mole of either substrate results in essentially the same total decrease in absorbancy at 450 m$\mu$; that is, the second molecule of DPNH effects a much larger change in absorbancy than does the first, whereas the reverse is true in the case of dihydroorotate. As will be seen in Fig. 6, the amount of semiquinone present is doubled upon the second addition of DPNH; and the total decrease in absorbancy, after two molecules of either substrate have been added, is sufficient to suggest that there then exists a similar, rather complex thermodynamic equilibrium among several reduced and partially reduced species of enzyme.

Further insight into the nature of the molecular species existing in a population of enzyme molecules treated with one or more moles of substrate per mole of enzyme was gained from the experiment shown in Fig. 7. In this instance, enzyme was treated, anaerobically, with varying amounts of DPNH, and after 40 msec, the system was brought to 90°K and examined by electron spin (paramagnetic) resonance (ESR) spectrometry. Other experiments, not shown here, indicated that, by 40 msec, the system had come to thermodynamic equilibrium. It will be seen that the signal at $g = 2.00$, presumably here indicating flavin semiquinone, is about half-maximal after the addition

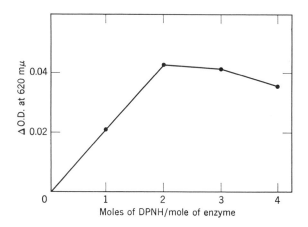

**Fig. 6.** Semiquinone formation during titration of DHOD with DPNH. DPNH was added, anaerobically, to the enzyme, and equilibrium was achieved after each addition of substrate. The reaction was followed at 620 m$\mu$.

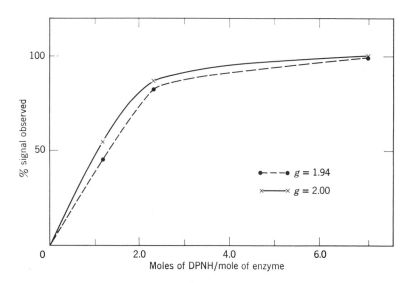

**Fig. 7.** ESR study of the reduction of DHOD by DPNH, added under anaerobic conditions. After 40 msec of reaction at room temperature, the sample was quick-frozen at $-181°C$ and recordings were taken from these samples.

of one molecule of DPNH per mole of enzyme, and almost maximal after the addition of the second mole of substrate. This is in excellent conformity with the data shown in Fig. 5 with respect to absorbancy at longer wavelengths. Equally important, it will be seen that the signal at $g = 1.94$ behaves in identical fashion. This is the signal which has been attributed to a form of reduced iron present in this diverse group of iron flavoproteins, as well as in reduced preparations of succinic dehydrogenase, DPNH dehydrogenase, and the more recently observed iron protein of mitochondria (4, 5). Perhaps most convincing is the fact that this signal is elicited by treatment of the flavin-free iron protein of aldehyde oxidase with dithionite.

$A$.  $FADH_2$—$Fe^{3+}Fe^{3+}$—FMN
$B$.  $FADH\cdot$—$Fe^{2+}Fe^{3+}$—FMN
$C$.  FAD—$Fe^{2+}Fe^{2+}$—FMN
$D$.  FAD—$Fe^{3+}Fe^{2+}$—$FMNH\cdot$
$E$.  FAD—$Fe^{3+}Fe^{3+}$—$FMNH_2$
$F$.  $FADH\cdot$—$Fe^{3+}Fe^{3+}$—$FMNH\cdot$

**Fig. 8.**    Possible reduced species of DHOD with equimolar amount of DPNH.

At this time it is uncertain what arrangement of iron atoms or what valence state of the component iron atoms is responsible for the signal. Our previous data suggest strongly that the signal originates only when iron atoms are paired in very close association, but it is not apparent whether the signal requires both members of the pair to be in the reduced (ferrous) condition, or whether, as we prefer to think, it arises after reduction of only one member of the pair. This problem makes definitive interpretation of the data already presented impossible at this time.

Figure 8 indicates some of the possible molecular species which might be considered as being present in a solution of enzyme which has been reduced by one molecule of substrate. On the arbitrary assumption that the FAD molecule is at the DPNH site while the FMN is at the orotic acid site, from the spectrophotometric data species $E$ would appear to represent the state of the enzyme after the addition of one molecule of dihydroototic acid. However, depending on which form of the iron pair is required to provide the iron signal, addition of DPNH results either entirely in the formation of species $B$ or in the formation of an equal mixture of species $B$ and $C$. The geometrical arrangement of the iron atoms and flavin components must be all important in this regard. At this writing, it seems most likely that the $g = 1.94$ signal denotes existence of an $Fe^{2+}$-$Fe^{3+}$ couple; and in considering changes in the magnitude of the semiquinone signal, one must remain aware of the unlikelihood of observing a $g = 2.00$ signal if an $Fe^{3+}$ atom is lodged quite close to an actual semiquinone. It seems most unlikely, in view of the nature of the enzyme species formed by titration with 1 mole of dihydroorotate and the data previously presented with respect to the "switching" action of the enzyme sulfhydryl group, that, upon addition of a single mole of DPNH, any electrons find their way to the FMN side of the transport system. If the couple $Fe^{2+}$-$Fe^2$ does *not* give the $g = 1.94$ signal, then the most likely arrangement after addition of 2 moles of either dihydroorotate or DPNH would be as follows:

$$FADH\cdot—Fe^{2+}\text{-}Fe^{3+}—FMNH_2$$

In any case, the number of possible electronic arrangements of the enzyme should become more apparent after ESR studies of titration of the native enzyme with dihydroorotate and of the *p*-CMB-treated enzyme with DPNH. Such studies are now in progress.

## D. Kinetic Course of the DHOD Reaction

Relatively crude kinetic studies have indicated that, when the enzyme is reduced by a stoichiometric amount of DPNH, the initial event appears to be formation of a fully reduced flavin which is then partially reoxidized, so that

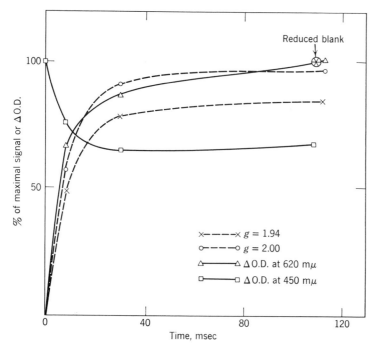

**Fig. 9.** ESR study of the approach of DHOD to the steady state. A solution containing DPNH and orotate in fifteen and fivefold molar excess over enzyme, respectively, was reacted anaerobically for the indicated durations. The reaction mixtures were then quick-frozen and studied by ESR and reflectance spectrometry.

at equilibrium semiquinone and reduced iron are apparent. The initial event, therefore, is probably transfer of a hydride ion from DPNH to FAD. Thereafter, the subsequent rates of appearance of flavin semiquinone and of reduced iron, as indicated by their respective ESR signals, are essentially identical. Moreover the rates of formation of semiquinone and of reduced iron, as well as the rates of their disappearance during the oxidative phase, are entirely

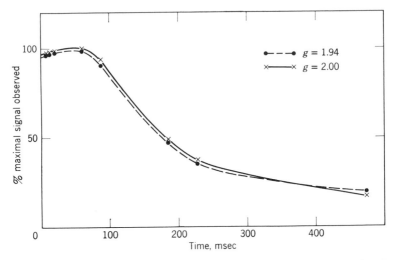

Fig. 10. Reoxidation of reduced DHOD. An anaerobic solution of DPNH and enzyme (3.8:1 molar ratio) was allowed to react at room temperature for 30 msec. The mixture was then treated with orotate (fortyfold excess) for the specified duration. Samples were quick-frozen and studied by ESR.

compatible with participation of these species in a normal catalytic cycle. These concepts are illustrated in Figs. 9 and 10. Thus, for example, the turnover time of the enzyme at $V$ is of the order of 1200 molecules of substrate per mole of enzyme per minute or approximately 1 mole of substrate/50 msec. Examination of Fig. 10 reveals that this is approximately the time required for the disappearance of both the $g = 2.00$ and the $g = 1.94$ signals as enzyme which had previously been fully reduced by 2 moles of DPNH is reoxidized by orotate.

## III. OPTICAL ROTATORY DISPERSION OF IRON PROTEINS

Optical rotatory dispersion studies of proteins have generally revealed a relatively featureless dispersion except for a Cotton effect at lower wavelengths, the magnitude of which has been related to the extent of helix content in the polypeptide chain. On the other hand, studies of the optical rotatory dispersion of metal chelates, particularly those in which optical activity is engendered in the complex from a mixture of non-optically active components, have been extremely fruitful in revealing the nature of such complexes. With such considerations in mind it seemed appropriate to attempt an investigation of the optical rotatory dispersion characteristics of iron proteins. Vallee and his colleagues (6) have reported a study of a series

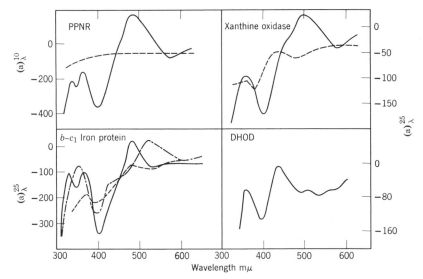

Fig. 11. Optical rotatory dispersion spectra of iron-containing proteins. PPNR: ———, native protein; – – – –, acid-denatured protein. Xanthine oxidase: ———, native protein in 0.05 $M$ phosphate buffer, pH 7.8; – – – –, reduced with xanthine. $b$–$c_1$ Iron protein: ———, native protein in 0.05 $M$ phosphate buffer, pH 7.8; — · — ·, oxidized with ferricyanide; – – – –, reduced with dithionite. DHOD: ———, native enzyme in 0.1 $M$ phosphate buffer, pH 6.5.

of heme proteins as well as that of PPNR*. The latter showed a rather dramatic optical rotatory dispersion curve with a pronounced Cotton effect in the visible region of the spectrum. Moreover, this curve was altered profoundly by addition of acid, which may be presumed to have displaced the iron atoms of this iron protein from one or more of their ligands.

Figure 11 compares the optical rotatory dispersion of PPNR (taken from the literature) with that of xanthine oxidase, DHOD, and the iron protein recently obtained from mitochondria (5). The dispersion curves of milk xanthine oxidase and rabbit-liver aldehyde oxidase are virtually identical; therefore, the curve for aldehyde oxidase is not shown. The general similarities among the curves for PPNR, xanthine oxidase, and the mitochondrial iron protein will be apparent. Indeed the resemblance between the dispersion

* Photosynthetic pyridine nucleotide reductase (chloroplast ferridoxin).

curves of PPNR and the mitochondrial protein in the region 300–450 m$\mu$ is quite remarkable. Both appear to differ significantly from the dispersion of xanthine oxidase in this region, whereas at longer wavelengths these are generally similar. The iron protein here utilized was a generous gift from Dr. Rieske of the University of Wisconsin. According to our information, such a preparation is "partially reduced." Accordingly three curves will be seen. In one instance the preparation was treated with ferricyanide to convert it to the fully oxidized form. The resultant curve, which resembles that of PPNR, also resembles that of xanthine oxidase at lower wavelengths, but at longer wavelengths the resultant curve is displaced considerably toward the red region of the spectrum. Upon reduction of this protein with dithionite, a profound alteration occurs which, however, has the general character of that induced in xanthine oxidase by reduction with its substrate or in PPNR by treatment with acid. These changes strongly imply reduction of the iron atoms—although the number of reduced iron atoms per mole cannot be stated—by substrate in the case of xanthine oxidase and by dithionite in the case of the mitochondrial protein. Moreover, they suggest strongly that, in consequence of reduction in the valence state, attachment to certain ligands, the nature of which is uncertain, is broken in a manner similar to that effected in PPNR by titration with acid.

The optical rotatory dispersion of DHOD stands in distinct contrast to that of the other proteins here considered. The curve resembles that of xanthine oxidase in the region 300–450 m$\mu$. However, at longer wavelengths as compared to the dispersion produced by xanthine oxidase, that of DHOD appears to be inverted. This observation suggests that the ligands to which the iron moieties of DHOD are affixed differ from those which obtain in xanthine oxidase and the other two iron proteins. Reduction of DHOD by its substrate again results in a profound alteration in optical rotatory dispersion, indicating, presumably, reduction of the iron components and release of appropriate ligands. Hopefully, an extension of these studies will prove of use not only in demonstrating the similarities among such proteins but also in the absolute identification of the ligands responsible for iron binding.

## IV. THE ROLE OF MOLYBDENUM IN XANTHINE AND ALDEHYDE OXIDASE

Previous studies (1, 7) using ESR spectrometry have demonstrated that the molybdenum moiety of xanthine and aldehyde oxidase is reduced upon incubation with substrate. Moreover kinetic studies revealed that in the course of reduction of enzyme by substrate the molybdenum of each of these enzymes was the first component of its internal electron-transport system to be reduced, while during the aerobic oxidation of the fully reduced enzyme the molybdenum components were the last to be reoxidized. Such data suggested therefore that molybdenum may well be the acceptor of electrons closest to the oxidizable substrates. Even were it not the immediate acceptor from the substrate, reduction of the molybdenum of aldehyde oxidase, for example, certainly seems to occur before reduction of the flavin, coenzyme $Q$, or iron components. The data did not eliminate the possibility that there is some other unidentified component of the transport system, which does not yield an ESR signal, reduction of which might be effected before that of molybdenum. Taken together with the finding that there is a sulfhydryl group at the substrate-binding site of aldehyde oxidase, attack of which by sulfhydryl reagent is competitively prevented by substrate (9), these data suggested that, among other ligands responsible for molybdenum binding, this metal may exist in covalent linkage to a sulfhydryl sulfur and that the reduction of this complex may be the initial event in transfer of electrons from substrate. This concept is compatible with recognition of the fact that the oxidations effected by both xanthine and aldehyde oxidases may, more properly, be regarded as hydroxylations (8).

The observations which will be reported below lend strong support to these concepts. Of a large number of enzymes tested, milk xanthine oxidase and liver aldehyde oxidase proved to be uniquely susceptible to progressive inhibition by methanol. As shown in Fig. 12a, development of this inhibition was contingent upon the operation of the enzyme in the presence of substrate. Prolonged preincubation of enzyme with methanol at concentrations up to 1 $M$ was essentially without any effect, whereas subsequent addition of substrate resulted in the development of inhibition exactly as shown in Fig. 12a. Several observations suggest that the methanol must be operative at or close to the substrate-binding site or the site at which the electrons are first introduced into the enzymes in the electron-transport system. Thus, as shown in Fig. 12b, this effect of methanol is competitively prevented by higher concentrations of substrate. Enzyme which had been progressively inhibited by 0.5 $M$ methanol could be reisolated readily by ammonium sulfate precipitation. Such preparations were devoid of catalytic acitivity, and addition of substrate resulted in no change in the absorption spectrum of the enzyme. However, activity reappeared in considerable measure when such preparations were subjected to prolonged dialysis against buffer.

Methanol-inhibited xanthine and aldehyde oxidases were prepared as described above and examined by ESR spectrometry. The results are shown in Fig. 13. Native aldehyde oxidase in its oxidized form invariably exhibits at $g = 1.97$ a small signal which is enormously heightened upon reduction by substrate. This is the signal which has been attributed to the molybdenum moiety. Xanthine oxidase does not show such a signal in its oxidized form, whereas an identical signal is apparent upon reduction by substrate. However, as will be seen, in both instances the reisolated, methanol-inhibited

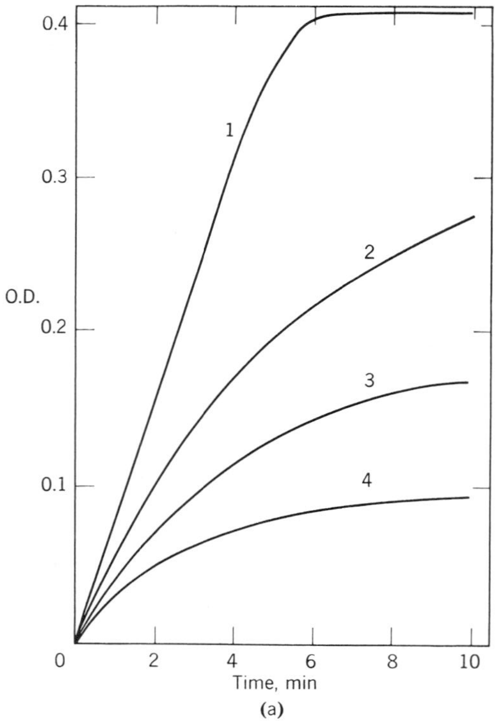

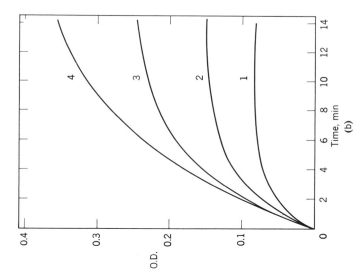

**Fig. 12a.** Inactivation of milk xanthine oxidase by methanol. 1, control (xanthine, 5 × 10⁻⁵ *M*); 2, 3, and 4, plus 0.5 *M*, 1.0 *M*, and 1.5 *M* methanol, respectively. [Rajagopalan and Handler, *J. Biol. Chem.*, **239**, 2027 (1964).]

**Fig. 12b.** Effect of substrate concentration on the rate of inactivation of xanthine oxidase by 1 *M* methanol. 1–4, 1.35 × 10⁻⁵ *M*, 5 × 10⁻⁵ *M*, 1.5 × 10⁻⁴ *M*, and 5 × 10⁻⁴ *M* xanthine, respectively. [Rajagopalan and Handler, *J. Biol. Chem.*, **239**, 2027 (1964).]

enzyme exhibits an extremely large and complex signal about $g = 1.97$. The precise meaning of the fine structure of this signal is as yet uncertain. However, there can be little doubt that it reveals the molybdenum of the methanol-inhibited enzymes to exist in the reduced form ($Mo^{5+}$). The bizarre and complex nature of this signal strongly suggests also that it is ligation of one

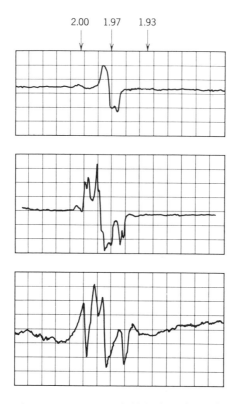

**Fig. 13.** ESR spectra of methanol-inactivated aldehyde and xanthine oxidases. Top curve, native O·A; middle curve, methanol-inactivated A·O, bottom curve, methanol-inactivated X·O.

or more molecules of methanol to this molybdenum which serves to inhibit the enzyme. When methanol-inhibited enzyme is subjected to prolonged dialysis, it would appear that the methanol is exchanged for water, and the enzyme reverts to its normal condition. The complete inactivity of methanol-inhibited enzymes and the failure of such preparations to exhibit any change in absorbancy at 450 m$\mu$ in the presence of substrate indicate clearly that reduction of molybdenum is a necessary prelude to reduction of the flavin and iron components of these enzymes. When taken in conjunction with the competitive nature of the inhibition by methanol (Fig. 11b), these findings seem definitely to establish the presence of molybdenum at the substrate-binding site and its role as initial electron acceptor.


## V. OBSERVATIONS CONCERNING THE MECHANISM OF CYTOCHROME *c* OXIDASE

Perhaps the most challenging question with respect to the mechanism of action of cytochrome oxidase is the manner in which it accomplishes the four-electron reduction of oxygen. Numerous investigators have speculated concerning the possibility of free-radical intermediates during this process. However, no categorical evidence in this regard has been described, and the initial possibility, the superoxide anion ($O_2^-$), has been thought unlikely in view of the alleged low potential of this species. Nevertheless, this possibility warrants re-examination, if indeed there exists as a transient intermediate the "oxygenated" cytochrome oxidase, described earlier and more recently supported by the findings of Davison and Wainio (9). This appears to be reduced enzyme to which is bound molecular oxygen in a state not unlike that of oxyhemoglobin. This complex has been stated to go over to the ordinary oxidized form in the presence of ferricytochrome *c* (9).

In an earlier communication Fridovich and Handler (10), suggested the participation of free-radical intermediates in the reduction of oxygen by cytochrome oxidase and postulated that these remain bound to the enzyme, from which only hydroxyl ions were thought to be released. The evidence in support of this suggestion was the initiation of the autoxidation of sulfite when the latter ion is incubated with cytochrome oxidase, ferrocytochrome *c*, and oxygen (10). As stated earlier, this phenomenon, originally observed with xanthine oxidase, has been extended also to aldehyde oxidase and DHOD. The $O_2^-$ radical, bound to the iron of these enzymes, is considered to be the reagent responsible for initiation of sulfite autoxidation as well as for chemiluminescence in the presence of luminol and for reduction of cytochrome *c* by these iron flavoproteins, which show an absolute dependence on oxygen for this reaction. The initiation of sulfite autoxidation has been used to demonstrate the formation of oxygen free radicals at an oxygen electrode, in illuminated dye solutions, as well as in such systems as azide-catalase plus peroxide, peroxidase in the presence of both peroxide and peroxidizable substrate, lipoxidase, and liver microsomes in the presence of TPNH. In contrast, none of the following enzymes, in the presence of their substrates and oxygen, is capable of initiating sulfite autoxidation: L-amino acid oxidase, tyrosinase, succinic dehydrogenase, glucose oxidase, D-amino acid oxidase, alcohol dehydrogenase, lactic dehydrogenase, or uricase. Since they showed that initiation of sulfite autoxidation could be effected equally as well with the particulate cytochrome oxidase preparation of Smith and Stotz (11) as with the purified, soluble preparation obtained from Green and his co-workers (12) and that, further, this process was strongly inhibited by cyanide, Fridovich and Handler concluded that the reduction of oxygen by cytochrome oxidase proceeds by successive univalent steps yielding free-radical, enzyme-bound intermediates of oxygen.

Related to these observations is the fact that, when spectrophotometry is used to follow the process, the activity of cytochrome oxidase appears to be first order at all concentrations of cytochrome $c$. In manometric and polarographic assays, in which ascorbate is employed to keep all the cytochrome $c$

TABLE 2

**Effect of Tiron and Globin of Myoglobin on Cytochrome $c$ Oxidase**

| Initial Concentration, $\times 10^5 M$ | | Initial Rate | | Stimulation, % |
|---|---|---|---|---|
| Cyt. $c^{2+}$ | Cyt. $c^{3+}$ | $-$ Globin | $+$ Globin[a] | |
| 5.15 | 1.3 | 0.244 | 0.315 | 29 |
| 5.15 | 3.0 | 0.168 | 0.234 | 39 |
| 5.15 | 4.6 | 0.126 | 0.190 | 51 |
| | | $-$ Tiron | $+$ Tiron[b] | |
| 4.70 | 1.73 | 0.175 | 0.325 | 86 |

[a] 50 $\mu$g/ml.
[b] 0.01 $M$.

in the reduced condition, this is not the case (13, 14). More pertinent still is the fact that in spectrophotometric assays ferricytochrome $c$ appears to act as an "inhibitor" of cytochrome oxidase activity (15, 16).

It seemed possible that these various observations could be reconciled by a single hypothesis, namely, that in the ordinary course of catalysis reduced cytochrome oxidase binds molecular oxygen; subsequent electron transfer results in the formation of an enzyme-bound, free-radical reduced form of oxygen. If this complex is capable of reducing ferricytochrome $c$, by analogy to the reduction of ferricytochrome $c$ effected by our various iron flavoproteins in the presence of oxygen, then an excess of free ferricytochrome $c$ would appear to be an inhibitor, electrons flowing from ferrocytochrome $c$ to enzyme to oxygen to ferricytochrome $c$. Since the concentration of ferricytochrome $c$ would increase, however, during the course of enzymic activity, it would begin to inhibit, and the reaction would appear to obey first-order, kinetics at all concentrations of ferrocytochrome $c$.

The experiment described in Table 2 was devised to test this hypothesis. It will be seen that, at constant concentration of ferrocytochrome $c$, increasing concentrations of the oxidized form of cytochrome $c$ were inhibitory, a threefold increase in concentration effecting a 50% decrease in initial reaction velocity. These observations confirm and extend those previously described in the literature.

More revealing, however, are the effects of globin and tiron. Repeatedly in this laboratory, the globin obtained from horse-heart myoglobin has been demonstrated specifically to inhibit the oxygen-dependent reduction of cytochrome $c$ by our three iron flavoproteins, as well as to prevent chemiluminescence and sulfite autoxidation initiation. Tiron is even more effective in this regard. Were these two materials, globin and tiron, also similarly operative in the cytochrome oxidase system, i.e., were they able to react with an oxygen radical such as $O_2^-$, while bound to the enzyme surface, this would prevent the reduction of ferricytochrome $c$ and hence be apparent as an increase in the rate of oxidation of ferrocytochrome $c$ under these circumstances. As shown in Table 2, 50 $\mu g/ml$ of globin was able to effect a 50% increase in the *apparent* rate of oxidation of ferrocytochrome $c$ when ferricytochrome $c$ was initially present at a concentration of $4.6 \times 10^{-5}\,M$. Tiron, at a concentration of 0.01 $M$, was even more effective, causing almost a doubling of the apparent rate of oxidation of ferrocytochrome $c$ when ferricytochrome $c$ was present at an initial concentration of $1.7 \times 10^{-5}\,M$.

These observations, therefore, strongly suggest that oxygen radicals are indeed formed as intermediates in oxygen reduction by cytochrome oxidase, that such radicals remain enzyme bound until further reduced, and that, under the artificial circumstances prevailing in many investigative situations, ferricytochrome $c$ present in the medium can partially obscure the oxidation of ferrocytochrome $c$ by itself serving as ultimate oxidant for the enzyme-oxygen radical complex.

## ACKNOWLEDGMENT

These studies were supported by Research Grant GM-0091 from the Division of General Medical Sciences, National Institutes of Health.

## REFERENCES

1. P. Handler, K. V. Rajagopalan, and V. Aleman, *Federation Proc.*, **23**, 30 (1964).
2. I. Lieberman and A. Kornberg, *Biochim. et Biophys. Acta*, **12**, 223 (1953).
3. H. C. Friedman and B. Vennesland, *J. Biol. Chem.*, **235**, 1526 (1960).
4. H. Beinert, W. Heinen, and G. Palmer, "Enzyme Models and Enzyme Structure," *Brookhaven Symposia in Biol.*, No. 15, p. 229 (1962).
5. J. S. Rieske, D. H. MacLennan, and R. Coleman, *Biochem. Biophys. Research Communs.*, **15**, 338 (1964).
6. D. D. Ulmer and B. L. Vallee, *Biochemistry*, **2**, 1335 (1963).
7. R. C. Bray, R. Pettersson, and A. Ehrenberg, *Biochem. J.*, **81**, 178 (1961).

8. K. V. Rajagopalan and P. Handler, *J. Biol. Chem.*, **239**, 2027 (1964).
9. A. J. Davison and W. W. Wainio, *Federation Proc.*, **23**, 323 (1964).
10. I. Fridovich and P. Handler, *J. Biol. Chem.*, **236**, 1836 (1961).
11. F. G. Smith and E. Stotz, *J. Biol. Chem.*, **179**, 819 (1949).
12. R. S. Criddel and R. M. Bock, *Biochem. Biophys. Research Communs.*, **1**, 138 (1959).
13. E. Stotz, A. M. Altschul, and T. R. Hogness, *J. Biol. Chem.*, **124**, 745 (1938).
14. E. C. Slater, *Biochem. J.*, **44**, 305 (1949).
15. L. Smith and H. Conrad, *Arch. Biochem. Biophys.*, **63**, 403 (1956).
16. K. Minnaert, *Biochim. et Biophys. Acta*, **50**, 23 (1961).

## ADDENDUM

Since preparation of this manuscript, subsequent studies have revealed that the molecular weight of DHOD is about 120,000. The molecular weight assigned to this enzyme in this paper was a minimum value based on its flavin content. In the studies reported herein, all references to reagents or substrates added "per mole of enzyme" should be regarded as added per functional grouping of FAD, FMN, two iron atoms, and two acid-labile sulfides.

*Discussion*

HANDLER: Our paper is really four papers. The paper itself is rather straight-forward, and very few additional comments are warranted.

The effect of methanol on our molybdo-flavoproteins was encountered accidentally, but its meaning is clear. The data in Figs. 12a and b (p. 394 of this book) leave little doubt that (a) methanol affects the enzymes only when they are turning over during normal catalysis, and (b) although substrate is imperative to the phenomenon—presumably as a reductant—it is also protective. Indeed, it is protective even at a concentration at which, in the absence of methanol, one normally observes "excess substrate inhibition." One can only conclude that methanol reacts with the reduced form of enzyme and that the law of attack by methanol is at, or close to, the substrate binding site. Both notions are confirmed by the data of Fig. 13 (p. 395). The ESR signals clearly reveal that enzyme thus inhibited by methanol is "frozen" in a state in which the molybdenum is in the $Mo^{5+}$ condition. We infer from the bizarre fine structure of the ESR signal that methanol has replaced some normal ligand, and it is this fact that results in the failure of the $Mo^{5+}$ to reoxidize. The fact that this inhibited form fails to show any evidence of reduction of the flavin or iron components as judged by absorbancy at 450 and 550 m$\mu$, strengthens the arguments advanced by Drs. Bray and Beinert, as well as ourselves, that the molybdenum is the first component of the electron-transport chain of xanthine and aldehyde oxidases to undergo reduction by substrate.

Of incidental interest is the failure of methanol to influence the slow oxidation of DPNH by xanthine oxidase, the only activity of this enzyme which is also insensitive to cyanide inhibition. This strongly suggests that electrons from DPNH enter the enzyme's electron-transport chain at a point subsequent to the molybdenum and, furthermore, as we have suggested elsewhere, that molybdenum is the component of these enzymes which is attacked by cyanide, leading to irreversible inhibition.

There is a real possibility that the presence of molybdenum in these two enzymes is related to the fact that the reactions which they catalyze are "hydroxylations" rather than dehydrogenations, e.g., hypoxanthine to xanthine, N-methylnicotinamide to its pyrridone, aldehydes to acids. In each instance, the oxygen atom introduced into the product is derived from the aqueous medium.

Next, I should like to direct your attention to a few aspects of our studies of dihydroorotic acid dehydrogenase. We chose this enzyme because it seemed the simplest of all iron flavoproteins, with only one FAD, one FMN, and two iron atoms per mole (62,000 = molecular weight).

Of particular significance are the following facts. The enzyme is a reversible dehydrogenase but can also catalyze reduction of $O_2$ by both DPNH and dihydroorotic acid (DHOA). Aerobically, like xanthine and aldehyde oxidases, it initiates sulfite autoxidation and, in the presence of luminol, chemiluminescence. Like these other iron proteins, it shows an obligatory dependence on $O_2$ in order to accomplish reduction of cytochrome $c$.

The data in Table 1 (p. 383) suggest operation of an internal "switching" mechanism. In the presence of cysteine, the flow of electrons between substrates is maximal, as is the ability of DHOA to reduce $O_2$, whereas, with DPNH as substrate, electrons from DPNH are "deflected" from $O_2$ to orotic acid. If the enzyme is oxidized or treated with one $p$-CMB per mole, transfer of electrons between substrates and from DHOA to $O_2$ is markedly inhibited, while there is little effect on the DPNH $\rightarrow$ $O_2$ reaction. Assuming, entirely arbitrarily, that FAD is at the DPN-DPNH site and that FMN lies at the DHOA-OA site, these data suggest a transport arrangement as follows:

$$
\begin{array}{ccc}
\text{DPNH} \\
\phantom{x} \Big) \text{FAD---Fe---Fe---} \rightarrow \text{---FMN} \Big( & \begin{array}{c} \text{DHOA} \\ \\ \text{OA} \end{array} \\
\text{DPN}^+ & \begin{array}{c} | \\ \text{H} \\ | \\ \text{---S---} \end{array}
\end{array}
$$

This concept is certainly fortified by the data obtained by spectrophotometrically following the titration of enzyme by its two reduced substrates (Fig. 1, p. 381).

Clearly, whereas one mole of DHOA results in an absorbancy change equal to full bleaching of one flavin/mole with no sign (at 620 m$\mu$) of free radical, the first mole of DPNH seems to reduce flavin only to the level of flavoquinone, as shown also in Fig. 6, p. 387. The latter data are confirmed by the ESR data shown in Fig. 7, p. 387. Thus, introduction of electrons from the two sides results in quite different consequences to the enzyme. However, after two pairs of electrons have entered, regardless of substrate, the enzyme appears to be brought to the same condition, if sufficient time is allowed for equilibration.

The simplest interpretation of these data is that, even when the "switch" is in the sulfhydryl condition, the first pair of electrons to enter the oxidized enzyme remains on the side of the switch at which it entered! This leads to full bleaching of FMN by DHOA, but distribution of the electron pair among the FAD and the iron atoms when DPNH is the electron source. In either case, introduction of a second pair of electrons succeeds in crossing this barrier.

The kinetic data are of great interest. They clearly demonstrate that the rates of appearance of the $g = 1.94$ and $g = 2.00$ signals are identical. Furthermore, when the enzyme, fully reduced by DPNH, is reoxidized by OA, the two signals disappear at the same rate, and, moreover, that rate is compatible with $V$ for the enzyme under comparable conditions!

The absorption spectrum of the iron protein prepared from dihydroorotic acid dehydrogenase by methanol precipitation is shown in Fig. 3, p. 382. It is essentially identical with that which we have described for the equivalent proteins prepared from xanthine and aldehyde oxidases. Moreover, when reduced by dithionite, these iron proteins yield the characteristic $g = 1.94$ signal, which disappears as the reduced proteins are reoxidized by oxygen. Clearly, the flavin component is not required for signal production, which must reflect reduction of the iron component, a phenomenon which, in the absence of flavin, is observed equally well by ordinary spectrophotometry.

That dihydroorotic acid dehydrogenase is a superb object for study must be abundantly evident. We continue to study it as intensively as possible. Unhappily, it cannot really be obtained in quantity; 1500 gal of a culture of *Zymobacterium oroticum* yields only 500 mg of purified enzyme! This means that one must be rather conservative in its use. Perhaps this accounts for the fact that our attempts to estimate the labile sulfide have never yielded values stoichiometric with the iron. The values are always substantially less than unity.

I must also confess my frustration in being unable to be certain of the events which occur during titration of the enzyme with DPNH and DHOA. The available data simply cannot be reconciled, or at least so it seems. Most probably, after adding 2 moles of either substrate, the enzyme is: $FADH\cdot—Fe^{2+}—Fe^{3+}—FMNH_2$, but we cannot be equally confident of the state of the enzyme after addition of one DPNH mole. Hopefully, this problem will be resolved by the studies now in progress.

KING: You mentioned that the sulfide to iron ratio is less than unity.

HANDLER: I don't know that it is really less than that in the enzyme. In doing these determinations we simply haven't gotten unity.

KING: What I want to say is that it is mysterious. We have scanned the whole spectrum of this methylene blue compound, and the methylene blue compound which came from inorganic sulfite is somewhat different from the methylene blue compound which came from PPNR, kindly supplied us by Dr. San Pietro, and also different from the methylene blue compound formed from succinate dehydrogenase. There is not too much difference. It is just that the ratio of the maxima to the minima is different.

HANDLER: Well, we have done that only once. We got the same spectrum with aldehyde oxidase as that of a commercial sample of methylene blue. It's the only time we made this comparison.

MASON: I wonder what exactly sulfite-chain initiation means in terms of free-radical involvement in mechanism. Actually, it seems to me that the key to the meaning of this technique is a correlation between the rate of enzyme action and the rate of chain initiation, not simply the observation of the initiation. After all, Parravano, years ago, used simple chain initiation to pick up free-radical formation but could never be certain that the free radicals were an integral part of the enzyme mechanism.

HANDLER: I don't know that I can provide an answer to that, Dr. Mason. The fact remains that three flavoproteins, and only three, do this. These are the three that have iron, that show an oxygen dependence for cytochrome $c$ reduction, and that will cause chemiluminescence in the presence of luminol and other such materials. You can also cause initiation of these chain phenomena simply at an oxygen electrode. This is essentially the phenomenon which happens when a beaker of sulfite stands around in your laboratory and goes over to sulfate. You can stop that with versene. The mechanism which we use is the same as that which inorganic chemists have been using for a long time to account for the spontaneous autoxidation of sulfite in a beaker exposed to the air. A trace metal, cuprous, ferrous, etc., reduces oxygen, and then two materials which should react in a two-electron fashion get started in a one-electron fashion, resulting in a chain reaction. Perhaps you will recall that with xanthine oxidase, for example, this chain length is as long as forty thousand, that is, for every xanthine oxidized, some forty thousand sulfites are oxidized. How can one ascertain whether this happened only in 1% of all instances, with chains that are four million units long? Yet that is what you really ask. I don't know how to do the kinetics of the process. All I can say is that most certainly there is a restricted group of enzymes which do this. And if one is fully to understand such an enzyme, one must be able to accommodate in the mechanism the fact that it initiates this process. Please understand that a free-radical intermediate is absolutely required to initiate a free-radical chain. This simple observation and the conclusions it compels are just as definitive as an absorption spectrum or ESR signal.

SINGER: We, too, have been under the impression that the presumed exact coincidence between "labile sulfide" and non-heme iron is probably not as real as it would appear from the papers on photosynthetic pyridine nucleotide reductase and ferrodoxin. In the case of DPNH dehydrogenase, in about fifteen different preparations at various stages of purification, the ratio of labile sulfur to iron varied from about 1.1 to 1.3, and the experimental error is of the order of 5% for the combined determinations. In Ziegler's succinate CoQ reductase, the ratio is 1.15 to 1.2 rather than 1.0. Ordinary inorganic sulfide seems to contain some impurities. the nature of which I don't know. If gaseous $H_2S$ is used as a standard, one gets exactly the same absorption spectrum in the resulting colored complex, either in the methylene blue method or in Rabinowitz's modification, as with $H_2S$ liberated from labile sulfide-containing enzymes.

BEINERT: By extending previous work on *Azotobacter vinelandii*, we have recently obtained what we think is the strongest evidence so far that the signal at $g = 1.94$ is really due to iron. When particles prepared from *Azotobacter vinelandii* are reduced with dithionite, a signal at $g = 1.94$ appears. We compared ESR spectra from bacteria grown on $^{56}Fe$ and on $^{57}Fe$. Since $^{56}Fe$ has no nuclear magnetic moment, whereas $^{57}Fe$ does (spin $= \frac{1}{2}$), one would expect two lines from $^{57}Fe$ where one line is observed from $^{56}Fe$. If the splitting is small, as expected from $^{57}Fe$, one might expect only line broadening, as the two lines are no longer resolved. In the spectra of particles prepared from *Azotobacter* grown on $^{57}$Fe, small broadening could be seen [*Brookhaven Symposia in Biol.*, No. 15, 247 (1962)]. However, the biochemists said, "It is such a small effect! Can you make a point out of this?" The physicists said, "$^{57}$Fe has a very low nuclear moment (0.09). You can't expect an effect as big as what you see." Now, there I was. For one group it was too small; for the other one it was too big.

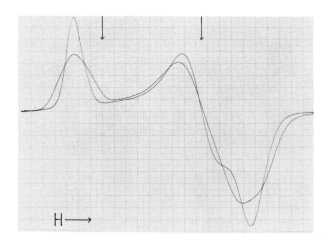

**Fig. 1.** EPR spectra of iron proteins isolated from $^{56}$Fe- and $^{57}$Fe-grown *Azotobacter Vinelandii*. The preparations were reduced with dithionite, and the spectra were recorded at 95°K at a power of 25 mwatt and a modulation amplitude of 3 gauss. The magnetic field is increasing to the right, and the two markers indicate $g = 2.00$ (left) and $g = 1.94$ (right). The spectrum showing sharper lines of higher amplitude is that of the $^{56}$Fe protein. The integrated intensities were matched to represent equal iron content. (According to experiments by Shethna, Wilson, Hansen, and Beinert.)

This time I think that we have more to show. In collaboration with Dr. Perry Wilson and Dr. Shethna of the Department of Bacteriology at Madison, we have isolated an iron protein from *Azotobacter* (we were no longer satisfied with particles) and have in this way reduced the signal-to-noise ratio to a comfortable level (Fig. 1). To the left is the $g = 2.00$ signal; and to the right the 1.94 signal. There is a definite kink, indicating that we have three $g$ values: $x$, $y$, and $z$ ($x$ and $y$ at $g \approx 1.94$, $z$ at $g = 2.00$). The iron protein isolated from the cells grown on $^{57}$Fe gives the spectrum which is shown superimposed on the $^{56}$Fe signal. The spectra are superimposed for equal iron content of the preparation. The shoulder is wiped out, because $^{57}$Fe would split the lines into two and cause overlapping of the lines at $g_x$ and $g_y$. Although $^{57}$Fe has a relatively small nuclear magnetic moment, the effect would depend on the extent of splitting that is observed, which we are not completely sure of because we have no model compound. We have grown batches of bacteria twice on $^{57}$Fe and many times on $^{56}$Fe. The spectra superimpose exactly for $^{56}$Fe-grown and $^{57}$Fe-grown bacteria. We have superimposed the spectra with the

Varian Fieldial so that they are exactly superimposed. The observed effect would, I think, for all reasonable purposes, mean that the signal is indeed due to an iron species. I would not want to say that sulfur is not in the coordination sphere of that iron. We don't know, but it is likely that it is. But on the basis of the presented evidence I think that the signal itself is not due to sulfur, although it may be modified by a sulfur ligand. Concerning the valence of the iron, I have to admit that this cannot be derived from our data as long as we have no model compound. Our idea that we are dealing with a reduced species of iron derives only from the experience that the more one reduces, the more of the $g = 1.94$ signal is generally seen. You cannot get this signal unless you have a reducing condition. It is, therefore, relatively hard to visualize trivalent iron being maintained under such conditions.

HANDLER: Dr. Beinert, could you tell us about the absorption spectrum of that iron protein?

BEINERT: It looks as you would expect. There is a sloping absorption from the ultraviolet to 600 m$\mu$.

CHANCE: Are the physicists now satisfied that the effect is not still larger than you would expect for an iron with no nuclear magnetic moment? In other words, don't you have to consider that there might be an appreciable contribution from the sulfur as well, in order that the effect be so little diminished by the lack of a nuclear magnetic moment of the iron?

BEINERT: On this point I have to rely completely on what others say. Dr. Vänngård from Uppsala, who visited us, has looked at the spectra. He said that in the absence of knowledge of the type of compound one cannot say exactly what the splitting should be. He thought it entirely reasonable that one would get such an effect, even with a relatively small nuclear magnetic moment, which is about 0.1 for $^{57}Fe$ as compared, for instance, with the moment of 0.4 for $^{14}N$, which gives well-defined splitting.

BRAY: I should just like to add a word about the susceptibility measurements which Dr. Ehrenberg carried out on xanthine oxidase. While there is no evidence from the ESR itself as to the valence of the iron, it is clear, as Dr. Ehrenberg showed (Fig. 2, p. 376), that the susceptibility change does parallel the $g = 1.9$ signal. I think that the susceptibility changes can best be explained in terms of a reduction of the iron from the $Fe^{3+}$ low-spin configuration to the $Fe^{2+}$ high spin, and in the case of xanthine oxidase the data fit fairly well quantitatively for two out of the eight irons being reduced.

MASSEY: I should like to present some relevant work of Dr. R. W. Miller and myself which bears on the nature of the $g = 1.94$ signal and the role of iron in metalloflavoproteins. This research is with dihydroorotic dehydrogenase. Figure 2 shows the rate of reduction of the iron in the presence of $o$-phenanthroline, studied by the stopped-flow method. The bottom trace shows the changes in optical density at 510 m$\mu$ when enzyme is reacted anaerobically with DPNH at 25° in phosphate, pH 6.6. Curve 2 shows the same experiment, but carried out in the presence of 2.5 × 10$^{-4}$ $M$ $o$-phenanthroline. Curve 3 is a difference curve between curves 2 and 1 and, therefore, represents the rate of formation of ferrous $o$-phenanthrolinate. It is obvious that the rate of reduction of the iron by DPNH is quite slow. From these results, an apparent first-order rate constant of about 2 min$^{-1}$ can be calculated.

This should be compared with the catalytic turnover of about 1200 under the same conditions. As a check that the rate-limiting step is not the reaction of *o*-phenanthroline with the enzyme ferrous iron, we also incubated enzyme and DPNH for 10 min before reacting with *o*-phenanthroline. The results are shown in curve 4; clearly the ferrous form of the enzyme can react very rapidly with *o*-phenanthroline. Substantially the same results are obtained when the reaction is carried out with dihydroorotate, except that now the rate of reduction is about ten times slower even than with DPNH. These results are also in very good agreement with those

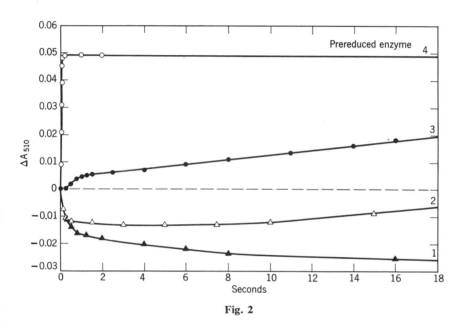

**Fig. 2**

obtained if the valence state of the iron is determined at various times by the anaerobic denaturation technique used a long time ago with succinic dehydrogenase [V. Massey, *J. Biol. Chem.*, **229**, 763 (1957)]. Even slower rates of reduction of iron have been observed with succinic dehydrogenase or with xanthine oxidase [P. E. Brumby and V. Massey, *Biochem. J.*, **89**, 46P (1963)]. Thus, we are forced to the conclusion that either the $g = 1.94$ signal is not due to iron or, more reasonably in view of Dr. Beinert's latest results, that it is due to some complex of the iron which remains in the ferric state, even in the presence of reducing agents.

HANDLER: In "rebuttal" I can offer the figures already reported to you. The data in Figs. 9 and 10, pp. 389 and 390, report not dissimilar experiments. Quite clearly the $g = 1.94$ and $g = 2.00$ signals go up and down in unison. If, as we believe, the $g = 1.94$ signal reflects iron reduction even though the entering electron may be delocalized and really part of a Fe-S system, then certainly the catalytic cycle of the enzyme entails iron reduction and reoxidation.

MASON: Why isn't there a signal for the ferric state? Did I correctly understand

Dr. Bray to say that magnetic susceptibility measurements indicated that, upon reduction, the system goes from one unpaired electron to four unpaired electrons? BRAY: Yes.

MASON: There is still an unpaired electron to be accounted for, and this signal is sufficiently big that one-quarter of the integrated area should be apparent. I should like to ask Dr. Beinert whether the iron protein of *Azotobacter*, from which this signal was taken, contained any flavin. How much iron did it have?

BEINERT: The iron protein from *Azotobacter* is at a stage where it contains about 4 $\mu$moles of iron and 0.25 $\mu$mole of flavin per gram of protein, so we have been able to eliminate the flavin quite well. It is also still possible that there is extra iron present (iron not giving the $g = 1.94$ signal) and that the flavin would have an equivalent amount of $g = 1.94$ iron associated with it. We are analyzing the signal quantitatively now, which should answer this.

May I say something in reply to Dr. Massey's comment on the dihydroorotic dehydrogenase? I think that chemical examination of valence states is inherently unreliable, and I am, therefore, not worried by data obtained with *o*-phenanthroline. However, we have tried experiments similar to those Dr. Massey has reported. I don't have the data here, but we have found that the $g = 1.94$ signal appears, as Dr. Handler has shown, at the rate commensurate with appearance of the flavin semiquinone signal and with the over-all reaction, whereas the phenanthroline color shows up considerably later. We have done this by simultaneous reflectance and ESR spectroscopy. Therefore, I think that what is measured with phenanthroline is the formation of the phenanthroline-iron complex, rather than the reduction of the iron. The other experiment which Dr. Massey mentioned, where the enzyme was prereduced with DPNH, may, from our experience at least, have had the flaw that these flavoproteins, when reduced with substrate and left together with substrate, even for a minute, undergo changes which are not readily reversed. We have evidence here from ESR measurements that this is so. I wonder, therefore, whether one can trust the immediate reduction of the phenanthroline in the experiments described by Dr. Massey when prereduction of the enzyme for longer periods has taken place.

SINGER: I think that quite possibly both Dr. Handler and Dr. Massey are right. And maybe we don't have to invoke the very plausible interpretation that Dr. Beinert has just mentioned. The experiments of Drs. Massey and Handler are not really comparable. Dr. Handler is measuring, to use his interpretation, the rate of reduction of enzyme-bound non-heme iron by the substrate. On the other hand, Massey measured the rate of reduction of enzyme-bound ferric *o*-phenanthrolinate by the substrate. It is well known that ferric iron also chelates *o*-phenanthroline. The rate of electron flux within the enzyme may be quite different, depending upon whether the enzyme-bound iron atoms are chelated or unchelated.

ESTABROOK: What control has Dr. Massey used for the chemical determination? Dr. Beinert has indicated that he has combined spectrophotometric and spin resonance. Has Dr. Massey also combined spectrophotometric and chemical analyses as a control for his method?

MASSEY: The encouraging thing about the experiment I just reported is that the results are in substantial agreement with the chemical method of determination in which you denature the enzyme with trichloracetic acid in the presence of *p*-chlorophenyl mercuric sulfonate. You cannot detect any difference in the rate of the iron reduction. I think the point which Dr. Singer raised—that we are following the reduction of ferric *o*-phenanthrolinate by substrate—is not really valid for succinic dehydrogenase, although I cannot say for dihydroorotic dehydrogenase. With succinic dehydrogenase, the reduction of the iron by dithionite is an extremely slow process, and you can show quite readily that it goes at a certain slow rate. If you do a series of experiments in which you have *o*-phenanthroline and dithionite present at zero time and follow the time course of the reaction at 510 m$\mu$, there is a slow increase in absorption. If you do another experiment in which you add the dithionite first and then add the *o*-phenanthroline at a later time, you get an immediate increase in optical density at 510 m$\mu$ up to that of the first curve, and so on. The present experiment indicates the same thing. To come back to Dr. Estabrook's question, I find it difficult to see what other controls you can have in this sort of experiment. The point I am trying to make is that if these types of estimations are valid (and at the moment I see no good evidence to indicate that they are not valid), then the iron is not being reduced. Is this not at least worthy of discussion?

SINGER: I should like to quote Massey's statement that you can't use an enzyme from one source as evidence about the mechanism of action of an enzyme from another source. There is no analogy here. Succinate dehydrogenase iron is slowly reactive, while the iron moieties of these enzymes are apparently quite rapidly reactive with chelators.

WINFIELD: I do not think it has been made clear enough that if you produce an enzyme reaction, for example, a free radical on an oxygen or a sulfur atom, and that atom happens to be part of a ligand attached to iron, then you will not see a free-radical signal. You will see a signal like that of an iron atom which scarcely knows that there is a free radical in the vicinity.

If one can judge the spectra of some of the cobalt complexes in which an unpaired electron is confined to the metal atom, there may be much the same *g*-value and much the same kind of signal that are obtained if the electron is in fact spending part of its time on several nearby atoms. But it is just possible that you will find hyperfine structure more readily in the case where the electron is spread over several atoms instead of being confined to the cobalt. The hyperfine structure is, however, quite difficult to find in some compounds. Detection of the signal sometimes requires careful control of pH, and sometimes rather critical control of temperature, and "unusual" temperatures. Many people to whom I have spoken about polysulfide enzymes believe that, after adding an electron to their assembly of iron atoms, they have not indeed induced change in the valence of the iron in the sense that they don't see an optical spectral change corresponding to the presence of iron in two valence states. Now, if this is true, it seems to me that we must be able to deduce something.

KING: Dr. Beinert, you said that there is an irreversible change of the enzymes in the presence of the substrate. What do you really mean?

BEINERT: I said that there are changes which are not readily reversed. I didn't say "irreversible," because we have not investigated this yet, but I can show you a very nice example of what I meant. Figure 3 shows an experiment with aldehyde oxidase under two different conditions. On the ordinate, we show per cent of reduction, and on the abscissa, time in milliseconds. At the left two different experiments are superimposed; they agree reasonably well. The kinetics of the ESR signals of semiquinone, molybdenum, and $g = 1.94$ are shown. The experiment was done by reducing aldehyde oxidase with N-methylnicotinamide, which is a good substrate for it, putting it in the syringes of the rapid-mixing apparatus, and then shooting it against buffer containing oxygen, resulting in reoxidation.

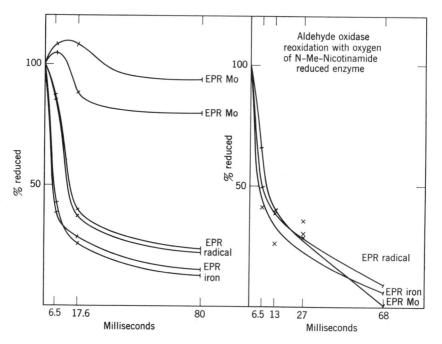

**Fig. 3.** Time course of reoxidation of electron carriers of aldehyde oxidase by oxygen, after previous reduction with N-methylnicotinamide. *Left portion of figure:* The enzyme was reduced with substrate, filled into one syringe of the Bray apparatus, and mixed with oxygenated buffer. The enzyme remained in the reduced state in this procedure from 10 to 30 min. *Right portion of figure:* The enzyme was mixed with substrate in the rapid-mixing apparatus and left in contact with substrate for <1 min. This solution was then immediately mixed in a second mixing chamber with oxygenated buffer from a third syringe. (According to experiments by Rajagopalan, Handler, Palmer, and Beinert.)

In this case (left side) molybdenum hardly changes at all, as is evident in both experiments, whereas free radical and iron are going down, which means oxidation. We were not satisfied with this, since we had other evidence that molybdenum is an active electron carrier. Then we used a three-syringe setup in which we first mixed with two syringes aldehyde oxidase with the substrate, so that reduction took place, and about 1 min later we shot in oxygenated buffer to reoxidize it. This time we got the kinetics shown at the right, demonstrating that in this case the molybdenum is fully active, as one would expect in this enzyme. Then we took a closer look at the signal. The signal obtained in the two-syringe experiment on prolonged reduction differs from signals obtained on brief (1-min) reduction. The signals show very markedly different saturation behavior. We have not investigated how one could eventually revert the "long-reduced" to the other "active" form, but it is obvious that the contact with substrate in this case does something to the enzyme which impairs the reaction of the molybdenum. Similar things occur very obviously in xanthine oxidase and also in DPNH dehydrogenase, as Dr. Singer, Dr. Palmer, and I have seen [*Biochem. Biophys. Research Communs.*, **12**, 432 (1963)]. I should like to actually stress the contribution of Dr. Palmer, who was a coauthor and had a very substantial hand in all this work.

CHANCE: You didn't say whether the form on the left or the right was the active one of the enzyme.

BEINERT: Well, I would assume the one that reacts, that is, to the right.

CHANCE: Undoubtedly you are defining this by whether the molybdenum changed.

BEINERT: I would suspect that, if anything is active, it is the one that had the shorter treatment.

KING: Dr. Beinert, have you tried a succinate dehydrogenase in the presence of succinate?

BEINERT: We have done experiments with succinic dehydrogenase of the Singer and Ziegler type, and we do see the reduction of what we call the iron ($g = 1.94$) in these enzymes and also see the formation of semiquinone, presumably of the flavin. Now, what are you driving at?

KING: I meant the irreversible change or the so-called irreversible change.

BEINERT: There are lots of changes when you let the enzymes sit or add cyanide or things of that sort, but we have not done the type of experiment in which substrate was incubated with enzyme for longer periods.

ROSENBERG: If one takes seriously the model of electron transport in enzyme systems where an electron moves from one site on the protein molecule to another site some large distance away, then the electron must be conceived to spend some time (the transit time, or a fraction of it) in a free state as a "conduction" electron. If the density of such electrons is large, and in an effective enzyme operating at maximum rate it ought to be substantial, the free electron should produce an ESR signal. I wonder whether anyone has attempted to look for this signal, or whether any of the unexplained signals found can be accounted for by this mechanism.

BEINERT: It is true that in biological materials very often you find more unexplained signals than you want to cope with, but in isolated enzymes, even in these enzymes with several built-in carriers, we have not found any strange unexplained signals. It could be that small radical signals, since they are not very different from each other, could easily have been superimposed on other signals, and we could have missed them. I think that it would be extremely difficult to pin this kind of phenomenon down.

To come back to an earlier point, what is the possibility that one would have a configuration in which iron would stay trivalent but the electron would be found with the ligand—in this case, let's say, a sulfur ligand?

HEMMERICH: Dr. Massey raised the question as to whether the radical might be associated with sulfur or iron. Certainly all the evidence available points to the fact that the sulfur which is present in the enzyme is associated with iron. And since Dr. Beinert has shown by his [57]Fe experiments that there is some spin density at the iron, we ought to accept that the signal of 1.94 is associated with a certain Fe-S system. In that way Dr. Massey's and Dr. Beinert's thoughts could be reconciled.

CHANCE: Dr. Beinert read into the record that chemical determination of valence states is unreliable. Maybe he just meant that in a special context.

BEINERT: I mean of course that chemical determinations may be right, but you can't be sure. As I see it, if you get results that may be right but may also be wrong, you can consider the method as unreliable.

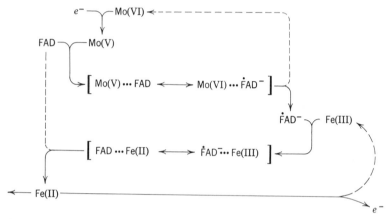

**Fig. 4.** Schematic representation of interactions of electron carriers in a Mo-Fe flavo-protein during electron transport.

CHANCE: This is true not of all compounds, but just some particular compound. I'm trying to say that you have made a very general statement.

BEINERT: The ideas that Dr. Hemmerich's chemical studies have brought into the flavin field, taken together with our findings on flavin saturation and the kinetic data we have obtained with Dr. Palmer, Dr. Handler's group, and Dr. Singer, would indicate that all this information can perhaps be reconciled. Dr. Hemmerich and I have composed a scheme shown in Fig. 4 which may account for some of the things that are going on. This describes electron transfer in enzymes such as xanthine oxidase and aldehyde oxidase. The way we have written it here does not take account of the fact that the carriers, molybdenum, flavin, and the irons are, probably, pretty well fixed in their locations. While it might seem as if they can float around freely, this is not meant. They are fixed, but of course they have to come together some way. Now, when an electron passes into xanthine oxidase (top line), it would first reduce molybdenum(VI), which would go to molybdenum-(V), and then to the flavin resonance form shown. According to Dr. Hemmerich's work with models, molybdenum(V) and oxidized flavin are in resonance with molybdenum(VI) and flavin radical. Eventually a flavin radical dissociates from the molybdenum(VI) and encounters the trivalent iron on the other side. This would again form the next resonance system of iron(III) and flavin radical, which is in resonance with oxidized flavin and iron(II). This would eventually have an iron dissociated out of the complex, iron(II), which would be ready to interact with oxygen. This would take account of our saturation data, indicating that there is really a measurable interaction of flavin radical and metal. There are, of course, also objections to such a scheme. Dr. Vänngård has pointed out to me that when you have a considerable amount of such a resonance system, as is shown in the brackets, you would expect to see this in the signals. You might not, however, see any molybdenum signal under these conditions, or you might get a changed radical signal. We in fact do get a changed radical signal insofar as the saturation changes. It should be pointed out that in these proteins only about 30%, or at the best 40%, of the molybdenum can be found by integration, so the rest of the molybdenum is never seen. Maybe this is the portion present in the resonance form, but I would not say that this is the only way to explain the data. It seems that the scheme shown gets all the information nicely together.

WINFIELD: I'm still not clear about what Dr. Beinert means in his last scheme when he shows an FAD radical near a molybdenum atom. I'm very pleased to see something concrete; but I would have thought that if the flavin radical were coordinated in any way to the metal atom, he would get quite a different spectrum. The fact that he obtains a free-radical signal with decreased saturation suggests that the molybdenum atom is not chemically attached. Perhaps the presence of molybdenum in the general vicinity of the free radical is able to ease the relaxation problem.

BEINERT: I did mention that this was an objection to the scheme. When you have a resonance system such as that presented, the molybdenum might grossly change the signal or it might not give a molybdenum signal at all. It may be that we are, in fact, never observing all of the molybdenum—and maybe the molybdenum which is in the resonance form is the one that we are not seeing.

WINFIELD: This doesn't really satisfy me because I still am looking at this problem in another way. I feel that, if your free radical were near the molybdenum, you wouldn't see a radical signal. If it were near in the sense of being chemically bonded, you would see what looked to be a metal signal.

BEINERT: Perhaps so. We see only part of the flavin in the free-radical form, and perhaps that part which belongs to the resonance form is not seen at all.

ESTABROOK: Isn't part of the discussion related to the question of how quantitatively you can evaluate your data in the spin resonance technique? If you do not believe any of the chemical analyses, how do you know how much iron you are reducing, and how can you therefore quantitate what you are identifying with the spin resonance signal?

BEINERT: Dr. Estabrook, I do not want to discredit chemical iron analysis! If you look in the literature, you will still find people referring to my methods for microanalysis for iron and copper. I just don't believe that you can reliably determine the valence state of a metal in a metal protein. This is another matter, but otherwise I do agree with you. The second point, that ESR integrations and quantitative evaluations are very shaky and that very often you have to be satisfied to be within a factor of 2, is certainly at the moment a serious drawback of much of the ESR work. This is definitely true in the work on xanthine aldehyde oxidase.

SINGER: I'd like to come to Dr. Beinert's rescue, lest he go on record as the only person feeling that valence-state determinations by chemical methods are unreliable. I think that he is referring to the fact that, in a joint review with Dr. Massey published in 1958, it was shown that data published before that time regarding the valence of iron in metal flavoproteins, as determined by chemical methods, turned out to be erroneous. Several papers have appeared since then dealing with the same problem but using new methods. Although this has not been published, several laboratories find these new methods to be just as unreliable as those published before 1958. Thus, there is still no unequivocal chemical method to determine the valence of iron in iron flavoproteins.

EHRENBERG: I wanted to mention that we have made some calibrations and tried to compare the measurement of free radicals in irradiated materials in a number of laboratories. A simple system, irradiated glucose, was used which gives fairly stable radicals and should produce very good results. There were seven laboratories involved [Köhnlein et al., Second International Congress of Radiation Research, Harrogabe, 1962; for details cf. J. W. Boag, in M. Ebert and A. Howard, Eds., Radiation Effects in Physics, Chemistry, and Biology, North-Holland Publishing Co., Amsterdam, 1963, p. 194] and there is a factor of 1.5 or so between the quantitative measurements of the different laboratories on exactly the same samples.

MASSEY: Can we hear why these methods are unreliable? If this is supposed to be a scientific conference, it's not good enough just to say that they are unreliable. Let's have some information.

MASON: In reply to Dr. Massey, the reason why the chemical determination of valence in metalloproteins is unreliable is that if the protein contains any oxidizing equivalents or any reducing equivalents, other than those in the metal, at the moment at which the metal is released from its protein ligand either oxidation or reduction can occur, and the valence of the metal can change before the chelating agent picks it up for determination.

MASSEY: Well, having myself demonstrated that because of extraneous reductive processes these methods are unreliable, I am willing to accept that part of Dr. Mason's statement, but what about the oxidative ones? What are we going to use to oxidize ferrous iron to ferric? Presumably flavin radical would be preferred in order to do this. In this case, if you are going to get reoxidation of ferrous iron, you should now get $FADH_2$. Now we have looked for this; and although these are certainly only preliminary experiments, we can't find that we get $FADH_2$ out of semiquinone with these metalloflavoproteins when we denature.

SLATER: I should like to defend the standpoint of Dr. Massey. Surely it would be nice to have chemical evidence too that the iron is being reduced in the course of this reaction. There is no doubt from the beautiful data of Beinert that whatever is responsible for the $g = 1.94$ signal follows kinetically the same course as the free radical and that it is very likely to be involved in the enzyme reaction. The point that Dr. Massey is making is whether or not an actual reduction of the iron is involved in the appearance of the $g = 1.94$ signal. I don't see how you are going to answer that question until you face up to the problem of trying to do some chemical analyses of the valence state of the iron.

CHANCE: I think what Dr. Slater means is that you need more model compounds for ESR and better oxidants and reductants.

BEINERT: I think that the answer will come from finding a model compound for the $g = 1.94$ signal, and making sure what valence the iron in these model compounds has. I think that I would consider this approach much more promising than trying to decide this by chemical methods. Now, in regard to why chemical determinations of the valence state in metal proteins are unreliable, I point out in my contribution to this symposium that the oxidant could be a sulfur system, or it could be in what is being added. In our case it was the $p$-CMS we were adding that brought about oxidation via a S-S, SH system.

CHANCE: I suppose we would satisfy everyone by saying that, when you have the model compound, you'll determine its valence by chemical methods.

HANDLER: You will recall that the circumstances under which one obtains the $g = 1.94$ signal are those in which one also observes characteristic bleaching of every one of these iron proteins in the visible region of the spectrum. This is one of the criteria that Dr. Winfield proposed, and it has been completely satisfied. This is what led to the present studies of changes in optical rotatory dispersion as this same group of iron flavoproteins undergoes reduction. Each shows a pronounced Cotton effect in the visible portion of the spectrum, but clearly these curves are not absorption spectra and the changes in dispersion do not simply mirror the change in absorbancy at any wavelength. Each represents a solution of a protein at comparable iron concentration. Even though the flavin is bleached, the dispersion changes seen upon reduction of aldehyde oxidase, xanthine oxidase, and the $b$-$c$ iron protein are similar in character. However, although the absorption spectrum of the dihydroorotic acid dehydrogenase iron protein resembles that of the other members of this group, its reduction by dihydroorotate and the reduction of the derived iron protein by dithionite yield rather different changes in dispersion at longer wavelengths, indicating that, although the ligands about the iron of this enzyme may resemble those in the other members of the group, the conformational change induced by reduction is rather dramatically different. None of these changes, however, is as profound as that induced in PPNR by acid.

KING: It seems to me that these spectra can be better explained (if not better, equally well explained) by conformational changes of the proteins. Of course, conformational change of a protein may be effected by causes other than oxidation-reduction states of the protein.

HANDLER: I think the answer to that statement is that, for the enzymes of a different category (i.e., lactic dehydrogenase in the presence of lactate—enzymes which do not have functional metals), the presence of a substrate simply does not elicit any change in conformation evident in the visible portion of the spectrum. Proteins generally show a rather characterless optical rotatory dispersion except down at very low wavelengths, and that seems to reflect the amount of helix in the protein.

YONETANI: I believe that these enzymes show absorption changes during oxidation-reduction. If so, these observed changes in ORD merely reflect spectral, not conformational, changes.

HANDLER: I am sorry. That is not so. Remember that what is being measured is the optical rotation of the enzyme protein at each wavelength along that curve; that is, you are not looking at an absorption curve at all.

YONETANI: I mean that these changes in Cotton effect could be caused by changes in absorption as well as conformation. Therefore, without measuring Moffit-Yang parameters, you cannot say whether or not conformational changes are involved in these cases.

HANDLER: You're quite correct. But you can't have this happening unless at the same time there is a conformational change; otherwise you wouldn't see this. It is not merely a function of the absorption at those wavelengths, because the change in absorbancy doesn't follow that pattern at all. It follows a quite different pattern.

KING: In reply to Dr. Handler's examples for lactic dehydrogenase and so forth, I think that is the beauty of metalloprotein, because those proteins contain different transition elements and ligands change with oxidation states. That is why I am worried about the conformational changes. What I am getting at is that the conformations of metalloproteins change with oxidation or reduction.

HANDLER: That is precisely what we were trying to demonstrate!

MORRISON: If rotation measurements are made through the region of an absorption maximum which is an optically active absorption band, a Cotton effect will be observed. If the chromaphore is altered, thus changing the spectrum, there will, of course, be changes in the optical rotatory dispersion curves. These changes will be most dramatic in the regions of the Cotton effect, as Dr. Handler observed. This does not mean that the configuration of the protein has changed. It reflects the changes in the chromaphore.

We have been interested in the changes in configuration of proteins and polypeptides, because we felt that in most of the enzymes being discussed this is the rate-limiting phenomenon. The rate-limiting steps in the turnover of the cytochromes are really in the changes in conformation of the protein. Therefore, we have also looked into optical rotatory dispersion, and I am pleased to be able to show you some really spectacular results.

This study was performed in conjunction with Dr. Jack Duffield and Paige Hooper of Cary Instrument Company. The instrument was a prototype of the Cary Spectrapolarimeter model 60 and a prototype magnet. Figure 5 shows the ORD (optical rotatory dispersion) curves of reduced cytochrome $c$.

You will note the marked Cotton effect at the absorption maxima at 550 and 415 m$\mu$ with less clear but discernible effects in the regions of the $\beta$-peak. Now, if you take the more dilute preparation of cytochrome $c$, 0.007 $mM$, and place it in a magnet field, you get the magnetically induced optical rotation, a truly spectacular change from the ORD curve. A great deal of fine structure is apparent in the curve of Fig. 6. One of the most interesting things about this fine structure is that the wavelengths at which the Cotton effects occur are reminiscent of the maxima in the spectrum of cytochrome $c$ at the temperature of liquid air. I wonder whether some of the theoreticians in the group would be able to give us some comments on this.

CHANCE: What is that 549 m$\mu$ peak? Is that the room-temperature spectrum? Why do you say liquid nitrogen?

MORRISON: All the spectrum were at room temperature. In the ideal Cotton effect, the wavelength at which there is zero rotation is identical with the absorption maximum. 549 m$\mu$ is the peak of the Cotton effect but does not coincide with the absorption maxima. The point I was making is that the multiple Cotton effects

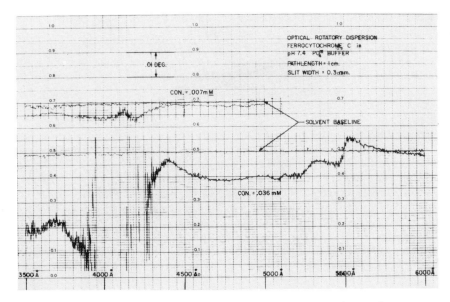

**Fig. 5.** The optical rotatory dispersion of reduced cytochrome *c*. The cytochrome *c* was purified by the column chromatography [Morrison, Hollocher, Murray, Marinetti, and Stotz, *Biochem. et Biophys. Acta*, **41**, 334 (1960)] and reduced with solid dithionite. The solvent was 0.05 *M* phosphate buffer, pH 7.4. The concentrations of cytochrome *c* were 0.036 *mM* and 0.007 *mM* as indicated. (Unpublished data, Morrison, Duffield, and Hooper.)

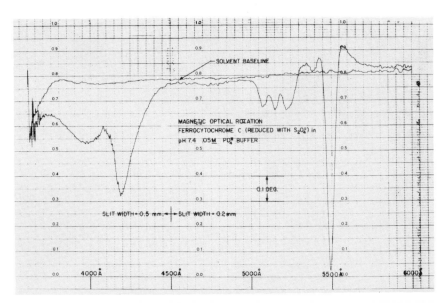

**Fig. 6.** Magnetically induced optical rotation of reduced cytochrome *c*. The cytochrome *c* was the same as that used for Fig. 5. The concentration of cytochrome *c* was 0.007 *mM*. (Unpublished data, Morrison, Duffield and Hooper.)

and their positions are reminiscent of the low-temperature spectrum of cytochrome $c$.

CHANCE: Did you look at lower wavelengths?

MORRISON: No, we haven't looked at lower wavelengths. We have looked at denatured cytochrome $c$, however, and we can't see very much difference.

CAUGHEY: I just wondered what magnetic field was used.

MORRISON: The mean magnetic field is 5000 gauss.

CHANCE: This is a remarkable figure. The magnetic field didn't affect your detector?

MORRISON: No.

KING: What is the difference between the dispersion changes you find and those of Eichhorn and Cairns [*Nature*, **181**, 994 (1958)]?

MORRISON: I didn't bring that out, but our results differ from theirs. The data are not plotted in exactly the same way. The data in our figures have not been replotted. Their data were plotted on a molar basis. But we are not in agreement.

KING: You mean that their results are wrong?

MORRISON: Yes.

# Generation of Active Oxygen
# for Mixed-Function Oxidation

... I. C. GUNSALUS, H. E. CONRAD,
and P. W. TRUDGILL

## I. NATURE OF MIXED-FUNCTION OXIDATION

Among the most important biological conversions in the initial stages of metabolic degradation of many substrates are those in which molecular oxygen is incorporated into the substrate molecule. The oxygen-fixing reactions are ubiquitous in nature, occurring in plants, animals, and microorganisms. They represent a general biological means for primary attack on cyclic and acyclic hydrocarbons and their derivatives. In addition, they participate in several important biosynthetic reactions, such as the formation of tyrosine (1), the cyclization of squalene (2), and the desaturation of fatty acids (3). An organism which lacks the capacity to carry out such reactions is usually unable to utilize these substrates or to form certain essential metabolites.

The mixed-function oxidases, with which this report is concerned, are characterized by the cleavage of molecular oxygen with the incorporation of one atom into the substrate and the reduction of the other to water (4). The reactions catalyzed by this mechanism include hydroxylations of aliphatic or aromatic carbons, epoxidations of double bonds, lactonizations of cyclic ketones, and conversions of acyclic ketones to esters. With some substrates several oxygenations may occur in sequence with one such reaction generating the substrate for a subsequent one. For example, in the pathway shown in Fig. 1, conversion of the C-5 methylene group of camphor (I) to a ketone by hydroxylation and dehydrogenation yields the cyclic ketone substrate for the mixed-function oxidative lactonization of IX to yield X.

Although only a few mixed-function oxidase systems have proved amenable to detailed study (5–9), several general characteristics of this group of enzymes have emerged. In addition to molecular oxygen, a two-electron donor is required, and water is formed from the atom of oxygen not incorporated into the substrate. The electron donor may be reduced pyridine nucleotide

(5, 6), ascorbic acid (9), or even the substrate to be oxygenated (7, 8). In most of the systems which have been studied in detail a metal ion plays a functional role in the oxygenation, presumably serving as the site of activation of the oxygen molecule. The metal ion most commonly associated with these systems is iron, but copper has also been reported (4). The iron is dipyridyl-reactive and is thus non-heme iron. More recently, dissociable electron carrier cofactors have been implicated in several mixed-function oxidase

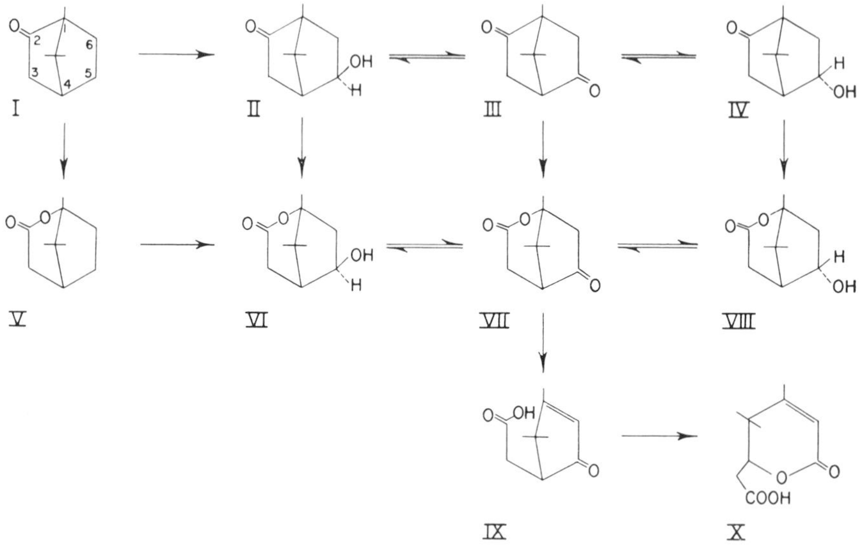

Fig. 1. The lactonization reaction in metabolism of camphor by pseudomonads.

systems. To date these cofactors have been either pteridines (5) or flavins (6, 10–12).

Other general characteristics of mixed-function oxidases have been some-what on the negative side. For example, the mammalian hydroxylating systems are frequently localized in mitochondria or microsomes, and attempts to purify these activities have been attended with the usual difficulties associated with fractionation of particulate systems. In microbial systems, especially in *Pseudomonas* and *Mycobacterium* species, where mixed-function oxidases are found often, the enzymes are less commonly associated with particulate systems, but fractionation attempts have still resulted in rapid and irreparable loss of activity. Sulfhydryl compounds and chelating agents added in attempts to stabilize enzymes often have proved inhibitory. These difficulties are compounded by enzyme assays rendered tedious by use of highly reduced substrates often having solubilities below the concentrations required for enzyme saturation and by products lacking functional groups which would facilitate rapid assay.

## II. THE LACTONIZATION REACTION

Several years ago our studies of the inducible metabolism of camphor (I, in Fig. 1) by pseudomonads (13) led to the discovery of a soluble mixed-function oxidase system for the lactonization of camphor and several of its metabolites as shown in Fig. 1 (6). Similar reactions occur in fungal conversions of the steroid rings A and D (14). Their catalyses by extracts of such organisms have been described (15, 16). The lactone ring oxygen derives from molecular oxygen by reactions which require an electron donor (15). Thus, this type of reaction is a *bona fide* mixed-function oxidation.

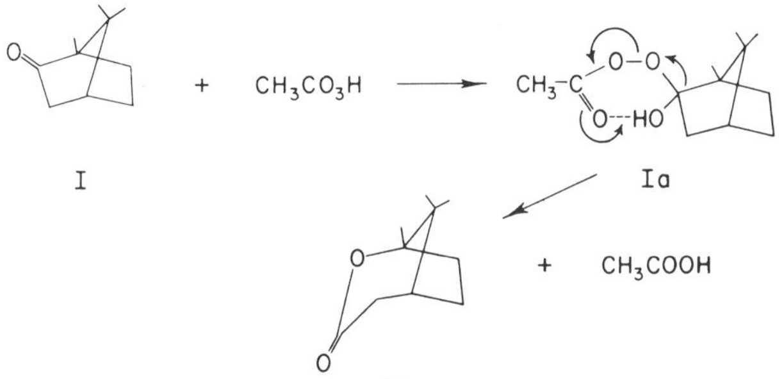

Fig. 2.   Baeyer-Villager oxidation of camphor. [From (17) by permission of the *Journal of the American Chemical Society.*]

The organic conversion of camphor to its 1,2-campholide (V) is accomplished by treatment with peracetic acid in the Baeyer-Villager reaction (17). The mechanism proposed for this conversion requires a nucleophilic attack of the peracid anion on the carbonyl carbon followed by the migration of the bridgehead carbon to the peroxide of the adduct and elimination of acetic acid (Fig. 2). This mechanism is fairly well established and lacks much of the ambiguity associated with the several proposed mechanisms for hydroxylation (4, 5). Thus, to the extent that the Baeyer-Villager reaction represents a valid model system for enzymatic lactonization, it is clear that the function of the enzyme system is to generate an active peroxide and to exert the specificity observed in the metabolic conversions. In our system, the raw materials for peroxide generation are DPNH and $O_2$.

Since our initial observation (18, 19) of the biological counterpart of the Baeyer-Villager reaction, these investigations have developed through a recognition of the enzymes and cofactors involved and a formulation of their mode of participation in lactonization (6, 20, 21). The enzymes have been purified, and some of their physical and chemical properties examined (6, 21).

The stereochemical specificity of enzyme induction by camphor and structurally related compounds has been studied (22, 23). In addition the nature of the catalytic site of lactonization has been considered by analysis of the structures of compounds serving as substrates or inhibitors (24, 25). Upon directing our attention to the nature of the coupling of the enzyme components of the lactonizing system, we found that the enzymes and cofactors can be purified as an enzyme complex (24). The ensuing development of the concept of a loosely associated electron-transport complex which interacts specifically and characteristically with different types of substrates and inhibitors (25) has led to the formulation of a general working model for mixed-function oxidation. These studies serve as a basis for the present report.

## III. CHARACTERIZATION OF THE OXIDASE-KETOLACTONASE ENZYME SYSTEM

### A. Reaction Sequence

Early in this work it became clear that our system was composed of two enzymes, $E_1$ and $E_2$, and a flavin cofactor which dialyzed readily from the initial *Pseudomonas* cell extracts (6). Maximal lactonization activity was attained with FMN at $10^{-5} M$; FAD at the same concentration was only one-third as active. It also developed early that the lactonization was strongly inhibited by $10^{-4} M$ dipyridyl and that the functional metal ion, iron, was bound to the enzyme which interacted directly with oxygen and the

TABLE 1

Cofactor Content of Purified Enzymes

| Cofactor | Moles/Mole Enzyme[a] | |
| --- | --- | --- |
| | Oxidase (S.A.[b] = 28) | Ketolactonase (S.A.[b] = 0.75) |
| Total iron | 0.11 | 1.01 |
| Heme iron | <0.005 | 0.015 |
| Flavin | 0.016 | 0.094 |
| Molybdenum | ... | <0.001 |
| Copper | ... | 0.076 |

[a] The molecular weights of oxidase and ketolactonase were taken as 50,000 and 80,000, respectively, based on sucrose density gradient centrifugation.

[b] Specific activities = units/mg protein when 1 unit = 1 $\mu$mole substrate converted/min.

cyclic ketone substrate; see Table 1. These observations led to a tentative formulation of the reaction sequence as follows:

$$DPNH + H^+ + FMN \xrightarrow{E_1} DPN^+ + FMNH_2 \tag{1}$$

$$FMNH_2 + E_2 \cdot 2Fe^{3+} \longrightarrow FMN + E_2 \cdot 2Fe^{2+} \tag{2a}$$

$$FMNH_2 + O_2 \longrightarrow FMN + H_2O_2 \tag{2b}$$

$$E_2 \cdot 2Fe^{2+} + O_2 + I + 2H^+ \longrightarrow E_2 \cdot 2Fe^{3+} + V + H_2O \tag{3}$$

$$DPNH + H^+ + O_2 + I \longrightarrow DPN^+ + V + H_2O \qquad \text{Sum: } 1 + 2a + 3$$

where I = camphor, and V = 1,2-campholide, Fig. 1. As indicated in this formulation, $E_1$ is simply a DPNH oxidase which reduces free FMN. The rapid rate of auto-oxidation of reduced FMN (equation 2b) permits assay of $E_1$ by measurement of the rate of DPNH oxidation in the presence of a catalytic but saturating amount of FMN.

## B. Oxygen Stoichiometry

The early assays of lactonization were carried out by Warburg respirometry, using camphor as substrate. The DPNH was generated from DPN and

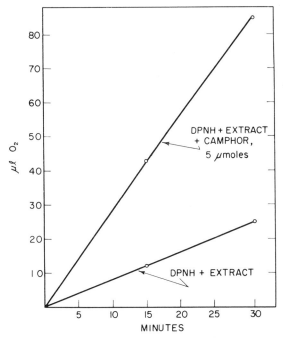

**Fig. 3.** Warburg assay of lactonization. Assays contain in $\mu$moles/1.3 ml: 50 Tris, pH 7.2; 1 DPN; 20 G-6-P, and the following enzymes: 1.6 units G-6-P DH; 0.1 ml = 2 mg cell extract or lactonizing complex; G-6-P DH unit converts 1 $\mu$mole G-6-P/min.

glucose-6-phosphate by the glucose-6-phosphate dehydrogenase from *Leuconostoc mesenteroides* (26). Incubation of this DPNH generating system with cell extracts and camphor gave the results shown in Fig. 3. The $O_2$ uptake with DPNH alone was attributed to reactions $1 + 2b$, in which loosely bound flavin was readily autoxidized to yield $H_2O_2$. The initial extracts contained catalase, and the assumption was made that for each mole of $H_2O_2$ formed (and consequently for each mole of DPNH oxidized) $\frac{1}{2}$ mole of $O_2$ was returned to the system. For this sequence, therefore, $\frac{1}{2}$ mole of $O_2$ is taken up per mole of DPNH oxidized, and 1 mole of water is formed. In the presence of camphor, however, reactions $1 + 2a + 3$ were assumed to prevail with a stoichiometry of 1 mole of oxygen taken up per mole of DPNH oxidized. Thus, the respiration data were rationalized on the basis of the ultimate fate of the DPNH electrons, assuming the rate of DPNH oxidation to be identical in the presence and the absence of camphor. This assumption seemed likely at the time but was not tested.

## C. Enzyme Assays

To purify $E_1$, the DPNH oxidase, and $E_2$, the ketolactonase, reproducible assays for both crude and fractionated cells extracts were needed. An assay for $E_1$ was based on the rate of DPNH oxidation with a saturating level of FMN ($2 \times 10^{-5}\,M$) added. A reliable assay for $E_2$, however, presented several problems. The oxygen uptake stimulated by camphor as described above did not prove to be a reproducible measure of lactonization because of the high rate of oxygen uptake in the absence of camphor and the variable rates of competing reactions in its presence. Furthermore, upon fractionation of the system, loss of flavin results in loss of lactonization activity, and the concentration of FMN added back becomes quite critical in terms of an $O_2$ uptake assay for reasons which will be described later. Therefore, a suitable assay for lactonization was developed in which the conversion of III to IX via the unstable intermediate lactone VII (6) was measured, thus taking advantage of the high extinction coefficient of IX ($E_{235} = 15,000\,\text{cm}^2/\text{mmole}$). Upon incubation of appropriate levels of $E_1$ and $E_2$ with DPN, glucose-6-phosphate, glucose-6-phosphate dehydrogenase, FMN, and III on a Dubnoff shaker, the rate of IX formation is proportional to the amount of $E_2$ added as determined from the O.D.$_{235}$ read against a blank from which III is omitted, after the reaction is stopped by addition of metaphosphoric acid.

This assay has several anomalous kinetic properties which, in the main, are attributed to side reactions—i.e., reactions other than 1, 2a, and 3—of $O_2$, FMN, and DPNH. First, it is not possible to saturate $E_2$ with $E_1$ (Fig. 4a). This is attributed to the failure to achieve levels of $FMNH_2$ sufficient to saturate $E_2$ because of the rapid autoxidation of $FMNH_2$. Therefore, to assay $E_2$ a fixed level of $E_1$ is chosen such that an approximately linear rate

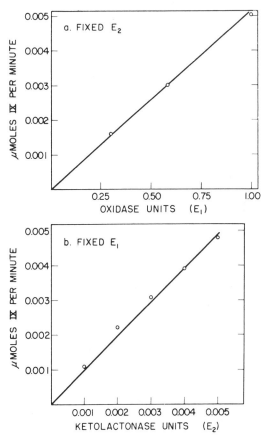

**Fig. 4.** Effect of oxidase and ketolactonase concentration on lactonization rate. Assay contained in $\mu$moles/0.2 ml: 10 Tris, pH 7.2; 0.06 DPN; 0.002 FMN; 6 G-6-P; 0.2 2,5-diketocamphane; and enzyme units = 0.33 G-6-P DH; fixed $E_1$ = 0.17; fixed $E_2$ = 0.001. Incubation 15 min, 30°C. Reaction stopped 0.8 ml 5 % $H_3PO_4$; IX estimated O.D.[235] ($E_{1\,cm}^{M}$ = 15,000 cm²/mmole).

of IX accumulation as a function of $E_2$ added is attained (Fig. 4b). Second, in this assay the concentrations of both DPN and FMN are critical. For maximal rate of IX formation it is necessary to use a level of DPN insufficient to saturate $E_1$. Higher DPN concentrations lower the lactonization rate markedly. This inhibition is ascribed to destruction by DPNH of the enzyme-activated oxygen, as will be discussed in section VIC of this paper. Similarly, there is an optimum FMN concentration for lactonization, $10^{-5}$ $M$; see Fig. 5. In contrast, for the $E_1$ assay, an increase in FMN concentration beyond the lowest saturating level does not alter the rate of DPNH oxidation (Fig. 5).

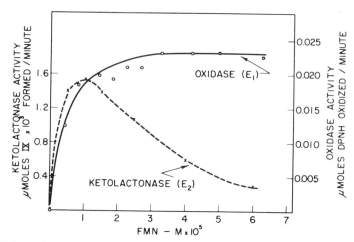

**Fig. 5.** Effect of FMN concentration of oxidase and ketolactonase activities. Assays: oxidase ($E_1$) contains in $\mu$moles/1.3 ml: 50 Tris, pH 7.2; 1 DPNH; FMN as indicated. Enzyme about 0.02 unit purified oxidase; 1 unit = 1 $\mu$mole DPNH oxidized/min. Keto-lactonase ($E_2$): conditions as for Fig. 4. Enzyme about 0.0015 unit. 1 unit = 1 $\mu$mole IX formed/min.

## D. Purification of $E_1$ and $E_2$

Using the assays described above, $E_1$ has been purified fifty-fold to a specific activity of 40 $\mu$moles DPNH oxidized/min/mg of protein; $E_2$ has been purified thirty-fold to a maximum specific activity of 1.5 $\mu$moles III lactonized/min/mg of protein. The purest preparations of $E_1$ show two major components in the ultracentrifuge, while $E_2$ at its maximum specific activity sediments as a single peak with an $S_{20,w}$ of 4.4. By sucrose density gradient centrifugation, molecular weights have been estimated at 50,000 for $E_1$ and 80,000 for $E_2$. The cofactor contents of the two enzymes are shown in Table 1. Although $E_1$ is devoid of cofactors, $E_2$ contains significant levels of bound iron and flavin (estimated as FMN). Heme, present in the early stages of purification, is reduced to a low level in the purest $E_2$ preparations. That heme does not play a functional role in the lactonization reaction is suggested by the failure of CO, $CN^-$, or $N_3^-$ to inhibit the reaction; see Table 8.

## IV. THE COUPLING OF OXIDASE ($E_1$) WITH KETOLACTONASE ($E_2$)

In the assay described above for $E_2$, a large proportion of the DPNH electrons is drained off by autoxidation of reduced FMN to form $H_2O_2$. It can be shown that this $H_2O_2$ does not participate in the lactonization, since catalase does not inhibit the reaction and glucose oxidase, which generates

$H_2O_2$, does not replace the DPNH-$E_1$-FMN system in the $E_2$ assay. From this experiment we have concluded that the active oxygen for lactonization is generated on $E_2$ by combination of the reduced enzyme with $O_2$, probably at the iron site. To determine whether the poor efficiency is an uncoupling of the system which results on aging or fractionation of the extracts, we attempted to re-examine the coupling between $E_1$ and $E_2$ in the fresh, alumina-ground extracts by two procedures.

## A. Centrifugation and Coupling

First, it was felt that, if $E_1$ and $E_2$ were coupled in these extracts, they might sediment together in a sucrose density gradient at a rate greater than that of either purified enzyme. Comparison of the sedimentation rates of purified $E_1$ and $E_2$ in a sucrose gradient with the rates of these activities present in a particle-free unfractionated extract, freshly prepared by grinding cells with alumina, has shown, however, that the major portions of the $E_1$ and $E_2$ activities of the extract separate and sediment at rates similar to those of their "purified" counterparts. Thus, if physical coupling of these two enzymes exists in the intact cell, it appears to be of such low strength that it is broken either during grinding of the cells or during centrifugation in the high sucrose concentration.

## B. Substrate Requirement for DPNH Oxidation

In a second attempt to measure coupling of oxidase and ketolactonase, we re-examined the oxygen uptake rates, comparing them with rates of DPNH oxidation and product accumulation in the enzyme reaction. First the rates of $O_2$ utilization were examined. It must be recalled that this assay system is essentially a cell extract to which is added an optimum level of DPNH-generating system for lactone formation. In the early Warburg experiments we had not realized that flavin participates in lactonization or that two enzymes are involved; therefore, in these experiments only the FMN contained in the cell extracts was present. This amount of flavin is sufficient for lactonization to occur, as indicated by increase in oxygen uptake rate on addition of camphor to the system (Fig. 3). Since the extracts of camphor-induced cells are quite yellow and analyze for $10^{-4}$ $M$ FMN (difference in O.D.$_{450}$ after dithionite reduction), it is apparent that the amount of extract used for Warburg assays furnishes a final FMN concentration of approximately $10^{-5}$ $M$, which is near the optimum for maximum rates of lactonization as measured by product accumulation and $E_1$ activity (Fig. 5).

Next the rates of DPNH oxidation were examined. The rate of DPNH oxidation in the $E_1$ assay to which excess flavin ($2 \times 10^{-5}$ $M$ FMN) is added is found to be far in excess of that calculated from the rate of oxygen uptake with extract plus DPNH in the absence of camphor, provided the stoichiometry of equations 1 + 2b + the catalase reaction is valid. Since the FMN concentration in the extracts is sufficient to saturate the oxidase ($E_1$), i.e., $10^{-5} M$ (see Fig. 5), it can only be concluded that the flavin in the extract is not autoxidizable, as required in the oxidase assay. Therefore, we have concluded that the two enzymes must be coupled in a way to make the flavin poorly accessible to $O_2$ and that the rate of $FMNH_2$ autoxidation is limiting the rate of DPNH oxidation. This concept is confirmed by the demonstration of substrate (camphor) stimulation of the DPNH oxidation rate, apparently resulting from a more rapid flow of electrons through the system to $O_2$ via the lactonization mechanism than by $FMNH_2$ autoxidation.

## C. Uncoupling with Dipyridyl

In earlier experiments we had observed that the lactonization inhibitor dipyridyl, at $10^{-4} M$, stimulates the rate of $O_2$ uptake by cell extracts in the absence of added substrate (camphor) or FMN. Since dipyridyl does not inhibit the oxidase assay but does react with the iron in purified lactonase after it is reduced by oxidase or dithionite (6), one may conclude that chelation of the ferrous iron of the ketolactonase ($E_2$) uncouples oxidase-ketolactonase complex, permitting autoxidation of the bound FMN. If this explanation is correct, addition of dipyridyl to the coupled system should enhance the DPNH oxidation, and the amount of stimulation of these rates by camphor should be markedly reduced. It has, in fact, been found that the DPNH oxidation and the oxygen uptake rates catalyzed by cell extracts are increased by dipyridyl to a rate equivalent to that obtained with camphor, and that camphor does not further enhance this rate.

## D. FMN-Coupled $E_1 \cdot E_2$ Complex

These two sets of experimental results have led to the hypothesis that, other observations to the contrary, $E_1$ and $E_2$ in initial cell extracts are actually complexed through FMN and that the FMN is bound in a manner which precludes rapid autoxidation. According to this hypothesis, the rate of DPNH oxidation catalyzed by the extracts alone is determined by the rate of egress of electrons from the complex to oxygen. When no lactonization substrate is present, electrons presumably are lost via slow autoxidation of the bound FMN. Addition of substrate allows an increased rate of electron egress via the lactonization mechanism. Added dipyridyl chelates the iron, uncoupling the complex and allowing an increased rate of egress via the autoxidation of FMN. The predicted stimulation of rates by both substrates is seen in Table 2. Camphor stimulates equivalent molar rates of DPNH and $O_2$ consumption. The excessive rate of diketocamphane-stimulated

## TABLE 2

### Substrate-DPNH Coupling in Cell Extracts

| Substrate | Additions | Rates, $\mu$moles/min/mg protein | | |
|---|---|---|---|---|
| | | DPNH Oxidation[a] | $O_2$ Uptake[b] | Cyclopentenone Formation[c] |
| None | ... | 0.014 | 0.015 | ... |
| (+)-Camphor (I) | ... | 0.060 | 0.069 | ... |
| Diketocamphane (III) | ... | 0.430 | 0.068 | 0.017 |
| None | $\alpha,\alpha'$-Dipyridyl 7.5 $mM$ | 0.030 | 0.030 | ... |

[a] Assay contained in $\mu$moles/1.3 ml: 50 Tris, pH 7.2; 1 DPNH; 1 substrate; and 0.62 mg protein. $\Delta$ O.D.$_{340}$ followed in $\frac{1}{2}$ cm curvette at 25°.

[b] Assay contained in $\mu$moles/1.3 ml: 50 Tris, pH 7.2; 1 DPN; 20 G-6-P; 5 substrate; and 1.6 units G-6-P DH plus 3.1 mg protein. $O_2$ measured in Warburg at 30°.

[c] Warburg runs above stopped with 1.0 ml 5% $H_3PO_4$, precipitated protein centrifuged, and O.D.$_{235}$ of diketocamphane sample read against sample with no substrate. IX calculated using $E_{1cm}^M = 15,000$ cm$^2$/mmole.

DPNH oxidation reflects lactonization of the substrate plus its reduction to the two keto alcohols (II and IV, Fig. 1) by the dehydrogenases present. The stimulation of $O_2$ uptake with the diketocamphane, however, is due solely to increased lactonization. The bottom line shows the enhanced rates attributed to uncoupling by dipyridyl. Thus, the $O_2$ stoichiometry observed during the initial stages of this work can be explained in terms of the $E_1$-$E_2$ coupling without invoking the dismutation of $H_2O_2$ by catalase. Furthermore, our confidence in the cell's ability to conserve DPNH has been restored.

## V. PROPERTIES OF LACTONIZING COMPLEX

### A. Purification

Study of the properties of the oxidase-ketolactonase complex has necessitated its preparation free of the camphor metabolite dehydrogenases. The coupled activity is assayed by measuring the increase in DPNH oxidation rate when camphor is added to a cuvette containing enzyme and DPNH, but no added FMN. Under these conditions the increment of DPNH oxidation rate dependent on camphor addition is considered to proceed by a stoichiometry of 1 mole each of DPNH, $O_2$, and substrate used per mole of lactone formed. The DPNH-$O_2$ stoichiometry for camphor is shown in

Table 2. Later experiments with fractionated extracts confirm this stoichiometry. Purification of the complex is shown in Table 3. These steps actually give a marked decrease in the specific activity of coupling and poor recovery of activity, but the removal of catalase and of the camphor metabolite dehydrogenases has permitted the determination of specificity and stoichiometry of lactonization which was not possible earlier.

### TABLE 3

#### Purification of the Lactonization Complex

| Fraction | Volume, ml | Protein, mg | Coupling Activity with Camphor | | |
|---|---|---|---|---|---|
| | | | Units,[a] total | Rec., % | S.A.,[b] unit/mg |
| Cell extract | 162 | 5020 | 258. | 100 | 0.052 |
| Concentrate from DEAE eluate, 0.25–0.34 $M$ KCl | 92 | 920 | 21.5 | 8.3 | 0.023 |
| AmSO$_4$ fraction, 0.34–0.50 sat. | 8 | 450 | 6.3 | 2.4[c] | 0.016[d] |

[a] Assay contained in $\mu$moles/1.3 ml: 50 Tris, pH 7.2; 1 DPNH; 1 camphor; and enzyme to give $\Delta$ O.D.$_{340}$ up to 0.200/min in $\frac{1}{2}$ cm cuvette. One unit = camphor-stimulated DPNH oxidation of 1 $\mu$mole DPNH/min.

[b] Specific activity = units/mg protein.

[c] Final product contains 12% of original E$_1$ activity and 8% of original E$_2$ activity.

[d] The purified complex has E$_1$ specific activity = 0.97 and E$_2$ specific activity = 0.15 unit/mg; see Table 1.

### B. Cofactor Content

Analyses of the purified complex for cofactors are shown in Table 4. Although this preparation is by no means pure E$_1$ · E$_2$ complex, for convenience the molar concentrations of cofactors are calculated on the basis of 130,000 g of protein, i.e., the sum of the molecular weights of the oxidase and ketolactonase. It is readily apparent that iron, which is essential for lactonization, is present at a relatively high level, whereas the concentration of flavin, equally essential, is much lower. These data suggest that the loss of activity during the purification results from removal of flavin from its specific binding site in the complex. The heme present is not considered to participate in the catalysis of lactonization, as indicated from earlier studies in which hemoproteins disappeared from purified ketolactonase as specific activity was increased.

## TABLE 4
### Cofactor Analyses of Purified Complex

| Cofactor | Concentration, moles/130,000 g Protein[a] |
|---|---|
| Total iron | 0.640 |
| Heme | 0.053 |
| Flavin | 0.069 |

[a] Enzyme preparation analyzed had the following specific activities: oxidase, 1.2; ketolactonase, 0.12; 2.5-diketocamphane coupling, 0.018; see Tables 1 and 3.

### C. Substrate Specificity

The purified complex catalyzes the lactonization of all the D-(+)-camphor analogs of these oxidation pathways (i.e., I–IV, Fig. 1) regardless of the substituent on the 5-carbon. The maximum turnover rates and affinity constants ($K_m$'s) for these substrates are shown in Table 5. The $K_m$'s range over more than one order of magnitude, but the maximum velocities are

## TABLE 5
### Specificity, Kinetics, and Stoichiometry of Lactonizing Complex

| Substrate | Stoichiometry | | | Kinetic Properties | |
|---|---|---|---|---|---|
| | Substrate Added, $\mu$moles | $O_2$ Used, $\mu$moles | Product Formed, $\mu$moles | $K_m,^a$ $M \times 10^5$ | $V,^a$ S.A.$^b \times 10^2$ |
| Camphor | 2.5 | 2.6 | ... | 19.0 | 1.6 |
| 2,5-Diketo-camphane | 5.0 | 4.6 | 4.9[c] | 1.9 | 2.7 |
| 5-*exo*-Hydroxy-camphor | 5.0 | 5.3 | ... | 33.0 | 1.7 |
| 5-*endo*-Hydroxy-camphor | 5.0 | 4.6 | ... | 6.1 | 2.5 |
| DPNH | ... | ... | ... | 2.9[d] | 2.7[d] |

[a] $K_m$ and $V$ values from Lineweaver-Burk plots.
[b] S.A. = $\mu$moles DPNH oxidized/min/mg protein.
[c] Cyclopentenone (IX).
[d] With 2,5-diketocamphane as substrate.

similar. When pairs of substrates are added together to the enzyme-DPNH mixture, the rates of DPNH oxidation are intermediate between those obtained when these substrates are assayed separately. That is, the individual rates of lactonization of these substrates by the complex are non-additive; thus, it is concluded that a single lactonizing site catalyzes conversion of these four substrates to their corresponding lactones.

The oxygen-substrate stoichiometry for lactonization when these substrates are cleaved by the dehydrogenase-free complex is shown in the left-hand part of Table 5. The mixed-function oxidase stoichiometry, requiring 1 mole of $O_2$ per mole of substrate converted to lactone, is apparent for all four substrates. The stoichiometric conversion of 2,5-diketocamphane to product (cyclopentenone) is also shown. The lactone products from the other substrates are less easily quantitated, but their formation has been demonstrated qualitatively by vapor-phase chromatography.

### D. L-(−)-Camphor Lactonization

LeGall et al. (22) have shown that the pseudomonad in use here, strain $C_1$, grows equally well on L-(−)-camphor and on the D-(+)-enantiomer. During its growth on L-(−)-camphor, one observes accumulation of the enantiomers of compounds II, III, IV, IX, and X obtained from D-(+)-camphor (see Fig. 1). The enantiomers of III and IX were prepared in quantity and rigorously characterized. The others showed the predicted rotations and VPC retention times. The L-camphor and the enantiomers of II, III, and IV (Fig. 1) isolated

**TABLE 6**

**Substrate Stereospecificity of D-Camphor-Induced Lactonizing System**

| Substrate | Lactonization Rate, $\mu$moles × $10^2$/min/mg protein, of Substrate Derived from: | |
| --- | --- | --- |
| | D(+)-Camphor | L(−)-Camphor |
| Camphor (I) | 1.7 | 0.05 |
| Diketocamphane (III) | 2.1 | 0.2 |
| exo-Hydroxycamphor (IV) | 1.7 | 0.3 |
| endo-Hydroxycamphor (II) | 2.0 | 0.1 |

from D-(+)-camphor- and L-(−)camphor-grown cultures were tested as lactonization substrates for the $E_1 \cdot E_2$ complex derived from the D-(+)-camphor-grown cells. The data in Table 6 show that only the intermediates of the D-camphor series are lactonized. Thus D-camphor-induced $E_2$ is specific for lactonization of D-camphor metabolites and does not act on L-camphor metabolites.

The failure of the D-camphor-induced lactonizing system to act on the L-camphor metabolites implies the induction during growth on L-camphor of an analogous set of enzymes specific for conversion in the L series. The data shown in Table 7 demonstrate the induction of a lactonizing system for the L enantiomers. The L-camphor-induced cells also contain lactonizing enzyme activity for the D-camphor analogs. However, the optical rotatory

TABLE 7

Substrate Stereospecificity of L-Camphor-Induced Lactonizing System

| Substrate | Lactonization Rate, $\mu$moles $\times 10^2$/min/mg protein, of Substrate Derived from: | |
| --- | --- | --- |
| | D(+)-Camphor | L(−)-Camphor |
| Camphor (I) | 2.0 | 4.0 |
| Diketocamphane (III) | 1.8 | 2.2 |

dispersion curves indicate the presence of as much as 3% of the D isomer in the L-camphor used for induction. This may be a sufficient level to induce the D-camphor enzymes. The alternate possibility, coordinate induction of the two sets of enzymes by L- but not by D-camphor, is not ruled out but need not be pursued until the first explanation is tested critically. In any event the ketolactonase shows stereospecificity for cyclic ketone (D- vs. L-camphor), Oxidase specificity for the two ketolactonases remains to be tested.

## VI. MODE OF ACTION OF LACTONIZATION INHIBITORS

In addition to offering an explanation of the $O_2$ stoichiometry, the demonstration of the $E_1 \cdot E_2$ complex containing both iron and FMN leads to a clarification of the mode of action of many of the groups of compounds which exert potent inhibitory effects on lactonization. These inhibitors, listed in Tables 8 and 9, fall into several groups: metal ions, chelators, electron acceptors, electron donors, and other substrates, such as $\alpha$-keto acids.

### A. Metal Ions and Chelating Agents

The primary effect of metal ions on the lactonization reaction appears to be on the $E_1$ catalysis of reduction of FMN by DPNH. Purified $E_1$ is markedly inhibited by metal ions at $10^{-3}$ $M$. As noted in Table 8, lactonization is stimulated by $10^{-4}$ $M$ FeSO$_4$, but as the Fe$^{2+}$ concentration is raised,

## TABLE 8
### Effect of Inhibitors on Lactonizing Activity

| Addition | Conc., $mM$ | Activity, % | Addition | Conc., $mM$ | Activity, % |
|---|---|---|---|---|---|
| None | ... | 100 | Electron acceptors | | |
| Chelators | | | Methylene blue | 5.0 | 15 |
| Tiron | 1.0 | 52 | $K_3Fe(CN)_6$ | 0.5 | 69 |
| 2,2′-Bipyridine | 2.0 | 1 | FMN | 0.01 | 100 |
| EDTA | 2.0 | 67 | FMN | 0.04 | 41 |
| Heme reactive agents | | | FMN | 0.075 | 7 |
| Globin | 100 mg/ml | 67 | Luminol | 0.8 | 54 |
| Hemin | 0.03 | 25 | Benzoquinone | 0.5 | 2 |
| Hemin | 0.003 | 70 | Metals | | |
| $NaN_3$ | 1.0 | 104 | $FeSO_4$ | 0.1 | 192 |
| NaCN | 1.0 | 104 | $FeSO_4$ | 0.5 | 92 |
| KF | 5.0 | 78 | $CoCl_2$ | 0.5 | 36 |
| $H_2O_2$ | 5.0 | 100 | $ZnCl_2$ | 0.5 | 21 |
| CO | 0.8 CO, 0.2 $O_2$ | 100 | $FeCl_3$ | 0.5 | 69 |
| | | | $CuCl_2$ | 0.5 | 0 |
| | | | $MnCl_2$ | 0.5 | 72 |

the reaction is inhibited. No other metal ions tested over wide concentrations ranges have been found to stimulate lactonization. The simplest explanation of the $Fe^{2+}$ stimulation is that part of the iron from $E_2$ lost in the enzyme purification is replaced in the above experiment to give an enhanced rate. The level of iron in native $E_2$ requires further investigation.

The inhibition by chelating agents led us to the early implication of a functional metal ion in the lactonization system. The metal was later demonstrated to be iron which was bound to $E_2$. In purified $E_2$ iron undergoes oxidation-reduction and is dipyridyl-reactive only upon reduction. Either the DPNH-$E_1$-FMN system or dithionite is a suitable reducing agent (6). Therefore, the bound iron is visualized as accepting the DPNH electrons in the lactonization reaction. Inhibition by chelators which complex both ferrous and ferric ions further suggests the possibility that iron undergoes oxidation and reduction during the catalytic reaction. Since all chelators tested gave inhibition of lactonization, it was not possible to use chelators to protect the enzyme system from the metal-ion inhibition noted above.

### B. Electron Acceptors

The course of inhibition by electron acceptors is recognized most readily from the bleaching observed when methylene blue is added to the lactonization assay. The methylene blue appears to be reduced by the bound FMN, since its reduction by purified $E_1$ was shown previously to require added FMN. The rate of DPNH oxidation catalyzed by the purified complex is stimulated greatly by added methylene blue. This rate is not decreased when chelating agents are added. It is concluded, therefore, that electrons

## TABLE 9
### Effect of Inhibitors on Lactonizing Activity

| Addition | Conc., $mM$ | Activity, % |
|---|---|---|
| Electron donors | | |
| DPNH | 9.0 | 62 |
| Na ascorbate | 5.0 | 10 |
| $o$-Phenylenediamine | 1.0 | 38 |
| $p$-Phenylenediamine | 1.0 | 67 |
| Na benzoate | 1.0 | 19 |
| Na-$p$-hydroxybenzoate | 1.0 | 14 |
| Na-$p$-aminobenzoate | 1.0 | 11 |
| Resorcinol | 1.0 | 44 |
| Na salicylate | 1.0 | 0 |
| Catechol | 1.0 | 46 |
| $NaNO_2$ | 1.0 | 61 |
| Hydroquinone | 1.0 | 65 |
| Na urate | 1.0 | 39 |
| Tyrosine | 1.0 | 22 |
| Guaiacol | 1.0 | 81 |
| $o$-Toludine | 1.0 | 2 |
| Camphor metabolites | | |
| Camphor | 1.0 | 91 |
| 5-$exo$-Hydroxycamphor | 1.0 | 69 |
| 5-$endo$-Hydroxycamphor | 1.0 | 37 |
| Keto acids | | |
| Na pyruvate | 1.0 | 80 |
| K oxalate | 1.0 | 62 |
| Na-$\alpha$-ketoglutarate | 1.0 | 79 |
| Na oxaloacetate | 1.0 | 78 |
| Na-$\beta$-ketoadipate | 25.0 | 100 |

are transferred from the FMN bound in the complex to methylene blue and that the bound FMN precedes the bound iron in the electron-transfer sequence in the complex (Fig. 6). Addition of exogenous FMN to the DPNH-enzyme mixture also markedly stimulates DPNH oxidation; again the rate is not further altered by chelators. Therefore, the added FMN must also be intercepting DPNH electrons, either from the bound FMN or directly from $E_1$. The variation of lactonization activity with increasing FMN concentration in the assays of the dissociated, purified enzymes (shown in Fig. 5) can be explained therefore, first, as an increased recoupling of $E_1$ and $E_2$ to a maximum level, and then, with more FMN, as a diversion of electrons being transferred through the recoupled system by the excess FMN not bound in the reformed complex. Inhibition of lactonization by increased FMN is thus

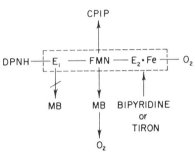

**Fig. 6.** Electron transport in mixed-function oxidative lactonization.

a consequence of an altered pathway of electron flow through flavin to $O_2$. An additional mode of inhibition by FMN is described below.

## C. Electron Donors

The electron donors, like the electron acceptors, markedly stimulate DPNH oxidation by the purified complex. It is noteworthy that these electron donors are peroxidase substrates, Table 9. Therefore, it is tempting to speculate that the activated oxygen in the lactonization system has properties similar to $H_2O_2$-peroxidase complex and that the peroxidase substrates inhibit lactonization by reducing the active oxygen to an inactive species. If this is true, one might expect that the lactonization system would catalyze the formation of the usual peroxidase products from these substrates. Attempts to detect such products have not been successful. This does not, however, rule out the mechanism of inhibition suggested above, since the DPNH required to generate active oxygen in the system would be expected to reduce the typical free-radical intermediates formed in the conversion of peroxidase substrates back to the original substrates (27). The levels of DPNH used in these studies completely block the horse-radish peroxidase conversions of o-toluidine and guaiacol to their chromaphoric products. It is interesting to note that cysteine, glutathione, and ascorbate, often added to stabilize enzymes, are among this group of inhibitors.

It is quite possible that the inhibition by DPNH referred to earlier may also be due to its reductive destruction of the active oxygen. In addition, it appears likely that the electron-acceptor inhibitors, described in section VIB, once reduced at the expense of the bound FMN, may also cause reduction of the active oxygen, thus compounding their felony.

## D. α-Keto Acids

The inhibition by α-keto acids has not been studied in detail. Again, they stimulate the DPNH oxidation by the complex. This effect is not observed with the β-keto acids tested, Table 9. Preliminary results obtained with pyruvate are consistent with the hypothesis that pyruvate is a substrate for the enzyme, as shown by a stoichiometric evolution of $CO_2$ when pyruvate is incubated with enzyme plus DPNH. This is reminiscent of the stoichiometry described by Sutton for lactic oxidative decarboxylase (7). Sutton showed that, in the absence of $O_2$, lactate reacts with the pure flavoprotein to give reduced flavoprotein plus enzyme-bound pyruvate. On admission of $O_2$,

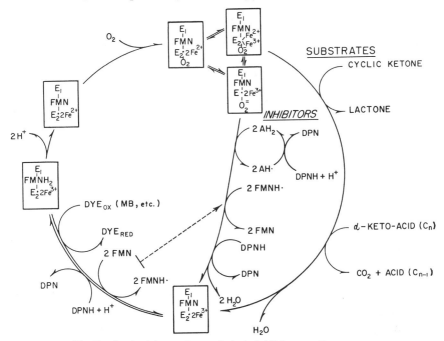

Fig. 7.  Lactonizing system, substrate-inhibitor reactions.

oxidized flavin color reappears and a mixed-function oxidative cleavage of pyruvate occurs between the carbonyl and carboxyl carbons to yield a mixed anhydride of acetic and carbonic acids. The anhydride apparently undergoes spontaneous hydrolysis to acetic acid and $CO_2$. The action of the lactonization system on pyruvate is viewed tentatively as a similar reaction. The several interactions of the components of the enzyme system, the substrates, and the possible sites of action of the various inhibitors with the activated oxygen are summarized schematically in Fig. 7.

## VII. FORMULATION OF OXYGEN REDUCTION
## AND TRANSFER SEQUENCE

The experiments described here establish a consistent formulation of the lactonization system as an electron-transport complex composed of two

proteins and bound FMN and iron. The electrons from DPNH are transferred in sequence through FMN and iron to generate the reactive species of
$O_2$, presumably a reduced form bound at the iron atom. The exact nature of
the reduced oxygen is a subject for further investigation, but several possibilities are apparent (28). Attack at the positively charged carbonyl carbon
in the lactonization suggests that the active oxygen carries a negative charge.
This negatively charged species might be generated either by a one-electron
reduction of $O_2$ to the superoxide ion or a two-electron reduction to the
hydroperoxide ion. Further addition of electrons to the peroxide would
yield oxygen species (hydroxyl ion and hydroxyl radical) deemed unlikely to
initiate the lactonization reaction. The high proton affinities of other
negatively charged oxygen species ($O^{2-}$ and $O_2^{2-}$) render their existence,
either free or enzyme bound, in aqueous solution improbable (28).

Molecular oxygen in solution is an exceptionally poor oxidizing agent in
its one-equivalent reduction to $O_2^-$ ($E_0' = -0.9$ volt) but a relatively good
oxidizing agent in its two-equivalent reduction to $HO_2^-$ ($E_0' = +0.27$ volt).
The effect of enzyme binding on the $E_0'$ of $O_2$ is not known, but to the extent
that enzyme-bound $O_2$ behavior parallels that of free $O_2$, hydroperoxide is
the more likely form of activated oxygen. This view is made more attractive
by the Baeyer-Villager reaction analogy and by the observed inhibition by
peroxidase substrates, both of which infer a reaction of active peroxide in the
lactonization. If the reactive species is an enzyme-bound peroxide, $O_2$ must
be uniquely reduced to this state by the reduced enzyme, since $H_2O_2$ generated
by glucose oxidase will not participate in the ketolactonase reaction.

The demonstrated essentiality of enzyme-bound iron for lactonization and
the known capacity of iron to coordinate $O_2$ imply that peroxide is generated
from an $O_2$ molecule coordinated to the iron atom. Present data do not
distinguish whether one or more than one iron atom is involved in the
reaction. A peroxide formed at an iron atom could be the actual active
oxygen in lactonization. On the other hand, an iron-bound peroxide could
be used to generate an enzymic peracid by interaction with the carboxyl
group of an adjacent acidic amino acid side chain in much the same manner
as peracids are generated in the Baeyer-Villager reaction by the reaction of
$H_2O_2$ with an organic acid. A further possible function of iron might be to
coordinate the carbonyl oxygen, thus acting as a binding site for substrate
and directing the reaction specifically toward the carbonyl carbon on the
substrate molecule (29). Such a dual function of iron in this catalysis is not
inconsistent with the data presented.

Depending upon the conditions used in the Baeyer-Villager reaction, an
oxygen atom may be inserted into the camphor molecule between either
carbons 1 and 2 or carbons 2 and 3 (see Fig. 1). Meinwald and Frauenglass
(17) have discussed the mechanism of the reaction from the standpoint of
electronic and steric effects which determine whether the primary group

(methylene carbon) or the tertiary group (the bridgehead carbon) migrates to the peracid adduct. By their formulation (Fig. 2), the hydroxyperester which will give the electronically favored product (bridgehead carbon migration) by the sterically favored transition state (chair conformation, as in V) is the exo compound (compound Ia). Since, in the enzymatic lactonization described here, only the bridgehead migration has been found, one might tentatively conclude that the active oxygen is added from the exo side of the carbonyl carbon.

Although all mixed-function oxidases have in common the capacity to reduce $O_2$ to an activated form, each of the several types (hydroxylase, epoxidase, ketolactonase, etc.) may have active oxygen species which differ in the mechanism of generation and mode of enzyme binding and perhaps in their oxidation level. In all cases, however, the activated form of oxygen appears to be similar in its extreme reactivity, a fact reflected in the increasing number of observations of the broad range of specificity for this class of enzymes (4, 30–32). In reaction specificity, any reducing agent which can come into close proximity with the activated oxygen is a potential "substrate." Therefore, the addition of such reducing agents to a mixed-function oxidase system would be predicted to inhibit conversion of the substrate by reducing the enzyme-peroxide intermediate. The marked inhibition of lactonization by a wide variety of electron donors might reasonably be explained on this basis.

## VIII. SUMMARY

We have reported the occurrence of two enzymatic lactonizing systems which differ in their specificity for D- and L-camphor metabolites. These systems show stoichiometry and properties consistent with Mason's definition (4) of a mixed-function oxidase. The ketolactonization proceeds by a reaction series consuming 1 mole each of DPNH, $O_2$, and cyclic ketone to form equal molar amounts of lactone and water. The lactonizing enzyme complex requires a lactonizable substrate for DPNH oxidation and $O_2$ utilization. On fractionation, this system separates into two protein components and an electron carrier, FMN. The separated proteins may be assayed separately, and on recombination with a suitable level of FMN they catalyze the lactonization of the cyclic ketones. The DPNH-reactive protein, $E_1$, couples to $O_2$ in the presence of excess FMN and thus functions as a DPNH oxidase. The second protein, $E_2$, contains iron and reacts with $O_2$ and substrate to convert cyclic ketones to lactones. The necessary electrons to cleave the oxygen molecule are furnished by DPNH via $E_1$ and FMN, presumably by reduction of the iron component of $E_2$.

In components and mechanism, this enzyme system finds its closest analogy in Kaufman's system (5) for hydroxylation of phenylalanine to yield tyrosine. In both systems two enzymes and an electron carrier participate. The first enzyme in each case catalyzes the reduction of an electron carrier by a reduced pyridine nucleotide, and the second enzyme, which contains iron, accepts the electrons and catalyzes the oxygenation of the substrate.

The turnover number for the lactonization system is 120 moles of cyclic ketone converted to lactone per mole of ketolactonase per minute. The maximum turnover reported for the phenylalanine hydroxylation system is 6 (calculated arbitrarily on a molecular weight of 100,000).

The inhibition of substrate oxygenation by metal ions, chelators, electron acceptors, and electron donors is similar for the ketolactonase and the phenylalanine hydroxylase. Other mixed-function oxidase systems, although not purified and studied in detail, show requirements for reducing agents and oxygen for activity and are subject to the same types of inhibition.

These strong parallels among mixed-function oxidase systems can be interpreted in terms of an electron-flow sequence, often with several enzymes coupled through electron carrier cofactors, which generates an activated oxygen hypothetically at a bound metal. The active oxygen of these mixed-function oxidases exhibits peroxide properties. The systems resemble peroxidases in their inactivation by reducing agents and by peroxidase substrates. Thus, the lactonizing system as here formulated is suggested as a model suitable for testing some of the numerous anomalous properties of mixed-function oxidase systems which have severely limited progress in the understanding of reductive oxygen fixation.

## ACKNOWLEDGMENTS

We wish to acknowledge the splendid technical assistance of René DuBus, Katherine Lieb, and M. J. Namtvedt in the performance of the experiments on which this work rests.

Our work was supported in part by a grant from the National Science Foundation (G-24037) and one from the United States Public Health Service (AM-00562).

## REFERENCES

1. S. Kaufman, in P. D. Boyer, H. Lardy, and K. Myrbäck, Eds., *The Enzymes*, 2nd ed., Vol. VIII, Academic Press, New York, 1963, pp. 373–382, 383.
2. T. T. Tchen and K. Bloch, *J. Am. Chem. Soc.*, **78**, 1516 (1956).
3. D. K. Bloomfield and K. Bloch, *J. Biol. Chem.*, **235**, 337 (1960).
4. H. S. Mason, in F. F. Nord, Ed., *Advances in Enzymol.*, **XIX**, 79–233 (1957).
5. S. Kaufman, in O. Hayaishi, Ed., *The Oxygenases*, Academic Press, New York, 1962, pp. 129–180.
6. H. E. Conrad, R. DuBus, and I. C. Gunsalus, *B.B.R.C.*, **6**, 293 (1961).
7. W. B. Sutton, *J. Biol. Chem.*, **226**, 395 (1957).

8. F. C. Charalampous, *J. Biol. Chem.*, **235**, 1286 (1960).
9. E. Y. Levin, B. Levenberg, and S. Kaufman, *J. Biol. Chem.*, **235**, 2080 (1960).
10. R. K. Gholson, J. N. Baptist, and M. J. Coon, *Biochemistry*, **2**, 1155 (1963).
11. M. Katagiri, S. Yamamoto, and O. Hayaishi, *J. Biol. Chem.*, **237**, PC2413 (1963).
12. A. J. Fulco and K. Bloch, *Biochim. et Biophys. Acta*, **63**, 545 (1962).
13. W. H. Bradshaw, H. E. Conrad, E. J. Corey, I. C. Gunsalus, and D. Lednicer, *J. Am. Chem. Soc.*, **81**, 5507 (1959).
14. E. Vischer and A. Wettstein, in F. F. Nord, Ed., *Advances in Enzymol.*, **XX**, 237–282 (1958).
15. R. L. Prairie and P. Tallalay, *Biochemistry*, **2**, 203 (1963).
16. J. Fried, personal communication; A. J. Laskin, P. Grabowich, C. De L. Meyers, and J. Fried, *J. Med. Chem.*, **7**, 406 (1964).
17. J. Meinwald and E. J. Frauenglass, *J. Am. Chem. Soc.*, **82**, 5235 (1960).
18. H. E. Conrad, E. J. Corey, I. C. Gunsalus, and R. Hartmann, *Federation Proc.*, **20**, 48 (1961).
19. J. Hedegaard, H. E. Conrad, and I. C. Gunsalus, *Bact. Proc.*, **1961**, 183.
20. H. E. Conrad, R. DuBus, and I. C. Gunsalus, *Federation Proc.*, **21**, 52 (1962).
21. H. E. Conrad, R. DuBus, M. J. Namtvedt, and I. C. Gunsalus, *J. Biol. Chem.*, **240**, 488 (1965).
22. J. LeGall, A. U. Bertland II, M. J. Namtvedt, and H. E. Conrad, *Federation Proc.*, **22**, 295 (1963).
23. L. A. Jacobson, A. U. Bertland II, and I. C. Gunsalus, *Bact. Proc.*, **1964**, 105.
24. H. E. Conrad, K. Lieb, and I. C. Gunsalus, *Federation Proc.*, **23**, 429 (1964).
25. H. E. Conrad, R. DuBus, K. Lieb, and I. C. Gunsalus, *Abstracts of the 6th International Congress of Biochemistry, New York, 1964*, p. 301.
26. R. D. DeMoss, in S. P. Colowick and N. O. Kaplan, Eds., *Methods in Enzymology*, Vol. I, Academic Press, New York, 1955, pp. 328–332.
27. T. Akazawa and E. E. Conn, *J. Biol. Chem.*, **232**, 403 (1958).
28. P. George and J. S. Griffith, in P. D. Boyer, H. Lardy, and K. Myrback, Eds., *The Enzymes*, 2nd ed., Vol. I, Academic Press, New York, 1959, p. 374.
29. R. Breslow and L. N. Lukens, *J. Biol. Chem.*, **235**, 292 (1960).
30. G. D. Auerback and W. B. Jakoby, *J. Biol. Chem.*, **237**, 565 (1962).
31. J. Renson, H. Weissbach, and S. Undenfriend, *J. Biol. Chem.*, **237**, 2261 (1962).
32. A. Ichihara, K. Adachi, K. Hosokawa, and Y. Takeda, *J. Biol. Chem.*, **237**, 2296 (1962).

## Discussion

GUNSALUS: We have been working with two mixed-function oxidases. I should like to supplement our manuscript discussion with a report on one of these and present a possible oxygen-iron-substrate reaction model. These systems, as defined by Howard Mason and as outlined in our manuscript, incorporate a single oxygen atom from $O_2$ into organic compounds. The first system converts a cycloketone into a lactone, operates with DPNH and FMN as cofactors, and contains bound non-heme iron. The second system converts methylene groups to secondary alcohols (a hydroxylase) by incorporating an oxygen atom between a carbon and a hydrogen and operates with TPNH and a pteridine. This discussion will concern the first system, termed a ketolactonizing complex, which can be extracted from *Pseudomonas* cells, in which it is inducible by the monoterpene, camphor, or by the terpenes, steroids. Sonic-treated or alumina-ground cells contain a complex of two enzymes with a sedimentation rate indicating a molecular weight of about $1.3 \times 10^5$. The complex can be separated into two protein fractions: $E_1$, an FMN-mediated DPNH oxidase of a molecular weight about $0.5 \times 10^5$, and $E_2$, the iron-containing enzyme which is substrate and oxygen reactive and to which we have applied the term "ketolactonase." Its molecular weight, from the sedimentation rate, is approximately $0.8 \times 10^5$. The rate of substrate turnover by the induced cells and extracted complex is 2–4 orders of magnitude more rapid than that of the mammalian microsomal oxygenases.

As outlined in our manuscript, the cleavage of a carbocyclic ketone ring with formation of a lactone can be accomplished chemically with peracetic acid and is referred to as a Baeyer-Villiger reaction (shown in Fig. 2, p. 419). With such a chemical analogy one can formulate for the enzymatic system a three-step sequence consisting of the addition of a molecular oxygen to a reduced enzyme—here written with a non-heme ferrous iron prosthetic group—to form a "peroxide" which serves as an oxygen donor. After loss of one atom of oxygen to substrate, the resultant enzyme-bound iron would best be written as ferric (3 + valence) with a bound atom of oxygen containing a negative charge, or on proton addition a bound hydroxyl. Regeneration of the ferrous enzyme for a second cycle of oxygenation would require two electrons and a second proton from the medium. These two electrons and one proton are ultimately furnished by DPNH and are visualized as transferred via enzyme $E_1$ and FMN. The second proton is furnished by the medium. A simplified model for the three-step sequence catalyzed by the second enzyme ($E_2$) may be formulated as shown in Fig. 1. This working model, based on one atom of iron per reaction site, is consistent with the available facts and would appear to be equally acceptable on theoretical grounds to more complicated models. The facts accounted for are (1) a substrate requirement for DPNH oxidation by the coupled $E_1 \cdot E_2$ system, (2) the formation of a colored bipyridyl complex on reduction, accompanied by a bipyridyl inhibition of the lactonization reaction, (3) the presence of non-heme iron approximating one atom per estimated molecular weight of active enzyme complex, and (4) the essentiality of $O_2$ and the lack of activity with $H_2O_2$ or $H_2O_2$-generating systems.

Evidence of the reduction steps, a two-electron step or two steps of one-electron each, is open; the latter is illustrated in Fig. 1 because the enzyme-bound iron exists in both oxidized and reduced states, as indicated by the bipyridyl and related inhibitor data.

To illustrate and summarize the catalytic nature of the complex ($E_1$ and $E_2$), its location and electron-transport properties and means of uncoupling, I should like to refer to Fig. 6 on p. 434. The components enclosed by the dotted line stay intact in cell extracts. As indicated at the left, the complex reacts with externally added DPNH, and the rate of DPNH oxidation is enhanced considerably by the presence of $O_2$ on addition of a lactonizable substrate, e.g., D-(+)-camphor or 2,5-diketocamphane. If one adds FMN at $10^{-4}$ $M$ without adding substrate, rapid DPNH oxidation ensues with $H_2O_2$ formation. Stimulation of DPNH oxidation rate with the complex, but not $E_1$ purified 50- to 100-fold, occurs on addition of methylene blue. With the purified $E_1$ one must add FMN to permit rapid DPNH oxidation in the presence of methylene blue.

GREEN: Is the FMN part of the $E_1$?

GUNSALUS: No—well, make up your own mind. One can remove the FMN; its dissociation constant is roughly $10^{-5}$ $M$.

GREEN: So you don't know of any other functional group besides flavin for that $E_1$?

GUNSALUS: No, not at this moment. Structurally, FMN either is at a very limiting level or is absent from $E_1$ as we purify this protein. Flavin has not been completely removed; there is still about 0.01 mole per 50,000 molecular weight.

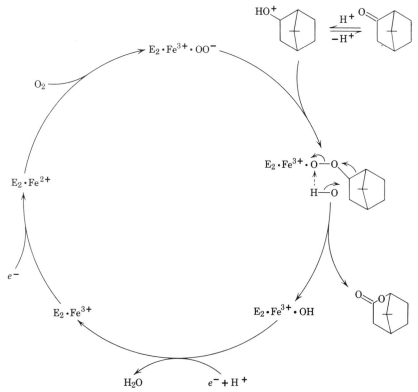

Fig. 1. Model for the three-step sequence catalyzed by $E_2$.

Methylene blue, as indicated, will not react directly with $E_1$ to oxidize DPNH, but will after addition of FMN; dichlorophenolindophenol reacts similarly to methylene blue. Either carrier can be used in the presence of FMN to assay $E_1$.

The cofactor and substrate specificities of the $E_1 \cdot E_2$ complex and of $E_1$ and $E_2$ can be described as follows. For the complex $E_1 \cdot E_2$ the camphor (substrate) requirement for a DPNH oxidation can be "uncoupled" by adding bipyridine. We consider this to indicate a reduction of the iron to the ferrous state and an uncoupling of the $E_2$ from $E_1$ with the unmasking of FMN in the complex to permit its reaction with oxygen. Since, with the addition of bipyridine to the $E_1 \cdot E_2$ complex, FMN addition is not required for enhanced rate of DPNH oxidation, we presume that the complex contains FMN which reacts with $O_2$, when $Fe^{2+}$ is bipyridine bound. Preparations of complex or of $E_2$ which have stood for some time with access to air become oxidized, since they do not develop a red color ($\epsilon_{max}$ = 540 m$\mu$) on bipyridine addition. If DPNH is added to the complex, or DPNH, FMN, and $E_1$ to $E_2$, adding bipyridine does develop the characteristic ferrous $a$ bipyridine complex color.

The stability of the 340 m$\mu$ extinction of DPNH at $10^{-4}$ $M$, in either cell extract or ammonium sulfate-precipitated DEAE eluate, and the FMN-stimulated oxidation certainly show the coupling of the two enzymes. The product of FMN-stimulated DPNH oxidation is $H_2O_2$, and of camphor-stimulated oxidation is a lactone. The over-all rate of lactone formation, measured by $\Delta_{340}$ spectral assay and checked by lactone accumulation (vapor-phase chromatography measurement), is greater than the rate measured by compound IX accumulation when enzymes 1 and 2 are recombined and incubated with III (for compounds IX and III, see Fig. 1 on p. 418). With the ammonium sulfate-precipitated complex which has passed a DEAE column, approximately 80% of the DPNH oxidase is accompanied by oxygen insertion into the camphor ring (lactonization of the ketone). This we refer to as the S → S·S·O conversion.

RACKER: Where does the substrate come from in Fig. 6 (p. 434)?

GUNSALUS: It is added, i.e., camphor, as indicated in the upper right-hand portion of Fig. 1, shown on p. 441 of this discussion.

RACKER: The substrate?

GUNSALUS: Surely, unless you want to call DPNH a substrate; it is, in fact, a second substrate, and the third substrate is, of course, $O_2$. Over-all substrate to product reaction is this: DPNH + $H^+$ + $O_2$ + S → DPN + $H_2O$ + S·O.

RACKER: According to your Fig. 6, you don't need FMN.

GUNSALUS: We do not need to *add* FMN; there is FMN in the complex, indicated by the reactants enclosed by the dotted lines in Fig. 6. I did not specify the amount of FMN present in the complex. As I told Dr. Green, FMN can be removed by separating E and $E_2$. After purification, $E_1$ will not react with methylene blue or dichlorophenolindophenol to oxidize DPNH unless FMN, FAD, or riboflavin is added. The FAD and riboflavin react more slowly and are required in higher concentration. I interpret the data presented in Table 4 on p. 429 to indicate that FMN is very probably the limiting factor in the complex as we use it here. The $E_1$ which has been separated from $E_2$ and purified has less than 1 part of flavin (as FMN)/100 parts of protein, on a molar basis. The complex $E_1$ + $E_2$ has flavin with it to the extent of about 0.2 mole/mole of protein. We cannot be definite about which component is rate limiting, but it could well be FMN.

RACKER: Carried through to the substrate?

GUNSALUS: Yes. The lactonization and the DPNH oxidation steps could both be rate limited by the low levels of FMN. The formulation of $E_2$ reactions shown in Fig. 1 on p. 418 was introduced as a simplified working hypothesis which covers the requisites of the oxygen-reducing reactions and coupling to a substrate. Thus one has substrate control on the reduction of oxygen, a facet which is missing from the regular electron transport via cytochromes terminating with $O_2$ reduction by cytochrome oxidase.

A more general summary of the $E_1$-$E_2$ interaction with both substrate and inhibitors is contained in Fig. 7 on p. 435, which I am using in this discussion to

$$\text{(benzene ring)} \begin{array}{c} -COOH \\ -OH \end{array} \quad + \quad NADH_2 + O_2^*$$

$$\Big\downarrow \quad FAD - enzyme$$

$$\text{(benzene ring)} \begin{array}{c} -\overset{*}{O}H \\ -OH \end{array} \quad + \quad CO_2 + NAD + H_2O^*$$

**Fig. 2**

answer questions and to summarize both our findings and the hypothesis we have constructed to relate the relevant but isolated observations from the literature. Detailed discussion is embodied in our paper, which is, of course, readable at your leisure.

HAYAISHI: I wonder if Dr. Gunsalus could tell me whether the enzyme $E_1$ is specific for $E_2$ or can be replaced by another similar enzyme, such as old yellow enzyme of NADH oxidase. The reason I am particularly interested in this aspect is as follows. We have recently described an enzyme from a *Pseudomonas* which catalyzes the formation of catechol from salicyclic acid (Fig. 2). This enzyme is an FAD-containing protein and requires NADH as an external hydrogen donor. This salicylate hydroxylase is now extensively purified, is not yet obtained in a crystalline form, but has proved to be homogeneous upon ultracentrifugation and electrophoresis, as shown in Fig. 3. The molecular weight is estimated to be about 57,000, and it has 1 mole of FAD per mole of enzyme protein. The oxidation of NADH and the reduction of FAD by this enzyme are dependent upon the presence of the substrate salicylic acid. As can be seen in Fig. 4, the rate of oxidation of NADH under aerobic conditions was markedly accelerated in the presence of this substrate. The presence of substrate not only affects the length of the NADH

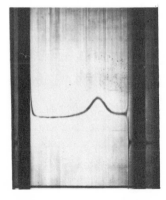
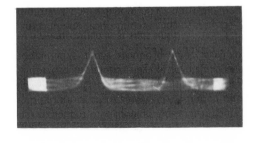

**Fig. 3**

| Salicylate, $M$ | NADH Oxidation, $\mu$/mg protein | $K_m$ for NADH, $M$ |
|---|---|---|
| $6.7 \times 10^{-5}$ | 13.5 | $2.6 \times 10^{-6}$ |
| 0 | 0.1 | $1.1 \times 10^{-3}$ |

**Fig. 4.** NADH oxidation and salicylate hydroxylation. The decrease in the absorbancy of NADH at 340 m$\mu$ was followed spectrophotometrically in the air. The reaction mixture contained purified salicylate hydroxylase, Tris-HCl buffer at pH 8.0, FAD, and NADH with or without potassium salicylate. One unit of enzyme was defined as that amount that caused the decrease of 1 $\mu$mole of substrate min at 20°.

oxidation but also changes the affinity of NADH to the enzyme protein. When the rate of FAD reduction in the presence of NADH was determined under anaerobic conditions (Fig. 5), then the reduction of FAD was almost absolutely dependent on the presence of salicylic acid. Therefore, in contrast with Dr. Gunsalus' enzyme, in our enzyme system salicylic acid hydroxylation appears to be tightly coupled with NADH oxidation and catalyzed by a single protein.

Another point of interest is the participation of metal in such a reaction. Our enzyme is inhibited 41% and 37% in the presence of $10^{-3}$ $M$ and $10^{-4}$ $M$ o-phenanthroline, respectively. However, when such a preparation is dialyzed, the enzyme activity is fully restored. Dr. Gunsalus suggested that the ferrous iron of diketocamphane lactonizing enzyme has a dual function, to activate oxygen and also to act as a binding site for the substrate. If the participation of ferrous iron in the activation of oxygen and the substrate is assumed, one can easily suggest a mechanism of action of this enzyme which is essentially analogous to what I have proposed for tryptophan pyrrolase and metapyrocatechase p. 526, Fig. 7). Well, this is essentially analogous also with Fig. 1, p. 441, which Dr. Gunsalus has just shown us,

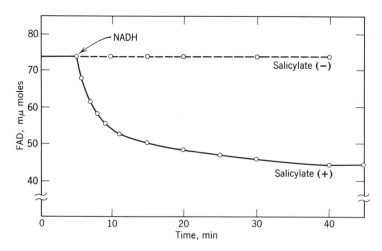

**Fig. 5**

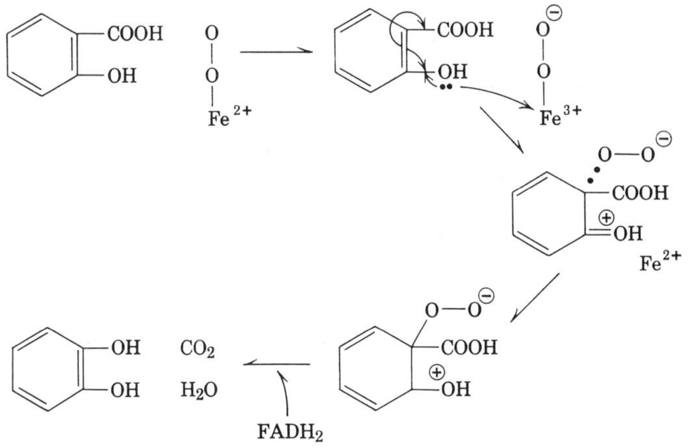

**Fig. 6**

so I won't go into detail. If the metal does not participate in the mixed-function oxidase reaction, then the reductant, for example, $FADH_2$ in this case, may fulfill the role of iron or metal in this scheme. In that case, the oxygen is activated by the reduced flavin, and the activated oxygen may attack the $\alpha$-carbon of the substrate in a manner similar to the foregoing mechanism (Fig. 7).

Now, I should like to ask Dr. Gunsalus two questions. First, is your enzyme $E_1$ specific for the lactonizing enzyme? Can it be replaced by another similar enzyme, such as NADH oxidase, diaphorase, or something like that? Second, is there any direct evidence suggesting binding between ferrous iron and the substrate, such as the competitive-type inhibition experiments which we demonstrated with meta-pyrocatechase?

GUNSALUS: The enzyme ($E_1$) is not completely specific, at least not the only means of $E_2$ reduction; it can be replaced by dithionite or several other reducing agents. Other flavoproteins tested are, however, not active. Thus we imply a

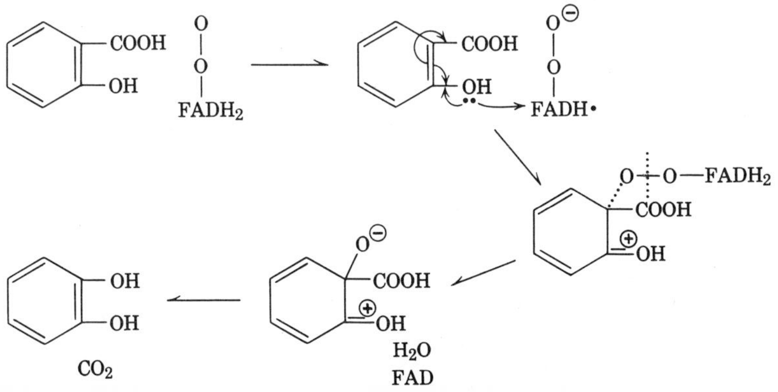

**Fig. 7**

coupling of this flavin-coupled $E_1$ to $E_2$ to have a measure of specificity. With the *Pseudomonas* used here, other mixed-function oxidases are inducible. To take one example, L-( — )-camphor enantiomer is metabolized and does induce the formation of a second ketolactonase and, as Dr. Trudgill recently found, a second DPNH-coupled enzyme (a DPNH oxidase). Incidentally, these data are in our paper, as are also the inhibitor data. These pairs of enzymes must be under genetic control; for the camphor enantiomers there seem to be two enzyme systems, each composed of two proteins. Not only the two substrate-coupled enzymes seem specific, but also the DPNH oxidases (the $E_1$-type enzymes) which reduce them.

Our enzyme system differs from Dr. Hayaishi's in three regards. First, we are dealing with the two protein components; he seems to be dealing with a single protein. Second, the FAD is tightly coupled to his enzyme, as is characteristic of flavoproteins, whereas the FMN in our system has a dissociation constant in the order of magnitude of $10^{-5}$. Third, the degree of coupling between our two proteins is satisfactory in cell extracts. Although it is possible to get small amounts of this system out of cells and fractionated without gross uncoupling, we are dealing with proteins which characteristically separate. The reducing one is the DPNH oxidase, which reacts spontaneously to reduce oxygen. Hayaishi's system, with one protein and bound FAD, seems to be more tightly coupled; e.g., there is a low rate of $O_2$ reduction without substrate. His enzyme should also be quite useful in studying the mechanism of oxygen reduction, providing, of course, that it is a mixed-function oxidase which produces water, whether or not it contains metals, for example, non-heme iron.

Dr. Hayaishi's second question concerns the evidence of interaction of the iron and substrate. The model which I wrote for the possible interaction of iron and camphor does suggest both a binding and an oxygen-carrying function. In Fig. 1 on p. 441, the iron is visualized as an oxygen carrier and as an integral part of the enolization reaction patterned to conform to the Baeyer-Villiger model. Once the enolization has occurred and the oxygen with negative charge is attracted to the polarized carbonyl group, a migration of the carbon bond with its electrons to the oxygen atom is visualized. I cannot at this moment furnish further evidence of mechanism beyond the essentiality of the components, the occurrence of the iron in both the $Fe^{2+}$ and $Fe^{3+}$ forms (bipyridyl reaction) and $Fe^{3+}$ reduction with DPNH·$E_1$. In order to study the mechanism we have tried to visualize a possible model compatible with the facts and helpful in untangling this rather complex series of events.

KING: Did I understand you to say that $E_1$ combines with $E_2$ in the presence of FMN structurally?

GUNSALUS: Yes.

KING: I think that is a better answer to Dr. Hayaishi. There is a kind of re-constitution there.

ESTABROOK: You didn't mention the catalase sensitivity of the reaction.

GUNSALUS: It is not catalase sensitive, nor can one replace the $E_1$ function with a hydrogen peroxide generator, e.g., glucose oxidase.

CRANDALL: I realize that you don't intend to discuss the other reaction you mentioned, but I suggest that you insert an oxygen between a carbon and a hydrogen.

GUNSALUS: You may call it a hydroxylation reaction. I was speaking of the stoichiometry and the transfer of an oxygen atom from $O_2$ directly to substrate. I did not intend to write a mechanism, and I would agree with your earlier suggestion that this is a hydroxyl transfer rather than an insertion of an oxygen with retention of hydrogen.

CRANDALL: But in the other reaction you don't displace the substituent hydrogen?

GUNSALUS: We have not studied the reaction in the detail required to answer your question. We know the stoichiometry and the products. We have been purifying the system. So far this is all that I am able to report to you.

# Comparative Biochemistry
# of Succinate Dehydrogenase:

# Forms and Functions

. . . THOMAS P. SINGER

## I. INTRODUCTION

Until a few years ago the impression was prevalent in biochemical circles that the enzymatic mechanism of a given metabolic transformation was very similar, perhaps even identical, in widely different organisms. This unitarian point of view of enzyme chemistry was probably a consequence of the fact that during that period interest was focused much more on defining the pathways of intermediary metabolism (which are impressively similar and often coincident in microorganisms, plants, and animal tissues) than on the structure and molecular properties of the enzymes involved. Thus it became customary to isolate enzymes from any convenient source available without regard to species differences, to use enzymes of widely different origin in coupled assays (e.g., horse-heart cytochrome $c$ in the assay of dehydrogenases from diverse mammalian species, yeast, or bacteria), and to reason about the properties of a given enzyme from those of its counterpart in other tissues.

Although a few pioneering investigations of the comparative biochemistry of enzymes date to the 1930's and 1940's, during the past decade a widespread interest has become evident in the differences among enzymes from different cell types for the catalysis of the same reaction ["heteroenzymes" in Wieland's nomenclature (1)]. At the same time there has been an upsurge of interest in the existence of multiple forms of enzymes in the same cell which catalyze a given reaction by the same mechanism ("isoenzymes") or by different mechanisms ["isoalloenzymes" (1)].

Our laboratory has devoted considerable efforts to the comparative study of respiratory chain-linked dehydrogenases from different organisms and to a search for multiple forms of the enzyme within one cell. We thought that those of our studies dealing with succinate dehydrogenase might be an appropriate subject for this symposium, since they suggest that in the evolutionary development of this enzyme in different species, as in the transition of a given cell from anaerobic to aerobic life, the properties of the dehydrogenase reflect in a gratifying manner the physiological needs of the organism.

## II. VARIATIONS IN THE PROPERTIES OF SUCCINATE DEHYDROGENASE FROM DIFFERENT SPECIES

### A. Mammalian Succinate Dehydrogenase

This summary of the properties of the dehydrogenase from mammalian heart muscle is intended only as a basis of comparison with the characteristics of the dehydrogenase from other sources. More detailed presentations of the subject may be found elsewhere (2, 3).

Although the enzyme has been extracted and partially purified from a variety of mammalian mitochondria (4, 5) and its catalytic properties in these sources have been found to be quite comparable to those of the dehydrogenase from beef heart, information on the molecular properties is available only for the beef- and pig-heart enzymes, since these are the only ones which have been obtained in homogeneous form (6, 7).

The dehydrogenase is structurally and functionally linked to the respiratory chain in mitochondria. Soluble, purified preparations contain 1 mole of flavin and 4 atoms of non-heme iron per mole of protein with a molecular weight of 200,000. The flavin dinucleotide is covalently bonded to a peptide chain and hence is not liberated in free form by denaturative procedures (8–10). Since succinate dehydrogenase appears to be the only enzyme in mammalian heart which contains this type of "bound flavin," covalently bound flavin content may be used to determine the concentration of the enzyme (and hence its turnover number) in all types of heart-muscle preparations (2, 11). The non-heme iron appears to be intimately related to the "labile sulfide" present in the enzyme (12, 13) and to be responsible for its anomalous spectrum, as in DPNH dehydrogenase (5), ferredoxin (14), photosynthetic pyridine nucleotide reductase from spinach (15), dihydro-orotic dehydrogenase (16), aldehyde oxidase (16), and xanthine oxidase (16), all of which contain non-heme iron and "labile sulfide" in essentially stoichiometric proportions. The non-heme iron of succinate dehydrogenase is also thought to be responsible for the asymmetric, temperature-sensitive $g = 1.94$ ESR signal (17, 18) which appears on the addition of succinate to suitable preparations of the enzyme.

One of the most characteristic properties of the heart enzyme is its activation by substrates and competitive inhibitors (19). The process involves an intramolecular transformation of the enzyme with a high activation energy from a form of very low catalytic activity to one of full activity and is reversed upon complete removal of the activator (20). The phenomenon has been studied in intact mitochondria, submitochondrial particles, and purified soluble preparations isolated by various procedures (19–21). Differences between the activated and non-activated forms are revealed readily by assays involving the complete respiratory chain or the direct reaction with phenazine methosulfate; the $FMNH_2$-fumarate reaction, however, is unaffected by activation. Thus the activation may be an intramolecular change affecting, perhaps, electron transport from the reduced flavin prosthetic group but not the flavin-substrate interaction.

It is well known that the dehydrogenase shows a high degree of selectivity toward electron acceptors. In soluble preparations the enzyme reacts rapidly only with N-alkylphenazonium derivatives and, more slowly, with ferricyanide, but a number of reduced dyes can serve as electron donors for the reduction of fumarate, of which $FMNH_2$ reacts best with the enzyme from heart muscle (23).

Although problems concerning the validity of different assay methods for succinate dehydrogenase are clearly outside the scope of this paper, certain points regarding activity determinations must be emphasized in order to enable the reader to evaluate the differences among succinate dehydrogenases from various species. As discussed later, among the most useful and interesting criteria of comparison are the $K_m$ and $K_i$ values for succinate, fumarate, and malonate, the turnover number per mole of active center, and the ratio of maximal rates of the forward and reverse reactions. Data of this type are summarized in Tables 1 and 2.

In regard to Michaelis constants it should be noted that such values are apt to be erroneously high unless the assay measures nearly the full activity of the enzyme. Thus for each preparation in Table 2 a number of electron donors (or acceptors) were tested and, except where otherwise noted, the values given are for $V$ with respect to the best electron carrier available. Turnover numbers for the enzyme from beef heart and yeast have been measured with phenazine methosulfate as the electron acceptor at $V$, since the natural reaction partner of the dehydrogenase in respiratory chain preparations is not definitely established (3, 36) and since even in tightly coupled mitochondria succinate oxidation via the complete respiratory chain is limited by the turnover rate of the cytochrome system, not that of the dehydrogenase (3). In fresh heart mitochondria, with suitable provisions for full activation and for penetration of the dye, the turnover number is 18,000 moles succinate oxidized/min/mole of bound flavin (3, 24) (Table 1). With the exception of ETP, mitochondrial fragments and other particulate preparations exhibit a lower turnover number, which suggests preparative modification of the enzyme (2, 31, 37). Depending on the method of isolation, soluble preparations show a much lower turnover number resulting, in part, possibly, from

## TABLE 1
## Comparison of Catalytic Activities of Succinate Dehydrogenases

| Preparation | Succinate Oxidation | | | Ratio of Rates of Succinate Oxidation to Fumarate Reduction | Reference |
|---|---|---|---|---|---|
| | Reaction | Temperature, °C | Turnover Number[a] | | |
| Beef-heart mitochondria[b] | Succ.-PMS[c] | 38 | 17,000 ± 1,000 | $\dfrac{\text{Succ.-PMS}^c}{\text{Fum.-FMNH}_2} = 62$ | (3, 24) |
| Beef heart, purified enzyme | Succ.-PMS[d] | 38 | | $\dfrac{\text{Succ.-PMS}^d}{\text{Fum.-FMNH}_2} = 9^e$ | (23) |
| Rat-brain mitochondria[b] | Succ.-PMS[d] | 38 | 19,200 | | (25) |
| Beef-liver mitochondria[b] | Succ.-PMS[c] | 38 | 9,300 | | (3, 24) |
| Rat-liver mitochondria[b] | Succ.-PMS[c] | 38 | 5,200 | | (3, 24) |
| Rat-liver mitochondria[b] | Succ.-PMS[d] | 38 | 5,900 ± 500 | | (25) |
| Baker's yeast "ETP" particles | Succ.-PMS[c] | 30 | 12,500 ± 1,000 | $\dfrac{\text{Succ.-PMS}^c}{\text{Fum.-FMNH}_2} = 34 \pm 2$ | (26) |
| Baker's yeast, soluble enzyme | | 38 | | $\dfrac{\text{Succ.-PMS}^d}{\text{Fum.-FMNH}_2} = 9^e$ | (27) |
| Propionibacterium pentosaceum, purified enzyme | | 30 | | $\dfrac{\text{Succ.-PMS}^d}{\text{Fum.-FMNH}_2} = 3$ | (28) |
| Proteus vulgaris, extract | | 38 | | $\dfrac{\text{Succ.-PMS}^d}{\text{Fum.-LMV}^g} = 0.11$ | (29) |
| Micrococcus lactilyticus, homogeneous enzyme | Succ.-PMS[d] | 38 | 2,590 | $\dfrac{\text{Succ.-PMS}^d}{\text{Fum.-LMV}^g} = 0.026^h$ | (30) |

All assays refer to $V$ with respect to the dye.

[a] Moles of succinate oxidized/min/mole flavin. Note that the turnover number based on covalently bound flavin in the case of liver preparations may be low because of the possible presence of flavin peptides not originating from succinate dehydrogenase in this tissue (cf. text).

[b] Determined in the presence of phospholipase A for full penetration of the electron carriers. Lower values in the literature (2, 31) were obtained with $Ca^{2+}$ instead of phospholipase to allow penetration of the dyes.

[c] Spectrophotometric phenazine methosulfate-DCIP assay (22).

[d] Manometric phenazine methosulfate assay. At 38° this may give somewhat lower rates than the spectrophotometric modification (22).

[e] For an explanation of the lower ratios obtained with soluble than with particle preparations see text. The value given for mitochondria is considered representative of the unmodified enzyme.

[f] The same ratio is obtained when leucomethylviologen is substituted for $FMNH_2$.

[g] LMV = leucomethylviologen.

[h] Ratio at 30°.

## TABLE 2
### Kinetic Constants of Succinate Dehydrogenases from Various Sources

| Preparation | Succinate Oxidation | | | | Fumarate Reduction | | | | Reference |
|---|---|---|---|---|---|---|---|---|---|
| | Assay Conditions | $K_{m\ succ.}$, $mM$ | $K_{i\ fum.}$, $mM$ | $K_{i\ malon.}$, $mM$ | Assay Conditions | $K_{m\ fum.}$, $mM$ | $K_{i\ succ.}$, $mM$ | $K_{i\ malon.}$, $mM$ | |
| Beef heart, purified enzyme | 38°, pH 7.6, PMS[a] | 1.3 | 1.9 | 0.041 | | | | | (19) |
| Beef heart, purified enzyme | 22°–25°, pH 7.6, PMS[a] | 0.52 | 0.80 | 0.025 | 20°–23°, pH 7.6, FMNH$_2$ | 0.50 | 0.12 | 0.12 | (19, 23) |
| Aerobic yeast, purified enzyme | 38°, pH 7.8, PMS[a] | 1.0 | 1.03 | 0.01 | | | | | (27) |
| Pumpkin seeds, purified enzyme | 35°, pH 7.8, PMS[b] | 1.4 | 1.5 | 0.061 | | | | | (32) |
| Proteus vulgaris, aerobically grown, extract | 38°, pH 7.6, PMS[a] | 1.3 | 1.8 | | | | | | (4, 23) |
| Claviceps purpurea (ergot fungus), purified enzyme | 35°, pH 7.7, PMS[b] | 3.3 | 0.93 | 0.03 | | | | | (33) |
| Mytilus edulis (bay mussel), purified enzyme | 35°, pH 7.4, PMS[a] | 2 | 0.15 | 0.06 | | | | | (34) |
| Propionibacterium pentosaceum, purified enzyme | 30°, pH 7.4, PMS[a] | 2.2 | | | 30°, pH 5.4, FMNH$_2$ | 0.7 | | | (28) |
| Micrococcus lactilyticus, homogeneous enzyme | 30°, pH 7.6, PMS[a] | 5.3 | 0.22 | 0.23 | 30°, pH 7.6, LMV[c] | <0.3 | | | (35) |

All assays are at $V$ with respect to electron carrier, except as noted.

[a] Manometric phenazine methosulfate assay.

[b] Manometric assay but at fixed concentration of dye; hence values are subject to some revision.

[c] LMV = leucomethylviologen.

damage to the enzyme during extraction, in part from the loss of one of the two reaction sites for phenazine methosulfate. [The heart enzyme in the particle-bound form has two reaction sites for phenazine methosulfate, one of which is cyanide-sensitive and is lost on solubilization (38) but is regained (39) on reincorporation into the respiratory chain (40).] In view of these considerations it is clear that the most reliable value for the turnover number of the heart enzyme is that measured with fresh mitochondria.

Table 1 also shows, for comparison, the apparent turnover numbers of succinate dehydrogenase in other mammalian tissues. Rat brain gives about the same value as beef heart, rat, and pig heart, but the values in beef and rat liver and in kidney appear to be much lower. Although the possibility cannot be excluded that the enzyme from these sources has a lower catalytic activity, a more likely explanation is that the bound flavin content of these tissues, on which the turnover numbers are based, is not due entirely to succinate dehydrogenase. The possible presence of covalently bound flavin in sarcosine and dimethylglycine dehydrogenases from liver mitochondria has been, in fact, reported (41).

The third parameter of comparison among succinate dehydrogenases given in Table 1 is the relative rates of the forward/reverse reactions under optimal conditions (and the most highly active electron carrier) in each assay. It should be clear that these are not equilibria, since the dyes used in the two directions of catalysis are different in each case. Furthermore, these are not absolute characteristics of the individual enzymes, for if a better electron donor (or acceptor) were found for a particular preparation, the ratio might change materially. A case in point is that on extraction of the dehydrogenase from heart mitochondria the ratio of rates of the succinate-phenazine methosulfate/fumarate-$FMNH_2$ reactions falls from about 60 to about 9 (2). This is due only partly to the lowering of the turnover number of the forward reaction on extraction, as noted above; in part it is the result of an *increased* turnover number in the fumarate-$FMNH_2$ assay on solubilization and purification of the enzyme. It has been found that the interaction of external $FMNH_2$ with the bound flavin of the heart enzyme is hindered in the structure of the native enzyme by SH groups, but various manipulations such as those involved in the preparation of mitochondrial fragments, particulate complexes, and especially exposure to alkaline pH values result in oxidation of these thiols and a concomitant increase in the fumarate-$FMNH_2$ reaction (37, 39, 42).

Although these complications may appear formidable at first glance, actually it is quite easy to demonstrate that enzymes from aerobic organisms predominantly catalyze the oxidation of succinate, whereas anaerobes are geared for the reduction of fumarate. By testing a large number of electron carriers in both directions of catalysis with each of the enzymes listed in Table 1, this tendency has been amply demonstrated (29, 43, 44). Taken together with the respective $K_m$ values for succinate and fumarate, this property is of considerable physiological importance, as discussed in section IIF.

## B. Succinate Dehydrogenase from Yeast

It will be shown in section III that yeast cells contain three enzymes which catalyze the interconversion of succinate and fumarate. The present discussion will be limited to the mitochondrial enzyme.

In mitochondria from aerobic yeast, succinate dehydrogenase is linked to the respiratory chain in apparently the same manner as in mammalian tissues; the linkage is resistant to all agents which fail to solubilize the heart enzyme and is cleaved by alkaline extraction, after desiccation with organic solvents, as in mammalian tissues (27). The enzyme has been obtained in extensively purified form, and its properties have been shown to be remarkably similar to those of the heart enzyme (27). The estimated molecular weights and non-heme iron:flavin ratios of the heart and yeast enzymes are identical; their sedimentation constants, absorption spectra, kinetic constants, inhibition patterns, and specificities toward electron carriers are nearly the same. The flavin moiety of the dehydrogenase from yeast is also covalently bound. Chromatographic analysis of trypsin-chymotrypsin digests of highly purified preparations reveals a series of flavin peptides, but no FAD or FMN, as in the case of the heart enzyme (27). [The report (45) that tryptic digestion of yeast "ETP" results in the release of the succinate dehydrogenase flavin in the form of free FAD could not be confirmed in our laboratory (26); cf. also Fig. 3.]

The Michaelis constants of the dehydrogenase from aerobically cultured yeast are typical of strictly aerobic organisms (Table 2), and the enzyme catalyzes the oxidation of succinate much faster than the reduction of fumarate (Table 1). If allowance is made for the difference in assay temperature, the turnover numbers of the heart and yeast enzymes in intact respiratory chain preparations are also similar (Table 1).

Perhaps the only major difference found between the heart and yeast enzymes was that the latter did not appear to be activated by substrates or competitive inhibitors (23). With improved assays it has now been found that the yeast enzyme is activated by succinate, malonate, and phosphate in the same manner as the heart enzyme, but the activation is quite rapid and hence may escape detection in manometric procedures at 38° (26). As illustrated in Fig. 1, succinoxidase assays of yeast "ETP" preparations (45) show a pronounced lag which is minimized by brief anaerobic preincubation with phosphate and abolished by preincubation with malonate. Figure 2 shows the activation of the dehydrogenase in the spectrophotometric phenazine-DCIP assay.

There remain, however, some differences between the yeast and heart enzymes. The former is even more labile than the latter (27); even in the respiratory chain-bound form anaerobic incubation for a few minutes at 38° causes significant destruction (26), whereas the heart enzyme is quite stable

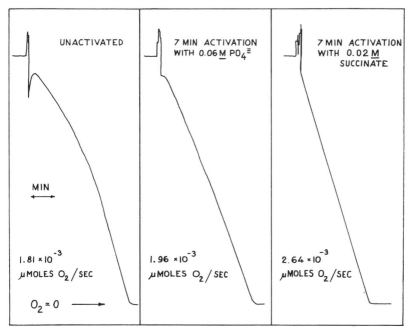

**Fig. 1.** Activation of succinate oxidase in yeast ETP preparation (45) by phosphate and succinate. The incubation mixture for activation contained in the main compartment of Thunberg tubes 0.15 ml 0.2 $M$ phosphate, pH 7.5, and 0.3 ml ETP (6.9 mg protein); the side arm contained 0.05 ml $H_2O$ (phosphate activation) or 0.05 ml 0.4 $M$ succinate. The tubes were repeatedly evacuated and filled with $N_2$ at 0°. After 3 min equilibration at 30°, the contents of the side arm were tipped. The tubes were maintained at 30° for the time indicated and then cooled to 0°. A 25 $\mu$l aliquot was immediately added to the assay mixture (already at 30°) containing 0.04 $M$ phosphate, pH 7.5, 0.05 $M$ succinate, and 0.4 mg horse-heart cytochrome $c$ in 2 ml final volume. Assays were performed with an $O_2$ electrode. The unactivated sample was added directly to the assay mixture without preincubation. The specific activity on full activation was 0.95 $\mu$mole succ/min/mg at 30°. [Data of Rocca *et al.* (26).]

under these conditions. The $K_i$ for malonate is somewhat lower for the yeast than for the heart enzyme, and the former reacts even less with ferricyanide than the latter (27). Furthermore, the pH-fluoroescence curves of the flavin peptides from heart and yeast succinate dehydrogenases are not identical (Fig. 3).

It has also been reported (38) that, whereas the incubation of respiratory chain preparations, but not of the soluble enzyme, from heart with cyanide

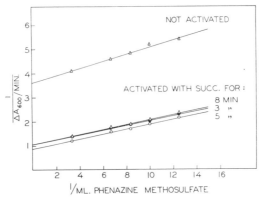

**Fig. 2.** Activation of succinate dehydrogenase in yeast ETP. Activation was performed in spectrophotometer cuvettes at 30° containing 0.12 mmole phosphate, pH 7.5, 0.06 mmole succinate, 0.115 mg ETP protein, and 0.003 mmole cyanide, in a volume varying from 2.6 to 2.82 ml, for the times indicated. The catalytic reaction was started by the addition of DCIP and phenazine methosulfate (0.33% solution, in amounts indicated on the abscissa), bringing the final volume to 3.0 ml. Assay was by the spectrophotometric method (22) at 30°. During assay the concentrations of succinate, phosphate, cyanide, and DCIP were 20 $mM$, 40 $mM$, 10 $mM$, and 0.063 $mM$, respectively. The specific activity was 1.56 $\mu$moles/min/mg on full activation. [Data of Rocca et al. (26).]

causes partial inactivation of the succinate-phenazine methosulfate reaction (and, hence, abolishes one of the two reaction sites of the dye), under similar conditions cyanide appears to have no effect on the succinate-phenazine methosulfate activity of yeast mitochondria. With improved assay procedures (spectrophotometric phenazine-DCIP method with provisions for full activation of the dehydrogenase) it has now been shown that the succinate dehydrogenase activity of yeast ETP is also cyanide sensitive (26). Hence, except for the quantitative differences noted above, the dehydrogenase from

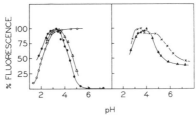

**Fig. 3.** Comparison of pH-fluorescence curves of FMN and of flavin peptides from heart muscle and yeast. ○, FMN; ●, pure flavin hexapeptide from heart succinate dehydrogenase (9); △ proteolytic digest of beef-heart Keilin-Hartree preparation (24); ▲, ETP from baker's yeast (26); ×, ETP from "petite" mutant (26). The ordinate denotes the relative intensity of the fluorescence of the particular sample, the maximum taken as 100. All preparations were exhaustively extracted with acid before trypsin-chymotrypsin digestion and were hydrolyzed to the mononucleotide level.

aerobic yeast mitochondria is extremely similar to its counterpart in animal tissues.

## C. Succinate Dehydrogenase in "Petite" and in Anaerobic Yeasts

In his classical studies on the respiratory enzymes of yeast, Slonimski (48) noted that in anaerobically cultured yeast several of the cytochromes and succinate dehydrogenase were absent, but these enzymes developed on exposure of the cells to $O_2$. "Petite" mutants, whether grown aerobically or anaerobically, were said to lack succinate dehydrogenase as well as the cytochrome system. Since the dehydrogenase was assayed in these studies with methylene blue as acceptor (48), a dye which was later shown (27) not to react with the enzyme from yeast mitochondria, these observations required re-examination.

As regards the mutant strain, recent studies (49, 50) contradict Slonimski's finding in that the dehydrogenase is reported to be present in "petites," but at much lower concentration than in normal cells. In a very recent report from Slonimski's laboratory (46) "petites" are said to exhibit only a slightly lower activity of the enzyme than wild-type cells. It appeared that these contradictory findings may have been due to the continued use of unsatisfactory assay methods (ferricyanide, DCIP, or phenazine-INT at fixed dye concentrations, without activation), which measured an uncertain fraction of the true dehydrogenase content. We have reinvestigated the problem, therefore, basing activity measurements on the more satisfactory phenazine-DCIP method and on estimation of the bound flavin content.

As shown in Table 3, succinate dehydrogenase is nearly absent in ETP preparations isolated from the respiratory-deficient "petite" mutants, whether grown anaerobically or aerobically in the medium specified. A very small amount of covalently bound flavin is present even after exhaustive washing with trichloroacetic acid, but this cannot be equated with succinate dehydrogenase, since the pH-fluorescence curve of flavin peptides obtained by proteolytic digestion of "petite" ETP appears to be different from that shown by samples isolated from commerical aerobic yeast (Fig. 3). Whether the bound flavin present in respiratory chain preparations of the mutants originates from another flavoprotein containing bound flavin is not known at present.

As regards succinate dehydrogenase in normal *anaerobic* cells, by means of the manometric phenazine methosulfate assay Hebb *et al.* (51) have shown that while these cells are totally devoid of succinoxidase and cytochrome oxidase, succinate dehydrogenase is present, but at a considerably lower concentration than in aerobic cells. During $O_2$ adaptation the dehydrogenase activity rose but not nearly as dramatically as succinate oxidation via the respiratory chain. Although these findings have been confirmed (52, 53), it

TABLE 3

Succinate Dehydrogenase and Bound Flavin Content of ETP
from Baker's Yeast and from "Petite" Mutants[a]

| Preparation | Succinate Dehydrogenase Activity,[b] $\mu$moles succ./min/mg | Bound Flavin Content,[c] m$\mu$mole/mg |
|---|---|---|
| ETP [Mackler et al. (45) preparation] from Red Star yeast | 1.5 | 0.15 |
| ETP [Mahler et al. (46) preparation] from Red Star yeast | 1.6–2.1 | 0.16–0.20 |
| ETP from "petite" mutants [Mahler et al. (46) preparation][d] | 0.007–0.02 | 0.02–0.03 |

[a] Unpublished data of Rocca et al. (26).

[b] $V$ phenazine methosulfate, spectrophotometric assay, 30°, fully activated samples, protein determined by Lowry method.

[c] Fluorometric analysis of proteolytic digests (11) of samples which had been extracted exhaustively to remove free flavin. Fluorescence was read at pH 3.8 (cf. Fig. 3).

[d] Acriflavin mutants of a strain isolated from Red Star yeast, grown on Hirsch's (47) medium aerobically or anaerobically.

would be desirable to re-examine the rate of synthesis of succinate dehydrogenase during $O_2$ adaptation of anaerobically cultured cells with the more satisfactory assay methods now available, in order to ascertain whether the increase in succinate dehydrogenase activity is induced by $O_2$ itself or by respiratory chain components arising during the adaptive process.

## D. Succinate Dehydrogenase in Higher Plants

In higher plants, as in animal tissues and aerobic yeast, the dehydrogenase is localized in the mitochondria and catalyzes the reversible oxidation of succinate, and catalytic activity in the direction of succinate oxidation predominates greatly over the reductive reaction (54). Although the dehydrogenase has not yet been obtained in highly purified form from higher plants, the properties of a partially purified preparation from pumpkin seedlings (32) appear to be comparable to those of the heart enzyme. The $K_m$ values of this preparation for succinate and fumarate are typical of succinate dehydrogenases from aerobic organisms (Table 2).

## E. Succinate Dehydrogenases in Invertebrates

Succinate dehydrogenase has been solubilized and partially purified from the posterior adductor muscle of *Mytilus edulis* (bay mussel) (34) by a procedure similar to that used earlier for the isolation of the beef-heart enzyme (6). Like the mammalian enzyme, soluble preparations from this invertebrate source react only with phenazine methosulfate and ferricyanide (34). The specificity toward electron donors in the reductive reaction and the relative rates of the forward/reverse reactions have not been reported. The $K_m$ value of the mussel enzyme for succinate is higher, and the $K_i$ for fumarate is lower, than corresponding values for typical aerobic organisms (Table 2), which may reflect adaptation to life at relatively low $O_2$ tensions (cf. below).

The parasitic worm *Ascaris lumbricoides* is adapted to life under the essentially anaerobic conditions prevailing in its natural habitat (55). Succinate is a normal fermentation product of the worm (56); its formation is thought to proceed by $CO_2$ fixation into pyruvate, followed by fumarase action; the fumarate is then reduced to succinate under the influence of succinate dehydrogenase and the reaction is coupled to the reoxidation of DPNH generated in anaerobic glycolysis (55). This role of fumarate as a terminal acceptor and the coupling of fumarate reduction to the oxidation of lactate are typical of many anaerobic bacteria, such as *Micrococcus lactilyticus* and *Clostridia* (cf. below). In accord with the physiological needs of such organisms the properties of their succinate dehydrogenases are admirably adapted to their function as terminal electron acceptor: their turnover numbers in the reductive reaction are usually very high, while their tendency to oxidize succinate is lower (Table 1). Further, their $K_m$ values for fumarate are usually very low, and their $K_i$ values for succinate are quite high. Thus the reduction of fumarate can proceed maximally even at very low substrate concentrations, without inhibition by the accumulated succinate (Table 2).

Known properties of succinate dehydrogenase from *Ascaris* appear to fit this general pattern in regard to both the higher reaction rate of fumarate reduction over succinate oxidation and the Michaelis constants for this substrate pair (55). In soluble preparations, extracted from acetone powders, as usual, phenazine methosulfate serves as the only satisfactory electron acceptor for the oxidation of succinate. Particulate, multienzyme preparations are devoid of the cytochrome system but possess an autoxidizable flavoprotein which accepts electrons from succinate dehydrogenase.

## F. Succinate Dehydrogenases from Various Microorganisms

Peck *et al.* (57) observed that cell-free extracts of the obligate anaerobe *M. lactilyticus* catalyze rapidly the reduction of fumarate but oxidize succinate only extremely slowly, even in the presence of phenazine methosulfate. Furthermore, the reduction of fumarate was not inhibited by succinate and was only slightly affected by malonate at concentrations which would completely inhibit fumarate reduction by succinate dehydrogenase from heart or aerobic yeast mitochondria. These properties were reminiscent of the "unidirectional fumurate reductase" claimed by Fischer and co-workers (58, 59) to be present in anaerobic yeast but were divergent from those of succinate dehydrogenases isolated from yeast and animal tissues.

In order to shed some light on the reasons for this remarkable behavior Warringa *et al.* (30) isolated the enzyme from *M. lactilyticus* in homogeneous form. The dehydrogenase was found to be a readily soluble, high-molecular-weight protein ($S_{20,w} = 54$ svedbergs) containing an extremely high complement of non-heme iron (40 g atoms/mole of FAD/460,000 g protein). The flavin is readily liberated by acid treatment and therefore is not covalently bound. Although the molecular weight is not known, in view of the high sedimentation coefficient several moles of FAD appear to be present per mole of enzyme (35). The absorption spectrum is typical of proteins containing large amounts of non-heme iron. Since the brown color of the enzyme is bleached by succinate and the original spectrum reappears on the addition of fumarate, at least some of the non-heme iron may be involved in the cyclic action of the enzyme. In regard to stability, kinetics, and specificity toward electron carriers, the dehydrogenase from *M. lactilyticus* differs markedly from the mammalian enzyme (35).

The enzyme has been shown to be readily reversible, but the conditions found to be optimal for the oxidation of succinate were different from those for the reduction of fumarate. A variety of conditions of inactivation causes the same loss of activity in either direction of catalysis. Furthermore, after the initial purification step (which, as discussed below, removes an inhibitor of succinate oxidation) the ratio of the relative rates of the forward/reverse reactions remains constant throughout isolation. Thus no evidence could be detected for the presence of more than one succinate dehydrogenase in the organism (30).

As shown in Table 1, the highly purified dehydrogenase catalyzes the reduction of fumarate far faster than the oxidation of succinate, even when both reactions are measured under optimal conditions. This property is well adapted to the functioning of fumarate as terminal acceptor in the normal metabolism of this organism, as are the respective $K_m$ values for fumarate and succinate (Table 2). The relative insensitivity of the enzyme to malonate when fumarate serves as substrate and the extensive malonate inhibition observed when succinate is oxidized are readily explained in terms of the respective $K_m$ and $K_i$ values (Table 2). The very slow rate of succinate oxidation in cell-free extracts, reported by Peck *et al.* (57), reflects in part the properties of the enzyme, and in part the different assay conditions required for maximal rates of succinate oxidation and fumarate reduction, respectively. Also, interestingly, crude extracts of the bacterium contain a heat-stable, non-dialyzable substance which differentially inhibits the oxidation of succinate without affecting the reduction of fumarate. The inhibitor, separated from the dehydrogenase by $(NH_4)_2SO_4$ fractionation, when added either to

## TABLE 4

### Effect of Inhibitor from *M. Lactilyticus* on Succinate Oxidation and Fumarate Reduction[a]

| Preparation | Succinate Dehydrogenase Activity[b] | | | Fumarate Reductase Activity[c] | | |
|---|---|---|---|---|---|---|
| | Without Inhibitor | With Inhibitor | Inhibition, % | Without Inhibitor | With Inhibitor | Inhibition, % |
| Keilin-Hartree particles from beef heart | 22.5 | 15.8 | 30 | 1.00 | 1.02 | 0 |
| Purified succinate dehydrogenase from *M. lactilyticus* | 7.32 | 5.37 | 28 | 258 | 259 | 0 |

[a] Unpublished data of A. Giuditta and T. P. Singer (1957). The inhibitor was a thoroughly dialyzed, boiled preparation of the 0.42–0.46 sat. $(NH_4)_2SO_4$ fraction of *M. lactilyticus* extracts (30); 1 ml of this solution was used per 3 ml assay mixture. The inhibitions found are by no means maximal but reflect the amount of inhibitor used. With Keilin-Hartree preparation inhibition was measured after 30 min of preincubation at 38°.

[b] Micromoles succinate oxidized/min/ml preparation at 38° in the case of the heart enzyme, 30° in the case of the bacterial enzyme, in the manometric phenazine methosulfate assay, at fixed dye concentration.

[c] Micromoles fumarate reduced/min/ml preparation; leucomethylviologen assay (30) ($V$ at 30°) with the bacterial enzyme, manometric $FMNH_2$ assay at 38° ($9.3 \times 10^{-4}$ $M$ $FMNH_2$) with the heart enzyme.

the highly purified *M. lactilyticus* enzyme or to Keilin-Hartree preparations of beef heart, differentially inhibits the dehydrogenation of succinate (Table 4). Thus the approximately threefold increase in the ratio of the forward to reverse reaction rates observed in the initial stages in the purification of the bacterial enzyme (30) is due largely to the removal of this inhibitor rather than to the presence of two succinate dehydrogenases.

In aerobic microorganisms, as in the dehydrogenase from aerobic yeast, the ratio of the maximal rates of the forward/reverse reactions and the Michaelis constants for succinate and fumarate are close to those found with the mammalian enzyme. The $K_i$ for fumarate of the dehydrogenase from the ergot fungus, *Claviceps purpurea*, is essentially the same as that of the heart enzyme, although the $K_m$ for succinate is reported to be somewhat higher (33) but still less than that given by the *M. lactilyticus* enzyme (Table 2).

We have studied the properties of succinate dehydrogenases from several facultative anaerobes over the years (29, 43, 60), but the bulk of the data has not yet been published. These studies have generally supported the hypothesis that in such organisms the parameters in question are in between those found in strict aerobes and obligate anaerobes (cf. *Proteus vulgaris* and *Propionibacterium pentosaceum* in Tables 1 and 2). The enzyme from *P. pentosaceum* (28, 43) is particularly interesting. Whereas on one hand in the anaerobic carbohydrate metabolism of this organism the oxidation of lactate to pyruvate is coupled to the reduction of fumarate to succinate (as in *M. lactilyticus* and in *Ascaris*) and thus the properties of the dehydrogenase must be such as to fulfill this important metabolic function, the organism is endowed also with the capacity for the aerobic oxidation of succinate. In fact, the dehydrogenase from this source, like that from another facultative anaerobe, *Corynebacterium diphtheriae* (61), appears to be inseparable from a *b*-type cytochrome to which it is structurally and functionally linked even in extensively purified preparations (28, 43).

Cell-free extracts of *P. pentosaceum* appear to contain two forms of succinate dehydrogenase, one readily soluble and another particle-bound. The latter has been solubilized by the procedure used in the extraction of the dehydrogenase from yeast mitochondria. Both forms of the enzyme have been purified, and, while they fractionated differently, in composition and catalytic properties they were indistinguishable (28). Both preparations contain a catalytically functional cytochrome *b* moiety and a high concentration of non-heme iron, but flavin has not been detected in either one. In regard to $K_m$ values for succinate and fumarate, selectivity toward electron acceptors, and the ratio of the maximal rates of the forward/reverse reactions, the properties of the *P. pentosaceum* enzyme are between those of mammalian preparations and the dehydrogenase from the obligate anaerobe, *M. lactilyticus* (Tables 1 and 2).

Numerous other examples could be cited in support of the thesis that the properties of succinate dehydrogenases, in the respects discussed, are adapted to the metabolic needs of the organisms. Perhaps one striking example will suffice, however. Hirsch *et al.* (62) have demonstrated that *E. coli* cells contain two succinate dehydrogenases, both of them reversible in their catalytic action. One of these, referred to as the "ratio 25 enzyme," catalyzes the oxidation of succinate by phenazine methosulfate some 25 times faster than the reduction of fumarate with $FMNH_2$ under the experimental conditions, while for the other enzyme (referred to as the "ratio 1.5 enzyme"), the rates of the forward/reverse reactions are in the ratio 1.5. The activities of the two enzymes vary independently with growth conditions; the "ratio 25 enzyme" is particularly high in aerobic cells grown on glucose and low in cells grown anaerobically on glycerol + fumarate. Although the two enzymes have not been separated by fractionation, their properties have been studied in extracts of mutants, which contain only "ratio 1.5 enzyme," and of normal aerobically grown cells, which contain largely the "ratio 25 enzyme." As shown in Table 5, $K_m$ values of the "ratio 25 enzyme" for

**TABLE 5**

**Michaelis Constants of Succinate Dehydrogenases from *E. coli* at 30°[a]**

| Source of Extract | $K_m$ for Succinate | $K_m$ for Fumarate |
|---|---|---|
| Aerobic normal cells grown on glucose[b] | $2.6 \times 10^{-4}$ | $4.5 \times 10^{-4}$ |
| Mutant grown anaerobically on glycerol and fumarate[c] | $1.0 \times 10^{-3}$ | $1.7 \times 10^{-5}$ |

[a] Data summarized from Hirsch *et al.* (62).
[b] Contains largely the "ratio 25 enzyme."
[c] Contains only the "ratio 1.5 enzyme."

succinate and fumarate are close to those found with aerobic organisms, whereas those of the "ratio 1.5 enzyme" are more typical of succinate dehydrogenases from anaerobes. The $K_m$ of the latter enzyme for fumarate is about sixtyfold lower than that for succinate, while the $K_m$ of the former enzyme for fumarate is higher than for succinate.

## III. MULTIPLE FORMS OF SUCCINATE DEHYDROGENASE FROM A SINGLE CELL TYPE

### A. Historical

In 1937 Fischer and Eysenbach (58) reported that purified preparations of the old yellow enzyme from yeast contain an impurity which reduces fumarate in the presence of leucosafranin and related dyes but cannot oxidize succinate with methylene blue. Since at the time methylene blue reduction was considered a *sine qua non* of succinate dehydrogenase action, the enzyme concerned was named "fumarate hydrogenase" and its catalytic action was considered to be unidirectional. It was further claimed that the prosthetic group of this enzyme is FAD and that reversible dissociation occurs on dialysis (58, 59), but the experimental basis of these conclusions was rather unsatisfactory (27, 63).

Some years later it was demonstrated that yeast mitochondria from both aerobic and anaerobic cells contain a succinate dehydrogenase which is very similar in all of its properties to the mammalian enzyme (27). Since the action of the enzyme was found to be readily reversible in mitochondria as well as highly purified preparations, since the ratio of the forward/reverse reactions remained constant from mitochondria to highly purified enzyme and did not change on denaturation by various methods, and since the fumarate-reductase (or "hydrogenase") activity attributable to conventional succinate dehydrogenase was far higher than the activities reported by Fischer and co-workers, the question of the existence of a second, unidirectional fumarate-reducing enzyme needed re-evaluation. It was suggested (27, 64) that the apparent lack of succinate dehydrogenase activity of Fischer's preparation was due to the use of methylene blue, which, for all practical purposes, does not react with succinate dehydrogenase from yeast mitochondria, and to differential inactivation of the succinate dehydrogenase activity without parallel loss of fumarate reductase activity during preparation and storage over a period of years, since such effects could be reproduced readily on even a few days' storage of the purified enzyme from mitochondria, a notoriously unstable protein. It was suggested (23) that "while the existence of a separate 'fumarate reductase' is not disproved, the 'reductase' activities of . . . yeast mitochondria may be readily accounted for by the reversible action of succinic dehydrogenase and that at present no unequivocal evidence points to the existence of a separate 'fumaric reductase.'" Similar conclusions were reached independently by Martin and Morton (54).

Somewhat later the existence of a fumarate hydrogenase, distinct from succinate dehydrogenase, in heart-muscle preparations was reported (65), but later these observations were shown to be due to conventional succinate dehydrogenase acting in reverse (64, 66).

The observations of Peck *et al.* (57) on an apparently unidirectional fumarate reductase in *M. lactilyticus*, discussed in section IIF, and, in particular, the apparent change in the ratio of fumarate reductase to succinate dehydrogenase on purification again raised the question of the coexistence of a succinate dehydrogenase and of a separate "fumarate reductase" in this anaerobe. As already discussed, both activities are due to the same enzyme, and the apparent change in ratio on purification was due to the removal of a selective inhibitor of succinate oxidation (30).

Later Kováč (66) presented new evidence for the possibility that yeast cells contain, besides succinate dehydrogenase, a second protein geared for fumarate reduction. Working with broken cell preparations and cell-free extracts, this author reported that malonate, succinate, and *p*-chloromercuribenzoate (*p*-CMB) inhibited the fumarate-leucosafranin interaction incompletely and that the inhibitor-resistant activity was greater in anaerobic than in aerobic yeast. Recognizing that the assay methods used were equivocal and that these observations could also be interpreted differently, Kováč concluded that his experiments were only suggestive of the existence of a second succinate dehydrogenase in yeast.

About the same time Lara (28) showed in our laboratory that extracts of *P. pentosaceum* contained both a particle-bound and a soluble form of succinate dehydrogenase which differed only in properties during fractionation but not in composition or kinetic properties.

## B. Succinate Dehydrogenases in *Escherichia coli*

The first clear-cut demonstration of the coexistence of two succinate dehydrogenases in the same cell, one typical of aerobic organisms and one

### TABLE 6

Oxygen Uptake by Intact and Disrupted Parental (K)
and Mutant (S⁻) Cells[a]

|                   | Rate of Oxygen Uptake[b] | | |
|-------------------|------------|------------|------------|
| Cell Preparation  | Endogenous | + Succinate | + Fumarate |
| K, intact         | 0.27       | 1.41       | 0.77       |
| K, disrupted      | 0.00       | 0.47       | 0.08       |
| S⁻, intact        | 0.40       | 0.39       | 0.86       |
| S⁻, disrupted     | 0.02       | 0.05       | 0.06       |

[a] Data from Hirsch *et al.* (62).
[b] Micromoles $O_2$/mg/hr at 37°.

resembling closely succinate dehydrogenases from obligate anaerobes, came from the studies of Hirsch *et al.* (62). They found a mutant (S⁻) which lacked the aerobic enzyme but not the anaerobic one and thus failed to grow on succinate but grew readily when growth conditions required fumarate reduction. By comparing the abilities of intact and disrupted cells to oxidize succinate (Table 6) it was shown that the mutation abolishes the formation

of the aerobic succinate dehydrogenase rather than the permeability of succinate. Since, under aerobic conditions of growth, both the succinate
dehydrogenase and fumarate reductase activities of the parent strain were
largely ascribable to the aerobic enzyme, while in the S⁻ mutant only the latter
was present, some of the kinetic properties of the two dehydrogenases could
be defined without separation of the proteins by purification techniques
(Table 5). It is clear, then, that *E. coli* contains two forms of the dehydrogenase, one evolved for reaction with $O_2$ via the cytochrome system, and one
to act as terminal electron acceptor in anaerobic fermentations, a remarkably
efficient arrangement, considering the physiological needs of this facultative
anaerobe.

### C. Multiple Forms of Succinate Dehydrogenase in Yeast

At the request of Dr. Kováč, we have re-examined the possibility of the
existence of a second succinate dehydrogenase in yeast cells. Since the
mitochondrial fraction had been conclusively shown to contain only one
enzyme (27), it remained to investigate the question of whether the extramitochondrial fraction might not contain a different enzyme for the
succinate ⇌ fumarate reaction. For assay purposes the $H_2$-hydrogenase-
ferredoxin-$FMNH_2$ system was used as electron donor to fumarate (67).

It was found that the cytoplasmic phase indeed contained a relatively low
fumarate reductase activity. By comparing the fumarate-$FMNH_2$ activities
of respiratory chain preparations from yeast mitochondria [yeast "ETP"
(45, 46)] and of the cytoplasmic compartment, it was found that malonate
inhibition was incomplete in both cases (although malonate inhibits completely the oxidation of succinate in yeast ETP). Only at very low concentrations was a greater inhibition of fumarate reduction by the respiratory
chain-linked enzyme than by the cytoplasmic one observed (68). Since
fumarate reduction by ETP is due entirely to the aerobic enzyme, the incomplete inhibition by malonate cannot be used as evidence for the existence
of a second enzyme.

The situation with regard to SH inhibitors was similar. It has been reported that highly purified *M. lactilyticus* succinate dehydrogenase is
inhibited extensively by *p*-CMB in the succinate dehydrogenase but not in
the fumarate reductase assay (35). Although evidence has been presented
that this is not due to dissociation of the mercurial by the hydrogenase
preparation used in the fumarate reductase assay, it was considered advisable
to use an irreversible SH inhibitor, such as N-ethylmaleimide (NEM), to test
the point. As shown in Table 7, this reagent inhibits extensively the succinate
dehydrogenase activity of the mitochondrial enzyme but does not inhibit
fumarate reduction either by the mitochondrial enzyme or by extramitochondrial preparations.

Unambiguous evidence for the existence of a second succinate dehydrogenase in yeast came from particle fractionations. Rigorous exclusion of mitochondria from commercial baker's yeast preparations by differential centrifugation has shown that the soluble (cytoplasmic) phase contains appreciable succinate dehydrogenase and fumarate reductase activities and that the ratio $V_{succ. + phenazine\ methosulfate} : V_{fum. + FMNH_2}$ at $30°$ is 33 in mitochondria, but only 3.6 in the cytoplasm (26, 68).

### TABLE 7

**Effect of N-Ethylmaleimide on Succinate Oxidation and Fumarate Reduction in Yeast**[a]

| | Succinate Dehydrogenase Activity[c] | | Fumarate Reductase Activity[d] | |
|---|---|---|---|---|
| Sample[b] | Micromoles Succinate Oxidized/min/ml Original Enzyme | Inhibition, % | Micromoles Fumarate Reduced/min/ml Original Enzyme | Inhibition, % |
| Cytoplasmic preparation | | | 0.041 | |
| Same + NEM | | | 0.041 | 0 |
| ETP | 32.4 | | 1.1 | |
| Same + NEM | 6.4 | 80 | 1.3 | 0 |

[a] Data from Rossi et al. (68).
[b] The respiratory chain preparation denoted as ETP was prepared from Red Star baker's yeast by the method of Mahler et al. (46). The cytoplasmic phase was the supernatant obtained on centrifugation of the mitochondria for 20 min at 105,000 × g. Treatment with N-ethylmaleimide was by incubation of the preparation with 0.5 volume of 10 $mM$ NEM at pH 7.0 for 10 min at 0°, followed by removal of unreacted NEM on Sephadex G-25.
[c] Phenazine methosulfate-DCIP assay at V, 30°, with activation.
[d] FMNH$_2$-fumarate assay at 30° at 1.33 $mM$ FMNH$_2$.

The properties of the extramitochondrial enzyme(s) differ markedly from those of the mitochondrial enzyme. In the first place, the latter is tightly bound to the respiratory chain and is solubilized only with difficulty (27), whereas fumarate reductase activity in the extramitochondrial fraction becomes soluble on mechanical disruption of the cells (68). Second, fumarate reduction by the cytoplasmic preparation is extremely stable to storage and to variations in pH, while the solubilized mitochondrial enzyme is quite unstable.

It became apparent soon that the extramitochondrial fraction contained not one but two* succinate dehydrogenases; one was completely excluded on Sephadex G-200, the other completely included on both Sephadex G-100 and G-200. The former was precipitated at low $(NH_4)_2SO_4$ concentrations,

---

* As detailed in the Discussion, more recently the low-molecular-weight enzyme has been separated into two components. The differences between these two components are documented in the Discussion. Because of these findings, a figure and table which appeared in the preprinted manuscript have been deleted.

whereas the latter, a yellow protein, was precipitated only at high $(NH_4)_2SO_4$ saturations. Chromatography on hydroxylapatite also afforded separation of the two enzymes. The enzyme of higher molecular weight oxidizes succinate in the phenazine-DCIP assay $(V_{succ. + PMS} : V_{fum. + FMNH_2} = 4$–$5$ at $30°$) and reduces ferricyanide and cytochrome $c$ more slowly and appears to be activable; the other enzyme does not reduce phenazine methosulfate, ferricyanide, or cytochrome $c$ significantly. As measured by the fumarate-$FMNH_2$ assay, the concentration of the G-200 excluded enzyme in the cytoplasm appears to be lower in the respiratory deficient "petite" mutant and virtually nil in anaerobic yeast, while that of the G-200 included enzyme is normal in "petites" and increased in anaerobic yeast. It may be noted further that, at least as measured in the $FMNH_2$ assay, the fumarate-reducing capacity of either enzyme is considerably lower than that attributable to mitochondrial succinate dehydrogenase in normal, aerobic cells.

These findings raise many interesting questions concerning the physiological functions of the two cytoplasmic succinate dehydrogenases, the nature of their natural electron donors, and, above all, their relations to each other and to succinate dehydrogenase in mitochondria.


## IV. CONCLUDING REMARKS

From the viewpoint of this symposium it is of interest that succinate dehydrogenases present a beautiful example of adaptation of the organism to aerobic or anaerobic types of existence. This is not surprising, since in cells which derive their energy requirements from oxygen-linked reactions succinate dehydrogenase plays a cardinal role in metabolism as a member of the tricarboxylic acid cycle and as an enzyme concerned with one of the metabolic steps whereby oxygen-linked reactions lead to energy conservation. In contrast, in anaerobic fermentations the succinate dehydrogenase-fumarate system often replaces $O_2$ as terminal electron acceptor, and thus succinate dehydrogenases from organisms which function in this manner must be equipped to catalyze the reduction of fumarate with maximum efficiency. Although the pathway from succinate to $O_2$ in aerobes has been elucidated in many cases, the identity of the physiological electron donor to succinate dehydrogenase in anaerobic fermentations remains to be elucidated. One might speculate that a protein of the ferredoxin type could act as the link between DPNH, or a flavoprotein not utilizing dissociable coenzymes, and succinate dehydrogenase in anaerobes.

From the evolutionary viewpoint the development of the succinate dehydrogenase molecule has not yet been adequately explored. Perhaps the prime reason is the difficulty of isolating this unstable enzyme of high molecular weight in sufficiently pure and unmodified form from different cells to permit tracing the evolution of its primary structure. While this is a forbidding limitation, perhaps certain unusual properties of the enzyme from aerobic forms of life, such as the presence of covalently bound flavin, the presence of activation by substrates, and catalytic properties, may permit some progress in this direction.

Lastly, it is of transcending interest that in organisms such as yeast, where these phenomena can be studied readily, genetic or environmental conditions which lead to disappearance of the respiratory chain also cause a considerable lowering or even complete disappearance of mitochondrial succinate dehydrogenase activity and that, conversely, on adaptation to $O_2$, synthesis of the dehydrogenase occurs along with that of the respiratory chain. Elucidation of the mechanism regulating the synthesis of the dehydrogenase in these instances is one of the fascinating problems of the future.

## ACKNOWLEDGMENTS

The original studies reported here were supported by research grants from the United States Public Health Service (HE-01995) and the National Science Foundation (G-20457), and by Contract No. Nonr 1656(00) between the Office of Naval Research and this Institute.

## REFERENCES

1. T. Wieland and G. Pfleiderer, *Advances in Enzymol.*, **XXV**, 329 (1963).
2. T. P. Singer and E. B. Kearney, in P. Boyer, H. A. Lardy, and K. Myrbäck, Eds., *The Enzymes*, Vol. VII, 2nd Ed., Academic Press, New York, 1963, p. 383.
3. T. P. Singer, in M. Florkin and E. Stotz, Eds., *Comprehensive Biochemistry*, Vol. 14, Elsevier, Amsterdam, 1964.
4. E. B. Kearney and T. P. Singer, *J. Biol. Chem.*, **219**, 963 (1956).
5. T. P. Singer and C. J. Lusty, unpublished data (1959–1963).
6. T. P. Singer, E. B. Kearney, and P. Bernath, *J. Biol. Chem.*, **223**, 599 (1956).
7. T. Y. Wang, C. L. Tsou, and Y. L. Wang, *Sci. Sinica (Peking)*, **5**, 73 (1956).
8. E. B. Kearney and T. P. Singer, in *Résumés des communications, 3ème Congrès intern. de biochemie*, Brussels, 1955, p. 54.
9. E. B. Kearney, *J. Biol. Chem.*, **235**, 865 (1960).
10. T. Y. Wang, C. L. Tsou, and Y. L. Wang, *Sci. Sinica (Peking)*, **7**, 65 (1958).
11. T. P. Singer, J. Hauber, and E. B. Kearney, *Biochem. Biophys. Research Communs.*, **9**, 146 (1962).
12. T. P. Singer and V. Massey, *Record Chem. Progr.* (*Kresge-Hooker Sci. Lib.*), **18**, 201 (1957).
13. V. Massey, *J. Biol. Chem.*, **229**, 763 (1957).
14. W. Lovenberg, B. B. Buchanan, and J. C. Rabinowitz, *J. Biol. Chem.*, **238**, 3899 (1963).
15. K. T. Fry and A. San Pietro, *Biochem. Biophys. Research Communs.*, **9**, 218 (1962).
16. P. Handler, K. V. Rajagopalan, and V. Aleman, *Federation Proc.*, **23**, Part I, No. 1, 30 (1964).

17. H. Beinert and R. H. Sands, *Biochem. Biophys. Research Communs.*, **3**, 41 (1960).
18. H. Beinert and W. Lee, *Biochem. Biophys. Research Communs.*, **5**, 40 (1961).
19. E. B. Kearney, *J. Biol. Chem.*, **229**, 363 (1957).
20. T. Kimura, J. Hauber, and T. P. Singer, *Biochem. Biophys. Research Communs.*, **11**, 83 (1963).
21. M. B. Thorn, *Biochem. J.*, **85**, 116 (1962).
22. O. Arrigoni and T. P. Singer, *Nature*, **193**, 1526 (1962).
23. T. P. Singer, E. B. Kearney, and V. Massey, *Advances in Enzymol.*, **XVIII**, 65 (1957).
24. T. P. Singer, J. Hauber, and C. J. Lusty, unpublished data (1962–1963).
25. P. Cerletti, R. Strom, M. G. Giordano, F. Balestrero, and M. A. Giovenco, *Biochem. Biophys. Research Communs.*, **14**, 408 (1963).
26. E. Rocca, E. B. Kearney, C. Machinist, and T. P. Singer, unpublished data (1964).
27. T. P. Singer, V. Massey, and E. B. Kearney, *Arch. Biochem. Biophys.*, **69**, 405 (1957).
28. F. J. S. Lara, *Biochim. et Biophys. Acta*, **33**, 565 (1959).
29. T. P. Singer, *Annals N. Y. Acad. Sci.*, **72**, 480 (1959).
30. M. G. P. J. Warringa, O. H. Smith, A. Giuditta, and T. P. Singer, *J. Biol. Chem.*, **230**, 97 (1958).
31. T. P. Singer, J. Hauber, and O. Arrigoni, *Biochem. Biophys. Research Communs.*, **9**, 150 (1962).
32. L. Kováč, *Collection Czechoslov. Chem. Communs.*, **23**, 1140 (1958).
33. T. E. King, C. A. Ryan, V. H. Cheldelin, and J. K. McDonald, *Biochim. et Biophys. Acta*, **45**, 398 (1960).
34. C. A. Ryan and T. E. King, *Biochim. et Biophys. Acta*, **62**, 269 (1962).
35. M. G. P. J. Warringa and A. Giuditta, *J. Biol. Chem.*, **230**, 111 (1958).
36. T. P. Singer, in P. Boyer, H. A. Lardy, and K. Myrbäck, Eds., *The Enzymes*, Vol. VII, 2nd ed., Academic Press, New York, 1963, p. 345.
37. T. P. Singer and T. Cremona, in F. Dickens, Ed., *Symposium on Oxygen in the Animal Organism*, Pergamon Press, London, 1964, p. 389.
38. A. Giuditta and T. P. Singer, *J. Biol. Chem.*, **234**, 666 (1958).
39. T. Kimura, J. Hauber, and T. P. Singer, *Nature*, **199**, 362 (1963).
40. D. Keilin and T. E. King, *Proc. Roy. Soc. (London)*, **B152**, 163 (1960).
41. W. R. Frisell and C. G. MacKenzie, *J. Biol. Chem.*, **237**, 95 (1962).
42. T. P. Singer and J. Hauber, *Federation Proc.*, **22**, 466 (1963).
43. T. P. Singer and F. J. S. Lara, in K. Ichihara, Ed., *Proceedings of the International Symposium on Enzyme Chemistry, Tokyo-Kyoto, 1957*, Academic Press, New York, 1958, p. 330.
44. M. G. P. J. Warringa, A. Giuditta, E. B. Kearney, and T. P. Singer, *Bacteriol. Proc.*, P4 (1957).
45. B. Mackler, P. Collipp, H. Duncan, N. Rao, and F. Huennekens, *J. Biol. Chem.*, **237**, 2968 (1962).
46. H. R. Mahler, B. Mackler, S. Grandchamp, and P. P. Slonimski, unpublished data circulated by I.E.G. No. 1, National Institutes of Health, 1964.
47. H. M. Hirsch, *Biochim. et Biophys. Acta*, **9**, 674 (1962).
48. P. P. Slonimski, *La formation des enzymes respiratoires chez la Levure*, Masson, Paris, 1953.
49. G. Schatz, H. Tuppy, and J. Klima, *Z. Naturforsch.*, **18b**, 145 (1963).
50. A. W. Linnane and J. L. Still, *Australian J. Sci.*, **18**, 165 (1956).
51. C. R. Hebb, J. Slebodnik, T. P. Singer, and P. Bernath, *Arch. Biochem. Biophys.*, **83**, 10 (1959).
52. G. Schatz, *Biochem. Biophys. Research Communs.*, **12**, 448 (1963).
53. D. R. Briggs and A. W. Linnane, *Biochim. et Biophys. Acta*, **78**, 785 (1963).
54. E. M. Martin and R. K. Morton, *Biochem. J.*, **62**, 696 (1956).

55. E. Bueding, in B. Wright, Ed., *Control Mechanisms in Respiration and Fermentation*, Ronald Press, New York, 1963, p. 167.
56. E. Bueding, H. Saz, and G. W. Farrow, *Brit. J. Pharmacol.*, **14**, 497 (1959).
57. H. O. Peck, Jr., O. H. Smith, and H. Gest, *Biochim. et Biophys. Acta*, **25**, 142 (1957).
58. F. G. Fischer and H. Eysenbach, *Ann.*, **530**, 90 (1937).
59. F. G. Fischer, A. Roedig, and K. Bauch, *Ann.*, **552**, 203 (1942).
60. T. P. Singer, *Abstracts of the 132nd Meeting, American Chemical Society, New York, September, 1957*, 41C.
61. A. M. Pappenheimer, Jr., and E. D. Hendee, *J. Biol. Chem.*, **180**, 597 (1949).
62. C. A. Hirsch, M. Rasminsky, B. D. Davis, and E. C. C. Lin, *J. Biol. Chem.*, **238**, 3370 (1963).
63. V. Massey and T. P. Singer, *J. Biol. Chem.*, **228**, 263 (1957).
64. K. Harrison, *Nature*, **172**, 509 (1953).
65. T. P. Singer, V. Massey, and E. B. Kearney, *Biochim. et Biophys. Acta*, **19**, 200 (1956).
66. L. Kováč, *Enzymologia*, **22**, 27 (1960).
67. T. P. Singer and P. Bernath, in S. Colowick and N. O. Kaplan, Eds., *Methods in Enzymology*, Vol. V, Academic Press, New York, 1962, p. 597.
68. C. Rossi, J. Hauber, and T. P. Singer, *Nature*, **204**, 167 (1964).

## Discussion

SINGER: I'd like to summarize briefly the recent findings from the study of yeast. Yeast mitochondria contain a typical aerobic succinate dehydrogenase which, except for slightly lower stability than that of the enzyme from animal tissues, is remarkably similar to what one encounters in higher forms of life. This mito-chondrial succinate dehydrogenase disappears completely in anaerobiosis and is also absent in the respiratory-deficient "petite" mutant. In accord with findings in other laboratories, Drs. Kearney and Rocca have found that succinate dehydro-genase is completely absent from the particulate fraction of "petite" cells, whether measured by catalytic activity in the phenazine-2,6-dichlorophenolindophenol assay or by the specific chemical determination of covalently bound flavin (acid non-extractable flavin). The very small amount of "bound flavin" (Table 1) found in "petite" cells is not succinate dehydrogenase flavin but another source of co-valently bound flavin which exhibits an entirely different pH fluorescence curve than succinate dehydrogenase flavin.

As for anaerobic cells, the situation is rather interesting: now that several workers have confirmed the presence of small but measurable succinate dehydrogenase activity in anaerobic yeast, we can't find any, at least in the several strains we currently have. Thus, we are in complete accord with Dr. Linnane's group [see p. 1102 of Volume Two; D. R. Briggs and A. W. Linnane, *Biochim. et Biophys. Acta*, **78**, 785 (1963)], who also cannot detect any succinate dehydrogenase in anaerobic yeast. Furthermore, NADH dehydrogenase is also very much lowered in anaerobic cells, as shown in Table 2, which also illustrates the oxygen-induced formation of these enzymes. The important point illustrated in this table is that as you go from completely anaerobic yeast, with $Q_{O_2} = 0$, to a reasonably aerobic yeast ($Q_{O_2} = 40$–$50$), succinate dehydrogenase activity, covalently bound flavin, and NADH dehydrogenase all increase but by no means at the same rate as the cytochrome system.

## TABLE 1

### Succinate Oxidase, NADH Oxidase, Succinate Dehydrogenase, and Bound Flavin in ETP Preparations from Yeast

| Growth Conditions | $Q_{O_2}$ (whole cells) | Succinate Oxidase | Succinate Dehydro- genase | DPNH Oxidase | Covalently Bound Flavin Content, $m\mu moles/$ mg |
|---|---|---|---|---|---|
| Commercial Red Star yeast | ... | 1.0–1.5 | 1.6–2.5 | 2.0–2.8 | 0.18–0.20 |
| Red Star, anaerobic growth | 0 | 0–<0.1 | 0–<0.1 | 0.01 | 0.01–0.03 |
| Red Star, aerobic growth | 34 | 0.05–0.09 | 0.02–0.13 | 0.11–0.35 | ... |
| Red Star, aerobic growth | 58 | 0.08 | 0.14 | ... | 0.08 |
| "Petite" mutant, aerobic or anaero- bic growth | 0 | 0 | 0–0.02 | 0.03 | 0.02–0.03 |
| D.I. yeast,[a] an- aerobic growth | 0 | 0 | <0.01 | 0 | 0.02 |
| D.I. yeast, aerobic growth, moderate aeration | 24 | ... | 0.09 | 0.05 | ... |
| D.I. yeast, aerobic growth, moderate aeration | 80 | 0.66 | 0.69 | 0.36 | ... |
| D.I. yeast, aerobic growth, high aeration | 164 | ... | 2.88 | 1.15 | ... |

Specific Activities in "ETP" Fraction, $\mu$moles substrate/min/ mg protein

[a] D.I. = Distillerie Italiane yeast.

This oxygen-induced formation of the respiratory chain-linked dehydrogenases is a very complex phenomenon. It is easy to rig an adaptation experiment in such a way to arrive at over 50% of the maximal synthesis of the cytochrome system and yet less than 5% of the normal aerobic succinate dehydrogenase content at the end of the adaptation. As to cytoplasmic enzymes, it was originally suggested by Fischer and coworkers [F. G. Fischer and H. Eysenbach, *Ann*, **530**, 90 (1937); F. G. Fischer, A. Roedig, and K. Bauch, *Ann.*, **552**, 203 (1942)] some 25 or 30 years ago that there was a specific fumarate reductase in yeast incapable of oxidizing

## TABLE 2

### Oxygen-Induced Synthesis of Respiratory Enzymes in Anaerobic Yeast

| Time of $O_2$ Adaptation, hr | $Q_{O_2}$ (glucose) | Succinate Oxidase | | Succinate Dehydrogenase | | Bound Flavin m$\mu$moles/mg mitochondria | NADH Dehydrogenase | |
|---|---|---|---|---|---|---|---|---|
| | | Total Activity, $\mu$moles/min | Specific Activity, $\mu$moles/min/mg | Total Activity, $\mu$moles/min | Specific Activity, $\mu$moles/min/mg | | Total Activity, $\mu$moles/min | Specific Activity, $\mu$moles/min/mg |
| 0 | 0 | 0 | 0 | 15.6 | 0.009 | 0.016 | 291 | 0.18 |
| 1.5 | 10.7 | 4.65 | 0.006 | 27.0 | 0.047 | 0.019 | 491 | 0.59 |
| 3 | 24.1 | 20.1 | 0.026 | 81.6 | 0.105 | 0.023 | 1013 | 1.31 |
| 5 | 47 | 63.9 | 0.071 | 166 | 0.184 | 0.042 | 2025 | 2.25 |
| 18.5 | 41 | 109 | 0.141 | 463 | 0.60 | 0.074 | 2455 | 3.19 |

Adaptation in 0.066 $M$ $KH_2PO_4$–1% glucose in dark at 28° with vigorous aeration. Succinate oxidase assay polarographically at 30° with activation; succinate dehydrogenase with phenazine-2,6-dichlorophenolindophenol spectrophotometrically at 30°; DPNH dehydrogenase activity at 25°. $Q_{O_2}$ refers to whole cells; other activities, to mitochondria isolated after sonication. Total activity refers to 100 gram wet weight of cells.

succinate in the methylene blue assay. However, we were unable to reproduce these findings of Fischer *et al.* as detailed in the text and elsewhere.

Recently Dr. Rossi and Mr. Hauber (described on p. 466 of this book; also unpublished data) in our laboratory reopened this question. Having ascertained that yeast mitochondria contain only one form of succinate dehydrogenase, the one which resembles its counterpart in animal tissues, they explored the possible presence of other succinate dehydrogenases, in the cytoplasm. The supernatant

### TABLE 3

### Distribution of Fumarate Reducing Enzymes in Cytoplasm of Red Star Yeast

| Sephadex G-200 Fractionation | % of Total |
| --- | --- |
| Excluded | 17 |
| Included | 83 |

fraction obtained on centrifugation of broken cells for 1 hr at 144,000 × $g$ contains three enzymes capable of fumarate reduction. One is of fairly high molecular weight (of the order of 200,000), which is excluded on Sephadex G-200; it is present in very low amounts, and so far we cannot distinguish it from the mitochondrial succinate dehydrogenase in regard to properties we have been able to study. The other two enzymes are of lower molecular weight, being included on Sephadex G-100 or G-200 (cf. Table 3), and differ markedly in properties from the mitochondrial enzyme. The fact that the high-molecular-weight (G-200 excluded)

### TABLE 4

### Properties of G-200 Excluded Enzyme

$$V\,\frac{\text{Succ.} - \text{PMS}}{\text{Fum.} - \text{FMNH}_2} = 7.6$$

| | |
| --- | --- |
| Reaction with Fe(CN)$_6^{3-}$, 2,6-dichlorophenolindophenol, and cytochrome $c$ | None |
| Activation by substrate | + + |
| Malonate sensitivity | High |
| In anaerobic yeast | Absent |

enzyme behaves in respects hitherto studied very much like succinate dehydrogenase solubilized from mitochondria is shown in Table 4. Thus the ratio of the forward to the reverse reactions is rather close to that of the mitochondrial enzyme in soluble form (about 8–10 in yeast); it oxidizes succinate with phenazine methosulfate but doesn't react with any of the electron acceptors which are unreactive toward the mitochondrial enzyme. It is activated by substrate; it is highly sensitive to malonate; and, significantly, it is here absent in anaerobic cells and in the "petite" mutant. Whether it is a normal cytoplasmic constituent or is derived from mitochondria during disintegration of the cells cannot be presently decided.

In contrast, the other two enzymes, which are included on Sephadex G-200 and G-100 and are, therefore, of lower molecular weight, have materially different properties. They are present in rather high concentrations in both aerobic and anaerobic yeast. As shown in Fig. 1, they can be separated from each other on

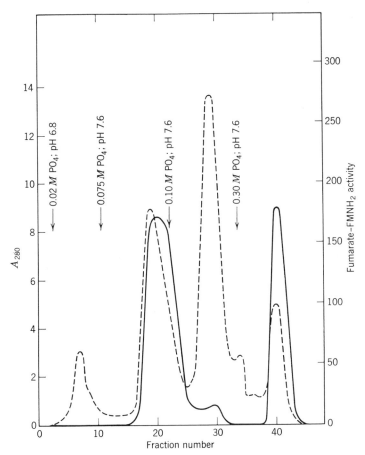

**Fig. 1.** Separation of the two low-molecular-weight fumarate reductases on hydroxylapatite. Solid line denotes activity in the fumarate-$FMNH_2$ assay; interrupted line, absorbancy at 280 m$\mu$. When rechromatographed on another hydroxylapatite column, both enzyme 1 (0.075 $M$ phosphate eluate) and enzyme 2 (0.3 $M$ phosphate eluate) gave single, symmetrical peaks.

hydroxylapatite columns. The solid line represents activity; the dashed line, protein. On rechromatography of each of the two enzymes thus separated a single symmetrical peak is obtained.

The properties of these two new fumarate reductases are compared in Table 5. There are significant differences in kinetic constants between the two enzymes. Type 1 is the one easily eluted from hydroxylapatite; type 2 is the enzyme eluted

## TABLE 5

### Comparison of Properties of G-200 Included Fumarate Reductases[a]

| Property | Type 1 | Type 2 |
|---|---|---|
| Mol. wt. | Near 50,000 | Near 50,000 |
| $K_m$ fumarate | 1.43 $mM$ | 0.89 $mM$ |
| $K_i$ succinate | 6.1 $mM$ | 4.2 $mM$ |
| $K_i$ malonate | 0.79 $mM$ | 0.49 $mM$ |
| Reaction with DCIP, PMS, cytochrome $c$, ferricyanide | None | None |
| Reaction with electron donors | $FMNH_2 > MV > BV$ | $FMNH_2 > BV > MV$ |
| pH optimum | 7.1–7.8 | 7.3–7.4 |
| $(NH_4)_2SO_4$ precipitation | 0.4–0.6 sat. | 0.5–0.7 sat. |
| Stability | Extremely stable | Relatively stable |

[a] DCIP, 2,6-dichlorophenolindophenol; PMS, phenazine methosulfate; MV, methylviologen; and BV, benzylviologen.

only at high ionic strengths. Both of these enzymes differ markedly from the mitochondrial enzyme or from the third cytoplasmic one in kinetic constants, reactivities with electron donors and acceptors, stability, etc. So far we have been unable to observe any oxidation of succinate with the acceptors listed with either "low-molecular-weight" fumarate reductase. As shown in Fig. 2, by measuring $H_2$ uptake in the presence of fumarate, hydrogenase, and ferredoxin and plotting

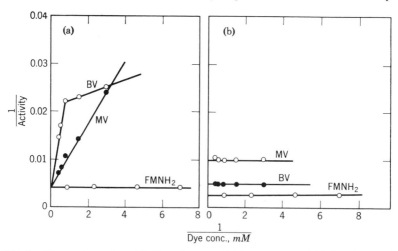

**Fig. 2.** Comparison of specificities of enzyme 1 (a) and enzyme 2 (b) for electron donors. MV, methylviologen; BV, benzylviologen. All assays were at 30°, pH 7.6 by manometric measurement of $H_2$ uptake in the presence of excess hydrogenase from *Cl. pasteurianum*. The biphasic curve seen with benzylviologen in (a) is often noted with this dye and is due to impurities present even in recrystallized preparations of the dye.

reciprocal activity against reciprocal dye concentration for a series of electron donors, both the $V$ and relative $K_m$ values for the dyes are found to be quite different for the two enzymes. Figure 3 demonstrates that these two low-molecular-weight enzymes also differ from each other and from the high-molecular-weight enzyme in their sensitivity to malonate.

The biological function of these different fumarate-reducing enzymes is presently a matter of speculation, but some possibilities might be considered. Perhaps the most interesting fact which has emerged from this investigation, as also demonstrated by Davis and coworkers for *E. coli* [C. A. Hirsch, M. Rasminsky, B. D. Davis, and E. C. C. Lin, *J. Biol. Chem.*, **238**, 3770 (1963)], is that there are certain

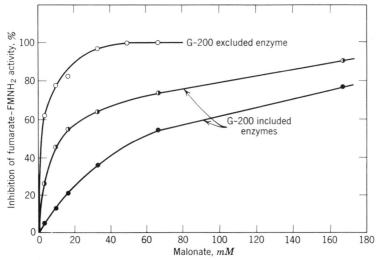

**Fig. 3.** Malonate sensitivity of fumarate-reducing enzymes from yeast cytoplasm. Activities noted on the abscissa refer to the fumarate-FMNH$_2$ assay at 30°, pH 7.6 in the presence of 2 *mM* fumarate. Open circles, enzyme 1; solid circles, enzyme 2; half-shaded circles, high-molecular-weight enzyme.

types of cells which can live successfully in both aerobiosis and anaerobiosis, under very different conditions of metabolism, depending on the presence or absence of oxygen. Such cells develop succinate dehydrogenases which fit the physiological needs of the cell in the particular environment. This is surely the most successful way of coping with the problems imposed upon the cell by extreme variations in oxygen tension.

LINNANE: I should like to make a comment on our work in regard to mitochondrial succinate dehydrogenase in yeast. We have not found significant quantities of the mitochondrial succinate dehydrogenase in anaerobically grown cells, and, also consistently with this data, our anaerobically grown cells as seen in the electron microscope are devoid of mitochondria. I am interested to learn that Dr. Singer would agree with this view at least with his present yeast strains. In regard to some of his earlier work in support of the presence of succinate dehydrogenase in anaerobically grown cells, I should like to know the localization of this enzyme in an anaerobically grown cell. Was this a particulate enzyme, and with what fraction was it associated? Dr. Singer, would you say that there are mitochondria in anaerobically grown yeast?

SINGER: At the time that this work was done, we put in a footnote to the effect that we did not wish to enter into an argument as to what to call the particles which come down in anaerobic yeast in the same sedimenting range as mitochondria do in aerobic ones. I surely have no opinions on the matter. The enzyme was certainly particulate; we made it by your method. These were time samples on fractions collected at high centrifugal fields between two sedimenting ranges and assayed as the particle-bound enzyme for cytochrome oxidase, succinate oxidase, succinate dehydrogenase, etc. In our joint study with Caroline Hebb [C. R. Hebb, J. Slebodnik, T. P. Singer, and P. Bernath, *Arch. Biochem. Biophys.*, **83**, 10 (1959)], we used a strain isolated from commercial Red Star yeast. However, the succinate dehydrogenase and oxidase activities of aerobic cells of Red Star yeast sold in 1956 were only about a tenth as high as the values found in current lots of Red Star yeast. Therefore, what appeared to be appreciable succinate dehydrogenase activity in anaerobic yeast 8 years ago is negligibly small compared with the succinate dehydrogenase activity in aerobic cells of the current strain. Schatz [G. Shatz, *Biochem. Biophys. Research Communs.*, **12**, 448 (1963)], however, reported very much higher succinate dehydrogenase activities in anaerobic yeast than other investigators have found. We have recently examined at least four strains of American and Italian yeast and cannot find any significant amount in anaerobically grown cells.

RACKER: I should like to make a brief comment regarding changes in yeast. Dr. Bermeyer of Boehringer's came to visit me a few months ago; I asked him why the supply of glucose-6-phosphate dehydrogenase in the United States had suddenly disappeared. He said, "Because of Fidel Castro." I was surprised to find that he had become Americanized so quickly that he blamed Fidel Castro for everything, but I finally got the full story. They had trouble at Boehringer's in making the enzyme for several months with different batches of yeast, and they just couldn't understand what the difficulty was. Finally they asked the firm that supplied the yeast and were informed that the firm had run out of Cuban cane sugar and had had to switch to beet sugar molasses. This completely changed the fractionation process in the enzyme.

SINGER: The α-hydroxyacid dehydrogenase both is low in quantity and differs in properties when the yeast is grown on sugar cane molasses, and for successful isolation the yeast should be cultured in a beet sugar medium. Let me tell one other thing that may be of some conceivable interest to those who don't have an excessively unitarian point of view about biochemistry. It may be that at least one of these two cytoplasmic enzymes is going to turn out to be an FMN enzyme. Neither one of the two "Sephadex-included" fumarate reductases contains covalently bound flavin. On deproteinization the flavin is removed from both enzymes. One of the two reductases has now been reversibly resolved by the acid-ammonium sulfate method, and while we get some reactivation with FAD, almost complete reactivation has been observed with FMN. FMN is also present in much larger amounts than FAD in preparations hitherto obtained, which are not yet homogeneous. It would be amusing to find a succinate dehydrogenase with FMN as the prosthetic group, since we traditionally think of succinate dehydrogenase as a FAD enzyme. It should be added that dialysis does not dissociate either enzyme; hence they cannot be identified with the reductase of Fischer *et al.*

LINNANE: I should like to ask Dr. Singer about his conditions for the oxygen-induced synthesis of succinate dehydrogenase in anaerobically grown yeast. These are not indicated in the paper. Our own experience with this enzyme and its induction is that it is under the influence of a glucose repression. What was the composition of the medium with regard to carbon and nitrogen sources, and what is the time course of the syntheses of the inductions of succinate dehydrogenase?

SINGER: To make a long story short, we have varied the strain of yeast, the time of growth, the composition of the culture medium in terms of glucose content (varying it from 0.6% to 5%), the source of nitrogen (inorganic or peptone), and finally the oxygen tension. The oxygen tension is by no means the only factor determining the rate of induction. We thoroughly agree with you on the induction of succinate. I might add that NADH dehydrogenase acts similarly under a whole variety of controls, because you can affect it profoundly by varying the glucose concentration. By using low glucose and peptone as the source of nitrogen and moderately high aeration, you may get a higher rate of synthesis of succinate dehydrogenase than that of the cytochrome system, but if you raise the glucose to about 1–1.5% in the aeration medium, you can have succinate dehydrogenase lag tenfold behind the synthesis of the cytochrome system. Glucose is one of the main repressing influences, but we don't know as yet all the other factors which influence the induction.

KING: I should like just to supplement two points which Dr. Singer did not describe in his paper. The reason I am going to bring them out, *inter alia*, is that some people not directly working in this field are desperately confused. (1) In all the descriptions Dr. Singer made in his paper in this book under the name succinate dehydrogenase, at least the isolated succinate dehydrogenase refers to the enzyme which catalyzes the oxidation of succinate only by artificial electron acceptors such as phenazine methosulfate. However, he did not mention another kind of succinate dehydrogenase which can use not only artificial acceptors but also the cytochrome system. The action of this succinate dehydrogenase toward the cytochrome system or the reconstitution of the respiratory succinate oxidase actually has no correlation with its artificial activity. This enzyme, i.e., reconstitutively active succinate dehydrogenase, has been documented in the literature since 1958 [e.g., King, *J. Biol. Chem.*, **238**, 4032 (1963); see previous references cited there]. The mammalian enzyme (I don't know about the others which he reported) described by Singer does not react to a cytochrome system at all. (2) Dr. Singer mentioned the homogeneity of his enzyme from mammalian source. Under the conditions conducted by Dr. Singer and co-workers for the test of homogeneity, the word homogeneous is meaningless because the functional test clearly reveals that the enzyme in air even at 0° is very unstable with a half-life of only a few hours *even* based on the phenazine methosulfate assay. In other words, his physical characterization is far from sensitive in comparison to the activity test even with an artificial acceptor and not, say, with reconstitution.

I don't think that I should bring out the whole story and point out many sophistic arguments in more than a half-dozen reviews written by Dr. Singer.

SINGER: It appeared to me that, since the point of view of this paper was one of comparative biochemistry, nomenclatural problems were not particularly relevant to the issue or even Dr. King's work on how many species of degraded forms of enzyme one can find. However, as long as the point has been brought up, I could make a few comments to this effect. We define homogeneity, as do most enzyme chemists, in terms of physical criteria. We have always been aware of the fact that these are not as sensitive as are some biological criteria, such as immunochemical methods. The problem in this case does not seem to be one of nomenclature, because all protein chemists know that sedimentation or diffusion analysis has a certain inherent source of error. What Dr. King is referring to perhaps is his worry about why some preparations of the soluble mammalian enzyme will "recombine" with an alkali-treated respiratory chain preparation, while others won't. Now, as you know, he has shown (and this can be readily confirmed) that none of the three *main* preparations of soluble succinate dehydrogenase from heart in the literature recombines with alkali-treated respiratory chain preparations. Each one requires some modification of the original method to do so. I am now citing Dr. King's work. The Wang et al. [T. Y. Wang, C. L. Tsou, and Y. L. Wang, *Sci. Sinica* (*Peking*), **5**, 73 (1956)] preparation of 1956 requires the omission of cyanide and then will recombine. The Singer et al. [T. P. Singer, E. B. Kearney, and V. Massey, *Advances in Enzymol.*, **XVIII**, 65 (1957)] preparation of 1956, according to Dr. King's publications [e.g., King, *J. Biol. Chem.*, **238**, 4032 (1963); see previous references cited there], has to be modified by the inclusion of succinate during the extraction and then will recombine. Now, Dr. Kimura and Mr. Hauber [*Biochem. Biophys. Research Communs.*, **13**, 169 (1963)] in our laboratory have published a paper showing that the situation is even more complex. Differential inactivation of succinate dehydrogenase in one kind of assay may occur much faster than in another, as we have known for well over 10 years. Furthermore, in terms of the reconstitution test any given preparation contains at least four and possibly five different species of succinate dehydrogenase. A soluble preparation, such as that used by Dr. King, can be resolved partially on Sephadex columns into various forms of succinate dehydrogenase, all of which are active in catalytic assays (such as phenazine methosulfate), and four of these five fractions do recombine (in terms of chemical analysis) with the alkali-treated preparation in stoichiometric amounts, but each type confers very different properties on the alkali-treated preparation. Only one of the five components, present in not more than 2% or so in a typical preparation, will reconstitute the system in all of its known properties. So the situation is pretty complex. I don't think that changing nomenclature will resolve the problem, since it is one of protein chemistry, which is not particularly germane to the present work.

KING: My answer to Dr. Singer's lengthy comment is very short. Here, it is not the polemics of nomenclature but the activity tests, artificial electron acceptors vs. reconstitution. Dr. Singer found perhaps four or five species of the so-called succinate dehydrogenase from the Sephadex column chromatography. These four or five species may be due to successive stages of irreversible denaturation of the active enzyme; I have discussed this point [*J. Biol. Chem.*, **239**, 3559 (1964)] elsewhere. Dr. Singer himself found that the half-life of succinate dehydrogenase for reconstitution is about 20 min [*Biochem. Biophys. Research Communs.*, **13**, 169

(1963)]. How could an enzyme with a half-life of 20 min stand chromatography under his conditions without inactivation?

SINGER: I don't think that anybody knows. By the way, this is not my work; it is Dr. Kimura's and Mr. Hauber's. They proposed that these are all modification products. I think that there is no basis whatsoever to call them successive ones. They may be formed simultaneously. The important point that was brought out in that paper is that a preparation which had hitherto been labeled as only reconstitutively active, in fact, contains a large variety of species of succinate dehydrogenase and only a very minor fraction is reconstitutively active in terms of a succinate oxidase test.

KING: Modification or inactivation and successive or otherwise are immaterial. You said that about 2% of your preparation of succinate dehydrogenase is reconstitutively active to form succinate oxidase. This is incompatible. In our hands, the reconstitution of succinate oxidase, using good, fresh succinate dehydrogenase (as the limiting amount), is always 100% based on the amount of the acid nonextractable flavin incorporated. 100%, no less!

RACKER: I was wondering whether you should call the decay (loss of activity) irreversible. It's irreversible until somebody finds that he can reverse it.

KING: Actually I should say that it is irreversible (denaturation) at the present time.

ESTABROOK: Do you, Dr. Singer, have any thoughts on the non-reactivity of succinate dehydrogenase with oxygen? How does this enzyme compare with other iron flavoproteins which do react to oxygen at rather high rates?

SINGER: I think that most workers in the field agree that the reaction of free FAD with $O_2$ is repressed in the succinate dehydrogenase molecule by the conformation of the protein. In other words, it is protected from rapid reoxidation by oxygen; nevertheless, there is a very slight autoxidizability (less than 0.1% of the turnover number of the enzyme) in preparations that we have examined.

ESTABROOK: Do you mean that the flavin is protected, or the iron is protected?

SINGER: I am speaking of the flavin moiety. The iron, according to Dr. Massey's work, is apparently in the ferric state in the isolated enzyme. Isn't that right, Dr. Massey?

MASSEY: The iron according to analysis was in the oxidized form and also was not reduced by substrate.

# PART V

# Heme-Containing Oxidases, I

# A Mechanism and Model
# of Peroxidase-Oxidase Reaction

. . . I. YAMAZAKI, K. YOKOTA,
and R. NAKAJIMA

## I. INTRODUCTION*

Peroxidase catalyzes a number of oxidations in which molecular oxygen serves as the electron acceptor. The theories which have been put forward to account for the oxidase reaction fall into two groups: those postulating the reduction of peroxidase to the ferrous form as an active state and those denying the participation of the ferrous form in the reaction. Recently, there have been accumulated a number of items of evidence that peroxidase-oxidase reactions are inhibited by CO, and ferroperoxidase-CO complex can be observed during the reaction under the limited conditions (1, 2, 3, 4, 5).

On the other hand, a free-radical mechanism has been proposed (4, 6, 7, 8) to show that the reactive intermediate is not ferroperoxidase-$O_2$ complex but free radicals produced in the reaction of donor with peroxidase-$H_2O_2$ compounds. The possibility of forming such free radicals has been suggested by George (9, 10), who found that a peroxidase-$H_2O_2$ intermediate, compound II, is in a one-electron oxidized state compared with free peroxidase. Chance (11) has also observed one-electron reduction from compound I to compound II. The mechanism of two-step oxidation in the peroxidase system has been confirmed directly by the observation of ESR signals during the reaction (12, 13).

In a previous paper (4) we presented a possible explanation of these results, showing that reduction of peroxidase is a side path which is not important for catalysis, but that CO can inhibit the reaction by removing the active form of the enzyme. In this paper we shall report some additional evidence and discuss the possibility of the participation of ferroperoxidase.

---

\* The following abbreviations are used in this paper: DHF, dihydroxyfumarate; ESR, electron spin (paramagnetic) resonance.

## II. EXPERIMENTAL DETAILS

Peroxidase (R.Z., $E_{403}/E_{278} = 3.0$) was purified and crystallized by the method of Kenten and Mann (14) from wild horse-radish (*Ainu wasabi*). Oxymyoglobin was purified and crystallized from fresh horse heart by the method reported elsewhere (15). Metmyoglobin was prepared from oxymyoglobin by oxidation with ferricyanide and separated from ferro- and ferricyanide with DEAE cellulose chromatography. The optical density was taken with a Hitachi recording spectrophotometer, and semiquinones were estimated with a Varian V-4502 x-band ESR spectrometer, utilizing 100-kc field modulation and Fieldial control of the magnetic field.

## III. RESULTS

### A. Reaction of Free Radicals with Oxygen

A free-radical mechanism for the peroxidase-oxidase reaction involves the reaction of free radicals with oxygen. This will suggest the consumption of oxygen during the oxidation of a certain donor with univalent oxidants. Figure 1 shows that $Ce^{4+}$ addition induced the consumption of oxygen

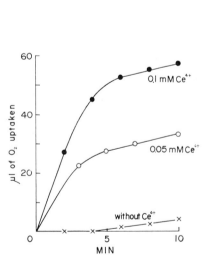

**Fig. 1.** $Ce^{4+}$-induced $O_2$ uptake in the presence of DHF. 2 $mM$ DHF, 0.05 $M$ acetate, pH 5.0, 25°C.

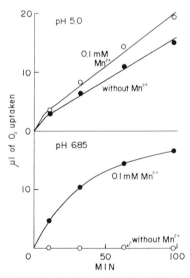

**Fig. 2.** Ferricyanide-induced $O_2$ uptake in the presence of NADH. 2 $mM$ NADH, 1 $mM$ ferricyanide, 25°C.

which depended on the amount of $Ce^{4+}$ added. Although the role of $Ce^{4+}$ was not catalytic, 1 mole of $Ce^{4+}$ induced the consumption of about 10 moles of oxygen. During the oxidation of NADH with ferricyanide, more sluggish consumption of oxygen could be observed at low pH, as shown in Fig. 2. In neutral pH, this oxygen consumption was induced only in the presence of $Mn^{2+}$.

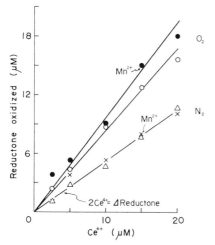

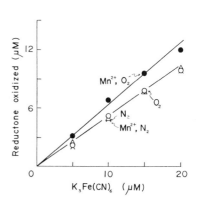

**Fig. 3.** Overoxidation of triose reductone with $Ce^{4+}$ in the presence (0.1 $mM$) and absence of $Mn^{2+}$. The solution was gassed with $O_2$ or $N_2$, pH 5.0.

**Fig. 4.** Overoxidation of triose reductone with ferricyanide in the presence (0.1 $mM$) and absence of $Mn^{2+}$. The solution was gassed with $O_2$ or $N_2$, pH 7.0.

The same kind of phenomena could also be shown by spectrophotometric methods. The very rapid oxidation of triose reductone took place when $Ce^{4+}$ and ferricyanide were added at low and neutral pH, respectively. Under the anaerobic conditions oxidation of triose reductone equivalent to the added oxidants could be observed, but in the presence of oxygen an amount of oxidized triose reductone was slightly over the added oxidants, which was enhanced in the presence of $Mn^{2+}$ (see Figs. 3 and 4). In the case of hydroquinone and ascorbate, no such excess oxidation could be observed spectrophotometrically even in the presence of $Mn^{2+}$.

## B. Potential of the First and Second Oxidation of Donor

According to Michaelis, if one distinguishes three oxidation levels, the reduced form ($R$), the semioxidized form ($S$), and the totally oxidized form ($T$) in a bivalent reversible system, which is not disturbed by any complications such as dimerization of any of the molecular species concerned, or by any subsequent irreversible process, the potentials of the three systems, $T \rightleftharpoons S$, $S \rightleftharpoons R$, and $T \rightleftharpoons S$, are

$$E = E_m + \frac{RT}{2F} \ln \frac{t}{r} \tag{1}$$

$$E = E_1 + \frac{RT}{F} \ln \frac{s}{r} \tag{2}$$

$$E = E_2 + \frac{RT}{F} \ln \frac{t}{s} \tag{3}$$

where $r$, $s$, and $t$ designate the molar concentrations of $R$, $S$, and $T$. The mean normal potential, $E_m$, has been determined for many bivalent systems, and $E_1$ and $E_2$ can be estimated when the constant for semiquinone formation, $k = s^2/rt$, is known.

$$E_1 = E_m - \frac{RT}{2F} \ln k \tag{4}$$

$$E_2 = E_m + \frac{RT}{2F} \ln k \tag{5}$$

Michaelis *et al.* have estimated $E_1$ and $E_2$ for phenanthrenequinone-3-sulfonate and pyocyanine by the analysis of potentiometric titration curve (16). This method can be applied only for the oxidation-reduction system which gives a large equilibrium concentration of semiquinone, usually for the system for which $k > 0.01$. Direct estimation of semiquinone concentration by ESR spectroscopy is a much more sensitive method for the estimation of $k$ than the analysis of titration curve. The equilibrium between $R$, $S$, and $T$ was confirmed from the result shown in Fig. 5. The equilibrium concentration of semiquinones depended greatly upon the pH of the solution. From the hyperfine structure of the ESR signal it is evident that the semiquinone of ascorbate and hydroquinone are completely dissociated above pH 5. At neutral pH, hydroquinone is in undissociated form and ascorbic acid is in monodissociated form. If the constants of semiquinone formation are expressed as

$$k_h = \frac{(A^-)^2(H^+)^2}{(A)(AH_2)} \quad \text{for hydroquinone} \tag{6}$$

$$k_a = \frac{(A^-)^2(H^+)}{(A)(AH^-)} \quad \text{for ascorbate} \tag{7}$$

where $R = AH_2$ or $AH^-$, $S = AH$ or $A^-$, $T = A$. Figure 6 shows that the dependency of $k_h$ and $k_a$ upon the pH of the solution is consistent with equations 6 and 7. Using equations 4 and 5, we can calculate the values of $E_1$ and $E_2$, which are plotted against pH in Fig. 7.

No semiquinones were detected from DHF and triose reductone under the

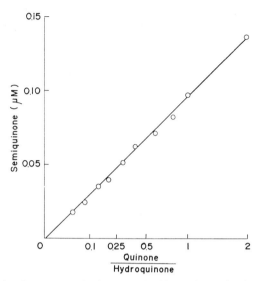

**Fig. 5.** Relation between semiquinone and added quinone in the presence of constant concentration of hydroquinone (0.35 $mM$). 0.05 $M$ phosphate, pH 6.5, 25°C. $p$-Benzoquinone concentration is plotted as the square root of the ratio of $p$-benzoquinone to hydroquinone.

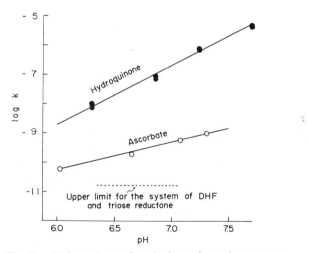

**Fig. 6.** pH dependence of semiquinone formation constant.

same experimental conditions. To judge from the sensitivity of the present ESR spectroscopy, the equilibrium concentration of semiquinones from DHF and triose reductone may be less than 0.02 $\mu M$. As the oxidized form of DHF, triose reductone, and ascorbate is supposed to be unstable, the mixed solution of the reduced and oxidized form was obtained using enzyme. A half of $AH_2$ was oxidized with $H_2O_2$ in the presence of peroxidase. At

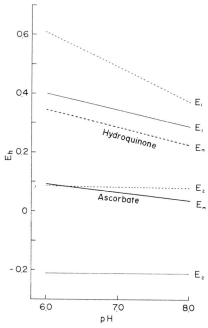

Fig. 7.   pH dependence of $E_m$, $E_1$, and $E_2$.   Solid lines, ascorbate;   dotted lines, hydroquinone.

neutral pH a part of the semiquinone of ascorbate accumulated during the enzymic reaction persisted after the reaction was over and kept a constant concentration during several runs of ESR measurement.   In the case of DHF and triose reductone, however, ESR signals which were observed during the enzymic reaction disappeared completely when the reactions were over.

## C. Reduction of Metmyoglobin by Peroxidase System

DHF could hardly reduce metmyoglobin, but the reduction was induced by the addition of a small amount of $H_2O_2$.   The reduction was accelerated in the presence of peroxidase.   Myoglobin thus reduced gave oxymyoglobin under the aerobic conditions and carboxymyoglobin when CO was gassed in solution (Figs. 8 and 9).   Figure 10 shows that the reduction of myoglobin was

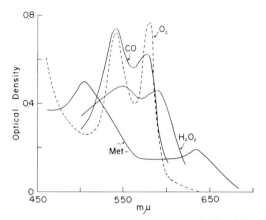

**Fig. 8.** Absorption spectra of metmyoglobin, oxymyoglobin, CO-myoglobin, and $H_2O_2$-metmyoglobin complex. 50 $\mu M$ myoglobin. [Reproduced from (21) by permission of the *Biochemical Journal* and from (15) by permission of the *Journal of Biological Chemistry*.]

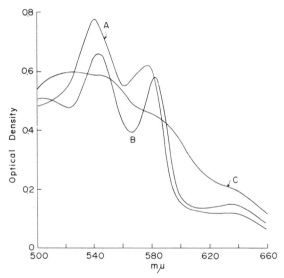

**Fig. 9.** Absorption spectra of myoglobin derivatives formed during the reactions. *A*. CO-myoglobin formed in solution of metmyoglobin, DHF, $H_2O_2$, and CO, pH 5.0; see Fig. 10. *B*. Oxymyoglobin formed in solution of metmyoglobin, DHF, and $H_2O_2$, aerobic, pH 5.0; see Fig. 10. *C*. $H_2O_2$-myoglobin compound formed in solution of metmyoglobin, DHF, and $Mn^{2+}$, aerobic, pH 5.0.

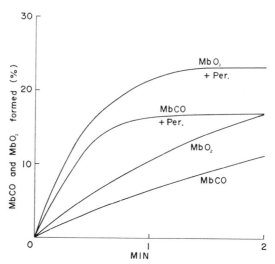

**Fig. 10.** $H_2O_2$-induced formation of oxy- and carboxymyoglobin from metmyoglobin in the presence of DHF (0.2 $mM$). The reaction started with the addition of 9 $\mu M$ $H_2O_2$. The solutions were bubbled with air or CO during the reactions. The formations of $O_2$ and CO-myoglobin were followed spectrophotometrically at 580 and 577 mu, respectively. 70 $\mu M$ metmyoglobin with or without peroxidase (1 $\mu M$), 0.05 $M$ acetate, pH 5.0. Room temperature.

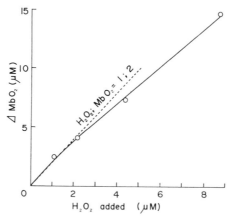

**Fig. 11.** Stoichiometry of metmyoglobin reduction with $H_2O_2$ in the presence of DHF (0.2 $mM$). 70 $\mu M$ metmyoglobin, 1 $\mu M$ peroxidase, 0.05 $M$ acetate, pH 5.0. Room temperature.

more effective in the presence of oxygen than of CO. Each of the myoglobin derivatives was identified by means of a recording spectrophotometer as shown in Fig. 9. Figure 11 shows the stoichiometric relation between oxymyoglobin formed and $H_2O_2$ added. It was found that 1 mole of $H_2O_2$ formed almost 2 moles of oxymyoglobin.

## D. Reduction of Peroxidase

In the previous paper, we reported the $H_2O_2$-induced formation of CO-peroxidase complex in the presence of DHF, triose reductone, and indole-acetic acid. Among these hydrogen donors, indoleacetic acid seemed to

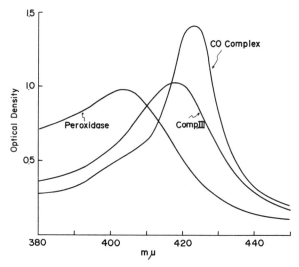

Fig. 12. Absorption spectra of peroxidase, CO-ferroperoxidase, and compound III in Soret band. 9 $\mu M$ peroxidase.

form a remarkably effective intermediate to reduce peroxidase. Figure 13 shows the time course of formation of CO-peroxidase complex during the continuous addition of $H_2O_2$ through a capillary (cf. Fig. 12). The steady formation of the complex was observed after a short lag period. Provided that the increase in optical density at 423 m$\mu$ is due only to the formation of CO complex, the rate of the complex formation is 16 $\mu M$/min, while the rate of $H_2O_2$ addition through a capillary is 23 $\mu M$/min.

## E. Compound III

DHF is known as only one substrate which gives compound III during the oxidase reaction. It was found that a stoichiometric amount of $H_2O_2$ was needed to form compound III in the presence of DHF and oxygen. When

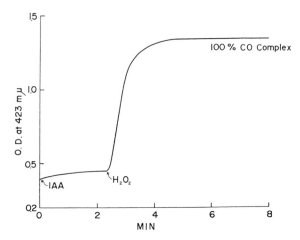

**Fig. 13.** H₂O₂-induced formation of CO-peroxidase complex in the presence of indole-acetate (IAA, 4 mg/6 ml). 2 *mM* H₂O₂ was added continuously through a capillary (0.07 ml/min), and the solution was gassed with CO. 0.05 *M* acetate, pH 5.0. Room temperature.

H₂O₂ was added to the system of DHF, oxygen, and peroxidase, very rapid formation of compound III was observed, as shown in Figs. 14 and 15. The steep slope of compound III formation in Fig. 14 shows that 1 mole of H₂O₂ converted almost 2 moles of peroxidase to compound III. The difference in the stability of compound III between the results shown in Figs. 14 and 15 indicates that the addition of an excess amount of H₂O₂ is not suitable for

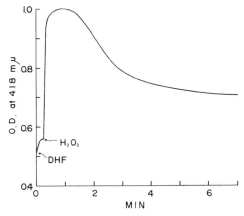

**Fig. 14.** H₂O₂-induced formation of compound III in the presence of DHF. 2 *mM* H₂O₂ was added continuously through a capillary (0.07 ml/min) with bubbling air. 9 *μM* peroxidase, 0.2 *mM* DHF, 0.05 *M* acetate, pH 5.0. Room temperature.

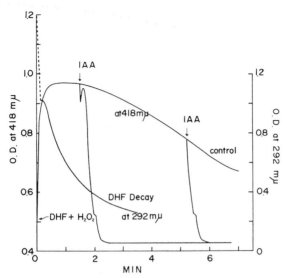

**Fig. 15.**  H$_2$O$_2$-induced formation of compound III and decay of DHF.  Indoleacetate (100 $\mu M$) was added at arrows.  0.2 $mM$ DHF, 10 $\mu M$ H$_2$O$_2$, 9 $\mu M$ peroxidase, 0.05 $M$ acetate, pH 5.0.  Room temperature.

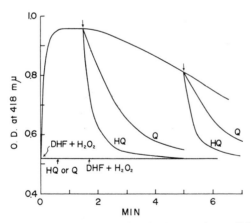

**Fig. 16.**  Effect of hydroquinone (0.1 $mM$) and $p$-benzoquinone (0.1 $mM$) on the stability of compound III.  The experimental condition was the same as that in Fig. 15.  No change in the absorbancy was observed when DHF and H$_2$O$_2$ were added after the addition of hydroquinone or quinone (base line in the figure).

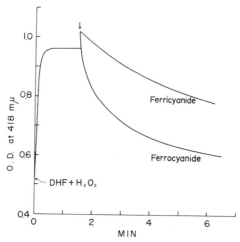

**Fig. 17.** Effect of ferrocyanide (0.1 *mM*) and ferricyanide (0.1 *mM*) on the stability of compound III. The experimental condition was the same as that in Fig. 15.

the maintenance of compound III. Various redox substances were added to find the effect on the stability of compound III. It might be said generally that the reduced forms were more effective for the decomposition of compound III than the corresponding oxidized forms, and anionic species were less active than cationic ones (Figs. 16, 17, and 18). Rapid disappearance of compound III was induced by the addition of indoleacetate (Fig. 15) and triose reductone (Fig. 18). On the other hand tryptophan, tyrosine, and salicylic acid had little effect on the stability of compound III.

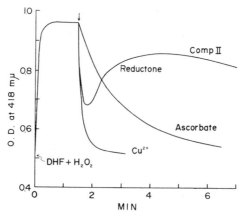

**Fig. 18.** Effect of $Cu^{2+}$ (0.1 *mM*), ascorbate (0.1 *mM*), and triose reductone (0.1 *mM*) on the stability of compound III. The experimental condition was the same as that in Fig. 15.

## IV. DISCUSSION

The mechanism presented in Fig. 19 is essentially the same as that reported in a previous paper (4) and will be discussed here in detail with the additional evidence.

### A. Formation of Free Radicals of Donor Molecules by Peroxidatic Oxidation, Reactions $(a)$, $(d)$, $(a')$ and $(f)$

In reaction $(a)$ 1 mole of hydrogen peroxide forms 2 moles of free radicals,

$$2YH_2 + H_2O_2 \xrightarrow{\text{peroxidase}} 2YH\cdot + (2H_2O) \qquad (a)$$

This stoichiometry of the reaction has been suggested by the titrimetric analysis of a peroxidase derivative, compound II (9, 10), and by the direct observation of monovalent conversion of another derivative, compound I to compound II (11) (see Fig. 20). The kinetic experiments with ESR spectroscopy (13) disclosed that the free radicals are free in solution and decay mostly by dismutation, reaction $(d)$ of Fig. 19. When reaction $(a')$ is much faster than reaction $(a)$, $XH_2$ promotes the peroxidatic disappearance of $YH_2$ and the formation of $Y^-$ (13). $Y^-$ thus formed is initiator of the oxygen-consuming chain reaction, and this is the reason why a trace amount of hydrogen peroxide is invariably needed to initiate the peroxidase-oxidase reactions.

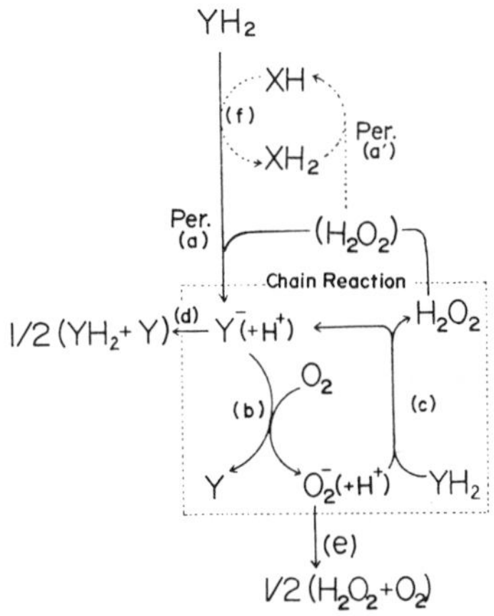

### B. Reduction of Oxygen by $Y^-$, Reaction $(b)$

This step in the free-radical mechanism of Fig. 19 has been most ambiguous because of the difficulty of direct confirmation of the reaction. The main decay of free radicals, $Y^-$, is dismutation, the rate constant being around $10^6 \sim 10^8 \, M^{-1} \, \text{sec}^{-1}$. At the usual speed of peroxidase reaction, for instance, $-(dYH_2/dt) = 10^{-6} \, M^{-1} \, \text{sec}^{-1}$, $1 \sim 0.1 \, \mu M$ of free radicals of donor substrates, such as ascorbate, hydroquinone, triose reductone, and DHF, was observed during the peroxidatic reactions. Only in the case of DHF, the ESR signal disappeared in the presence of oxygen and emerged again when

Fig. 19. Tentative scheme for $O_2$-consuming oxidation of $YH_2$ catalyzed by peroxidase. Broken line shows chain reaction. Reactions $(d)$ and $(e)$ are chain termination. $Mn^{2+}$ promotes reaction $(c)$ as a bridging substance when $YH_2$ molecule is anionic. The alternative path of the chain reaction is shown in Fig. 22.

oxygen was completely gone (4). It suggests that DHF semiquinone has a strong affinity for oxygen. This suggestion is confirmed by the observation that a monovalent oxidant can induce the oxygen consumption and that the addition of 1 mole of oxidant results in the consumption of about 10 moles of oxygen. This is due to a high degree of efficiency of the chain reaction in Fig. 19, especially when DHF is used as hydrogen donor. Although not so remarkable as DHF, the same phenomenon can be observed when NADH

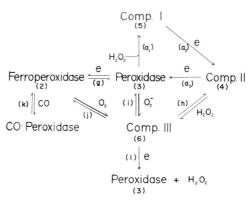

Fig. 20. Peroxidase derivatives related to the peroxidase-oxidase reaction. Numerals in parentheses show the number of the effective valence in the iron of peroxidase.

and triose reductone are used as electron donors (Figs. 2, 3, and 4). The chain reaction is shown to be effective in acidic pH, and $Mn^{2+}$ promotes the reaction in neutral pH. Now, it may be worthwhile to discuss reaction (b) of Fig. 19 from the standpoint of the potential of the two redox systems involved in this reaction.

$Y^- \leftrightarrows Y + e$ (8). The normal potential of this monovalent system can be estimated only when $E_m$ and $k$ are known; see equation 5. The hyperfine structures of semiquinones of DHF, ascorbate, hydroquinone, and triose reductone indicate that they are all in dissociated form in physiological pH. This means that the potential of the redox system equation 8 does not change around this pH. The estimated values are $-0.21$ volt for ascorbate and $+0.09$ volt for hydroquinone. For triose reductone and DHF, the upper limit of the potential, $E_2$, will be estimated when $E_m$ is known. Unfortunately, no data are available for the $E_m$ value of the DHF system, and only ambiguous data for that of the triose reductone system.

$O_2 + e \leftrightarrows O_2^-$ (9). There is no direct estimation for the potential of the first reduction step of oxygen. Many workers have calculated the value from the thermodynamic data based on the related reactions. George and Griffith (17) discussed the reliability of the calculation and selected the value of

−0.9 volt at pH 7.0 as the most reliable one. On the other hand, a great many experiments have been carried out polarographically to estimate the potential where oxygen is reduced by using mercury or platinum electrodes. These data are given in Table 1, which shows that oxygen is reduced when the electrode potential goes down around 0 volt; these are pH-independent. Although no direct relation can be expected between the electrode reaction and the intermolecular reaction (b), there might be an upper limit of the potential of the system equation 8 to enable the reduction of oxygen by $Y^-$. We may safely say that the potential is around −0.3 volt.

### TABLE 1

#### Reduction Potential of Oxygen (vs. N.H.E.)

Polarographic data.

|  | Volt vs. N.H.E. | pH | Reference |
|---|---|---|---|
| Mercury electrode | +0.15 | 1–10 | (22) |
|  | +0.09 | Body fluid | (23) |
|  | +0.18 | Physiological | (24) |
| Platinum electrode | +0.15 | Physiological | (25) |
|  | −0.08 | 3–12 | (26) |

### C. Activity of the Perhydroxyl Radical

The perhydroxyl radical is supposed to be strong acid and a dissociated form at pH 4.0. This radical can act as strong monovalent oxidant and reductant. The oxidation of $YH_2$ with this radical, reaction (c) of Fig. 19, is an important step to maintain the chain reaction. Reaction (c) usually takes place between anionic charged molecules, and the transfer of electron from $AH^-$ to $O_2^-$ is not so easy, especially at neutral pH. As a bridging substance for the electron transfer $Mn^{2+}$ seems to be effective. It is generally accepted that the dismutation of $O_2^-$, reaction (e), is very fast, and the steady-state concentration of this radical is very low. Another striking feature of this radical may be a presumed affinity toward the active center of peroxidase; this will be discussed next.

### D. Peroxidase Compound III and Oxymyoglobin

There is a remarkable similarity between plant peroxidase and metmyoglobin, in regard, for instance, to molecular weight, prosthetic group, and optical and magnetic properties. Both give the ferro form by reduction and react with $H_2O_2$ to give compound II type derivatives.

The differences in reactivity between these two molecules are as follows:

(*a*) the normal potential of the ferro-ferri system at pH 7.0 is $+0.05$ volt for myoglobin (18) and $-0.27$ volt for peroxidase (II type) (19), (*b*) a derivative corresponding to peroxidase-$H_2O_2$ compound I has not been observed from myoglobin, and (*c*) myoglobin combines with oxygen reversibly but peroxidase does not. The last point will be discussed here in detail.

In a previous paper (4), we proposed a mechanism which shows three different paths of compound III formation (Fig. 20). This mechanism indicates that compound III has a structure of oxygenated ferroperoxidase which is analogous to oxymyoglobin, as was suggested by Mason (20). This idea is supported by the following findings:

1. During the autoxidation of hydrosulfite-reduced peroxidase to free peroxidase, one can observe an intermediate compound which seems to be an oxygenated ferroperoxidase, the absorption spectrum being undistinguishable from compound III (4). The half-reaction time is $4 \sim 5$ min. Figure 15 also shows that the half-decay time of compound III is about 4 min. These values are relatively independent of pH.

2. There is a remarkable similarity in the formation of compound III and of oxymyoglobin from their corresponding ferri form. In both cases, $H_2O_2$ induces the formation, and the following stoichiometry is obtained:

$$2\,DHF + H_2O_2 + 2\,\text{Peroxidase} + (2O_2) \rightarrow (2DKS) + 2\,\text{Compound III}$$

$$(2DHF) + H_2O_2 + 2\,\text{Metmyoglobin} + (2O_2) \rightarrow$$
$$(2DKS) + 2\,\text{Oxymyoglobin}$$

Although it is unambiguous that these reactions are initiated by the formation of DHF semiquinone, the subsequent reactions may have two possible paths: (*a*) hemiprotein is reduced by DHF semiquinone and combines with oxygen, reactions (*g*) and (*j*) of Fig. 20, and (*b*) oxygen is reduced by DHF semiquinone to perhydroxyl radical, which reacts with hemiprotein, reactions (*b*) and (*i*). Figure 10 shows that the main reactions of the formation of oxymyoglobin are in path (*a*). On the other hand, the slow formation of CO complex in the solution of DHF, $H_2O_2$, CO, and peroxidase suggests path (*b*) for the reaction of compound III formation.

## E. Reactivity of Compound III

A few ideas are complicated in the problems of the reactivity of compound III. It has been generally accepted that compound III formed in solution of peroxidase and a large excess of $H_2O_2$ is an inactive form. On the other hand, many workers have suggested the participation of compound III (or oxygenated ferroperoxidase) in the peroxidase-oxidase reactions, though no direct evidence has been demonstrated. No explanation has been made as to why compound III appears only in the DHF system. The results presented

## TABLE 2
### The Effect of Reductants on the Conversion of Oxymyoglobin to Metmyoglobin

| Reductant | pH 4.8 | pH 7.0 |
|---|---|---|
| Ferrocyanide | + + + + | − |
| Hydroquinone | + + | − |
| Catechol | + | − |
| Resorcinol | + | − |
| o-Phenylenediamine | + | − |
| p-Phenylenediamine | ( + ) | − |
| Ascorbic acid | − | − |
| Cysteine | − | − |

in this paper will give direct evidence to discuss about these problems. As can be seen in Fig. 15, the DHF system gives a suitable experimental condition to estimate the reactivity of compound III. Many reducing agents were found to react with compound III and to convert it into free enzyme. It should be noted that the reactions of compound III with indoleacetate and triose reductone are very fast, but not the reaction with DHF. This is the reason why indoleacetate and $H_2O_2$ cause an accumulation of CO-peroxidase complex in the presence of CO but not of compound III under the aerobic condition. The reaction of indoleacetate with peroxidase is not so simple and will be reported elsewhere.

It might be worthwhile to compare the stability of compound III and of oxymyoglobin. Oxymyoglobin is unstable at acidic pH and is oxidized to metmyoglobin. The conversion of oxymyoglobin to metmyoglobin is extremely fast when ferricyanide and p-benzoquinone are added. In the presence of certain reducing agents, oxymyoglobin acts as an electron acceptor in acidic pH (see Table 2). The differences between compound III and oxymyoglobin in the reactivity against reductants and oxidants might be

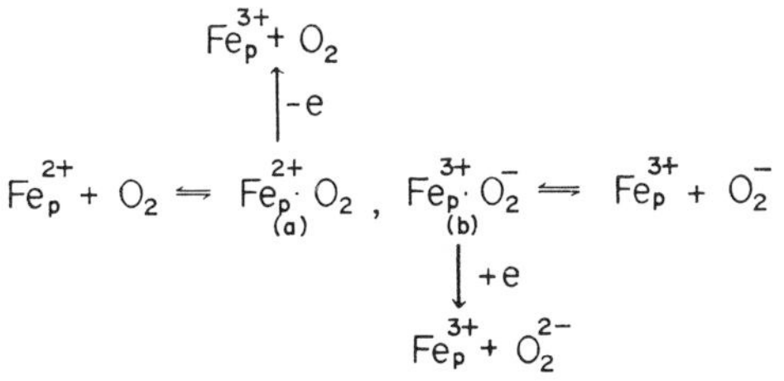

$$Fe_p^{3+} + O_2$$
$$\Big\uparrow -e$$
$$Fe_p^{2+} + O_2 \rightleftharpoons \underset{(a)}{Fe_p^{2+} \cdot O_2} , \quad \underset{(b)}{Fe_p^{3+} \cdot O_2^-} \rightleftharpoons Fe_p^{3+} + O_2^-$$
$$\Big\downarrow +e$$
$$Fe_p^{3+} + O_2^{2-}$$

**Fig. 21.** Oxymyoglobin and compound III. Oxymyoglobin [(a) > (b)] is sensitive for oxidants, and compound III [(a) < (b)] is sensitive for reductants.

explained as shown in Fig. 21. Structure (*a*) is dominant in oxymyoglobin, and structure (*b*) in compound III. The change to met- form is accelerated by oxidant in the case of oxymyoglobin and by reductant in the case of compound III.

## F. Mixed Feature of Peroxidase-Oxidase Reaction

As far as DHF oxidation is concerned, the free-radical mechanism shown in Fig. 19 can explain the majority of various properties of the reaction. Here, the reduction of peroxidase (CO inhibition) and the formation of compound III are side reactions. Compound III is accumulated during the reaction because of its low reactivity toward DHF.

On the other hand, indoleacetate reduces peroxidase effectively in the presence of $H_2O_2$ and also exhibits high reactivity toward compound III. Reaction (*a*) must be the essential step involved in all these peroxidase-oxidase reactions. However, three possibilities will be suggested for the further reactions of indoleacetate free radical (see Figs. 20 and 22): (i) the free radical reduces peroxidase and forms compound III, reactions (*g*) and (*j*); (ii) the free radical reduces oxygen, and perhydroxyl radical reacts with peroxidase to form compound III, reactions (*b*) and (*i*); (iii) the last mechanism is the same as that shown in Fig. 20. The first two mechanisms involve the re-

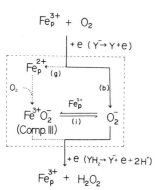

**Fig. 22.** Improved mechanism for chain reaction in Fig. 19. This is the general mechanism to explain the diverse features of peroxidase-oxidase reaction.

action of indoleacetate with compound III. Compound III is an enzymic intermediate and acts as an oxidant rather than a reductant. Although compound III seems to be much less active than perhydroxyl radical, a labile intermediate may increase the probability of the reaction with certain donor substrate by increasing the effective concentration combining with enzyme. If the free radical reduces peroxidase in the first place and compound III is the active form, the mechanism involves ferroperoxidase as an active intermediate. But the mechanism presented in Fig. 22 is different from the previous one, which suggests the only bivalent redox reactions in the decomposition of ferroperoxidase-$O_2$ complex.

It might be concluded that a beginning of the peroxidase-oxidase reaction is invariably reaction (*a*), and that the subsequent reactions differ from substrate to substrate. Oxygen is activated as perhydroxyl radical which continues the chain reaction as either the free state or the combined state in peroxidase.

# V. SUMMARY

The peroxidase-oxidase reaction begins with the peroxidatic reaction which forms free radicals of donor substrates. Three possible paths of the successive reactions are suggested. (a) The free radical reduces oxygen to perhydroxyl radical, which oxidizes the substrate and forms the free radical of the substrate again. This is the case of dihydroxyfumarate oxidation. (b) Perhydroxyl radical reacts with peroxidase to form compound III, which does or does not oxidize the donor substrate. The latter is the case in the oxidation of dihydroxyfumarate. (c) The free radical reduces peroxidase to ferroperoxidase, which reacts with oxygen to form compound III. It may oxidize the donor substrate. This mechanism seems to be involved in the oxidation of indoleacetate.

# ACKNOWLEDGMENTS

This work was supported by Research Grant AM-06518 from the United States Public Health Service and by a research grant from the Department of Education of Japan.

# REFERENCES

1. B. Swedin and H. Theorell, *Nature*, **145**, 71 (1940).
2. P. M. Ray, *Arch. Biochem. Biophys.*, **87**, 19 (1960).
3. Y. Morita and K. Kameda, *Mem. Research Inst. Food Sci., Kyoto Univ.*, **23**, 1 (1961).
4. I. Yamazaki and L. H. Piett, *Biochim. et Biophys. Acta.*, **77**, 47 (1963).
5. M. H. Klapper and D. P. Hackett, *J. Biol. Chem.*, **238**, 3743 (1963).
6. I. Yamazaki, *Proceedings of the International Symposium on Enzyme Chemistry (Tokyo and Kyoto), 1958*, p. 224.
7. I. Yamazaki and H. Souzu, *Arch. Biochem. Biophys.*, **86**, 294 (1960).
8. P. Nicholls, in O. Hayaishi, Ed., *Oxygenase*, Academic Press, New York, 1962, p. 273.
9. P. George, *Nature*, **169**, 612 (1952).
10. P. George, *Biochem. J.*, **54**, 267 (1953).
11. B. Chance, *Arch. Biochem. Biophys.*, **41**, 416 (1952).
12. I. Yamazaki, H. S. Mason, and L. H. Piette, *J. Biol. Chem.*, **235**, 2444 (1960).
13. I. Yamazaki and L. H. Piette, *Biochim. et Biophys. Acta.*, **50**, 62 (1961).
14. R. H. Kenten and P. J. G. Mann, *Biochem. J.*, **57**, 347 (1954).
15. I. Yamazaki, K. Yokota, and K. Shikama, *J. Biol. Chem.*, **239**, 4151 (1964).
16. L. Michaelis, in J. B. Sumner and K. Myrback, Eds., *The Enzymes*, Vol. II, Academic Press, New York, Part I, 1951, p. 1.
17. P. George and J. S. Griffith, in P. D. Boyer, H. Lardy, and K. Myrback, Eds., *The Enzymes*, Vol. I, Academic Press, New York, 1959, p. 347.
18. J. F. Taylor and V. E. Morgan, *J. Biol. Chem.*, **144**, 15 (1942).
19. H. A. Harbury, *J. Biol. Chem.*, **225**, 1009 (1957).

20. H. S. Mason, *Proceedings of the International Symposium on Enzyme Chemistry (Tokyo-Kyoto), 1957*, p. 223.
21. P. George and D. H. Irvine, *Biochem. J.*, **52**, 511 (1952).
22. I. M. Kolthoff and C. S. Miller, *J. Am. Chem. Soc.*, **63**, 1013 (1941).
23. H. K. Beecher, R. Follansbee, A. J. Murphy, and F. N. Craig, *J. Biol. Chem.*, **146**, 197 (1942).
24. R. Brdicka and C. Tropp, *Biochem. Z.*, **289**, 301 (1936).
25. P. W. Davies and F. Brink, *Rev. Sci. Instr.*, **13**, 524 (1942).
26. I. M. Kolthoff and H. A. Laitinen, *Science*, **92**, 152 (1940).

## Discussion

CHANCE: Certainly time doesn't allow a detailed discussion of Dr. Yamazaki's ingenious mechanisms, and I can only discuss perhaps one key point with respect to the idea of the ferrous oxygen compound, where he has reported an experiment on the reaction of dithionite with peroxidase. Actually the ferrous oxygen compound introduces an interesting facet into his mechanism, and this key experiment which he has reported in his paper forms the principal novelty of this mechanism over earlier mechanisms described by him in 1958 and 1963 and by me in 1962. Work on the reaction of dithionite in hemoglobin has been reported in detail by Dalziel and O'Brien [*Biochem. J.*, **78**, 236 (1961)]. Certainly we will agree it's not a simple reaction. It isn't simple with peroxidase either.

These experiments were done with crystalline horse-radish peroxidase which was saturated with hydrogen and mixed with dithionite in a rapid-flow apparatus.

Under experimental conditions where oxygen is excluded to the greatest degree possible from both the peroxidase and from the solvent for dithionite, the reaction kinetics of Fig. 1 are obtained. Here we plot, by the stopped-flow method, the time course of peroxidase reduction. The observation tube is filled with ferroperoxidase, the spent reactant from the previous experiment. On injecting fresh reactants into the observation chamber, the trace sweeps rapidly downward and, as the flow stops, sweeps back upward in exponential fashion. The upward sweep of the trace indicates an increased absorbancy at 440 m$\mu$. The half-time of the reaction with 85 $\mu M$ dithionite is 0.7 sec, and a second-order velocity constant of roughly $10^4$ $M^{-1}$ sec$^{-1}$ is calculated. It is possible, however, that the reaction velocity constant is even greater because any trace of oxygen would delay the reduction until the oxygen had reacted with the dithionite.

Two points are to be noted about the reaction product. First, it is stable, in the sense that the absorbancy increase remains at the same level for many minutes. Second, the absorbancy change in the region of 440 m$\mu$ agrees very well with that obtained under static conditions. An isosbestic point is found at 423 m$\mu$, and the $\Delta\epsilon_{440}$ is equal to 50 cm$^{-1}$ × $mM^{-1}$, as measured in the 1 mm circular capillary observation tube, as compared with 60 cm$^{-1}$ × $mM^{-1}$ when measured in the rectangular cuvette of a Beckman spectrophotometer.

On investigating the rate of formation of the reduced compound, the end-point calibrations of Fig. 2 become of considerable interest. This experiment records kinetics similar to those of Fig. 1, except that a wavelength of 430 m$\mu$ is used for recording and the dithionite concentration is 135 $\mu M$. Independent controls with

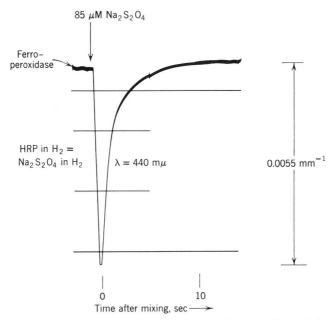

**Fig. 1.** Time course of peroxidase reduction as measured in the capillary of the 1 mm bore flow apparatus. The formation of ferroperoxidase 1.1 $\mu M$ horse-radish peroxidase reacts with 85 $\mu M$ $Na_2S_2O_4$. Both solutions bubbled with purified hydrogen. pH equals 4.5; 0.01 $M$ acetate buffer. $\lambda$ equals 440 m$\mu$ (Expt. 29C).

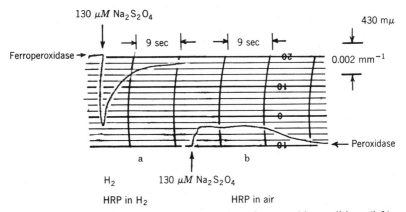

**Fig. 2.** A comparison of the reduction of peroxidase in anaerobic conditions (left) and under aerobic conditions (right). In the left-hand portion (a) 1.1 $\mu M$ horse-radish peroxidase is reacted with 130 $\mu M$ $Na_2S_2O_4$ in an atmosphere of hydrogen. (b) 1.1 $\mu M$ peroxidase in air-saturated buffer is reacted with 130 $\mu M$ $Na_2S_2O_4$ solution saturated with purified hydrogen. pH equals 4.7, 0.01 $M$ acetate buffer; 430 m$\mu$ (Expt. 32 D and E).

oscillographic recording indicate that the pen-and-ink recorder used in this experiment responds rapidly enough to measure the maximum absorbancy change indicated by the downward deflection of the trace during the discharge of reactants into the observation chamber. The exponential formation of the compound then occurs.

In order to determine whether the observation tube was filled with ferroperoxidase during the flow illustrated in Figs. 1 and 2a, we have included Fig. 2b. Here, at the end of the experiment, the dithionite is expended and ferriperoxidase is obtained. Sufficient oxygen (120 $mM$) is present in the peroxidase to expend the 135 $\mu M$ dithionite. Under these conditions, the spent material remaining in the observation tube from the previous experiment is free peroxidase. On refilling the observation

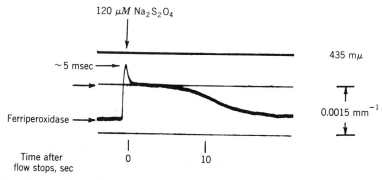

**Fig. 3.** An experiment similar to that of Fig. 2b but repeated with oscillographic recording, to show the early kinetics. 1.1 $\mu M$ peroxidase in air reacted with 120 $\mu M$ Na$_2$S$_2$O$_4$ in a solution of saturated and purified hydrogen. pH 4.5, 0.01 $M$ acetate buffer. Wavelength 435 m$\mu$. The flow velocity (monitored independently) during this experiment is sufficient to give a time after mixing of 5 msec at the time of the peak of the upward deflection on the trace at the point indicated by the arrow, "120 $\mu M$ Na$_2$S$_2$O$_4$" (Expt. 33C).

tube with fresh peroxidase, oxygen, and dithionite, the absorbancy change, even a few milliseconds after mixing, rises only to 20% of the absorbancy observed in the control experiment of Fig. 2a, in which ferriperoxidase was obtained. The absorbancy remains at the 20% level for approximately 15 sec and then declines to a level corresponding to that of the free enzyme.

It is apparent that ferroperoxidase cannot be obtained in the presence of oxygen; instead, a short-lived intermediate characteristic of the "high-spin" peroxidase compounds is obtained as shown by scanning through the spectrum. The absorbancy change in the region 425–440 m$\mu$ is already indicated in Fig. 2b to be small compared to that of ferroperoxidase, complex II or complex III. In the region 370–420 m$\mu$, the spectrum resembles that of peroxidase complex I, the isosbestic point being at 423 m$\mu$ (as compared with 427 m$\mu$ for complex II), and the $\Delta\epsilon_{395\ m\mu}$ being 35 cm$^{-1}$ $mM^{-1}$.

If the experiment of Fig. 2 is repeated with ascorbate present in the peroxidase, the lifetime and the absorbancy change of the intermediate are the same. The insensitivity of the intermediate to the reaction with ascorbate distinguishes it from complex I, which would be expected to react with ascorbate to form complex II, which, in turn, would disappear more rapidly in the presence of the hydrogen donor.

If the experiment of Fig. 2b is carried out with oxygen-saturated peroxidase rather than air-saturated peroxidase, the absorbancy change has a half-time of 85 sec, as compared with 19 sec. Interestingly, enough, the addition of 20 $\mu M$ $H_2O_2$ to the reaction mixture of Fig. 2b decreased the half-time from the 19 sec indicated by this figure to approximately 2 sec. These experiments indicate clearly that the compound formed in the presence of dithionite is not a peroxidase compound.

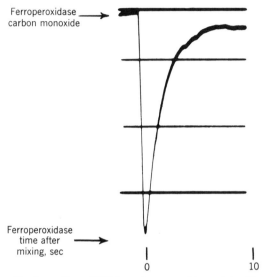

**Fig. 4.** The formation of CO from ferroperoxidase. 1.1 $\mu M$ peroxidase solution saturated with purified hydrogen, mixed with 550 $\mu M$ dithionite solution saturated with CO (approximately 1 $mM$); pH 4.5; 0.01 $M$ acetate buffer; 425 m$\mu$ (Expt. 29B).

If the experiment of Fig. 2b is recorded on a rapidly moving chart with an oscillograph galvanometer, as indicated in Fig. 3, it is seen that a small "pip" precedes the steady state of the intermediate complex. This pip suggests that the intermediate complex is preceded by an intermediate of higher absorbancy at 430 m$\mu$, presumably ferroperoxidase.

**Formation of the CO Compound.** An appropriate experimental procedure for measuring the kinetics of the formation of the CO compound is indicated by Fig. 4. Here, the peroxidase solution is saturated with purified hydrogen as before. The buffer for dissolving the dithionite is saturated with CO instead of with hydrogen. In addition, a high concentration of dithionite is used in order that the formation of the reduced form not be rate limiting; in this experiment, 550 $\mu M$ dithionite is sufficient to diminish the time for formation of the reduced compound considerably below the 0.7 sec value indicated in Fig. 1. The capillary observation tube of the apparatus having already been filled with the products of the previous experiment, the base line for the experiment of Fig. 4 corresponds to the absorbancy of the ferroperoxidase CO compound. The anaerobic peroxidase is rapidly mixed with 550 $\mu M$ dithionite and 600 $\mu M$ CO, sweeping out the reaction products from the observation chamber. As the flow stops, the formation of the CO compound proceeds in an exponential manner with a half-time of 1.1 sec. Assuming a second-order reaction, the velocity constant would be $1 \times 10^3 \ M^{-1} \sec^{-1}$.

If the experiment for Fig. 4 is repeated at various wavelengths, an isosbestic point is found at 407 m$\mu$, indicating that under these experimental conditions, with a large excess of dithionite, the CO compounds are formed essentially from ferroperoxidase as indicated in Fig. 5, which shows the spectra of ferroperoxidase and ferroperoxidase CO.

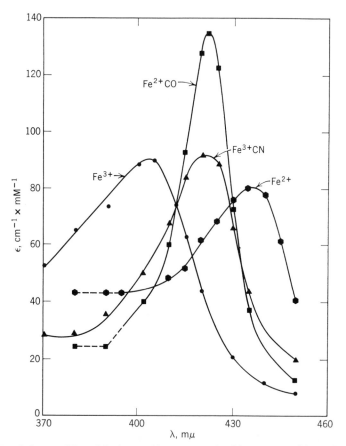

**Fig. 5.** A ferrous CO and ferric cyanide compounds of ferrous peroxidase. 1.6 $\mu M$ horseradish peroxidase plus 0.5 m$M$ Na$_2$S$_2$O$_4$. Ferrous peroxidase CO, 1.6 $\mu M$ peroxidase saturated with CO plus 0.5 m$M$ Na$_2$S$_2$O$_4$. Ferriperoxidase cyanide, 1.7 peroxidase plus 50 $\mu M$ cyanide. Ferroperoxidase, 1.7 $\mu M$ horseradish peroxidase. The extinction coefficient of horseradish peroxidase was taken to be 90 mm$^{-1}$ cm$^{-1}$ (see Colowick and Kaplan, Eds., *Methods in Enzymology*, Vol. II, p. 143, Academic Press, 1955); pH 7; 0.01 $M$ phosphate buffer, 25° (Expt. 283 and 285).

**The Reaction of Ferroperoxidase with Oxygen.** Figure 3 affords a basis for considering whether or not this important reaction can be measured under these experimental conditions. As noted above, it is clearly shown by Fig. 2 that the absorbancy value at the shortest time after mixing (around 5 msec) does not correspond to 100% ferroperoxidase; in fact, the small deflection observed during the flow is only 14% of the absorbancy change expected for the oxidation of ferroperoxidase. Converting this value to a pseudo first-order velocity constant, we obtain 400 $sec^{-1}$, and dividing by the oxygen concentration present (120 $\mu M$), we obtain a second-order constant of approximately $3 \times 10^6 \ M^{-1} sec^{-1}$. This, of course, is a minimum value, and other steps may have prevented the measurement of the true second-order velocity constant.

**Velocity Constant for the Dissociation of the CO Compound.** The dissociation velocity of the CO compound can be measured directly with the ordinary spectrophotometer. A solution formed under conditions similar to those of Fig. 1 is bubbled with oxygen for 2 min to remove the dithionite and partially to saturate the solution with oxygen. As shown in Fig. 6, the dissociation of the CO compound can be followed directly and has a half-time of about 6 min, corresponding to a velocity constant of $2 \times 10^{-3}$ sec. This velocity constant, which is slow compared to that of the cytochrome oxidase CO compound, would nevertheless not interfere with light reversal of CO inhibition of peroxidase-oxidase reactions, since the formation of the CO compound would greatly speed up this dissociation reaction.

The dissociation constant for ferroperoxidase CO, calculated on the basis of these kinetic data, corresponds to $1.5 \times 10^{-6} \ M$.

These experiments were carried out primarily to determine what would be expected if ferroperoxidases were formed in peroxidase-oxidase reaction, such as that obtained in the presence of DHF. In general, the results show that the CO compound would be expected to form with a half-time of approximately 1 sec from any mixture containing the ferrous compound. Therefore, a failure to obtain rapid formation of the CO compound from mixtures expected to contain this species strongly suggests that the ferrous compound is not present.

The reaction of peroxidase with dithionite is complex, as is to be expected from experience with the reaction of oxyhemoglobin with dithionite [Dalziel and O'Brien, *Biochem. J.*, **78**, 236 (1961)]. It is apparent from these studies that the formation of ferroperoxidase is preceded by a compound of a spectrum that can be generally classified as a "high-spin" type. The reaction sequence can be described as follows:

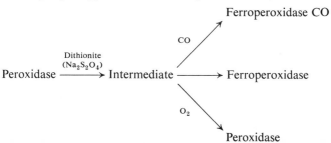

Insofar as our kinetic studies indicate, the three products, ferroperoxidase,

ferroperoxidase CO, and free peroxidase as well, involve this intermediate compound as a prior step.

The chemical nature of the intermediate compound is difficult to assess. It could be either an intermediate formed in the reduction of peroxidase or an intermediate in its oxidation, since chemical reactions must occur between dithionite and peroxidase in order to produce the reduced form. Opposed to the view that the intermediate compound is formed in the reduction of the peroxidase are experiments in

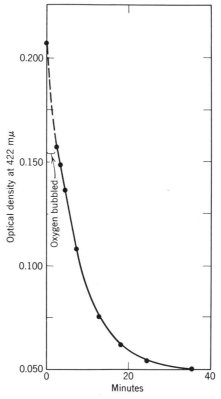

**Fig. 6.** The dissociation of ferroperoxidase CO. The solution of ferroperoxidase CO, prepared as indicated for Fig. 5, was bubbled with oxygen for 2 min, and the disappearance of absorption at 420 m$\mu$ was followed in the Beckman spectrophotometer (Expt. 283).

which peroxidase reduced by dithionite under hydrogen is reacted with oxygen with an increase in the lifetime of the intermediate. A more likely interpretation of the results is that dithionite reduces peroxidase without a spectroscopically detectable intermediate, but that traces of oxygen in the peroxidase solution may lead to the formation of the intermediate. This view is supported by the fact that when oxygen is present the lifetime of the intermediate compound is prolonged. It is appropriate to identify the compound tentatively with a ferrous oxygen intermediate. Final identification as an oxygen compound requires the detection of oxygen bound to the intermediate, an experiment of sufficient technical difficulty that it has not yet been attempted.

The spectral properties of this compound in relation to ferroperoxidase and peroxidase are appropriately identified by the traces of Fig. 2, where at 430 m$\mu$ the absorbancy due to the intermediate is less than one-fourth that of ferroperoxidase. This further indicates that the intermediate does not have a spectrum characteristic of a low spin state.

Attempts have been made to identify this intermediate with peroxidase complex I, first because of the general spectroscopic similarity and second because of the possibility that $H_2O_2$ is generated by dithionite in the reduction of oxygen or of peroxidase. The results are so far negative. First, the reaction with a typical donor, ascorbic acid, having high activity at the pH involved (4.5) failed to accelerate the decomposition of the intermediate. Similarly, the addition of $H_2O_2$, instead of prolonging the lifetime of the intermediate, actually diminished it; 20 $\mu M$ $H_2O_2$ diminished the lifetime by a factor of 6. These data suggest that the intermediate is of a reduced rather than an oxidized state and support the view that a ferrous compound of peroxidase is involved. Again, the question of whether it is an oxygen compound, or one involving oxidation compounds of dithionite, cannot be resolved without a measurement and direct identification of the ligand bound to peroxidase.

**Relationship to Peroxidase-Oxidase Activity.** Of first importance with relation to peroxidase-oxidase activities is the formation of the CO compound in a time of 1 sec in spite of the fact that an intermediate compound has preceded it. This result suggests that the rapid formation of the CO compound should be observed in an enzymatic sequence which involves this compound. It is clear from a number of results that the rapid formation of the CO compound does not occur; in fact, special conditions are required to form it at all.

**In Summary.** 1. Reduction under conditions which are as oxygen free as possible involves the formation in times of less than 5 msec of an intermediate compound from which ferroperoxidase forms, under particular experimental conditions, in a time of 0.7 sec.

2. The same intermediate compound is formed when peroxidase, in the presence of small concentrations of oxygen, is reduced by dithionite. The lifetime of the compound increases with the amount of oxygen present, is unaffected by the presence of ascorbic acid, and is decreased by the addition of $H_2O_2$.

A minimum value for a velocity constant for the formation of reduced ferroperoxidase by dithionite is $1 \times 10^4 \, M^{-1} \sec^{-1}$.

Ferroperoxidase has not been identified under conditions where oxygen is present. Its reaction with oxygen is extremely rapid, and a minimum value for the velocity constant is $4 \times 10^6 \, M^{-1} \sec^{-1}$.

The intermediate compound observed in the reaction of peroxidase with dithionite in the presence or absence of oxygen shows no properties similar to those expected for a low-spin ferrous oxygen intermediate such as complex III or oxymyoglobin. Instead the spectroscopic characteristics are similar to those of a high-spin intermediate such as complex I.

3. On a chemical basis the compound differs from complex I; its lifetime is not decreased by ascorbate but is decreased by $H_2O_2$.

4. The CO compound of ferroperoxidase is formed from the above-mentioned intermediate compound with a velocity constant, computed according to the second-order formula, of $1 \times 10^3 M^{-1} \sec^{-1}$. The ferroperoxidase CO compound associates with a first-order velocity constant of $2 \times 10^{-3} \sec^{-1}$, giving a minimum value of the dissociation constant of $1.5 \times 10^{-6} M$. The relationship of this intermediate compound to peroxidase-oxidase activities is discussed, and it is concluded that the intermediate compound bears no spectroscopic relationship to either complex II or oxymyoglobin.

YAMAZAKI: I think that your experimental conditions are slightly different from ours, because we tried several experiments using different concentrations of hydrosulfite and found that if we used slightly more hydrosulfite, some very different reaction occurs, and we did not observe compound III. We cannot observe any spectrum of compound III or of any myoglobin type if we use slightly more sodium hydrosulfite. If we decrease the hydrosulfite, then we can observe compound III very clearly. This compound decays according to first-order kinetics, and its halftime is around 5 min. The half-decay time of compound III formed in the dihydroxyfumarate system was almost the same. I think that the difference between Professor Chance's and our experiment is the amount of dithionite used.

CHANCE: Your paper mentioned a few crystals, and we actually said 85 $\mu M$, so I can't tell what the cause of the difference is, whether you had more than we did or less than we did. What molarity of dithionite are you referring to?

YAMAZAKI: I did not use a solution but a few crystal pieces. If, however, we increased the amount of hydrosulfite, we could not observe compound III.

MASON: With respect to Dr. Yamazaki's latest mechanism, in which compound III is converted to ferriperoxidase by substrate, Fig. 22 (p. 502) indicates that the substance was converted to the monodehydro substrate during the shift from $FeO_2$ to $Fe^{3+}$. I wonder whether Dr. Yamazaki has any direct evidence that his process, going from compound III to peroxidase itself, does take place in one electron step. What is the fate of the oxygen?

YAMAZAKI: I have no direct evidence because this is in principle impossible, I think our calcuation of reaction velocity between this compound III and this donor substrate has a constant at least of the order of $10^3$. Dr. Chance has estimated the rate constant between compound II and many organic molecules and gives much higher values for each donor substrate. The reaction of these donor substrates with compound I has been found to be much faster than with compound II, so the rate-limiting step of compound III reduction is

$$\text{Compound III} + AH_2 \rightarrow \text{Compound I} + AH\cdot$$

and it is impossible to observe compound I in the steady state. The only thing that I can say is that monophenol and ferrocyanide can reduce compound III.

MASON: One further point—isn't it quite possible that oxygen transfer takes place? And then oxidation of the ferroperoxidase which is formed?

YAMAZAKI: I have no evidence for such a mechanism.

CHANCE: I agree with Dr. Yamazaki that it is extremely difficult to measure the reaction because preparations of compound III that are 100% pure and not contaminated with some of compound II are very hard to prepare, and therefore a slight contamination with compound II, and the faster velocity constant, makes it really difficult to interpret the experiments of this kind.

YAMAZAKI: Yes, I quite agree. But this is actually a change to this ferric form without any appreciable intermediate. Therefore if no intermediate is observable, the rate constant estimated is that of the first reduction step of compound III.

NICHOLLS: In support of Dr. Yamazaki's concept that compound III is in fact a ferrous complex of the enzyme, I'd like to point out that catalase also forms compound III, and that the differences between the spectra of the compounds III of catalase and peroxidase are those which would be expected from ferrous compounds of the two enzymes. That is, the two compounds III fall in line spectroscopically with what would be predicted if each were a ferrous complex. The oxidation state of such a ferrous complex would be that of the oxygenated state, and the difficulty still unresolved, which Dr. Chance has emphasized, is that the autoxidation of either ferroperoxidase or ferrocatalase is much faster than the rate of decay of compound III. What one appears to get in an autoxidation mechanism is the ferric enzyme and not compound II, whereas one obtains compound II from compound III. In order to get the ferric enzyme from compound III, one has to add a donor like phenol. In the absence of the phenol, compound III is fairly stable. My suggestion, therefore, to the protagonists here is that there may be yet another ferrous state at the oxidation level of oxyferroperoxidase, which in fact has a different structure, for instance, an $HO_2^+$ complex of some sort.

MASON: Two substances at the oxidation level of compound III might be an oxygenated form of ferroperoxidase and a perhydroxyl complex of ferriperoxidase.

KING: I wonder whether we can agree on this reaction, namely,

$$FeO_2^{2+} \rightarrow Fe^{3+} + O_2^-$$

In spite of the fact that thermodynamically this reaction is slightly endergonic, it must go first; then we can have the others. Now let me extend this slightly. This $O_2^-$ reacts with a proton to give the ferrous peroxide radical ($HO_2^{\cdot}$). This ($O_2^- + H^+ \rightarrow HO_2^{\cdot}$) can be considered as a neutralization. The activation energy is practically zero. The $E_0'$ at pH 7 is about 0.5 volt. What I am getting at is that these two reactions may help us to speculate concerning a possible four-electron transfer reaction and four one-electron transfer steps.

# Activation of Tryptophan Pyrrolase by Reduction and Hematin

...W. EUGENE KNOX and K. TOKUYAMA

## I. INTRODUCTION

The tryptophan pyrrolases of animal liver and *Pseudomonas* bacteria are two very similar hemoprotein oxygenases. It is becoming clear that our immense backlog of information about hemoproteins in general will help elucidate the mechanisms involved in the specific addition of molecular oxygen to L-tryptophan that is catalyzed by these enzymes. Highly purified preparations of both enzymes are now available, and only a few uncertainties remain about the mechanism of their action. But even these complicate the assay of the enzyme in crude tissue extracts. Such assays remain important because of the attention given to the adaptive variations in concentration of the liver enzyme with administration of substrate or hormones, in different stages of development, in malignancies, etc. In the first instance, the concentration of the enzyme is measured by its activity in tissue preparations that are designed to extract all the enzyme and are therefore crude and complex mixtures.

## II. EXPERIMENTS AND DISCUSSION

### A. Assay of Crude Liver Extracts of Tryptophan Pyrrolase

The earliest and most commonly used assay employed liver homogenates and measured the kynurenine produced from tryptophan after an hour's incubation (1). A significant increase in the activity was obtained if hydrogen peroxide was generated during the reaction (2, 3, 4, 5). Its function was to reduce an inactive ferric porphyrin species of the enzyme to the active form (6). The rate of peroxide generation was critical, however, since too much inhibited. In addition, various liver preparations, for example, those from rats and C57BL mice, differed as much as tenfold in the optimal rates of

514

peroxide generation (3, 4). The optimal assay conditions were therefore highly empirical.

Two additional problems were raised when Feigelson and Greengard (7) introduced the use of the particle-free supernatant fraction for assay. An initial lag phase that was just detectable in the homogenates (8) was lengthened 10–40 min in the particle-free supernatants. This necessitated serial spectrophotometric measurements, for which this preparation was well suited. In addition, these authors discovered that some of the enzyme was not conjugated with its prosthetic group. The addition of hematin, which in the homogenates had leached into the soluble fraction from the microsomes, increased the activity of the particle-free preparations.

The above observations taken together suggested that there might be *two* inactive species of the tryptophan pyrrolase in the particle-free supernatants of liver: the ferric form activated by reduction with hydrogen peroxide, and the apoenzyme activated by hematin addition. The potential need for reduction as well as hematin addition to activate the apoenzyme (although reduction was not necessary under the conditions used when the hematin effect was discovered) was a subsidiary possibility.

Experiments showed that *both* hematin and peroxide were needed for the maximum tryptophan pyrrolase activity in particle-free supernatant fractions of rat liver (Ogata and Knox, unpublished). The activity of a non-induced rat-liver preparation was approximately doubled by addition of either hematin or an optimal amount of a peroxide-generating system. Both effects persisted in combination and were in fact synergistic. The combination of activators was 30% more effective than the sum of their separate effects in increasing the reaction rate. This synergism was anticipated if the apoenzyme required not only conjugation with hematin but also reduction to the active ferrous porphyrin form. The experiments thus identified and provided measures of two inactive species, as well as the active species of tryptophan pyrrolase as obtained from liver.

The relative amounts of the three known species of the enzyme in normal and induced rat livers are given in Table 1. These average values from several rats present the fractions of total activity (a) measured without additions (EH$^{2+}$: ferrous porphyrin enzyme); (b) appearing with reduction by peroxide (EH$^{3+}$: ferric porphyrin enzyme); and (c) appearing in the reduced enzyme when hematin was added (E: apoenzyme). The results confirmed the marked increase in the degree of conjugation of the tryptophan-induced enzyme found by Greengard and Feigelson (9, 10), which may provide a clue to the mechanism of the substrate-type induction. This highly conjugated preparation of the enzyme is also predominantly in the active, reduced form. Therefore, in an assay system which lacked maximal activation by hematin and reduction, all but the tryptophan-induced type of enzyme would be significantly underestimated.

TABLE 1

Relative Proportions of the Three Species of Tryptophan
Pyrrolase in Rat Livers

| Induction of Rat | Apoenzyme (E), % | Ferrienzyme (EH$^{3+}$), % | Ferroenzyme (EH$^{2+}$), % |
|---|---|---|---|
| None | 57 | 28 | 16 |
| Hydrocortisone | 55 | 30 | 20 |
| Tryptophan | 28 | 17 | 55 |

**The Optimal Steady-State Concentration of Peroxide.** The rate of peroxide generation for optimal activation of the tryptophan pyrrolase was too variable for easy use in routine assays. Figure 1 shows examples of the ten-fold differences in the optimal rates of peroxide generation for the maximal tryptophan pyrrolase activities of rat- and mouse-liver preparations. These

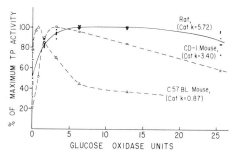

**Fig. 1.** Amounts of glucose oxidase for optimal rates of hydrogen peroxide generation in the tryptophan pyrrolase reaction of preparations with different catalase contents. (M. Ogata and W. E. Knox, unpublished.)

differences could be attributed to the variation in catalase contents. The preparations with more catalase needed more rapid peroxide generation for maximal activity. In a large number of such preparations, varying over tenfold in catalase content, there was a uniform ratio of the added glucose oxidase to the catalase at maximal tryptophan pyrrolase activity (Fig. 2). The steady-state concentration of hydrogen peroxide for maximal activity of the tryptophan pyrrolase can be calculated from this optimal ratio. It is 1–3 × 10$^{-10}$ $M$. With the help of this constant relationship between the rate of peroxide generation and catalase, the degree of empiricism may be lessened in choosing the optimal conditions of assay. Potential errors in the assay of tissue extracts without control of the catalase content or rate of endogenous peroxide generation are superimposed upon the differences between the types

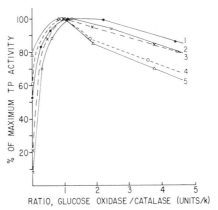

**Fig. 2.** Constancy of the ratio of added glucose oxidase to catalase content in rat- and mouse-liver preparations for maximum tryptophan pyrrolase activity. Absolute catalase contents ranged from 5.7 (curve 1) to 0.58 (curve 5) $k$/ml. (M. Ogata and W. E. Knox, unpublished.)

of enzyme preparations in Table 1 and are indicated by the range of activities shown along the abscissa of Fig. 1. Nearly any value may be obtained.

## B. Hematin and Its Reduction in the Purified Enzyme

Highly purified preparations of the tryptophan pyrrolase became available with the work of Greengard and Feigelson (11), who took advantage of the stabilization of the enzyme by its substrate and their discovery of the resolution of the enzyme to obtain an apoenzyme that was homogeneous in the ultracentrifuge. It was active only after addition of hematin. The specific activity represented a 300- to 1000-fold purification from the liver homogenate of tryptophan-induced rats (22–70 $\mu$moles/hr × mg protein at 37°). The substrate and the hematin prosthetic group mutually increased each other's affinity for the enzyme, resulting in a $K_m$ for tryptophan that fell from 3.0 to 1.5 × $10^{-4}$ $M$ as the hematin concentration was elevated, and a $K_m$ for hematin that fell from 2.5 to 1.2 × $10^{-8}$ $M$ as the tryptophan concentration was elevated. The mutually increased affinities of substrate and hematin probably explained the increased conjugation found by Greengard and Feigelson in the substrate-type induction of this enzyme by tryptophan (9) and by hematin (12).

The chemical state of the hematin was clarified by a similar purification of the hydrocortisone-induced enzyme, which gave a similar product with slightly lower specific activity (6 $\mu$moles/hr × mg protein at 25°) (13). The resolution and recombination of hematin was found to be sensitive to the valence state of the iron. Thus the dissociation of heme (ferrous porphyrin) and the recombination of hematin (ferric porphyrin) were the favored reactions.

The fact that the prosthetic groups of myoglobin behaved similarly (14) may indicate that hematin is chemically bound, whereas heme is merely entrapped by a non-polar environment in both the myoglobin and tryptophan pyrrolase proteins. Tryptophan prevented the dissociation of the heme. This probably explains the protection afforded by tryptophan against the inhibition caused by the hematin-binding property of albumin (15). It also indicates that some alteration in the enzyme molecule occurs upon combination with its substrate, although the role played by the combination with oxygen has not yet been assessed.

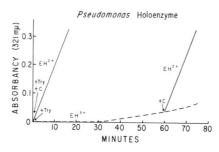

**Fig. 3.** The immediate reaction of the ferric form of tryptophan pyrrolase on reduction with ascorbic acid, and its indefinitely prolonged lag without reduction. Both experiments contained the complete reaction mixture of holoenzyme, L-tryptophan, and $O_2$. (K. Tokuyama and W. E. Knox, unpublished.)

The studies of Tokuyama and Knox (13) also demonstrated that the combination of the apoenzyme with added hematin was inactive until it was reduced by ascorbic acid, hydrogen peroxide, or certain other reductants, thus directly confirming the earlier identification in unresolved enzymes of the heme form as the active species of the enzyme. An example is shown in Fig. 3 of the immediate activation of the ferric form of the highly purified *Pseudomonas* enzyme by reduction with ascorbic acid, and its indefinitely prolonged lag period in the presence of substrate and oxygen without reduction.

**Mechanism.** Early studies recognized the requirement of the tryptophan pyrrolase reaction for molecular oxygen and demonstrated that it did not occur at a significant rate anaerobically with various electron acceptors (2). It therefore belonged to the subsequently defined family of "oxygenases," as the incorporation of $^{18}O_2$ into the product of the reaction demonstrated (16). The earliest reaction scheme resulted from the identification of hydrogen peroxide as an activator of the reaction, plus the fact that the reaction was inhibited by a series of reagents known to react with ferric and with ferrous forms of hemoproteins. A two-step reaction of a hemoprotein was conceived, each step catalyzed by one of the valence states of the enzyme. These were reduction of oxygen to peroxide followed by addition of the peroxide to the

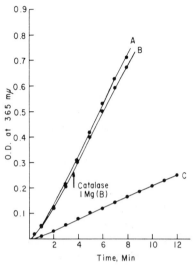

**Fig. 4.** The inhibition of liver tryptophan pyrrolase by catalase (1 mg) added immediately before the reaction (*C*) but not during the reaction (*B*). *A* is the control reaction. This experiment eliminated a role for hydrogen peroxide in the reaction itself and restricted it to a preparatory function. It reduced the inactive ferric porphyrin enzyme to the active ferrous porphyrin form. (T. Tanaka and W. E. Knox, 1959.)

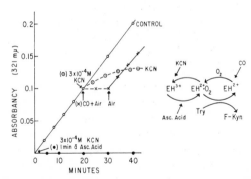

**Fig. 5.** The specificity of cyanide for the inactive ferric porphyrin ($EH^{3+}$) and CO for the active ferrous porphyrin ($EH^{2+}$) results in immediate inhibition of the enzyme by cyanide before reduction and by CO during the reaction. The slowly developing inhibition by cyanide added to the active ferrous enzyme results from the occasional "reaction inactivation" by oxidation to the ferric enzyme form. (K. Tokuyama and W. E. Knox, unpublished; cf. T. Tanaka and W. E. Knox, 1959.)

substrate intermediate to form the product. This so-called "peroxidase-oxidase reaction" scheme (17), patterned after the familiar oxidation of ethanol with oxygen catalyzed by xanthine oxidase plus catalase, was abandoned when the next experiments on mechanism were done. It is interesting to note that, when the original facts were rediscovered in 1963 (18), the same two-step scheme, with superoxy ($O_2^-$) instead of peroxide as intermediate, was again suggested.

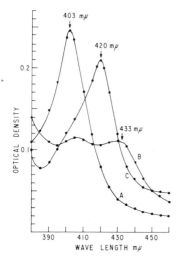

Since 1959 the two-step alternating-valence reaction scheme was untenable, following Tanaka's recognition that hydrogen peroxide is not an intermediate in the tryptophan pyrrolase reaction itself (6). The simplicity of this experiment has its own elegance (Fig. 4). The reaction was activated by hydrogen peroxide and inhibited by added catalase—*if the catalase was added before the reaction began.* Catalase was without effect after the reaction had begun. It followed that the role of peroxide was (largely) over after the reaction was started. Direct spectroscopic evidence was then obtained that the enzyme as prepared was in an inactive ferric porphyrin form, and that this was reduced by peroxide in the presence of tryptophan to the active ferrous porphyrin form.

**Fig. 6.** Spectrophotometric identification of the *Pseudomonas* tryptophan pyrrolase inactive ferric porphyrin form (*A*), the two active ferrous forms after aerobic reduction in the presence of tryptophan (*B*), and the conversion of both ferrous forms of *B* to a single CO derivative (*C*). (T. Tanaka and W. E. Knox, 1959.)

We have reconfirmed the observations of Tanaka and Knox on the mechanism with highly purified preparations of both liver and *Pseudomonas* enzymes. Figure 5 recapitulates some of the evidence from inhibitors for the reaction scheme shown in the same figure. Cyanide, which reacts with the ferric enzyme, promptly prevented the reaction if added before the reductant. Without cyanide, the enzyme was normally reduced by the added ascorbic acid and functioned in the ferrous form. Addition of CO to the going reaction promptly stopped it because the CO reacts specifically with the ferrous porphyrin enzyme. Addition of cyanide to the going reaction had no immediate effect but instead caused a cumulative inhibition as it trapped an occasional enzyme molecule which suffered "reaction inactivation" by being oxidized to the ferric form. The rate at which the inhibition developed under these conditions indicated that reaction inactivation occurred less than once per sixty catalytic cycles of the enzyme molecule.

Everything that we know is consistent with an analogy between the three forms of hemoglobin and the three forms of tryptophan pyrrolase: the met-, oxy-, and reduced hemoglobins resemble the ferric and the two ferrous forms of tryptophan pyrrolase. Two major uncertainties remain. The fast reduction of the enzyme to the active form by mild reductants has so far been possible only in the presence of oxygen and tryptophan. The mechanism of this reduction and the species involved are not known. No evidence was found for the possible participation of ferryl and higher-valence forms of iron (6). We are considering a preferential reduction to the oxyenzyme. After such reduction *two* different species of the enzyme are found, *both* identified as ferrous forms by their conversion to a common CO derivative (Fig. 6). One, with an absorption maximum at 430 m$\mu$, is identical with the chemically reduced (deoxygenated) ferrous form. The other, easily confused with the ferric form, which has a similar Soret band, may be the oxygenated ferrous form of the enzyme.

## REFERENCES

1. W. E. Knox and V. H. Auerbach, *J. Biol. Chem.*, **214**, 307 (1955).
2. W. E. Knox and A. H. Mehler, *J. Biol. Chem.*, **187**, 419 (1950).
3. S. Wood, R. S. Rivlin, and W. E. Knox, *Cancer Research*, **16**, 1053 (1956).
4. M. Civen and W. E. Knox, *J. Biol. Chem.*, **234**, 1787 (1959).
5. V. H. Auerbach, R. A. Pieringer, and H. A. Waisman, *Arch. Biochem. Biophys.*, **82**, 370 (1959).
6. T. Tanaka and W. E. Knox, *J. Biol. Chem.*, **234**, 1162 (1959).
7. P. Feigelson and O. Greengard, *J. Biol. Chem.*, **236**, 153 (1961).
8. H. M. Dyer, P. M. Gullino, and H. P. Morris, *Cancer Research*, **24**, 97 (1964).
9. O. Greengard and P. Feigelson, *Nature*, **190**, 446 (1961).
10. O. Greengard and P. Feigelson, *J. Biol. Chem.*, **236**, 158 (1961).
11. O. Greengard and P. Feigelson, *J. Biol. Chem.*, **237**, 1903 (1962).
12. P. Feigelson and O. Greengard, *Biochim. et Biophys. Acta*, **52**, 509 (1961).
13. K. Tokuyama and W. E. Knox, *Biochim. et Biophys. Acta*, **81**, 201 (1964).
14. H. E. Snyder, *Biochim. et Biophys. Acta*, **69**, 200 (1963).
15. P. Feigelson and O. Greengard, *J. Biol. Chem.*, **237**, 1908 (1962).
16. O. Hayaishi, S. Rothberg, A. H. Mehler, and Y. Saito, *J. Biol. Chem.*, **229**, 889 (1957).
17. W. E. Knox, *Biochim. et Biophys. Acta*, **14**, 117 (1954).
18. P. Feigelson, Y. Ishimura, and O. Hayaishi, *Biochem. Biophys. Research Communs.*, **14**, 96 (1963).

### Discussion

HAYAISHI: About six months ago P. Feigelson, Y. Ishimura, and I published a preliminary paper [*Biochem. Biophys. Research Communs.*, **14**, 96 (1963)] in which we proposed a mechanism for tryptophan pyrrolase involving a valence change of heme iron during the catalysis. The main body of evidence to support this idea is the fact that the native apoenzyme can be fully activated by hematin, and tryptophan can reduce hematin efficiently without any exogenous reductant. However, when the enzyme is further purified or is simply aged or denatured, the reduction of hematin enzyme by tryptophan becomes sluggish, and then there is a long lag period before the reaction starts unless ascorbic acid is added. I should like to present some of the latest experimental results with the more purified enzyme preparation which we think is somewhat denatured, but perhaps Dr. Knox would consider better, from work which we have been carrying out with Drs. Ishimura, Yamamoto, and Nosaki.

The absorption spectra of both the ferric and the ferrous states of such a highly purified enzyme preparation are shown in Fig. 1. The spectra are essentially the same as are shown by Dr. Knox in his paper, except that the Soret band of the

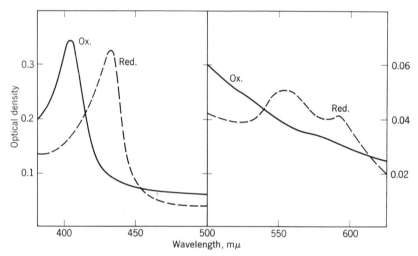

**Fig. 1.** Spectra of *Pseudomonas* tryptophan pyrrolase (————) and its reduced form obtained by the illumination of light under anerobic condition (– – – –; cf. legend for Fig. 2). Each solution contained 2.6 units (0.75 mg) of the enzyme/ml in 0.1 $M$ potassium phosphate buffer, pH 7.0, and the spectra were taken with a Cary automatic spectrophotometer model 15 at 24°C. One unit of the enzyme was defined as the amount of the enzyme which forms 1 $\mu$mole of L-formylkynurenine from L-tryptophan and oxygen/min at 24°C. The standard assay mixture contained in $\mu$moles: L-tryptophan, 9; L-ascorbic acid, 4; potassium phosphate buffer, pH 7.0, 250; and the enzyme in a final volume, 2.5 ml. The formation of L-formylkynurenone was measured by the increase of optical density at 321 m$\mu$.

reduced form of the enzyme shows only one distinct peak at 433 m$\mu$ in contrast with the two peaks Dr. Knox describes, because these are reduced in the presence of chemical reducing agents instead of enzymes and tryptophan. In the present discussion we would use the absorbancy at 405 and 433 m$\mu$ as the measure of oxidized and reduced forms of the enzyme, respectively. Recently, Dr. Ishimura in our laboratory observed that the enzyme becomes gradually reduced under anaerobic conditions without any exogenous reductant, and that this process is markedly accelerated by illumination (Fig. 2). About 0.1% solution of purified enzyme can be fully reduced in about 40 min when illuminated with a 350 watt light bulb at a distance of about 20 cm. The mechanism of this process is now under investigation, but this observation was utilized in the following experiments. When the enzyme in the ferric state was slowly reduced by light and the activity was determined at the different time intervals, the appearance of enzyme activity was exactly parallel with the rate of reduction (Fig. 3). Contrariwise, when the reduced enzyme was slowly oxidized, the disappearance of activity was exactly parallel with the rate of oxidation. These findings are in good agreement with those of Dr. Knox and his co-workers and also with recent findings on other oxygenases, such as metapyrocatechase and

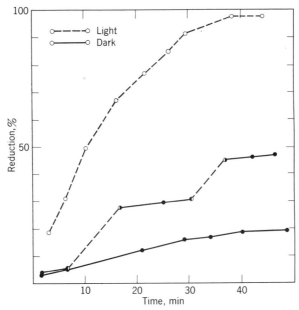

**Fig. 2.** The effect of light on the reduction of enzyme-heme under anaerobic conditions. Three Thunberg-type cuvettes which contained 0.1% solution of the enzyme at pH 7 (0.4 unit/ml) were evacuated, flushed with nitrogen stream, and again evacuated. This process was repeated 3 times. All operations were carried out in conditions as dark as possible. Then a cuvette was illuminated by three 150 watt tungsten lamps at a distance of 20 cm (○– – – –○), the second was placed in the dark (●————●), and the third was placed in dark and light alternately (●—◐—○). The amount of reduced enzyme was measured by the increase of absorbancy at 433 m$\mu$ at each time interval plotted in the figure. A 100% reduction was determined by the complete reduction with excess amount of $Na_2S_2O_4$. The temperature was controlled by a thermoregulator at 24°C.

pyrocatechase, that the iron in the oxygenase is in a divalent form in order to initiate the reaction. However, they do not tell us whether the iron undergoes a valence change or stays in a reduced state during the catalysis.

In order to solve this problem, the state of heme iron during the catalysis was examined with an automatic recording spectrophotometer. When the reaction was started by the addition of ascorbic acid and tryptophan to the ferric form of the enzyme as shown on the left-hand side of Fig. 4, the decrease of a trivalent form started almost immediately, whereas the increase of the ferrous form did not begin until the reaction had gone almost to completion. During the steady state of the reaction a new spectrum with a peak at about 420 m$\mu$ was observed, and a complete reduction of the enzyme occurred only after the reaction ceased. A similar spectral shift was observed when the reaction was started with the reduced form of the enzyme as shown on the right-hand side. This new peak during the steady state of catalysis is interpreted as due to a complex of enzyme, substrate, and oxygen, since

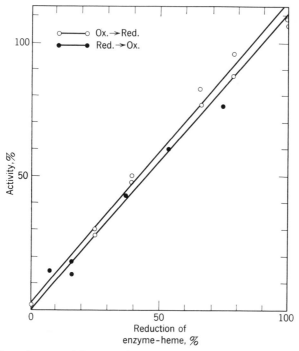

**Fig. 3.** The redox state of enzyme-heme and activity. The enzyme solutions, which contained various amounts of the reduced form, were prepared by the method described in the legend for Fig. 2. When the enzyme was reduced to the desirable degrees, nitrogen gas was introduced into the cuvette and an aliquot of the solution was quickly removed and assayed immediately (O————O) under the condition described in the legend for Fig. 1 except for the absence of ascorbic acid. The activity was also assayed when the fully reduced enzyme, obtained by the same procedure, were reoxidized to the desired degrees (●————●) by gentle agitation with air. The activity measured with the saturated amount of ascorbic acid was taken as 100%.

in the absence of oxygen no such spectral shift was observed. Further evidence to support this interpretation was provided by the following experiments. Another tryptophan pyrolase which acts specifically upon D-tryptophan was isolated from the rabbit intestine and was partly purified in our laboratory. A recent experiment by Dr. Yamamoto has shown that this enzyme catalyzes the conversion of D-tryptophan to formylkynurenine and is competitively inhibited by L-tryptophan. The absorption spectrum of the intestinal tryptophan pyrolase is very similar to that of the purified tryptophan pyrolase of liver and *Pseudomonas*, and when L-trypto-phan, a non-metabolizable substrate analog, was added to the enzyme solution, a new spectrum appeared with a peak of about 410 m$\mu$ (Fig. 5).

The difference spectrum shown at the right has a peak at about 420 m$\mu$ and is almost indistinguishable from the spectrum of the intermediate in the previous figures. These results are taken to indicate the presence of a ternary complex of heme, oxygen, and a substrate or substrate-analog during the steady-state catalysis.

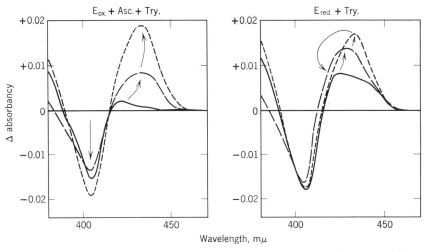

Fig. 4. Difference spectra of the enzyme during the catalysis. *Left:* The experimental cuvette contained in $\mu$moles: L-tryptophan, 9; acid, 20; potassium phosphate buffer, pH 7.0, 250; and 0.23 unit (0.75 mg) of oxidized form of the enzyme in a final volume of 2.5 ml. The reaction was started by the addition of ascorbate, and the reaction, judged by the formation of L-formylkynurenine at 321 m$\mu$, proceeded linearly for about $2\frac{1}{2}$ min. Then the rate of the reaction fell gradually because of the consumption of dissolved oxygen. Finally the reaction stopped at $3\frac{1}{2}$ min after the addition of the ascorbate. The difference spectra were recorded at 1 min (———), 3 min (— — —), and 10 min (- - - -) after the addition of ascorbic acid. The control cuvettes contained exactly the same components as the experimental cuvette except tryptophan. *Right:* The experiment was carried out under the same condition as described above except that ascorbic was omitted from the reaction mixture and the reaction was started by the addition of the reduced form of the enzyme. The time course of the reaction was essentially similar, and the spectra were recorded at the same time intervals as in the experiment portrayed in the left figure.

Figure 6 merely shows the inhibition experiment with cyanide and carbon monoxide; in this case the inhibition by cyanide occurs instantaneously and could be seen at any stage of the reaction.

On the basis of this experimental evidence, published before with Dr. Fiegelson and also in the present discussion, we should like to propose a hypothetical mechanism of reaction of tryptophan pyrolase and to invite some discussions and criticisms (Fig. 7). The oxygen and tryptophan combine with ferrous iron of the enzyme, and within this ternary complex oxygen is activated in such a way that the ferrous iron is almost oxidized to a trivalent state and the oxygen reduced to an amonic radical state. One of the unshared electrons on the nitrogen of the indole ring reduces ferric iron. The following rearrangement of electrons enables the activated oxygen to attack the $\beta$-carbon of the indole ring, thus forming an organic peroxide, which would cyclize and is cleared to form the product formylkynurenine.

KNOX: I don't think that we are in any serious disagreement any more. I can't comment on the interesting new development of another tryptophan pyrrolase, with which I have had no experience. I must reiterate that in the familiar liver tryptophan pyrrolase or the *Pseudomonas* tryptophan pyrrolase the identification of all that absorbs in the 405 m$\mu$ region of the enzyme with the ferric form may be

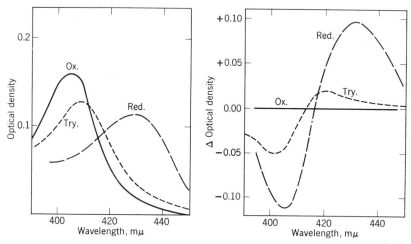

**Fig. 5.** Absorption spectra of intestinal tryptophan pyrrolase. The enzyme was isolated from rabbit small intestine and purified approximately 100-fold by protamine sulfate treatment, ammonium sulfate fractionation, calcium phosphate gel absorption, and solution and DEAE-Sephadex column chromatography. *Left:* the absolute spectra of the enzyme. Solid curve shows the spectrum of the enzyme in 0.1 $M$ potassium phosphate buffer at pH 7.5 (0.48 mg protein/ml). Broken curve (— — —) depicts the reduced form with sodium hydrosulfite, and dashed (– – – –) curve shows the spectrum observed in the presence of $3 \times 10^{-3}\,M$ L-tryptophan. *Right:* the difference spectra of the enzyme (0.12 mg protein/ml) recorded against the oxidized form. The conditions were the same as those in *Left*.

misleading. If the $Fe^{2+}O_2$ species absorbs there too, the difference spectra during the course of the reaction merely indicate a gradual using up of the ferrous-oxy form. In this case we are left with no evidence that any ferric form is cylically made in the reaction. But in the scheme that you have now presented, Dr. Hayaishi, a ferric form, properly so-called, was not included, if I understood you right. There was only the familiar ferric-OOH form ($Fe^{3+}\cdot O_2^- = Fe^{2+}\cdot O_2$).

HAYAISHI: Well, I think that we can describe this much better when I have the general mechanism of oxygenation with pyrocatechase and metapyrocatechase.

ESTABROOK: Perhaps one resolution of this oxygenated ferrous form might be through the measurement of a magnetic susceptibility of the enzyme to see whether

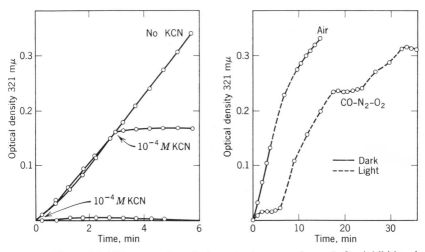

**Fig. 6.** Effect of inhibitors on intestinal tryptophan pyrrolase. *Left:* inhibition by potassium cyanide. The reaction mixture in 1 ml contained potassium phosphate buffer at pH 7.5 (100 $\mu$moles), methylene blue (5 m$\mu$moles), ascorbic acid (5 $\mu$moles), D-tryptophan (3 $\mu$moles), and the enzyme (63 $\mu$g). Absorption at 321 m$\mu$ was followed spectrophotometrically. Potassium cyanide (0.1 $\mu$mole) was added before the reaction was initiated or at the steady state of reaction. *Right:* inhibition by CO and reversion by light. The reaction mixture in 3 ml contained potassium phosphate buffer at pH 7.5 (300 $\mu$moles), methylene blue (15 m$\mu$moles), ascorbic acid (15 $\mu$moles), D-tryptophan (9 $\mu$moles), and the enzyme (83 $\mu$g). Absorption at 321 m$\mu$ was followed spectrophotometrically. A Thunberg-type cuvette containing the reaction mixture, in which the air was replaced by a gas mixture (20% CO, 20% $O_2$, and 60% $N_2$), was kept alternatively in the dark (———) or 10 cm from three 200 watt tungsten lamps (– – – –) at 24°. A control containing air was treated in a similar way.

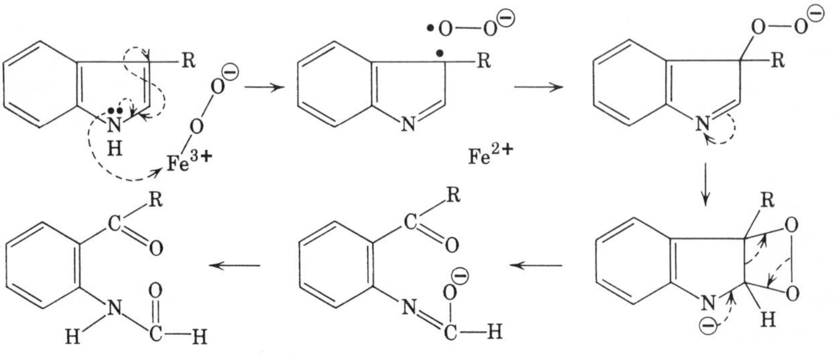

**Fig. 7**

the compound is diamagnetic. I wonder whether you have considered this possibility and what the results are.

KNOX: We have done only a few preliminary studies in collaboration with Dr. Mehler at NIH. We have been able to identify to our satisfaction the signal of the ferrous form during the reaction. It will take a great deal more work to go beyond that fact.

MASON: Dr. Hayaishi, in connection with the nomenclature of tryptophan pyrrolase, if the catalyzed reaction is actually the formation of either a peroxyl free radical or a peroxide, then in conformity with the principle that the name of an enzyme describes the reaction catalyzed a different name would have to be chosen for this enzyme.

HAYAISHI: I agree with you that the nomenclature and the classification of these enzymes should wait until the mechanism of action is clarified and well established. Until then I should like to call the enzyme an oxygenase since, in the over-all reaction, the substrate of tryptophan is oxygenated and the two atoms of oxygen added to the substrate were shown to be derived from the molecular oxygen. Besides, I never implicated hydrogen peroxide in the reaction scheme.

MASON: I think Dr. Hayaishi has raised an important issue when he accepts that the nomenclature of enzymes and oxidases is based on principles other than the identification of the reaction which is being catalyzed. Since the International Commission on Enzymes has to some extent done that also, I think that the subject is worth further discussion.

STAUDINGER: What about the ratio between carbon monoxide and oxygen in your inhibition experiments? And a second question: is this inhibition reversible by light?

KNOX: In that particular experiment the CO and oxygen were in the order of $80\%$ and $20\%$, respectively. The CO inhibition is reversible by light. It is done best, however, at a lower concentration—about $20\%$ CO, $20\%$ oxygen, the rest nitrogen. Then it is light reversible.

CHANCE: Referring to Dr. Staudinger's remark on the way in which these systems respond to CO and to light, we carried out a series of experiments on the oxidation of vitamin $K_3$ in the presence of peroxidase together with Dr. Klapper in order to determine how rapidly the CO compound of ferroperoxidase could be identified in the reaction mixture and to compare the rate of formation of the ferroperoxidase compound with the rate of the over-all activity. The results, which are still in the hands of Dr. Klapper, showed that there is no evidence of formation of ferroperoxidase CO compound at rates consistent with the rapid over-all rate of the reaction. This result is similar in some ways to those obtained with tryptophan pyrrolase and doesn't seem to be in accord with the role of the ferrous compound in the oxidase reaction. It seems that actually two mechanisms are being discussed here: one which is "mostly a ferric catalysis" and another which is "mostly a ferrous catalysis." There seem even to be mixtures of the two.

# The Status of RHP
# and Other Atypical Heme Proteins
# as Bacterial Oxidases

... MARTIN D. KAMEN

It is remarkable how little is known about oxidase systems in bacteria. For example, one of the most active oxidases known—that in *Azotobacter*—has never been isolated in a state sufficiently pure and active to permit characterization of its functional moiety. The list of oxidase systems in which the active terminal enzyme can be asserted to be a heme protein, and for which an oxidase function has been shown or suggested, is very short. Thus, there may be mentioned (i) the *a*-type cytochromes, such as occur in *Staphylococcus albus*, *Acetobacter* species, *Bacillus subtilis*, etc. (1, 2, 8), (ii) the "cytochrome *o*" pigments found in a wide variety of organisms (1), (iii) the soluble cytochrome *d* (formerly known as "$a_2$"), detected in *Escherichia coli* and *Acetobacter peroxidans* (14), (iv) the soluble diheme protein of *Pseudomonas aeroginosa*, classified as cytochrome *cd* (3, 4, 5), and (v) the soluble RHP-type proteins of the purple photosynthetic bacteria (12). In this report, major attention will be given to the fifth group of heme proteins.

In early studies with RHP, as isolated from *Rhodospirillum rubrum*, Bartsch and Kamen (16) observed that its rate of autoxidation was consistent with a possible function as an oxidase. Later, Horio and Kamen (17) showed that RHP, but not the homologous cytochrome $c_2$, of this microorganism was oxidized in aerated cell suspensions. Furthermore, they isolated and purified a pyridine-linked flavoprotein reductase which could reduce both RHP and cytochrome $c_2$ at comparable rates. They proposed on the basis of kinetic studies that RHP was an integral part, both of the oxidase system and of the photoactivated electron-transport system in *R. rubrum*, while cytochrome $c_2$ was involved wholly in the functional photo-oxidation pathway.

Chance and his colleagues (1), in their extensive spectroscopic studies of the CO-binding pigments in a variety of bacteria, had shown that the photochemical action spectrum for light relief of CO inhibition of oxygen uptake in *R. rubrum* mimicked closely the (CO, reduced-reduced) difference spectrum of the pure RHP from *R. rubrum*, at least in the Soret and visible regions of the absorption spectrum.

As against this evidence for an oxidase function, it was noted, first by Geller (15), and later by Taniguchi and Kamen (13), that RHP was not present in significant amounts in cells which had been grown aerobically in the dark and which had enhanced oxidase activity. Taniguchi and Kamen (13) prepared spheroplasts from dark-grown *R. rubrum* which exhibited strong oxidase activity and absorption spectra indicative of the presence of RHP, but from which no RHP could be extracted. Nor could they demonstrate the presence of a soluble RHP in crude extracts of dark-grown cells, using a sensitive assay based on agglutination with specific antisera directed against RHP. Furthermore, *Chromatium*, a strict anaerobe, extracts of which possessed weak oxidase activity but obviously no functional oxidase, contained significant amounts of an RHP-type heme protein (12).

Another characteristic of RHP is its midpoint potential ($E_{m,7}$) which normally has a value very close to that of the ascorbate system at pH 7 (i.e., $E_{m,7} \simeq 0.0$ volt). This potential would place RHP in the middle of an oxidase chain, rather than close to the terminal end. However, it may be argued that in the photosynthetic bacteria a truncated chain with an oxidase at a relatively low potential might be operative.

De Klerk, Bartsch, and Kamen (18) have found in a strain of *Rhodopseudomonas palustris* a form of RHP which exhibits a more positive $E_{m,7}$ (0.10 volt) and a very low rate of autoxidizability. This finding, coupled with the observation that this high-potential RHP can be modified by thawing and freezing to exhibit the usual low value of $E_{m,7}$ and a rapid rate of autoxidizability, suggests that all the RHP-type proteins formed previously may be modified or denatured representatives of the RHP pigment as it exists in its native state in the cell.

Another factor against RHP as a terminal oxidase is its failure to react with cyanide, even at very high concentrations of this reagent, which is a powerful inhibitor of respiration in *R. rubrum*. Again, this observation does not exclude RHP as a component in the oxidase system close to the terminal end, any more than its ability to bind CO proves that it is the terminal oxidase.

To add further complications, Taniguchi and Kamen (13) have found that a purified highly active particulate oxidase prepared from cell wall and membrane fragments of spheroplasts, obtained from dark-grown *R. rubrum*, shows absorption spectra which resemble closely those of RHP, in the range 400–600 m$\mu$, but fail to exhibit the characteristic hematin band of the oxidized form at 690 m$\mu$. In addition, the major heme component in the preparation can be split out as protoheme with dilute acid-acetone, whereas authentic RHP possesses the covalently bound mesoheme prosthetic group of *c*-type cytochromes. The evidence to date suggests strongly that the true oxidase in *R. rubrum*, at least as grown non-photosynthetically, is a *b*-type cytochrome, with the unusual ability to bind CO. Furthermore, it would appear that this oxidase can be identified with the cytochrome *o* of Chance and his colleagues, and not with RHP.

Some very preliminary findings on the CO- and $O_2$-binding capacities of RHP, as determined by Gibson, Taniguchi, and Kamen (unpublished) using flash spectrophotometry, show that the two heme groups in RHP cannot be distinguished by differential rates of reaction, just as Horio and Kamen found by means of equilibrium redox titration procedures. Nor has it been possible to detect any intermediates in the reaction with oxygen which might indicate an oxygenated complex. Thus, Appleby failed to note any alterations in RHP spectra at very low partial pressures of oxygen, while Gibson, Taniguchi, and Kamen have seen no spectral shifts attributable to intermediate species in the early stages of oxidation of RHP (half-times $\sim 10^{-3}$ sec).

However, further studies are needed to assure that RHP, as studied, is in its native form.

## REFERENCES

1. L. N. Castor and B. Chance, *J. Biol. Chem.*, **234**, 1587 (1959).
2. H. W. Taber and M. Morrison, *Arch. Biochem. Biophys.*, **105**, 367 (1964).
3. T. Horio, T. Higashi, H. Matsubara, K. Kusai, M. Hakai, and K. Okunuki, *Nature*, **182**, 1307 (1958).
4. T. Yamanaka, *J. Biochem. (Japan)*, **46**, 1289 (1958).
5. T. Higashi, *J. Biochem. (Japan)*, **47**, 326 (1960).
6. Y. Iwasaki, *Plant and Cell Physiol. (Japan)*, **1**, 207 (1960).
7. M. Kono, S. Taniguchi, and F. Egami, *J. Biochem. (Japan)*, **44**, 615 (1957).
8. L. Smith, *Arch. Biochem. Biophys.*, **50**, 299, 315 (1954).
9. L. P. Vernon and F. G. White, *Biochim. et Biophys. Acta*, **25**, 31 (1957).
10. M. I. H. Aleem and A. Nason, *Biochem. Biophys. Research Communs.*, **1**, 323 (1959).
11. T. Yamanaka and K. Okunuki, *Biochim. et Biophys. Acta*, **67**, 1379, 394, 407 (1963).
12. M. D. Kamen and R. G. Bartsch, in J. E. Falk, R. Lemberg, and R. K. Morton, Eds., *Haematin Enzymes*, Pergamon Press, Oxford, 1961, pp. 419 et seq.
13. S. Taniguchi and M. D. Kamen, *Biochim. et Biophys. Acta*, **96**, 395 (1965).
14. R. Lemberg and J. W. Legge, in *Hematin Compounds and Bile Pigments*, Interscience Publishers, New York, 1949, pp. 367 et seq.; see also *Report of the Committee on Enzymes*, IUB, Pergamon Press, New York, 1961, Vol. 20, p. 58.
15. D. M. Geller, *J. Biol. Chem.*, **237**, 2947 (1962).
16. R. G. Bartsch and M. D. Kamen, *J. Biol. Chem.*, **230**, 41 (1958).
17. T. Horio and M. D. Kamen, *Biochemistry*, **1**, 1141 (1962).
18. H. de Klerk, R. G. Bartsch, and M. D. Kamen, *Biochim. et Biophys. Acta*, **97**, 275 (1965).

References 6, 7, 9, 10, and 11 are included to provide examples of papers which relate to the study of bacterial oxidases.

*Discussion*

KAMEN: Since the preparation of the preceding Abstract, some data have become available which provide evidence substantiating the proposal that cytochrome *o* is a protoheme protein.

Taniguchi and I [*Biochim. et Biophys. Acta*, in press] have found that the absorption peak in the α-region (556–560 m$\mu$) of membrane-bound *b*-type proteins of the oxidase in *Rhodospirillum rubrum* consists of two *b*-type heme proteins which can be differentiated by their response to ascorbate or to the ascorbate-dichlorophenolindophenol (DCPI) sample. Addition of ascorbate yields ~80% of the CO-binding pigment found when reduction is complete, i.e., after addition of dithionite. Approximately 35% of the absorption at the α-peak of the *b* complex, found under the same conditions with argon as gas phase replacing CO, is associated with the appearance of this ascorbate-reduced CO-binding pigment.

Almost all of both the *b*-type cytochrome and CO-binding α-peaks are produced by incubation of the partially purified oxidase system with succinate or NADH. Only about one-third of the α-peak of the total *b*-complex absorption is found after incubations with ascorbate or ascorbate-DCPI. The addition of the DCPI appears to accelerate the reduction of the CO-binding pigment. Thus, the heme protein which is reduced almost completely by ascorbate, or ascorbate-DCPI, accounts for all the CO-binding capacity but for only about one-third of all the *b*-complex absorption.

Furthermore, in the presence of 2-heptyl, 4-hydroxyquinoline-N-oxide, HOQNO, about 50% of the total *b* complex is unaffected by the presence of CO when succinate is added. The block in the electron-transport chain effected by HOQNO appears to favor accumulation of the *b*-type cytochrome, which is unreactive with CO.

It may be concluded that the *b*-type complex which is responsible for the α absorption peak at 562–564 m$\mu$ consists of a *b*-type cytochrome and an autoxidizable protoheme protein with CO-binding capacity. The redox potential of the latter is higher than that of the former.

These results are very similar to those reported by Taber and Morrison [*Arch. Biochem. Biophys.*, **105**, 367 (1964)] for the oxidase system in *Staphylococcus albus*, with the difference that they also have found an *a*-type cytochrome. However, as they have emphasized, this *a*-type cytochrome is not the oxidase. A protoheme protein component (cytochrome *o*) appears to function in this capacity. The spectroscopic properties of this oxidase are very similar to those found by Taniguchi and Kamen for the *R. rubrum* CO-binding pigment in their oxidase preparations.

A comparison of the properties of membrane-bound CO-binding pigment and of soluble RHP from *R. rubrum* is given in Table 1. Marked divergences in redox potential and particularly in affinity for oxygen may be noted. Minor differences appear in spectrochemical behavior in the Soret and visible regions of the absorption spectra for the CO complexes, but the major discrepancy, as noted above, is the failure to find the characteristic hematin band of oxidized RHP at 630 m$\mu$ in the absorption spectra of the membrane fragments which contain the active oxidase. Finally, the prosthetic groups of the two proteins are totally dissimilar.

It appears necessary to conclude that RHP is not the terminal oxidase of the dark-grown *R. rubrum*, and also that it does not represent a solubilized form of the oxidase.

MORRISON: I wonder if the cytochrome *b* and so-called "cytochrome *o*" are in any way analogous to that unmentionable enzyme which contains *a*-type hemes.

### TABLE 1

**Properties of CO-Binding Pigment of Particulate Oxidase System and Isolated RHP, Prepared from Exponential-Phase *R. rubrum* Grown Aerobically in the Dark**

| Property | Membrane-Bound CO-Binding Pigment | RHP |
|---|---|---|
| $K_m$ for oxygen ($\mu M$) in oxidase reaction | 0.50; substrate, succinate | 300–400 substrates, NADH-reductase, or ascorbate |
| Co pressure (mm Hg) for 50% inhibition of respiration at 240 $\mu M$ $O_2$ | 70 ± 20 | 125 ± 25 |
| $K_m$ for combination of reduced form with CO ($\mu M$) | 11 ± 2 | 15 ± 2 |
| Position of α-peak (m$\mu$, 77°K) | 566–568 | 560 |
| Absorption maxima (↑) and minima (↓) of CO complex; 1 atm CO | 419–421 (↑), 433 (↓), 527 (↓), ~540 (↑), 560 (↓), ~573 (↑), ~592 (↓) | 417 (↑), 434 (↓), ~505 (↓), 534 (↑), 553 (↓), 569 (↑), 590 (↓) |
| $E_{m,7}$ (mv) | >350 (?) | −10 mv |
| Prosthetic group | Protoheme(s) | 2 mesohemes/mol. |

KAMEN: You may wonder.

CHANCE: Is there some inconsistency between the CO concentrations for 50% inhibition, which are not too different, and the $K_m$'s for oxygen, which are very different? One would expect that RHP would have been 50% inhibited by a very low CO concentration because of its $K_m$ for oxygen.

KAMEN: I have noticed this also, and it really surprises me. Actually this is a very peculiar situation. RHP is very hard to understand on the basis of its reactions with oxygen and its CO binding. We have been looking at this with Quentin Gibson and have noted very peculiar kinetics. This work is in progress and does not provide a basis for understanding these differences as yet.

CHANCE: Well, a possible point is that the turnover numbers are very different in the two kinds of determinations.

KAMEN: Yes. Oxygen consumption in membrane preparations involves a number of systems. In this case we are talking about a soluble preparation in which we are adding as substrate NADH plus a reductase or ascorbic acid. So it may be that this is not really typical of the terminal oxidases, but of the systems in which the studies were made.

SMITH: Were these cells grown anaerobically in the dark long enough so that there was no effect of light on the respiration?

KAMEN: Yes.

SMITH: Under these conditions is there any RHP in the particulate fraction?

KAMEN: Only a trace. We can alter the concentration of RHP per milligram of protein so that the light-grown cells contain 3–4000 times as much as the dark-grown cells. Ken Gummer was able to bring the amount of RHP per milligram protein down to a very low value by careful culturing in the dark and a series of transfers. The organism was completely bleached out, and, when grown, we could detect no soluble RHP.

SMITH: Do you think that the RHP is on the same particulate fraction in the light-grown cell?

KAMEN: I don't know.

SMITH: As you know, we don't get the same data that you do in our cells grown in the dark in the presence of air. We don't get any inhibition of respiration by CO, and we don't get an absorption peak with CO at 420 m$\mu$ either. I don't know what the difference is due to.

KAMEN: I don't either. We have been able to do this over and over again, and I can tell you some horror stories about changes in strains if you want to hear.

SMITH: No, I don't.

ESTABROOK: I wondered whether you would draw a scheme indicating the sequence between the CO-binding pigment, the other cytochrome $b$, cytochrome $c_2$, RHP, oxygen, light, and substrate.

KAMEN: We begin with substrate. This can be any dicarboxylic acid or a number of different alcohols and also some inorganic substrates in the case of the anaerobes. We go through the usual dehydrogenase and the flavins to cytochrome $b$ and then cytochrome $o$ to oxygen. We also have a pathway through cytochrome $c$ and then through chlorophyll to something which is the reducing end of the photosynthetic chain.

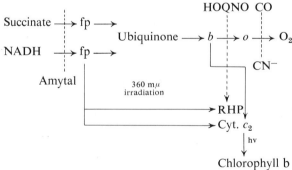

GREEN: Dr. Kamen, could you say a word about the integrated particle before you have taken it apart? Is there any indication that you can obtain a particle that contains all these components and that it can be separated from other parts of the bacterial cell?

KAMEN: No, I have no further data. We can get these fragments if we make spheroplasts. The spheroplasts contain all the oxidase activity. If we break them up, the membrane fragments contain all the components of the respiratory chain, including flavins and the antimycin and HOQNO-inhibited sites. We can do inhibitor studies just as you do in mitochondria. All these things are parallel to the mitochondrial case, but we haven't had these preparations long enough to characterize them further than that.

RACKER: Did I understand that you have respiratory control in your particles?

### TABLE 2

### Oxygen Affinities of Hemoproteins Containing Protoheme

| Hemoprotein | Half-Saturation Pressures,[a] mm Hg |
|---|---|
| Hemoglobin | 25 |
| Myoglobin | 2.5 |
| Leghemoglobin | 0.05 |
| RHP | 0[b] |

[a] All data at comparable temperatures and ionic strengths.

[b] See accompanying discussion.

KAMEN: I don't know. However, I did indicate that illumination does not affect respiration in these cells, whereas it does affect the light-grown cells. The light, in fact, makes ATP, which probably has something to do with the control.

ROSENBERG: Do you know if the CO binding is light reversible?

KAMEN: Yes, it's light reversible—extremely sensitive to light reversal.

ERNSTER: I should like to mention that Loeb and Afzelius in our laboratory have shown that chromataphores from R. rubrum show the same type of repeating units on the surface of the membrane as do mitochondria.

MORRISON: I wonder what this kind of system would imply, since the nature of the hemes is quite different from that of the mammalian cytochrome c oxidase. Does the heme structure have a great deal to do with both the oxygen-binding capacity and the oxidase activity of hemoproteins?

KAMEN: Well, it is protoheme in b and in o. We also have protoheme in myoglobin, in catalase, and in leghemoglobin. The oxygen affinities and reactions are fantastically different, yet there's no difference in the heme at all. Therefore, unless I'm not reading your leading question right, I think that this set of data shows that it isn't necessary to worry about the side groups in so far as some very important functions are concerned. In the series leghemoglobin, myoglobin, hemoglobin, and RHP, all these have very different reactivities with oxygen, as shown in Table 2. The binding constants vary greatly, and they all have the same protoheme prosthetic group. The affinity of RHP for oxygenation is zero, since it acts as an autoxidizable oxidation catalyst.

SMITH: When we measure the anaerobic minus aerobic difference spectra in packed dark-grown cells, we do see a $c$-type cytochrome. This doesn't represent all the cytochrome $c$ in the cell (some of it doesn't become oxidized), but there certainly is evidence for a cytochrome $c$ in the dark-grown chain that does become oxidized and reduced on addition of oxygen. There is also evidence for $c$ that doesn't. If you've isolated only one type of $c$, this may mean that part of it is in the right place and part of it isn't.

KAMEN: Yes, this is something else. You can add an exogenous $c$ to this preparation and oxidize and reduce it.

SMITH: Very slowly.

KAMEN: Yes. We have accounted for 90% of all the mesoheme by pyridine hemochromogen extraction as bound cytochrome $c_2$. About 5 or 10% mesoheme is not accounted for, and we were interested in seeing whether that could be the CO-binding pigment. But it can't be, because you'd have to assume an extinction coefficient of something like 2000 in order to account for all the CO-binding capacity in this membrane fragment. That's the point I want to bring out.

Now, as far as cytochrome $c_2$ is concerned, I have a certain amount of shock value for you. Cytochrome $c_2$ in the dark is not identical with cytochrome $c_2$ in the light. This is known because we are now able to do some analyses of proteins that are more refined than merely looking at the solubility in ammonium sulfate and the molecular weight from the centrifuge, and using other gross and inexact methods. What we do now is sequence analysis. We have seen that in the cytochrome $c_2$ in the dark there are a number of simple substitutions in amino acid sequence which occur in going from light to dark and which would never appear in any chemical or chromatographic analyses. Yet they are simple substitutions which don't change the structure, such as aspartic for glutamic, serine for alanine, and so on. But they are occurring, and we have found that in some of the cultures that we grew without taking great pains to have everything in the dark or everything in the light under intense illumination, we would get mixtures of all the gradations in between in the different monoamino acid compositions which are essentially moderate. We had been puzzled by this for quite a while. We were getting differences in sequence composition in different batches of *R. rubrum*, because some were grown in thick bottles and some in thin bottles. There are some things happening that we have to keep in mind in regard to the fine structure of these proteins.

KING: Is cytochrome $b$ slightly autoxidizable?

KAMEN: Yes, it is.

KING: What is its product, water or hydrogen peroxide?

KAMEN: I don't know. I don't even know what the product of RHP oxidation is.